Biology
of Humans

Concepts,
Applications,
and Issues

CONNECT WITH THE BIOLOGY OF HUMANS

Known for its unique "Special Topic" chapters and emphasis on everyday health concerns, the **Sixth Edition** helps learners apply course material to their everyday lives, making the science information more accessible as they build twenty-first century skills. The authors give students a practical and friendly introduction for understanding how their bodies work and for preparing them to navigate today's world of rapidly expanding—and shifting—health information.

ABUNDANT APPLICATIONS

EMPHASIS ON SKILL BUILDING

Finding and Evaluating Information

E-cigarettes are becoming increasingly popular in the United States, including among children and teens. We have seen that the cells of the linings of the air tubules are the first cells exposed to environmental substances. They protect us against harmful substances we may inhale. For this reason, researchers wanted to determine the effect of vapor from the liquid in e-cigarettes on cells of the air tubule lining of young people. Using tissue cultures from deceased children who had donated their bodies to research, they exposed epithelial cells from air tubules to vapors from e-cigarettes. After 10 minutes of exposure to the vapors, the cells were damaged and were more susceptible to rhinoviruses, which cause the common cold. The damage occurred whether or not the liquid contained nicotine.

The authors concluded:

"This is the first study to demonstrate the adverse effects of e-cigarettes on primary airway epithelial functions from young people. Our data suggest that even nicotine-free e-liquid promotes pro-inflammatory response and HRV infection. Moreover, both e-liquid without nicotine and with nicotine inhibits lung innate immunity (e.g., SPLUNC1) that is involved in lung defense against HRV (human rhinovirus) infection."

You can read the entire study at: Q. Wu et al., "Electronic cigarette liquid increases inflammation and virus infection in primary human airway epithelial cells," *PLoS ONE* 9(9) [2014]: e108342. doi:10.1371/journal.pone.0108342

1. What problems might there be with applying data from cells in tissue cultures to living people?

2. How would you design the experiment to confirm these data on living people?

3. Use reliable sources to investigate the evidence for and against adverse health effects of e-cigarettes.

CONSIDER THIS CASE

You spend the day with your Aunt Sally on her 55th birthday. She has a salad for lunch and suffers no ill effects. When she indulges in fried chicken and fries for dinner, however, she is rushed to the emergency room a few hours later with severe pain on the right side of her abdomen. She reports that she has had bouts of pain over the past month or so.

■ What do you think is wrong with Aunt Sally?

■ Why isn't the pain continuous?

NEW CASE EXERCISES

APPLY AND USE SKILLS IN CONTEXT

CONSIDER THIS CASE

Elsa, a high school and college tennis champion, had begun to work her way up through the ranks in professional tennis. Her training regimen involved daily matches against the best players she could find. After one professional win, her opponent Maria confessed to news reporters, "It is a great challenge to return a serve from Elsa's powerful right arm."

Over the holidays Elsa returned home to Vermont for a family celebration. While she was there, she slipped on the ice and fell forward. She was able to keep her face from hitting the ground with her outstretched arms, but found that she had broken her left arm.

- Why would you expect that only her left arm broke when there was equal force on both arms?
- How would you test your hypothesis?

NEW! Consider This Case exercises close each chapter with a scenario relating to the chapter content, followed by critical thinking questions that ask students to apply what they've learned in the chapter.

NEW! Finding and Evaluating Information activities present a brief excerpt from an intriguing article or blog post and ask students to evaluate the information and conclusions presented, as well as to explore other reliable sources of information on the topic.

Finding and Evaluating Information

An important function of skin is to be a protective barrier against infectious organisms. Cleanliness is important to the skin's ability to perform this function, and hand sanitizers are a popular way to achieve cleanliness. But are all sanitizers created equal? Below are excerpts from R. Babeluk et al., "Hand hygiene—evaluation of three disinfectant hand sanitizers in a community setting."[1] The entire article can be found at: www.plosone.org/article/info%3Adoi%2F10.1371%2Fjournal.pone.0111969

This study involved "sixty undergraduate students . . . (who had) no prior training in hand hygiene and were therefore believed to be representative of the general (non-healthcare) population. . . . The 60 volunteers were briefed to attend the two testing sessions at the University, using public transport. They were also asked to contaminate their hands by touching typical everyday surfaces (i.e. hand rails, door handles, vending machines, money) with both hands prior to testing.

"On arrival at the University laboratory, a swab of each subject's left palm and finger tips was taken and cultured on agar plates to determine a maximum spectrum of microbes present. This provided the base line for the testing.

"The volunteers were randomized into three groups of 20, each group was allocated one of the three hand sanitizers."

[1] R. Babeluk et al., "Hand hygiene—evaluation of three disinfectant hand sanitizers in a community setting," *PLoS One 9* (2014): e111969.

The participants then cleaned their hands with the assigned sanitizer. Their hands were swabbed and the swabs were plated as before.

"Before disinfection . . . there was no significant difference between the groups in the bacterial load detected on hands." Following disinfection, "there was a significant overall reduction in bacteria following hand disinfection with all three products."

Two of the three sanitizers "led to a satisfactory bacterial reduction." The researchers conclude that there "are significant differences in efficacy between products that have been certified in accordance with the applicable European standards, compared to the non-certified product. The two certified products achieved superior outcomes compared to the non-certified product."

1. Is the conclusion in the paper valid based on the experimental design and results?

2. It is often difficult to determine the truth behind claims made in the media. For cleaning hands, is hand washing with soap superior to using hand sanitizers? Which hand sanitizers are most effective? Does use of these sanitizers lead to the development of antibiotic-resistant bacteria? Do these products contain toxic ingredients? Use reliable sources of information (books, newspapers, magazines, journals, or trustworthy websites) to find answers to these questions so you can make an informed decision on whether to use hand sanitizers. Create a list of guidelines for the use of hand sanitizers. Cite your sources.

APPLY YOUR LEARNING **TO EVERYDAY LIFE**

IN THE PREVIOUS CHAPTER, we learned how food is broken down into its subunits, which are then absorbed and used to build new body molecules or are used to release energy for ATP production. Next we considered nutrients and how the body uses them. Finally, we explored ways to plan a healthy diet by selecting foods containing a balance of nutrients. In this chapter, we will consider obesity, which results when we choose an improper mix or amount of foods.

15a.1 What Is Obesity?

Although *overweight* and *obese* are both terms used to describe people who have excess body weight, they do not have exactly the same meaning. An obese person is overweight because of excess fat. An overweight person weighs more than the ideal on a height and weight chart. An athletic person whose muscles are well developed may weigh more than the weight listed as desirable on height–weight tables, but such a person is not obese. However, most people who are overweight have too much body fat. *Overweight* and *obese* generally refer to ranges of weight considered to be unhealthy.

Body Mass Index

The body mass index (BMI) is a number that provides a reliable indicator of body fat because it evaluates your weight in relation to your height (Figure 15a 1). A BMI greater than 30 is generally considered unhealthy and an indication of obesity. However, [it is possible for a] very muscular person to have a BMI above 30 and not be considered [obese, or a] person in the healthy weight range to have too much fat and litt[le muscle.]

Ten Special Topic chapters explore high-interest health topics more thoroughly than can be accomplished in a brief essay.

NEW! Special Topic Chapter 15a
The Sixth Edition features a new **Special Topic** chapter, titled The Obesity Epidemic. Focusing on the problem of obesity, this chapter covers topics such as:

1.   Health risks associated with obesity

2.   Regulation of food intake

3.   Weight management.

Expanded Did You Know? boxes now open every chapter, link directly to the chapter opening photo, and pique students' interest with fascinating and little-known facts about the topic that follows.

CONSIDER THE ISSUES BEFORE FORMING AN OPINION

ENVIRONMENTAL ISSUE

Noise Pollution

It is difficult to escape the din of modern life—noise from airports, city streets, loud appliances, mobile music players. Noise pollution threatens your hearing and your health. Exposure to excessive noise is to blame for the hearing loss of one-third of all hearing-impaired people. Loud noise damages the hairs on the hair cells of the inner ear. When the hairs are exposed to too much noise, they wear down, lose their flexibility, and can fuse together (Figure 9.A). Unfortunately, there is no way to undo the damage; you cannot grow spare parts for your ears.

The loudness of noise is measured in decibels (dB). The decibel scale is logarithmic. An increase of 10 dB generally makes a given sound twice as loud. The decibel ratings and effects of some familiar sounds are shown in Table 9.a. Most people judge sounds over 60 dB to be intrusive, over 80 dB to be annoying,

and over 100 dB to be extremely bothersome. The federal Occupational Safety and Health Administration (OSHA) has set 85 dB as the safety limit for 8 hours of exposure. The threshold for physical pain is 140 dB.

A surprising number of young people also have impaired hearing. The culprit is most likely noise—probably in the form of music. How can you protect yourself? Don't listen to loud music. Keep it tuned low enough that you can still hear other sounds. If you are listening with ear buds, no one else should be able to hear the

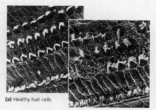

(a) Healthy hair cells

(b) Hair cells damaged by loud noise

Figure 9.A The hair cells of the inner ear can be permanently damaged by loud noise.

Table 9.a Loudness of Fa...
Sound Source
Jet plane at takeoff
Rock-and-roll band (at maximum
Jet plane at 152 m (500 ft)
Electric blender
Traffic noise
Soft background music
Whisper

Three categories of **Special Interest Essays** use the basic scientific content of the chapters to explore issues having broader impact on individual health, society, and the environment.

HEALTH ISSUE

Breast Cancer

Breast cancer usually begins with abnormal growth of the cells lining the milk ducts of the breast, but it sometimes begins in the milk glands themselves. Some types of breast cancer aggressively invade surrounding tissues. Typically, cancerous cells begin to spread when the tumor is about 20 mm (about 3/4 in.) in diameter. At this point, they break through the membranes of the ducts or glands where they initially formed and move into the connective tissue of the breast. They may then move into the lymphatic vessels or blood vessels permeating the breast or into both; the vessels may transport the cells throughout the body.

Detecting Breast Cancer

Early detection is a woman's best defense against breast cancer. A monthly breast self-exam (BSE) is helpful in detecting a lump early (Figure 17.A). If a woman begins doing regular breast self-exams in early adulthood, she becomes familiar with the consistency of her breast tissue. With this experience, it is easier to notice changes that might be signs of breast cancer. Mammograms, which are x-ray exams of breast tissue, can also help detect early breast cancer because they can reveal a tumor too small to be felt as a lump. A tumor large enough to be felt contains a billion or more cells—a few of which may already have spread from the tumor to other tissues of the body. After cancer cells spread, the woman's chance of survival decreases dramati-

cally. An added benefit of mammograms is that they can detect tumors small enough to be removed by a type of surgery called *lumpectomy*, which eliminates the lump but spares the breast. At later stages of breast cancer, the entire breast may have to be removed in a type of surgery called *mastectomy*.

Risk Factors

Many of the factors that increase the risk of breast cancer cannot be altered. The most important factor is gender. Although men can develop breast cancer, it is much more common in women. The genes a woman inherited from her parents also alter breast cancer risk. Mutations in at least two known genes,

woman ovulates is, in turn, affected by factors such as the following:

1. **Age when menstruation begins.** Ovulation usually occurs in each menstrual cycle. Thus, the younger a woman is when menstruation begins, the more opportunities there are for ovulation and the greater her exposure to estrogen.
2. **Menopause after age 55.** The older a woman is at menopause, the more menstrual cycles she is likely to have experienced. Estrogen levels are low and ovulation ceases after menopause.
3. **Childlessness and late age at first pregnancy.** Ovulation does not occur during pregnancy. Thus, pregnancy gives the ovaries a rest. Furthermore, the hormonal patterns of pregnancy appear

ETHICAL ISSUE

Gene Testing

Genetic screening is the practice of testing people who have no symptoms to determine whether they carry genes that will influence their chances of developing certain genetic diseases. Genetic screening technologies are advancing rapidly, and their use is gaining popularity. However, genetic screening raises many ethical questions.

Among the advantages of genetic testing is that it enables people who discover they are at risk for a treatable or preventable condition to take steps to reduce their risk. By informing people that they carry a recessive allele they were unaware of or a dominant allele that is not expressed until late in life, genetic screening can also help reduce the incidence of serious genetic disorders in future generations. Consider Tay-Sachs disease, an autosomal recessive disorder that causes the death of children, usually by the age of 5. Tay-Sachs disease is especially prevalent in descendants of Jewish people from eastern Europe. As a result of voluntary screening programs, the number of children born with Tay-Sachs disease has decreased tenfold in many communities.

Genetic testing also has a dark side. The psychological consequences of test results can be devastating. Many genetic disorders cannot be prevented or treated. How does a person who may have one of these disorders prepare for the

consequences of knowing now what will result in his or her death? Huntington's disease, for example, is caused by a dominant allele that provides no hints of its existence until relatively late in life, usually past child-bearing years. About 60% of people with Huntington's disease are diagnosed between the ages of 35 and 50. The gene causes degeneration of the brain, leading to muscle spasms, personality disorders, and death, usually within 10 to 15 years. Because Huntington's disease is caused by a dominant allele, a bearer has a 50% chance of passing it to his or her children. Thus, a person whose parent died of Huntington's disease might well be tested and receive the good news that the test did not detect the allele. But it is equally likely that the allele will show up in the test. Many persons at risk for Huntington's disease prefer to live without knowing their possible fate.

There is also concern that the results of genetic tests will not remain private information but instead be used by employers as well as life and health insurers. If you were an employer who had genetic information about prospective employees, would you choose to invest time and money in training a person who carried an allele that increased the risk of cancer, heart disease, Alzheimer's disease, or alcoholism? As an insurer, would you knowingly cover such a carrier?

The results of genetic testing can have both positive and negative consequences for individuals being tested and

for their families. Who, then, should decide whether screening should be done, for which genes, on whom, and in which communities? At first blush, one might be tempted to say, "There oughta be a law!" Should we leave ethical issues to judges and legislators? Should moral matters be decided by society or clergy? Or should they be personal decisions? These are not easy questions to answer, or even to think about—yet if we do not take part in the debate, we will be allowing others to decide these crucial issues for us.

Questions to Consider

- If genetic testing is done, should the person being tested be told the results no matter what? If the affected person is an infant, should the parents always be told the results, even if the condition is poorly understood? How do we balance helping such children with the possibility of stigmatizing them?
- We live in a world of limited resources. In addition to deciding who should be tested, we must decide who should pay the bill. Both testing and treatment are expensive. Should testing be done only when treatment or preventive measures are available? How much say should the agent that pays for the procedure have in deciding who is tested and who receives medical treatment?

Questions to Consider

- If genetic testing is done, should the person being tested be told the results no matter what? If the affected person is an infant, should the parents always be told the results, even if the condition is poorly understood? How do we balance helping such children with the possibility of stigmatizing them?
- We live in a world of limited resources. In addition to deciding who should be tested, we must decide who should pay the bill. Both testing and treatment are expensive. Should testing be done only when treatment or preventive measures are available? How much say should the agent that pays for the procedure have in deciding who is tested and who receives medical treatment?

Questions to Consider conclude each box and ask students to think about the ethical implications of certain behaviors (such as taking anabolic steroids) or medical procedures (such as generating extra embryos as part of infertility treatments).

MasteringBiology®

is an online homework, tutorial, and assessment program that helps you quickly master biology concepts and skills. Self-paced tutorials provide immediate wrong-answer feedback and hints to help keep you on track to succeed in the course.

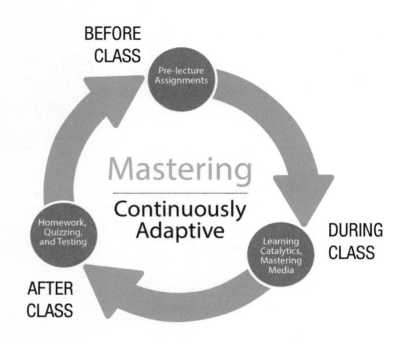

BEFORE CLASS

Mastering

Continuously Adaptive

DURING CLASS

AFTER CLASS

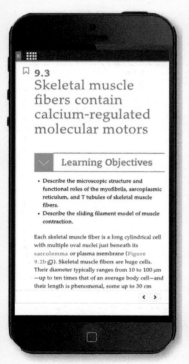

eText 2.0

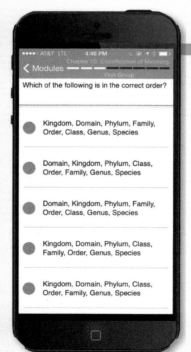

Dynamic Study Modules

BEFORE CLASS

NEW! eText 2.0 Allow your students to access their text anytime, anywhere.

- Now available on Smartphones and Tablets.
- Seamlessly integrated digital and media resources.
- Fully accessible (screen-reader ready).
- Configurable reading settings, including resizable type and night reading mode.
- Instructor and student note-taking, highlighting, bookmarking and search.

NEW! Dynamic Study Modules help students acquire, retain, and recall information faster and more efficiently than ever before. These convenient practice questions and detailed review explanations can be accessed using a smartphone, tablet, or computer.

DURING CLASS

NEW! **Learning Catalytics** is an assessment and classroom activity system that works with any web-enabled device and facilitates collaboration with your classmates. Your MasteringBiology subscription with eText includes access to Learning Catalytics.

NEW! **Everyday Biology Videos** briefly explore interesting and relevant biology topics that relate to concepts in the course. These videos, produced by the BBC, can be shown in class or assigned as homework in MasteringBiology.

AFTER CLASS

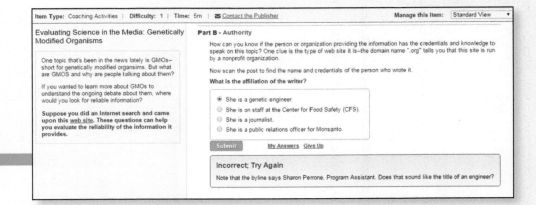

A **wide range of question types and activities** are available for homework assignments, including the following **NEW**assignment options for the Sixth Edition:

- **Interactive Physiology 2.0** help students advance beyond memorization to a genuine understanding of complex physiological processes. Full-color animations and videos demonstrate difficult concepts to reinforce the material. IP 2.0 features brand new graphics, quicker navigation, and more robust mobile-ready interactivities where students can explore, experiment, and predict.

- **Evaluating Science in the Media** challenge you to evaluate various information from websites, articles, and videos.

PEARSON

Judith Goodenough • Betty McGuire

Biology of Humans
Concepts, Applications, and Issues

Custom Edition MacEwan University

Taken from:
Biology of Humans: Concepts, Applications, and Issues, Sixth Edition
by Judith Goodenough and Betty McGuire

Pearson Education, Inc., 330 Hudson Street, New York, New York 10013
A Pearson Education Company
www.pearsoned.com

Printed in the United States of America

0002000010272118071

KM

ISBN 10: 1-323-77877-2
ISBN 13: 978-1-323-77877-7

10 2020

Brief Contents

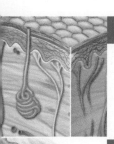

Detailed Contents

PART VI

22   Evolution and Our Heritage   470

Special Interest Essays

ENVIRONMENTAL ISSUES

ETHICAL ISSUES

HEALTH ISSUES

Judith Goodenough

Judith Goodenough

Judith received her B.S. in biology from Wagner College (Staten Island, NY) and her doctorate in biology from New York University. She has more than 35 years of teaching experience at the University of Massachusetts, Amherst, until recently specializing in introductory-level courses. In 2009, she was selected as a College of Natural Sciences Fellow for Blended Learning and developed a hybrid course in introductory physiology. She has experience teaching in the classroom, hybrid courses, and online courses. Her insights into student concerns and problems—gained from more than 30 years of teaching human biology and 20 years of team-teaching the biology of social issues—have helped shape this book. In 1986, Judith was honored with a Distinguished Teaching Award from the University of Massachusetts. In addition to teaching, she has written articles in peer-reviewed journals, contributed chapters to several introductory biology texts, and authored numerous laboratory manuals. With the team of McGuire and Jakob, she is also the coauthor of *Perspectives on Animal Behavior,* Third Edition.

Betty McGuire

Betty McGuire

Betty received her B.S. in biology from Pennsylvania State University, where she also played varsity basketball. She went on to receive an M.S. and Ph.D. in zoology from the University of Massachusetts, Amherst, and then spent two happy years as a postdoctoral researcher at the University of Illinois, Champaign-Urbana. Her field and laboratory research emphasizes the behavior and reproduction of wild and domestic mammals. She has published more than 60 research papers, coauthored the text *Perspectives on Animal Behavior* as well as several introductory biology study guides and instructor manuals, and served as an associate editor for *Mammalian Species,* a publication of the American Society of Mammalogists. At Smith College, Betty taught human biology, introductory biology, vertebrate biology, and animal behavior. Now at Cornell University, she teaches vertebrates: structure, function, and evolution and vertebrates: advanced topics in morphology, development, and evolution.

DEDICATION

To Stephen, my husband,
best friend, personal hero,
and the funniest person I know.
To Aimee and Heather, my daughters,
who fill me with love, wonder, and amazement.
To Betty Levrat, my mother,
an excellent role model
and endless source of support and encouragement.
To "The Group," friends for more than 40 years,
who help me hold it all together.

—J. G.

In loving memory of James Patrick McGuire.
To Willy, Kate, and Owen Bemis,
and to Dora, Kevin, and Cathy McGuire.

—B. M.

Preface

HUMANS ARE CURIOUS BY NATURE. This book was written to stimulate that curiosity, inspiring appreciation for the intricacy of human biology and the place of humans in the biosphere. To satisfy that curiosity with solid and current information, we provide students with a conceptual framework for understanding how their bodies work and for dealing with issues relevant to human health in the modern world. We sustain the student's interest by continually illustrating the connections between biological concepts and issues of current social, ethical, and environmental concern. Our central belief is that the application of biological concepts to familiar experiences is the key to helping students see the excitement of science and understand its importance in their lives.

This edition builds on the Fifth Edition's strengths of clarity, liveliness, consistency, currency, and relevance. The writing is engaging, the explanations straightforward, and the pedagogical framework meticulously constructed. All features are designed to help students identify important facts and ideas, understand them, and appreciate why they matter.

Application of the material to students' interests brings concepts to life and illustrates the ethical and social relevance of human biology. This strategy is especially apparent in the "Special Topic" chapters and the dozens of Special Interest Essays distributed throughout the other chapters.

Practical Goals and Special Features

The principal goals of this textbook are (1) to give *a clear presentation of the fundamental concepts* of human anatomy, physiology, development, genetics, evolution, and ecology; (2) to *apply these concepts* in ways that will both interest and benefit students; (3) to help students *develop reasoning skills* so they can make use of their newly acquired knowledge in the situations they face in daily life; (4) to help students *evaluate the many sources of information* available to them and to select those that are reliable and accurate; and (5) to give students an understanding of how the choices they make can *affect society and the planet, as well as their own quality of life.*

Much of the material covered in human biology has a bearing on ethical, social, and environmental issues that are important to us all. Connections between human biology topics and ethical, social, and environmental issues help students develop a global perspective on their impact on the biosphere and will prepare them to be responsible citizens of their country and the world. Society is currently immersed in many pressing biological debates, and students need the tools to understand these issues and make informed decisions.

New to This Edition

The Sixth Edition includes new features and information that increase application of the material to students' everyday lives and make it more accessible as well as help them build twenty-first century skills.

- A new **Consider This Case** feature at the end of every chapter presents a scenario relating to the chapter content, followed by critical thinking questions that ask students to apply what they've learned in the chapter.

- A new **Finding and Evaluating Information** feature at the end of each main chapter presents new research highlighted in current media, and asks students to evaluate the information and conclusions presented, as well as to find other reliable sources of information on the topic.

- A new **Special Topic** chapter, titled The Obesity Epidemic, has been added. Focusing on the problem of obesity, this chapter covers topics such as (1) health risks associated with obesity; (2) regulation of food intake; and (3) weight management.

- Expanded **Did You Know?** boxes now open every chapter, link directly to the chapter opening photo, and pique students' interest with fascinating and little-known facts about the topic that follows.

- A new, inviting design makes the Sixth Edition more student-friendly, easier to read, and reflective of the course level. The new design also helps facilitate an integrated reading experience by using step numbers in complex process figures to connect the text and art.

- The MasteringBiology online homework, tutorial, and assessment system replaces the Human Biology Place companion website of previous editions. Each end-of-chapter review includes a reminder that directs students to MasteringBiology to access related quizzes, activities, and more.

- New to this edition are online Dynamic Study Modules, which help students study effectively on their own by continuously assessing their activity and performance in real time.

Special Topic Chapters

The text contains 10 **Special Topic** chapters: Chapter 1a, Becoming a Patient: A Major Decision; Chapter 8a, Drugs and the Mind; Chapter 10a, Diabetes Mellitus; Chapter 12a, Cardiovascular Disease; Chapter 13a, Infectious Disease; Chapter 15a, The Obesity Epidemic; Chapter 17a, Sexually Transmitted Diseases and AIDS; Chapter 18a, Autism Spectrum Disorder; Chapter 19a, Stem Cells—A Repair Kit for the Body; and Chapter 21a, Cancer. Created to further motivate students to learn, each of these short chapters builds on the "pure biology" presented in the immediately preceding chapter to cover issues likely to be of personal interest. The discussions these chapters contain are more thoroughly developed than would be possible in a boxed essay. Even if instructors do not include these special topics in their reading assignments, we believe the issues are so pertinent to students that they will read the Special Topic chapters of their own volition, or at least refer to them occasionally as guides to a healthier lifestyle.

Much of the information offered in the text is practical: What can be done to prevent the spread of sexually transmitted diseases? How can one take steps to prevent or treat obesity? The body each of us is born with is a most intricate machine, but it does not come equipped with an owner's manual. In a sense, this book can be the students' owner's manual. Studying and applying the lessons to their individual lifestyles and health issues can help students live longer, happier, and more productive lives.

Special Interest Essays

Three categories of **Special Interest Essays** use the basic scientific content of the chapters to explore issues having broader impact on individual health, society, and the environment.

Environmental Issue essays deal with ways in which human activities alter the environment or, conversely (sometimes simultaneously), ways in which the environment influences human health. Among the topics discussed in **Environmental Issue** essays are asbestos, genetically modified foods, and noise pollution.

Ethical Issue essays explore ethical and social issues related to the topics in a chapter. They explore questions concerning such subjects as anabolic steroid use, gene testing, and the use of nonhuman primates in research.

Finally, **Health Issue** essays deal primarily with personal health topics. They provide current information on certain health problems that students, their families, or their friends might encounter. Topics discussed in **Health Issue** essays include acne, osteoporosis, treatments for the common cold, and disparities in health and health care.

All of these essays include **Questions to Consider,** which ask students to think about the ethical implications of certain behaviors (such as taking anabolic steroids) or medical procedures (such as generating extra embryos as part of infertility treatments).

Stop and Think Questions

The **Stop and Think** questions scattered throughout each chapter are intended to promote active learning. They invite students to pause in their reading to think about the information that was just presented and apply it to a new and interesting situation. These periodic checks allow students to determine whether they have followed and understood the basic chapter content. In the Sixth Edition we have increased the number of **Stop and Think** questions in each of the main chapters and added these questions to the Special Topic chapters.

What Would You Do? Questions

The **What Would You Do?** questions, which are also placed throughout each chapter, challenge the student to form an opinion or to take a stand on a particular issue that society faces today, as well as to identify the criteria used in reaching that opinion or decision. These questions help students see the relevance of biology to real-life problems and foster the practice of thinking through such complicated issues as the use of sperm-sorting technology by parents to select the gender of their offspring and strategies for slowing the growth of human populations. When the subject of one of these questions is controversial, the text presents examples of arguments from both sides, as well as evidence in support of competing arguments.

Enticing Illustration and Design Program

Users of previous editions—instructors and students alike—were unreservedly enthusiastic in praising the illustrations for their appeal and helpfulness. The visual program consists of simple but elegantly rendered illustrations that have been carefully designed for effective pedagogy. Their very beauty stimulates learning. This is particularly true of the many vibrant, three-dimensional anatomical figures, whose realistic style and appropriate depth and detail make them easy for students to interpret and use for review. Micrographs often appear side by side with illustrations to aid interpretation and understanding and to give the actual view of a structure or process being studied.

Within each category of illustrations—from molecular models to depictions of human tissues and organs—the figures are consistent in plan and style throughout the text. Numerous key figures pull concepts together to present the "big picture." Reference figures help students locate particular structures within the body. Flowcharts walk students through a process one step at a time so they can visually follow the progress of a discussion after they have read an explanation in the body of the text. Similarly, step-by-step figures break complex concepts down into simpler components. Finally, color is used in the visual program as an effective means of organizing information and maintaining consistency throughout the text.

Figure Questions

A question accompanies at least one figure in each chapter. This feature asks a question prompting students to pause and critically examine the information in the figure. Answers are provided in Appendix 3.

Engaging Design

This Sixth Edition of *Biology of Humans* presents an engaging design that was created to complement the vibrancy of the illustrations, clarify the organizational structure of the chapters, and increase overall readability.

Organization and Pedagogy

After an introductory chapter on the science of biology, the text presents a discussion of the chemistry of life; proceeds through cells, tissues, organs, and organ systems; and ends with discussions of genetics, evolution, and ecology. As teachers ourselves, we understand the difficulty of covering all the topics in a human biology text in one semester. Instructors are inevitably forced to make difficult decisions concerning what to include and what to leave out. We also know there are many equally valid ways of organizing the material. For this reason, the chapters in this text are written so as not to depend heavily on material covered in earlier chapters. The independence of each chapter allows the instructor to tailor the use of this text to his or her particular course. At the same time, we provide cross-references where they may be helpful to direct students to relevant discussions in other chapters.

The pedagogical features that provide a consistent framework for every chapter have been designed not only to help students understand the information presented in their human biology course but also to help them study more effectively. Some of the most important of these elements are described next.

Chapter Outlines and Introductions

Each chapter begins with a list of the chapter's main topics constructed from the major headings. Because it identifies the chapter's important concepts and the relationships between them, this feature provides a conceptual framework on which students can mentally organize new information as they read. Special Interest Essay boxes are also included in this outline.

Key Terms and Glossary

Because this text is intended for students who are not science majors, we have held the use of technical language to a minimum. Important terms are set in bold type where they are formally introduced, and they are listed as key terms at the end of each chapter. Other terms of lesser importance are set in italics. The **Recognizing Key Terms** list also provides chapter page numbers indicating where each term is defined. The **Glossary** at the end of the book contains definitions for all the key terms and many of the terms set in italics.

Looking Ahead (and Back)

It's widely known that students often compartmentalize chapters and have trouble seeing how one chapter relates to the next. To address this issue, we conclude each chapter with a **Looking Ahead** box to show students how the following chapter will build on the one they have just finished reading. In addition, we begin each chapter with an introductory paragraph that clearly explains how the material from the previous chapter relates to what they're about to read in the present chapter. This **Looking Ahead** (and back) approach draws explicit ties between chapters.

End-of-Chapter Questions

The questions provided at the end of each chapter are designed in several formats to encourage students to review and understand the relevant material instead of simply memorizing a few salient facts. Some, specifically **Reviewing the Concepts,** are intended simply as content review. Others—particularly those under the heading **Applying the Concepts**—require critical thinking and challenge students to apply what they have learned to new situations. Answers to all **Reviewing the Concepts** questions are provided in Appendix 1, and hints for answering the **Applying the Concepts** questions can be found in Appendix 2. These hints, which help students identify the information needed to answer each question, are intended to guide students in their thinking process instead of simply providing a quick answer.

Finding and Evaluating Information

A new **Finding and Evaluating Information** feature prompts students to explore and evaluate resources beyond the text and can be used as a starting point for developing research papers or reports. Students are presented with a synopsis of (and often an excerpt from) new research featured in current media and asked key questions to evaluate the information and conclusions and to find other reliable sources of information on the topic.

Chapter Updates

All of the material in the book has been carefully reviewed, revised, and updated. The latest statistical information and medical advances have been incorporated throughout. The following is a list of some of the more significant changes in each chapter.

Chapter 1 The discussion of the scientific method has been modified to improve clarity, following reviewer suggestions. Several figures have been modified. Two additional levels of biological organization—atom and organelle—have been added to Figure 1.3. The figure supporting the experiment described in the section on the scientific method has been altered to indicate the research begins with a question. A graph of increased use of cell phones has been added.

Chapter 1a A new section specific to young adults and health care has been added. Estimates of medical errors have been updated. A figure showing the new bedside handoff procedure used by nurses has been included. In response to reviewer comments, new secondary headings have been incorporated into several sections of text, and examples of reliable health care websites are now included.

Chapter 2 The figure of the periodic table has been replaced with a simpler version, and an expanded description is now included in the figure caption. There is a new **Stop and Think** on atomic number and atomic mass that requires students to use the periodic table. The **Environmental Issue** essays on radon exposure in homes and worldwide water shortages have been expanded and updated. There is a new figure showing levels of protein structure.

Chapter 3 The figure of the eukaryotic cell has been enlarged, as requested by reviewers. The **Environmental Issue** essay on asbestos has been updated to include global production and use of asbestos. The **Health Issue** essay on mitochondrial diseases contains new information on maternal age effects and mutations in mitochondrial DNA. Two new **Stop and Think** features have been added; one concerns water intoxication and the other, cellular respiration.

Chapter 4 The discussion of homeostasis has been trimmed to avoid overlap with Chapter 2. The drawing of skin is now three-dimensional and is combined with a micrograph of skin. The micrographs of cell junctions are new.

Chapter 5 The role of calcitonin in bone remodeling has been clarified. The discussion of suture joints and synovial joints has been enhanced.

Chapter 6 Following reviewer suggestions, several figures were modified to increase clarity. The discussion of anabolic steroids now includes reference to the alleged use of anabolic steroids among professional baseball players. There is a short discussion on the new phenomenon "text neck," which is caused by the increased frequency of texting.

Chapter 7 The figure showing the ionic events during an action potential and the figure illustrating the changes in voltage during an action potential have been made clearer.

Chapter 8 Within the **Health Issue** essay on traumatic brain injury, the focus has shifted from IED injuries to injuries in the NFL. The discussion of the brainstem parts has been reorganized to enhance clarity. The figure showing the organization of the nervous system has been altered so students will understand the divisions more readily.

Chapter 8a The discussion of marijuana, including both medical and recreational use, has been updated and expanded. The connection between prescription pain medication and heroin use is explained.

Chapter 9 The section on noise pollution was trimmed to highlight the most important information. The **Environmental Issue** essay now includes information on hearing loss in young people that is probably caused by loud music. The photographs illustrating differences in normal vision, farsightedness, and nearsightedness have been improved to help the student understand these differences. A photograph of a cataract has been added.

Chapter 10 A new figure of an exocrine gland has been included to highlight the structural differences between exocrine and endocrine glands. Two new **Stop and Think** features have been added, one concerning types of hormonal interactions and the other, Addison's disease. A new figure illustrates how the hypothalamus and hormones of the adrenal glands regulate stress responses.

Chapter 10a The figure showing insulin regulation of blood glucose levels has been modified to improve clarity and flow of information. All statistics regarding prevalence of diabetes and all blood glucose values for diagnosing different forms of diabetes have been updated. The section on ways to self-administer insulin now includes a discussion of the insulin patch pump; this device is shown in a new photograph, which allows comparison with the traditional insulin pump, also depicted in a new photograph. Emerging treatments, such as the artificial pancreas for treating type 1 diabetes, are discussed. A new photograph shows the excessive growth characteristic of babies born to mothers with untreated gestational diabetes.

Chapter 11 The formed elements discussion is reorganized so that these elements are covered in the order of the student's familiarity with each. A new **Health Issue** essay on medical blood tests has been included to help students understand this common medical procedure. The discussion of intercalated discs is expanded.

Chapter 12 The size of several figures has been changed to reflect their importance in understanding the concepts. Lymphoid tissue is discussed at greater length than in previous editions. Multiple-choice questions, two of which involve the lymphatic system, were added to the end-of-chapter material.

Chapter 12a The discussion of HDL- and LDL-cholesterol has been expanded, and a new table has been included. In addition, references to HDLs and LDLs in other chapters have been added.

Chapter 13 Slight modifications have been made to several figures to increase clarity. New photos are intended to stimulate interest in the discussion of passive immunity.

Chapter 13a The material on emerging and reemerging diseases was expanded and updated. A discussion of disease transmission via IV drug use was added, as was a discussion of the role played by failure to vaccinate in the reemergence of disease. Several figures were slightly modified to enhance understanding.

Chapter 14 A discussion of COPD was added. Several figures were modified to increase clarity.

Chapter 15 To enhance clarity, steps were added to the text to accompany those in art. A new discussion predicts the 2015 Dietary Guidelines for Americans based on the recommendations from the committee.

Chapter 15a This new Special Topic chapter, The Obesity Epidemic, discusses biological issues of obesity. It begins by defining the problem and then explains the interrelationships among the three major health risks associated with obesity: cardiovascular disease, type 2 diabetes, and cancer. It continues by explaining the neural, hormonal, and genetic regulation of food intake. The discussion of genetic regulation of food intake includes the recently recognized role of epigenetics, which involves changes in gene activity produced by chemicals in the environment, including the diet. The chapter ends with suggestions for weight management.

Chapter 16 Discussions of the ways kidneys help regulate blood pH and promote the body's use of calcium and phosphorus have been expanded. Statistics on the need for kidney transplants have been updated. Several figures have been modified to address reviewer requests. Additional detail has been added to the figure showing the organ systems involved in eliminating wastes from the body. A new photograph of a patient undergoing dialysis with an artificial kidney machine replaces the line drawing in the previous edition. In the section on urinary tract infections, the figure showing the urinary bladder and urethra of males and females has been modified to promote ease of comparison. There is an updated version of the organ donor card.

Chapter 17 A description of the procedure for testicular self-exam has been added. Numerical steps were incorporated into the text to coordinate it more closely with the figure depicting the ovarian cycle.

Chapter 17a To better coordinate with the art, numbered steps have been added to coverage of the stages of syphilis and the replication of HIV. The discussion of HIV treatment has been updated and reorganized to explain more clearly how each treatment blocks a step in HIV replication.

Chapter 18 The figure showing early stages of human development in cross section now includes structures that develop from each of the germ layers. The **Health Issue** essay on disparities in health and health care has been updated to include results from two recent studies and goals of the Healthy People 2020 initiative. Coverage of possible causes of aging has been updated with new results from research on caloric restriction. In response to reviewer comments, the figure depicting development of the central nervous system has been simplified to promote clarity. A new photograph of a newborn with spina bifida is included to link central nervous system development and birth defects.

Chapter 18a Statistics regarding the prevalence of autism spectrum disorder (ASD) have been updated. Causes and treatments have been updated based on new research findings. A new photograph shows the use of robots to promote development of social skills in children with ASD. The section concerning vaccines has been updated, with results from additional studies indicating no link between vaccines and ASD; a photograph of a toddler with measles has been added to illustrate the consequences of not vaccinating infants and children.

Chapter 19 The diagram of the human life cycle has been modified slightly to enhance clarity. The dynamic, continuous nature of mitosis is now emphasized. The diagram showing nondisjunction of chromosomes has been improved.

Chapter 19a The discussion of techniques to produce human stem cells has been updated and simplified. The updated section on regenerative medicine includes the use of three-dimensional printers to "bio print" new organs. A new **What would You do?** asks the student to consider whether he or she would travel to another country for stem cell treatment. Modifications have improved the clarity of the art program.

Chapter 20 The material on prenatal testing has been shortened and now includes noninvasive prenatal testing. The figure showing Fragile X syndrome was improved by adding labels.

Chapter 21 A new discussion of epigenetics and the epigenome has been included. Numbered steps have been added to the text that describes eight figures, thereby promoting greater understanding of the concepts.

Chapter 21a A discussion on the relationship between cancer and epigenetics has been included, as well as a discussion of targeted cancer treatment. Some technical details have been removed to increase comprehension.

Chapter 22 Coverage of the origin of life has been updated to include new evidence that comets brought organic material to earth. Two new **Stop and Think** features have been added, one concerning microevolution and the other, preservation of soft tissues. A new figure depicts genetic drift. A new example of natural selection (lactose tolerance) replaces the previous example (antibiotic resistance). The section on human evolution has been updated to reflect recent discoveries and new interpretations. Figures with cladograms have been redrawn with a simpler style to improve clarity.

Chapter 23 The nitrogen cycle discussion has been reorganized for greater clarity. The Biodiversity section has been updated and reorganized.

Chapter 24 Population statistics have been updated throughout the chapter. The global climate change discussion has been updated with information from the Fifth Assessment of the Intergovernmental Panel on Climate Change (IPCC).

Teaching and Learning Solutions for Instructors and Students

Biology of Humans, Sixth Edition, is supported by a full complement of carefully designed materials for both students and instructors.

For Instructors

Instructor Resource DVD
0134313003 / 9780134313009
The Instructor Resource DVD provides a range of ready-to-use media supplements to help instructors teach the course, engage students, and accommodate different learning styles. Instructors can augment their lectures, show students the relevance of the subject matter, and increase student comprehension using the following tools:

- An image library of all the art, tables, and photographs from the book
- A selection of images with customizable labels and stepped-out art
- Editable PowerPoint lecture presentation slides with embedded links to *ABC News* videos and Human Biology Animations
- Clicker questions
- Human Biology Animations
- BioFlix and BioFlix PowerPoint slides
- *ABC News* video clips
- *Interactive Physiology* for human biology slides, worksheets, and answer sheets
- Interactive Quiz Show games
- Microsoft Word files for the Instructor's Guide and Test Bank
- Computerized test bank

Instructor's Guide
0134323890 / 9780134323893
The Instructor's Guide provides tips for making the material relevant, interesting, and interactive, especially for nonmajors. Each chapter includes the following:

- Learning Objectives that identify goals for students and instructors
- Lecture activity suggestions
- Suggestions for class demonstrations and student activities
- Resource listings of relevant websites

Test Bank
The Test Bank includes over 1000 multiple-choice, fill-in-the-blank, short answer, and essay test questions—and answers—originally created and reviewed by a panel of educators. All questions are correlated to Bloom's Taxonomy of learning. Microsoft Word and TestGen versions of the files are available on the Instructor Resource DVD and can be downloaded from MasteringBiology.

MasteringBiology
www.masteringbiology.com
MasteringBiology is an online homework, tutorial, and assessment product designed to improve results by helping students quickly master concepts. Students benefit from self-paced tutorials that feature immediate wrong-answer feedback and hints that emulate the office-hour experience to help keep students on track. With a wide range of interactive, engaging, and assignable activities, students are encouraged to actively learn and retain tough course concepts.

For Students

MasteringBiology™
Now integrated with the Sixth Edition, the **MasteringBiology** online homework, tutorial, and assessment system helps instructors teach more efficiently and is pedagogically proven to help students learn. It helps instructors maximize class time with customizable, easy-to-assign, and automatically graded assessments that motivate students to learn outside class and arrive prepared for lecture. The powerful gradebook provides unique insight into student and class performance even before the first test. As a result, instructors can spend class time where students need it most. The Mastering system empowers students to take charge of their learning through activities aimed at different learning styles and engages them in learning science through practice and step-by-step guidance—at their convenience, 24/7.

Acknowledgments
It takes more than authors to get a book to the readers, and many dedicated people have helped deliver this text into your hands.

The project was enthusiastically launched by Star Burruto, Senior Acquisitions Editor, who helped us plan this edition and assembled a team of professionals who brought our vision to reality.

We are especially thankful for the opportunity to work with Nicole George-O'Brien, who kept our vision for this edition in mind through the entire project and was involved at every level. We would also like to thank Project Manager Lori Newman, and Program Manager Anna Amato for keeping all aspects of the project running smoothly. Supervising Project Manager for Instructional Media Chelsea Logan, and Content Producers Lucinda Bingham and Chloe Veylit managed production of media. Thanks also to Executive Marketing Manager Lauren Harp and her team.

In addition, we would like to thank Linda Brooks, Triton College, River Grove, Illinois; Tonya Bates, University of North Carolina, Charlotte, North Carolina; William Cushwa, Clark College, Vancouver, Washington; and Robert Sullivan, Marist College, New York for their work on the print and media supplements.

Many thanks go out to all of the instructors who reviewed the book and provided us with the useful feedback that helped shape this new edition:

Eric Anderson, *East Carolina University*
Tonya Bates, *University of North Carolina, Charlotte*
Caralisa Breidenbaugh, *Kent State University, Ashtabula*
Linda Brooks, *Triton College*
David Evans, *Penn College*
Emily Flynn, *South Central College*
Diane Fritz, *Gateway Community and Technical College*
Rachel Lewis, *Austin Peay State University*
Joanne Oellers, *Yavapai College*
Walter Prothero, *Weber State University*
Susan Rohde, *Triton College*
Derek Sims, *Hopkinsville Community College*
Eileen Stein, *Hagerstown Community College*
Jay Zimmer, *Gardner Webb University*

We extend our thanks to the reviewers of the fifth edition:

Andrea Abbas, *Washtenaw Community College*
Gary Arnet, *California State University, Chico*
Samantha Butler, *University of Southern California*
Edward Gabriel, *Lycoming College*
Noah Henley, *Rowan-Cabarrus Community College*
Cynthia Littlejohn, *University of Southern Mississippi*
Dennis McCracken, *University of North Carolina at Pembroke*
Jean Shingle, *Immaculata University*
Renato Tameta, *Schenectady County Community College*
Jessica Thomas, *Eastern Connecticut State University*
Greg Thurman, *Central Methodist University*
Rebecca Vance, *University of Alabama at Birmingham*
Naomi Waissman, *El Paso Community College*
Muhammed A. Wattoo, *Cornell Medical College*

From Judith Goodenough
I thank my family and friends, who supported and encouraged me at every stage of this project. My husband, Steve, was a cheerleader and convinced me that I would complete this project. Without his witty quips, I would have lost my sanity. He reassures me that I'll always be his first wife. My daughters, Aimee and Heather, inspire me and continually remind me that

the people you love should always come first. Aimee Goode-nough Chianelli, a rehabilitation counselor for clients with traumatic brain injury, contributed the Chapter 8 essay, "Brain Injury: A Silent Epidemic."

Margaret Ludlam cheered me up and helped me cope when things got tense. Lee Estrin, one of "the group" of dear friends who have always provided moral support and advice, was always willing to visit for an "I need a break" weekend, even when I couldn't actually stop working completely.

From Betty McGuire

I thank my husband, Willy Bemis, for support and encouragement throughout this edition, and my daughter Kate and son Owen, for (usually) waiting patiently for me to complete just one more sentence or paragraph. Dora, Kevin, and Cathy McGuire were endlessly encouraging and understanding, as they have been throughout my life. Finally, Lowell Getz, my longtime friend and research colleague, waited with good humor as one after another of our papers took a backseat to a book chapter.

1 Humans in the World of Biology

DID YOU KNOW?

- Estimates of the total number of species on Earth range from 5 to 30 million, and only 1.7 to 2 million species have been formally identified (Millennium Ecosystem Assessment).

- Scientists have discovered two planets about the size of Earth orbiting a distant star, Kepler-438b and Kepler-442b. These planets may have environmental conditions that could sustain life.

IN THIS CHAPTER, we see that life has many levels of organization: individual, population, community, ecosystem, and biosphere. Throughout most of this book, we focus on the human individual—how the individual human body functions and the biological principles that govern those functions. However, we also examine many of the larger health, social, and environmental issues that we must be aware of, because they can affect all of life.

1.1 Basic Characteristics of All Living Things

We will begin by exploring the Amazon rain forest—a place that is teeming with life. Given the biodiversity of the rain forest, it is not surprising that scientists are in search of secrets it may reveal, including any plants that may have healing qualities (see the Environmental Issue essay, *Medicinal Plants and the Shrinking Rain Forest*).

We say that life is abundant in the rain forest, but how do you determine whether something unfamiliar to you is alive? In most cases, the question is easy to answer. Although the leaves around you have different shapes and sizes, a brief examination assures you that they are leaves and that the tree whose trunk you are exploring is clearly a tree—thus telling you that this tree specimen is indeed alive. But what about the gray material adhering to the trunk? Is it also alive?

Defining *life* might seem easy, but it is not. In fact, no single definition satisfies all life scientists. For example, if we say that something is alive if it reproduces, someone is likely to note that a page with a wet ink spot can fall on top of another page and reproduce itself almost exactly. If we say something is alive if it grows, what should we conclude about crystals? They grow, but they are not alive. And so it goes.

ENVIRONMENTAL ISSUE

Medicinal Plants and the Shrinking Rain Forest

The healing powers of many plants have been known for centuries. Historically, such knowledge was gained by trial and error and passed along by word of mouth. For example, many cultures have long known that tea made from willow bark relieves pain and reduces fever. Scientists learned that willow bark contains salicylic acid. They isolated the compound and developed it into the drug we know today as aspirin. Similarly, digitalis, a heart medication, was discovered after a patient with an untreatable heart condition was seen to benefit from an herbal drink provided as a folk remedy. The potion contained purple foxglove, which, like willow bark, is frequently mentioned in ancient texts as a healing herb. Broccoli, a more familiar plant, contains the anticancer chemical sulforaphane.

Figure 1.A *The rosy periwinkle* (Catharanthus roseus) *is a source of two anticancer drugs.*

More than 25% of the prescription medicines sold in the United States today contain chemicals that came from plants, and 70% of the newly developed drugs are from natural sources. Many more healing chemicals first discovered in plants used medicinally by native people are now routinely synthesized in laboratories. Unfortunately, however, there are many plants whose medicinal compounds scientists have *not* been able to synthesize.

Most plants that have proved to be medically useful are found in the tropics, regions where the human population is growing rapidly. Unfortunately, the forests in these regions are being cut to create living space and foster economic development. For example, Madagascar is the home of the rosy periwinkle (Figure 1.A), which is the source of two anticancer drugs. Humans have destroyed 90% of the vegetation in that nation. Considering that 155,000 of the known 250,000 plant species are from tropical rain forests, and that fewer than 2% of the known plant species have been tested for medicinal value, we have no way of knowing what potential new medicines are being destroyed.

Questions to Consider

- Should indigenous people be compensated for plants found in their locality if extracts of the plants become drugs?
- What steps might be taken to preserve biodiversity within the rain forest?

No single definition applies to all forms of life, so we find that instead of defining life, we can only characterize it. That is, we can only list the traits associated with life. Most biologists agree that, in general, the following statements characterize life.

1. **Living things contain nucleic acids, proteins, carbohydrates, and lipids.** The same set of slightly more than 100 elements is present in various combinations in everything on Earth—living or nonliving. However, living things can combine certain of these elements to create molecules that are found in all living organisms. These molecules include nucleic acids, proteins, carbohydrates, and lipids. The nucleic acid DNA (deoxyribonucleic acid) is especially important because DNA molecules can make copies of themselves, an ability that enables organisms to reproduce (Figure 1.1). The molecules of life are discussed in Chapter 2.

2. **Living things are composed of cells.** Cells are the smallest units of life. Some organisms have only a single cell (*unicellular organisms*); others, such as humans, are composed of trillions of cells (*multicellular organisms*). All cells come from preexisting cells. The ability of cells to divide to form new cells makes reproduction, growth, and repair possible. Cells are discussed in Chapter 3 and cell division in Chapter 19.

3. **Living things grow and reproduce.** Living things grow and ultimately generate new individuals that carry some of the genetic material of the parents. Some organisms, such as bacteria, reproduce simply by making new and virtually exact copies of themselves. Other organisms, including humans, reproduce by combining genetic material with another individual. Many organisms have stages of life. Humans progress from embryo to fetus, child, adolescent, and then adult. Reproduction and development are discussed in Chapters 17 and 18, respectively.

4. **Living things use energy and raw materials.** The term **metabolism** refers to all chemical reactions that occur within the cells of living things. Through metabolic activities, organisms extract energy from various nutrients and transform it to do many kinds of work. Metabolism maintains life and allows organisms to grow. Chemical reactions involved in the transformation of energy are discussed in Chapter 2.

5. **Living things respond to their environment.** A boxer weaves and ducks to avoid the blow of an opponent. A chameleon takes aim at and captures its prey. For a living thing to respond, it must first detect a stimulus and then have a way to react. As later chapters explain, your sensory organs detect stimuli. Your nervous system processes sensory input, and your skeletal and muscular systems enable you to respond. The skeletal and muscular systems are discussed in Chapters 5 and 6, respectively. The nervous system is discussed in Chapter 8, and sensory organs in Chapter 9.

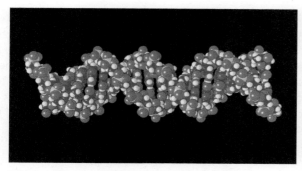

1. Living things contain nucleic acids, proteins, carbohydrates, and lipids.
This is a computer-generated model of the nucleic acid DNA, which carries genetic information.

2. Living things are composed of cells.
These are red blood cells (disks) and a white blood cell (sphere).

3. Living things grow and reproduce.
All organisms reproduce their own kind.

4. Living things use energy and raw materials.
This father is feeding his child.

5. Living things respond to their environment.
This chameleon sees and catches its prey.

6. Living things maintain homeostasis.
This person's body temperature will remain about 37°C (98.6°F) in spite of extreme environmental temperature.

7. Populations of living things evolve and have adaptive traits.
The orchid is adapted to live perched on branches of trees. It uses other plants for support so that it can receive enough sunlight to produce its own food by photosynthesis.

Figure 1.1 Characteristics of life

6. **Living things maintain homeostasis. Homeostasis** is the relatively constant and self-correcting internal environment of a living organism. We generally find that life can exist only within certain limits and that living things tend to behave in ways that will keep their body systems functioning within those limits. For example, if you become too cold, you shiver (a metabolic response). Shivering produces heat that warms your body. Alternatively, if you become too hot, your sweat glands will be activated to cool you down. In addition to these and other physiological responses, the sensation of being hot or cold may motivate you to behave in ways that cool you down or warm you up. We discuss homeostasis in Chapter 4, where we make an initial survey of body systems.

7. **Populations of living things have adaptive traits and evolve.** Members of a population of reproducing organisms possessing beneficial genetic traits will survive and reproduce better than members of the population that lack these traits. As a result of this process, called *natural selection,* each of the amazing organisms you see around you has **adaptive traits**—that is, traits that help it survive and reproduce in its natural environment. For example, most plants in the rain forest have shallow root systems, because the topsoil in the Amazon is thin and nutrients are near the surface. As a result, tall trees have developed, through evolution, supports like cathedral buttresses to hold them up, while vines climb over both roots and trees to reach the light. Many plants do not grow in the ground at all but live high above it in the canopy for greater exposure to sunlight, which provides energy to produce sugar. These plants, called *epiphytes,* are rooted on the surfaces of other plants. Rain forest animals also have adaptations—the ability to fly or climb, for example—that enable them to reach the plants for food. Adaptive traits and evolution are discussed in Chapter 22.

STOP and **THINK**

Scientists have discovered water and methane on Mars. Water is necessary for life. Solar radiation would quickly destroy methane, so "something" must be producing the methane we detect. If samples of water or soil from Mars were brought back to scientists on Earth, what characteristics of life could they look for to determine whether the samples contain anything that is or was once alive?

1.2 Evolution: A Unifying Theme in Biology

Evolution is a common theme in biology because it explains the unity and diversity of the at least 10 million species of organisms that live on Earth. Organisms are unified because all species descended from the first cells. However, as organisms adapted to different environments through evolution, diversity among species arose.

Scientists organize, or classify, living organisms in a way that shows evolutionary relationships among them. This means, for the most part, that organisms with the greatest similarity are grouped together.

Several classification systems have been proposed over the years. One system recently favored by many biologists recognizes three domains. Two of the domains, Bacteria and Archaea, consist of the various kinds of prokaryotes—all of which are very small, single-celled organisms that lack a nucleus or other internal compartments. All other organisms, including humans, belong to the third domain, Eukarya. Organisms in domain Eukarya have eukaryotic cells, which contain a nucleus and complex internal compartments called *organelles.* Domain Eukarya is subdivided into four kingdoms—protists, fungi, plants, and animals—as shown in Figure 1.2. Within

Domain Bacteria	Domain Archaea	Domain Eukarya			
Unicellular prokaryotic organisms 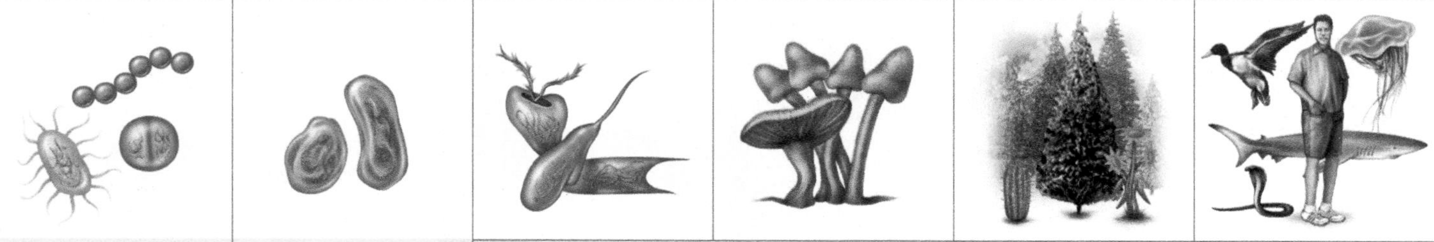	Unicellular prokaryotic organisms; most live in extreme environments	Eukaryotic cells that contain a membrane-bound nucleus and internal compartments			
		Kingdoms			
		Protists	**Fungi**	**Plants**	**Animals**
		Protozoans, algae, diatoms	Molds, mushrooms	Mosses, ferns, seed plants	Invertebrates and vertebrates

Figure 1.2 One classification scheme showing three domains and four kingdoms of life

each kingdom, organisms are further categorized into groups whose members share characteristics that distinguish them from members of other groups in the kingdom. These groups in turn are subdivided into smaller groups to show successively closer relationships.

As humans, we belong to a subdivision of the animal kingdom called *vertebrates* (animals with a nerve cord protected by a backbone) and, more specifically, to the group known as *mammals.* Two characteristics make us mammals: we have hair and we feed our young milk produced by mammary glands. However, we are further defined as belonging to the *primates,* along with lemurs, monkeys, and apes, because we share a suite of features that includes forward-looking eyes and a particularly well-developed brain. Humans, monkeys, and apes also have opposable thumbs (a thumb that can touch the tips of the other four fingers). Smaller details, such as tooth structure and skeletal characteristics, serve to divide the primates into smaller subgroupings.

STOP and **THINK**
If a new organism were discovered in the rain forest, what characteristic would you look for to decide whether the animal was a mammal?

1.3 Levels of Biological Organization

As we study human biology, we learn that life can be organized on many levels (Figure 1.3). Cells, the smallest unit of life, are themselves composed of molecules. A multicellular organism may consist of different tissues, groups of similar cells that perform specific functions. Organs also may consist of different types of tissue that work together for a specific function. Two or more organs working together to perform specific functions form an organ system. Humans have 11 organ systems, as we see in Chapter 4.

Life can also be organized at levels beyond the individual organism. A **population** is individuals of the same species (individuals that can interbreed) living in a distinct geographic area. Examples of a population include yellow-bellied marmots living in an alpine meadow or four-eyed butterfly fish living in a coral reef. A **community** is all living species that can potentially interact in a particular geographic area. Examples of a community include *all the species* that live and interact in an alpine meadow or *all the species* living in a coral reef.

An **ecosystem** includes all the living organisms in a community along with their physical environment. The size of the locality that defines the ecosystem varies with the interest of the person studying it. In other words, an ecosystem can be defined as the whole Earth, a particular forest, or even a single rotting log within a forest. Whatever its size, an ecosystem is viewed as being relatively self-contained.

The **biosphere** is that part of Earth where life is found. It encompasses all of Earth's living organisms and their habitats. In essence, the biosphere is the narrow zone in which the interplay of light, minerals, water, and gases produces environments

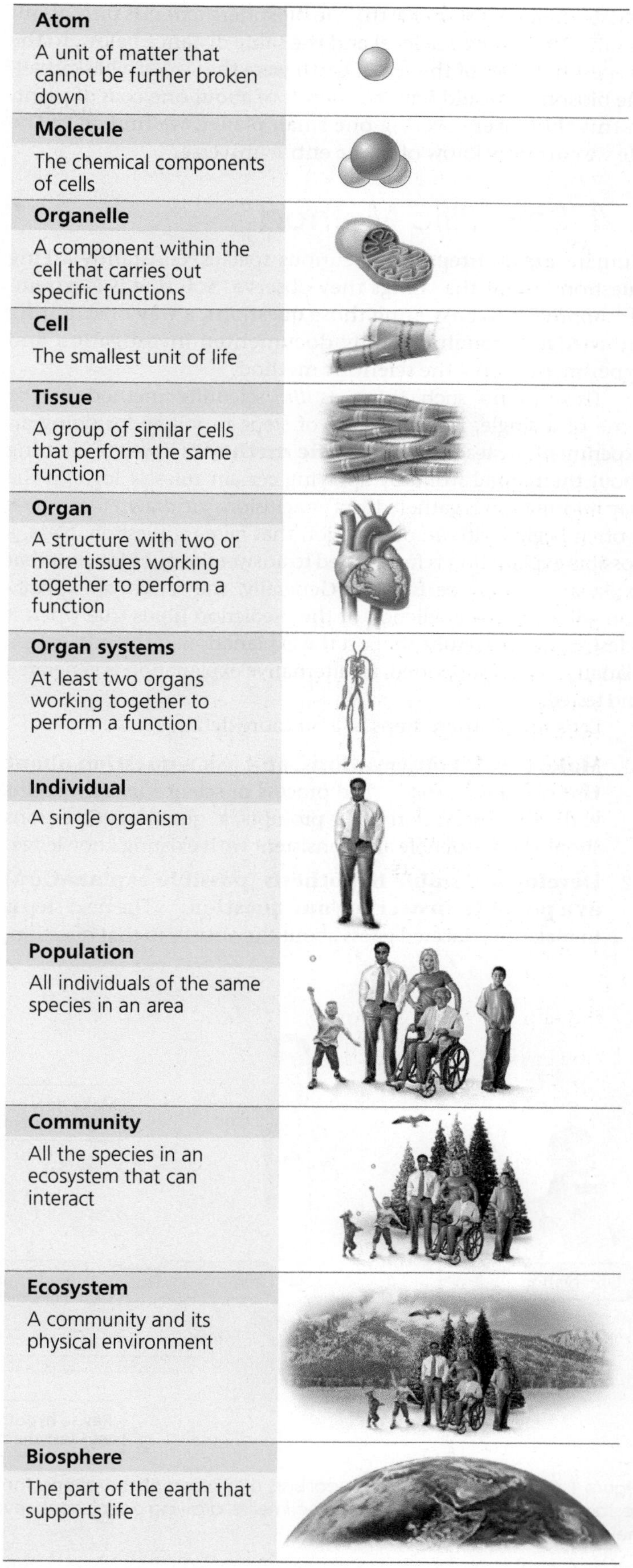

Atom	A unit of matter that cannot be further broken down
Molecule	The chemical components of cells
Organelle	A component within the cell that carries out specific functions
Cell	The smallest unit of life
Tissue	A group of similar cells that perform the same function
Organ	A structure with two or more tissues working together to perform a function
Organ systems	At least two organs working together to perform a function
Individual	A single organism
Population	All individuals of the same species in an area
Community	All the species in an ecosystem that can interact
Ecosystem	A community and its physical environment
Biosphere	The part of the earth that supports life

Figure 1.3 Levels of organization of life

where life can exist on Earth. The biosphere extends only about 11 km (7 mi) above sea level and the same distance below, to the deepest trenches of the sea. If Earth were the size of a basketball, the biosphere would have the depth of about one coat of paint. In this thin layer covering one small planet, we find all of the life we currently know of in the entire universe.

1.4 Scientific Method

Humans are an irrepressibly curious species, constantly asking questions about the things they observe. **Science** is a systematic approach to answering those questions, a way of acquiring knowledge through carefully documented investigation and experimentation—the scientific method.

There is no such thing as *the* scientific method in the sense of a single, formalized set of steps to follow for doing an experiment. Instead, the **scientific method** is a way of learning about the natural world by applying certain rules of logic to the way information is gathered and conclusions are drawn (Figure 1.4). It often begins with an observation that raises a question. Next, a possible explanation is formulated to answer the question, but that explanation must be testable. Generally, the tentative explanation will lead to a prediction. If the prediction holds true when it is tested, the test results support the explanation. If the original explanation is not supported, an alternative explanation is generated and tested.

Let's review these steps in a bit more detail.

1. **Make careful observations, and ask a question about the observations.** The process of science usually begins with an observation that prompts a question. Questions should be reasonable and consistent with existing knowledge.

2. **Develop a testable hypothesis (possible explanation) as a possible answer to your question.** The next step is to make an educated guess about the answer to that question, called a **hypothesis.** The hypothesis should be a clearly defined statement, not a question. It should be possible to test a hypothesis and to prove it false. Keep in mind that although a hypothesis can be shown to be false, it can never be proved to be true. You can collect data that support a hypothesis, but you must also rule out other possible explanations (alternative hypotheses).

Generally, the hypothesis leads to one or more predictions that will support the hypothesis if they hold true when tested. Depending on the hypothesis, the test may involve further observations or experimental manipulation.

Different hypotheses can sometimes lead to identical predictions. In such a case, a test can support or refute both hypotheses, depending on the outcome. In this event, it is necessary to make other predictions that will allow us to reject one of the hypotheses. When we find that the results of various tests are more consistent with one hypothesis than with others, we must still be cautious. New evidence may come to light that will disprove the hypothesis, or a new hypothesis may be proposed that is also consistent with the observations.

3. **Make a prediction based on your hypothesis, and test it with a controlled experiment.** Now you make a prediction regarding what should occur if the hypothesis is correct. This prediction will determine the experiment or observations that are necessary to test the hypothesis.

Ideally, your experiment will be designed in such a way that there can be only one explanation for the results. In such an experiment, called a **controlled experiment,** the research subjects are randomly divided into two groups. One group is designated as the **control group** and the other one as the **experimental group.** Both groups are treated in the same way except for the *one* factor, called the independent **variable,** whose effect the experiment is designed to reveal.

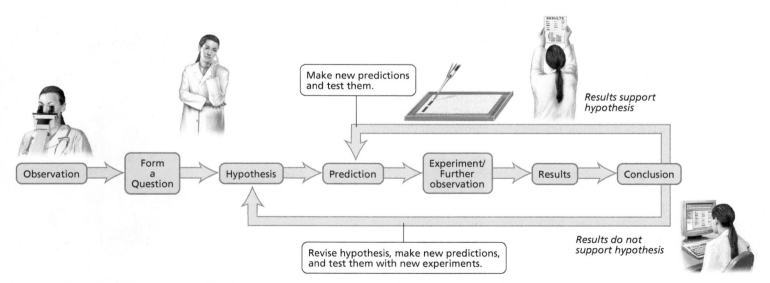

Figure 1.4 The scientific process consists of making observations, formulating questions, creating testable hypotheses, conducting experiments, drawing conclusions, revising hypotheses, and designing new experiments.

Q: How would you modify this diagram to indicate that testing alternative hypotheses is part of the scientific method?

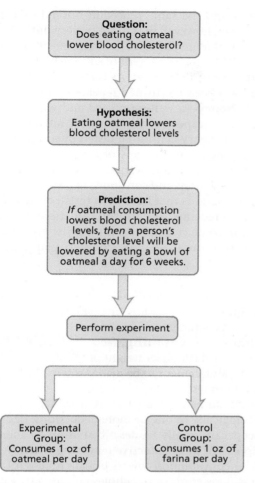

Figure 1.5 The design of an experiment to test the prediction that oatmeal lowers blood cholesterol levels

In a scientific study, additional variables that have not been controlled for, and may have affected the outcome, are called *confounding variables.* When there are confounding variables, we cannot say for sure which variable or variables caused the effect.

Let's see how the scientific method works. An advertisement on television proclaims that eating a daily bowl of oatmeal lowers blood cholesterol levels. Lowering levels of blood cholesterol is desirable because elevated cholesterol is related to atherosclerosis, a condition in which fatty deposits clog blood vessels. In turn, atherosclerosis increases one's risk of having a heart attack or stroke.

What observation(s) led to this claim? Oatmeal contains the soluble fiber ß-glucan. We begin to gather information about soluble fiber and learn the following:

- Soluble fiber binds to bile in the intestines, preventing bile from being reabsorbed into the body.

- Bile is high in cholesterol.

- Bile bound to soluble fiber is removed from the body in feces.

- The liver then removes cholesterol from the blood to synthesize new bile.

What experiment would support the claim that oatmeal lowers blood cholesterol? Scientists would first formulate a hypothesis.

In this case, the hypothesis might be that ß-glucan in oatmeal lowers blood cholesterol levels. They would then make a prediction that will hold true if the hypothesis is correct: *If* oatmeal consumption lowers blood cholesterol levels, *then* a person will lower his or her cholesterol level by eating a bowl of oatmeal a day for 6 weeks (Figure 1.5). The component of total cholesterol measured was the LDL (low-density lipoprotein) cholesterol-carrier, because this "bad" form of cholesterol promotes atherosclerosis. To test this hypothesis, we could gather adults whose LDL cholesterol levels are similar—between 4.5 mmol/L and 5.5 mmol/L—and divide them randomly into two groups. Volunteers in the experimental group consume a 1 oz packet of oatmeal per day for 6 weeks. Those in the control group eat a 1 oz packet of farina, a wheat cereal lacking ß-glucan. At the end of 6 weeks, the blood level of LDL cholesterol of each volunteer is measured again.

STOP and THINK

Why is randomly dividing the volunteers into groups a better experimental design than allowing the volunteers to choose their group?

4. **Draw a conclusion based on the results of the experiment.** Next, you arrive at a **conclusion,** which is an interpretation of the data. The results of a scientific experiment are often summarized in a graph, such as the one shown in Figure 1.6, which presents the results of the experiment we just described. When you read a graph, first look at the axes. The horizontal line, or x-axis, shows the independent variable—the variable altered by the researcher. In this case, the independent variable is the amount of soluble fiber consumed. The vertical line is the y-axis; it presents the dependent variable, that is, the variable that was changed by the independent variable. In this experiment, the dependent variable was the blood level of LDL cholesterol. Always read the labels on the axes to see what the graph pertains to, and notice the scale so that you can appreciate the extent of variation. In this case, we use a bar graph to present the results, because each treatment is a discrete category. Notice in Figure 1.6 that blood levels of LDL cholesterol declined more in the

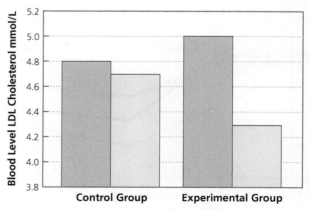

Figure 1.6 Cholesterol level in blood decreases with increased consumption of oatmeal.

experimental group than in the control group. Thus, we might conclude that eating oatmeal lowers blood LDL cholesterol.

Could these results be due to chance alone? Scientists base conclusions on the **statistical significance** of the data, which is a measure of the possibility that the results were due to chance. A probability of less than 5% (written as $p < 0.05$) that the results are due to chance is generally acceptable. The lower the number, the more confidence we have in the accuracy of the results. In this experiment, the differences in blood LDL cholesterol at the end of the treatment phase were statistically significant from the starting values.

5. **Make new predictions, and test them.** The experiment supports our hypothesis: ß-glucan in oatmeal lowers blood LDL cholesterol levels. We might, therefore, make two additional predictions: (1) If one consumes greater amounts of oatmeal, then the cholesterol-lowering effect should be greater; and (2) if one stops eating oatmeal, then blood LDL cholesterol levels should rise again.

We could test these predictions by gathering another, larger group of volunteers with blood LDL cholesterol levels between 4.5 mmol/L and 5.5 mmol/L and dividing them randomly into four groups. In the three experimental groups, volunteers consume one, two, or three 1 oz packets of oatmeal per day. Volunteers in the control group eat a 1 oz packet of farina. Levels of LDL cholesterol in the blood are measured 6 weeks after the volunteers begin eating their designated type and amount of cereal, and again 6 weeks after the volunteers stop eating cereal.

This time we use a line graph to indicate the changes in LDL cholesterol over time. In this experiment, the dependent variable, indicated on the vertical y-axis, is the blood level of LDL cholesterol. The independent variable is the amount of soluble fiber consumed over time. Notice in Figure 1.7 that the cholesterol-lowering effect of oatmeal increases with the amount of oatmeal consumed and that this effect slowly reverses once cereal consumption stops.

Another requirement of scientific inquiry is that experiments must be repeated and yield similar results. Other scientists following the same procedure should obtain a similar outcome. Note, however, that it can be very difficult to identify all the factors that might affect the outcome of an experiment.

The testing and refinement of a hypothesis represents one level of the scientific process. As time passes, related hypotheses that have been confirmed repeatedly can be fit together to form a **theory**—a well-supported and wide-ranging explanation of some aspect of the physical universe. Because of its breadth, a theory cannot be tested by a single experiment but instead emerges from many observations, hypotheses, and experiments. Nevertheless, a theory, like a hypothesis, leads to additional predictions and continued experimentation. Among the few explanations that have been tested thoroughly enough to be considered theories are the cell theory of life (which says all cells come from preexisting cells) and the theory of evolution by natural selection (which you learn about in Chapter 22).

Inductive and Deductive Reasoning

Scientific investigation usually involves two types of reasoning: inductive and deductive.

In **inductive reasoning,** facts are accumulated through observation until the sheer weight of the evidence allows some logical general statement to be made. You use inductive reasoning to develop a testable hypothesis.

Deductive reasoning begins with a general statement that leads logically to one or more deductions, or conclusions. The process can usually be described as an "if-then" series of associations. We used deductive reasoning when we predicted, "*If* oatmeal consumption lowers blood cholesterol levels, *then* a person will lower his or her cholesterol level by eating a bowl of oatmeal a day for 6 weeks." This prediction helped us decide whether the results of the experiment supported or refuted the hypothesis.

Clinical Trials

Before testing a new drug or treatment on humans, scientists must take steps to ensure that it will not do more harm than good (Table 1.1). Usually a drug is tested first on animals, such as laboratory rodents. Rats and mice are mammals, so some aspects of their physiology are similar to, and can be generalized to, human physiology. Using rodents to test drugs offers a number of advantages: they are relatively inexpensive to use, have short life spans, and reproduce quickly. Research on animals also helps determine how the body handles the drug, which

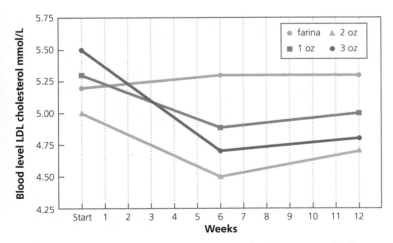

Figure 1.7 Oatmeal's cholesterol-lowering effect increases with the amount of oatmeal consumed.

Table 1.1	Tests Performed on a New Drug before It Is Approved by the Food and Drug Administration (FDA)
Tests on laboratory animals	
Is the drug safe for use on animals?	
Clinical trials	
Phase I	Is the drug safe for humans?
Phase II	Does the drug work for its intended purpose?
Phase III	How does the new drug compare with other available treatments?

helps determine dosage. Most medical advances, including vaccinations, chemotherapy, new surgical techniques, and organ transplants, began with animal studies. Strict rules safeguard the care and use of animals in research and testing.

If no ill effects are discovered in animals receiving the drug, then studies on humans, called *clinical trials,* may begin. In all phases of clinical testing, the studies are done on people who volunteer. In phase I of a clinical trial, the drug is screened for safety on fewer than 100 healthy people. At this stage, researchers hope to learn whether they can safely give the drug to humans, determine the effective dosage range, and identify side effects.

If the drug is found to be safe, it is tested further. In phase II of a clinical trial, a few hundred people with the target disease are given the drug to see whether it works for its intended purpose. If it does, the new drug will be compared with alternative treatments in phase III trials. Thousands of participants are involved in phase III of a clinical trial. The U.S. Food and Drug Administration (FDA) approves only those drugs or treatments that have passed all three phases of human-subjects testing.

what would YOU do? The job of the FDA is to ensure the safety and effectiveness of new drugs and treatments. It must balance the patients' desires for access to new treatments against the government's desire to protect patients from treatments that may be unsafe or ineffective. The drug approval process is painstakingly slow, usually taking more than 8 years. Do you think that the FDA should bypass certain steps of the approval process to make new drugs available to critically ill patients who may not be able to wait? If you do, what criteria should be used to decide the degree of illness that would warrant treatment with a drug that was not yet approved? Who should be held responsible if early access to a drug of unknown safety causes a patient to suffer serious side effects or premature death? ■

Recall that a well-designed experiment has both an experimental group and a control group. Clinical studies are no different. In a drug trial, the experimental group receives the drug under consideration. The control group receives a **placebo,** an innocuous, nondrug substance made to look like the drug being tested. Study participants are randomly assigned to either the control group or the experimental group and do not know whether they are receiving the treatment or a placebo. When neither the researchers nor the study participants know which people are receiving treatment and which are receiving the placebo, the study is described as being *double-blind.* It is important that participants not know whether they are receiving the placebo or the drug because their expectations about the drug could affect the way they respond. Similarly, researchers should not know which people are in the experimental or control groups because their expectations or desire for a particular result could affect their interpretation of the data.

Finally, it is extremely important, and legally required, that study participants give their **informed consent** before the trial begins. An informed consent document lists all the possible harmful effects of the drug or treatment and must be signed before a person can take part in the study. To give informed consent, study participants must be mentally capable of understanding the treatment and risks, so they cannot be mentally impaired as a result of mental retardation, mental or other illness, or substance abuse.

Epidemiological Studies

Human health can also be studied without clinical trials. In an epidemiological study, researchers look at patterns that occur within large populations. For example, an epidemiological study to investigate the effects of air pollution on asthma (a condition in which airway constriction causes breathing problems) would look for a correlation of some kind between the variable of interest (air pollution) and its suspected effects (worsening of asthma). If the researchers' hypothesis is that air pollution aggravates asthma, they might predict and then look for evidence that the number of people admitted to hospitals for asthma-related problems rises with increased levels of air pollution.

Recent epidemiological studies have asked the question, "Does using a cell phone increase your risk of developing brain cancer?" Cell phones emit radiofrequency waves and are usually held to one's ear (Figure 1.8). Based on a 2011 review of epidemiological studies of cell phone use and brain cancer, the World Health Organization (WHO) stated that cell phone use is "possibly carcinogenic to humans." The WHO statement is a cautious recommendation based largely on a study in which researchers tracked nearly 13,000 cell phone users from 13 countries over 10 years. A comparison of brain cancer rates of *all* people who used cell phones and *all* people who never used a cell phone did not show a difference in brain tumor rates. However, when the heaviest cell phone users were compared with all others (cell phone users and nonusers), researchers found a slight increase of brain cancer among heavy cell phone users. Thus, this study does not conclusively demonstrate a link between cell phone use and cancer, but it doesn't rule out the possibility.

Soon after the WHO report, a new epidemiological study was released—the largest to date. In the new study, researchers followed more than 350,000 cell phone users for over 10 years.

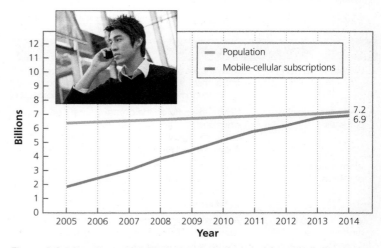

Figure 1.8 More than 4.6 billion people in the world use cell phones.

They did not find a dose-response relationship between cell phone use and the development of cancer. In other words, the incidence of brain tumors did not increase with the length of cell phone use and was not greater in the regions of the brain most heavily exposed to cell phone radiation. Nearly all studies to date have failed to show a link between cell phone use and brain cancer. Although these results are reassuring, additional research must be done. Cell phone use is a relatively new practice, and many cancers take years to develop. You can find current information on cell phones and cancer on the website of the American Cancer Society.

1.5 Critical Thinking to Evaluate Scientific Claims

Few of us perform controlled experiments in our everyday lives, but all of us must evaluate the likely validity of scientific claims. We encounter them in many forms—as advertisements, news stories, and anecdotes told by friends. We often must make decisions based on these claims, but how can we decide whether they are valid? Critical-thinking skills can help us analyze the information and make prudent decisions.

The key to becoming a critical thinker is to ask questions. The following list is not exhaustive, but it may help guide your thinking process.

1. **Is the information consistent with information from other sources?** The best way to answer this question is to gather as much information as possible from a variety of sources. Do not passively accept a report as true. Do some research.

2. **How reliable is the source of the information?** Investigate the source of the information to determine whether that person or group has the necessary scientific expertise (Table 1.2). Is there any reason to think the claim may be biased? Who stands to gain if you accept it as true? For example, the FDA is probably a more reliable source of information on the effectiveness of a drug than is the drug company marketing the drug. If a claim is controversial, listen to both sides of the debate, and be aware of who is arguing on each side.

3. **Was the information obtained through proper scientific procedures?** Information gathered through controlled experiments is more reliable than anecdotal evidence, which cannot be verified. For example, your friend might tell you that his muscles have gotten larger since he started using some special exercise equipment. But you cannot be sure unless measurements were taken before and after he began to use it. Even if your friend can prove his muscles are bigger with such measurements, there is no guarantee that exercising with this equipment will build *your* muscles.

4. **Were experimental results interpreted correctly?** Consider, for example, a headline advertising capsules containing fish oils: "Fish Oils Increase Longevity." It may be tempting to conclude from this headline that you will live longer if you take fish oil supplements, but in fact the headline is referring to an experiment in which *dietary* fish oil increased longevity in *rats*. Rats fed a diet high in fish oils lived longer than did rats on a diet low in fish oil. The claim that taking fish oil supplements will increase longevity is not a valid conclusion based on the experiment. First, the study was done on rats, not on humans. Not all aspects of rat physiology generalize to humans. For example, rats are more resistant to heart disease than are humans. Second, the amount of dietary fish oil, not the amount of fish oil from capsules, was the variable in the study the headline refers to. Supplements of fish oil may not have the same effect as dietary fish oils. It could be that taking fish oil supplements would boost the amount of fish oil in your body to unhealthy levels.

5. **Are there other possible explanations for the results?** Suppose you learn that the fish oil headline is based on a study showing that people who eat fish at least three times a week live longer than people who eat fish less frequently. In this case, the data indicate that there is a correlation between fish in the diet and length of life. However, a correlation between two factors does not prove that one *caused* the other. Instead, the two factors may *both* be caused by a third factor. In this case, the difference in longevity may be due to other differences in the lifestyles of the two groups. For instance, people who eat fish may exercise more frequently or have less stressful jobs or live in areas with less pollution.

As your critical-thinking skills develop, so should your information literacy skills. **Information literacy** involves the ability to recognize what you need to know, locate relevant information, evaluate it, apply it to the problem at hand, and communicate it effectively. These skills are important in our personal lives, as well as in education, the workforce, and society.

We are presented with a wealth (or some might say a glut) of information, much of which comes to us through technology. When in need of an answer, many of us find "an app for that." Thus, **information technology literacy** is also essential.

Throughout your life you will be asked to make many decisions about scientific issues. Some will affect your community

Table 1.2	How to Identify a Reliable Website
Who is the author?	Does the website provide information about the author? If not, try "Googling" the author's name to learn more about his or her affiliations.
Who is the publisher of the site?	Notice the suffix on the domain name (.edu = educational; .gov = government; .org = nonprofit organization; .com = commercial). A commercial site is likely to be more biased.
What is the purpose of the website?	Is it a report on a study by a reliable organization? Is its purpose to promote scholarship? Is its purpose to market a product? Is its purpose to present personal opinion?
When was the information posted?	Are there older or more recent websites that support or contradict the information presented in this website?

and even beyond. For example, should we eliminate genetically modified food? Should stem cell research be permitted? Should companies polluting the atmosphere be taxed at a higher rate? We will raise these and similar questions throughout this textbook. You will encounter such questions in your studies, and you will find others every day in the local and national news media.

Although you may never be one of the lawmakers deciding these issues, you are a voter who can help choose the lawmakers and voice your opinions to the lawmakers who will decide. Scientists can provide facts that may be useful as we all struggle to answer the complex questions facing society, but they cannot provide simple answers. As scientific knowledge grows and our choices become increasingly complex, each of us must stay informed and review the issues critically.

LOOKING AHEAD

In this chapter, we considered the characteristics of life and the nature of scientific thinking. In the next chapter, we will explore ways to use critical-thinking skills to make wise decisions as health care consumers.

CONSIDER THIS CASE

A major drug company has asked Maribel to test a rain forest plant that, according to what a rain forest native told her, brings relief to people who are having difficulty breathing. She suspects that it might be a good treatment for asthma, a condition in which constriction of airways causes breathing problems. She isolated a component of this plant as a drug. Tests on animals show that it is effective.

- How should Maribel design an experiment for phase I of the clinical trials? What will be the variable? What will be the control? If the results are positive, what can Maribel conclude?

- What experimental design should Maribel use in phase II of the clinical trials? What will be the variable? What will be the control? If the results are positive, what can Maribel conclude?

- How should Maribel design an experiment for phase III of the clinical trials? What will be the variable? What will be the control? If the results are positive, what can Maribel conclude?

Chapter Review   MasteringBiology®

Students Go to MasteringBiology for assignments, the eText, and the Study Area with animations, practice tests, and activities.

Professors Go to MasteringBiology for automatically graded tutorials and questions that you can assign to your students, plus Instructor Resources.

Highlighting the Concepts

1.1 Basic Characteristics of All Living Things (pp. 1–4)

- Life cannot be defined, only characterized.
- Living things contain nucleic acids, proteins, carbohydrates, and lipids; are made of cells; grow and reproduce; metabolize; detect and respond to stimuli; and maintain homeostasis. Populations of living things evolve over long periods of time.

1.2 Evolution: A Unifying Theme in Biology (pp. 4–5)

- Classifications of living organisms reflect the evolutionary relationships among them. One currently popular classification system recognizes three domains: Bacteria, Archaea, and Eukarya. Domain Eukarya consists of four kingdoms: protists, fungi, plants, and animals.
- Humans are classified as animals, vertebrates, mammals, and primates.

1.3 Levels of Biological Organization (pp. 5–6)

- Human biology can be studied at different levels. Within an individual, the levels of increasing complexity are molecules, cells, tissues, organs, and organ systems.
- Beyond the level of the individual are populations, communities, ecosystems, and the biosphere.

1.4 Scientific Method (pp. 6–10)

- The scientific method consists of making observations, formulating a question and a good hypothesis (a testable, possible

explanation), conducting experiments (performed with controls), and drawing a conclusion, which may lead to further experimentation.
- As evidence mounts in support of related hypotheses, the hypotheses may be organized into a theory, which is a well-supported explanation of nature.
- Inductive reasoning uses a large number of specific observations to arrive at a general conclusion. Deductive reasoning, in contrast, uses "if-then" logic to progress from the general to the specific.
- Strict rules govern experiments on humans and other animals. Drugs are usually tested on animals before humans. Phase I trials determine whether the drug is safe for humans, phase II determines whether it works for its intended purpose, and phase III determines whether it is more effective than existing treatments.
- The design of a human experiment often includes an experimental group that receives the treatment and a control group that receives a placebo. In what is known as a double-blind experiment, neither the study participants nor the researchers know who is receiving the real treatment.
- Study participants must sign an informed consent document indicating that they were made aware of the possible harmful consequences of the treatment.
- Epidemiological studies examine patterns within populations to find a correlation between a variable and its suspected effects.

1.5 Critical Thinking to Evaluate Scientific Claims (pp. 10–11)

■ Critical thinking consists of asking questions, forming hypotheses, gathering information, and evaluating evidence and its source carefully before drawing conclusions.

■ Information literacy involves the ability to identify what you need to know, locate relevant information, evaluate it, apply it to the problem at hand, and communicate it effectively.

■ Information technology literacy involves knowing how to effectively use technology to answer questions and solve problems.

Recognizing Key Terms

cell *p. 2*
metabolism *p. 2*
homeostasis *p. 4*
adaptive trait *p. 4*
population *p. 5*
community *p. 5*
ecosystem *p. 5*

biosphere *p. 5*
science *p. 6*
scientific method *p. 6*
hypothesis *p. 6*
controlled experiment *p. 6*
control group *p. 6*

experimental group *p. 6*
variable *p. 6*
conclusion *p. 7*
statistical significance *p. 8*
theory *p. 8*
inductive reasoning *p. 8*

deductive reasoning *p. 8*
placebo *p. 9*
informed consent *p. 9*
information literacy *p. 10*
information technology
   literacy *p. 10*

Reviewing the Concepts

1. What is the highest level in the classification of life?
a. genus
b. kingdom
c. family
d. domain

2. Forward-looking eyes are characteristic of
a. eukaryotes.
b. mammals.
c. primates.
d. animals.

3. Which of the following is an example of a population?
a. all individuals of the same species in an area
b. all the species that can interact in an ecosystem
c. a community and its interaction with the physical environment
d. the part of Earth that supports life

4. Which of the following is an example of an epidemiological experiment?
a. To test the effectiveness of a drug, researchers administer it to an experimental group of subjects but not to a control group of subjects.
b. Researchers look at the pattern of cancer development across populations in New England.
c. Researchers conduct a clinical trial to determine whether a treatment for multiple sclerosis is effective.
d. Researchers conduct a double-blind study to determine whether fish oil supplements reduce the frequency of heart attacks.

5. A theory is
a. a testable explanation for an observation.
b. a conclusion based on the results of an experiment.
c. a wide-ranging explanation for natural events that has been extensively tested over time.
d. the factor that is altered in a controlled experiment.

6. Which of the following is *not* an example of a good scientific question?
a. Does obesity reduce one's life expectancy?
b. Does dietary fat increase a woman's chance of developing breast cancer?
c. Does a full moon cause people to behave irrationally?
d. Does temperature alter the rate of an enzymatic reaction?

7. A trait that increases the chance that an organism will survive and reproduce in its natural environment is described as being
a. adaptive.
b. inductive.
c. hypothetical.
d. deductive.

8. A hypothesis is
a. a conclusion that has been tested repeatedly.
b. a significant result from an experiment.
c. a testable explanation for an observation.
d. a relationship between two factors.

Applying the Concepts

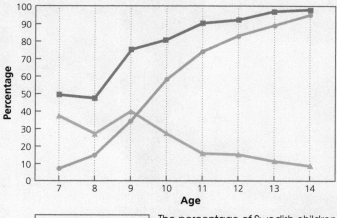

- ■ Do you have access to a mobile phone?
- ▲ Do you use a mobile phone that you share in the family?
- ● Do you have a mobile phone of your own?

The percentage of Swedish children questioned who answered yes to three questions about cell phone use.

F. Soderqvist et al., "Ownership and use of wireless telephones: a population-based study of Swedish children aged 7–14 years," BMC Public Health 7 [2007]: 105–113, (fig. 1, p. 107).

1. Interpret the accompanying graph to answer the questions.
   a. What percentage of these 7-year-old children have access to a cell phone?
   b. At a young age, these children share a cell phone with their family. At what age does sharing begin to decline?
   c. What percentage of 10-year-old children own their own cell phone?
2. Find an advertisement that makes a scientific claim. Use your critical-thinking skills to evaluate that claim.

Finding and Evaluating Information

Most of us agree that trees enhance the quality of our lives. Researchers[1] have found a connection between health and the loss of trees in the community. See the excerpt below from The U.S. Department of Agriculture Forest Service's report on this research. As you read, consider what you have learned about the scientific method. The entire report can be found at: www.fs.fed.us/pnw/sciencef/scifi158.pdf

"Humans have intuitively understood the value of trees to their physical and mental health since the beginning of recorded time. A scientist with the Pacific Northwest Research Station wondered if such a link could be scientifically validated. His research team took advantage of an infestation of emerald ash borer, an invasive pest that kills ash trees, to conduct a study that gets closer to a definitive connection between the loss of trees and increased human mortality.

Researchers analyzed data on demographics, tree loss from the emerald ash borer, and human mortality from lower respiratory disease and cardiovascular disease for 1990 through 2007. Results showed that the spread of the emerald ash borer across 15

states—first recorded in 2002—was associated with an additional 15,000 deaths from cardiovascular disease and an additional 6,000 deaths from lower respiratory disease. Human mortality increased the longer emerald ash borer was present and killing trees. Deaths occurred at higher rates in wealthier counties, where more trees are typically found than in urban areas."

Although the study doesn't establish causation, it does suggest a link between trees and human health. This information can be applied to a range of fields including public health, urban forestry, and urban planning.

1. How reliable is the source of the information?

2. Are the conclusions in the paper valid based on the experimental design and results?

3. List some alternative explanations for results and explain how or why they could (or can) be ruled out?

4. Many factors in the environment may influence our health. Use reliable sources of information (books, newspapers, magazines, journals, or trustworthy websites) to identify sources that indicate the environment does (or does not) influence human health. Begin by planning a strategy for your search. Keep a log of each source you use, and evaluate it for reliability and helpfulness. Provide a citation for each source you use.

[1]Donovan, G.H.; Butry, D.T.; Michael, Y.L.; Prestemon, J.P.; Gatziolis, D.; Mao, M.Y. 2013. The relationship between trees and health: evidence from the spread of the emerald ash borer. *American Journal of Preventive Medicine*. 44: 139–145. http://www .treesearch.fs.fed.us/pubs/45049.

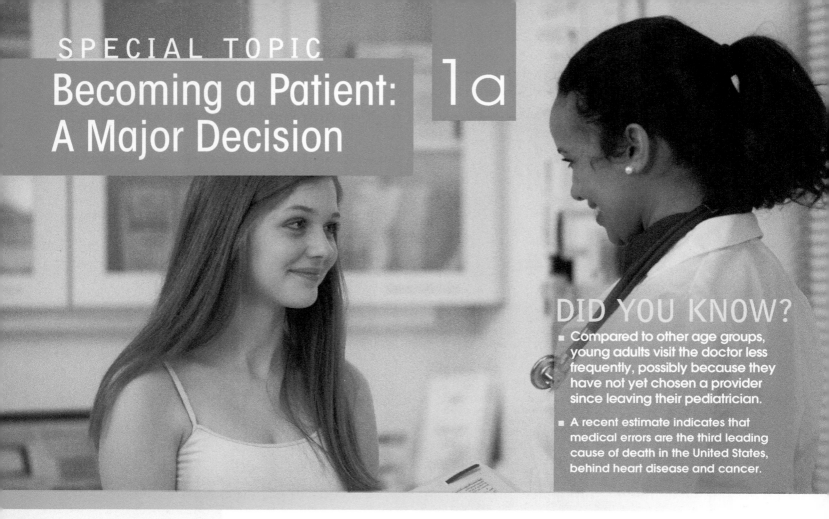

DID YOU KNOW?

- Compared to other age groups, young adults visit the doctor less frequently, possibly because they have not yet chosen a provider since leaving their pediatrician.

- A recent estimate indicates that medical errors are the third leading cause of death in the United States, behind heart disease and cancer.

THE INSTITUTE OF MEDICINE estimates that nearly half of all adults in the United States have inadequate health literacy, which means they have difficulty accessing, understanding, and using health information to make appropriate health decisions. In Chapter 1 we considered several aspects of critical thinking, including the importance of asking questions, gathering information, and evaluating sources of information to make an informed decision. In this chapter, we show how to apply your critical-thinking skills when you become a patient. We emphasize the importance of asking questions about your personal health and health care, and we describe how and where to find reliable medical information. Our goal is to help you be an active and informed participant in decisions regarding your health and health care.

1a.1 Young Adults and Health Care

When compared with other age groups, fewer young adults, defined as those between 18 and 25 years of age, use health care systems. In fact, compared with those immediately younger (adolescents, 12 to 17 years of age) and older (adults, 26 to 44 years of age), young adults have significantly lower rates of office-based visits, such as regular physical and dental checkups. These lower rates do not necessarily reflect better health in young adults than in the other age groups. One explanation, identified by the Institute of Medicine in its 2014 report titled "Investing in the Health and Well-Being of Young Adults," is the challenge of transitioning from pediatric/adolescent care to adult care. During this transition, young adults face the daunting task of finding a new set of health care providers. And unlike when they were adolescents, young adults often must find new care providers independently of parents or guardians. This chapter will help you make the transition to adult health care.

1a.2 Selecting a Primary Care Physician

Do you have a primary care provider? If your answer is "no" or "I don't know," then here are some steps that you can follow to become an active participant in your own health care. We hear a great deal about health care in the media every day, especially about the need for taking personal responsibility for our health. Finding a primary care provider you can work with to maintain and improve your health is a critical step in this process. Here we focus on primary care physicians. However, some patients have a physician assistant or a nurse practitioner, rather than a doctor, as their primary care provider. These providers consult with physicians. The general steps for selecting a physician assistant or a nurse practitioner are similar to those we describe for doctors.

Responsibilities of Primary Care Physicians

A primary care physician has training in family medicine, general internal medicine, or general pediatrics. This type of physician treats common medical conditions and advises patients on broad aspects of health care, including preventive care. He or she provides care in non-emergency situations, usually in an office or clinic. Patients requiring urgent medical attention typically visit an urgent care facility or an emergency room, commonly known as the ER. Visits to the ER are appropriate for severe illnesses or injuries but not for routine examinations. A primary care physician is often your gateway to more specialized services, should you need referral to a medical specialist. If you are admitted to the hospital, your primary care physician may oversee or participate in your care. As your primary care physician will be an important person in your life, you should think carefully about the qualities you are seeking in him or her.

Primary Care Physician Settings

Some primary care physicians have their own private practice, while others work as part of a team in large health centers and health maintenance organizations. Large health centers offer the convenience of "one-stop shopping" because they provide most basic medical services, including blood drawing, x-ray exams, and pharmacy, with the separate departments housed under one roof. The downside of such an arrangement is that you may not always see the same primary care physician. At the other extreme, if your primary care physician is in private practice, then you may have to visit several physical locations to obtain needed services, cope with different billing arrangements, and take greater personal responsibility for following through with recommended tests. The big advantage is that you will always see the same physician, and this may lead to a more rewarding and long-term doctor–patient relationship that promotes continuity of care.

Evaluating Primary Care Physicians

The keys to finding a primary care physician include obtaining a list of providers from your insurance organization, knowing the minimum requirements, and then considering features related to style of care. Asking for a list of providers early in the process helps to ensure that your insurance company will not contest future medical bills. At a minimum, your primary care physician should have excellent skills at record keeping, a patient-oriented approach, and strength of character, for doctors sometimes have to deliver bad news. Having an accessible location is also important. Most physicians do not communicate with their patients via e-mail or other electronic media. Nor do they generally answer personal health questions over the telephone. You will need to visit the office, so it should be conveniently located. Finally, make sure that you can get an appointment with your doctor in a reasonable amount of time after you request one.

Next, you should consider style of care, which varies among doctors. For example, one physician may emphasize friendly, informal conversation as a way to engage you in your care, inviting your involvement in decision making. Another may sit formally with you in the examination room or office, in a more authoritarian approach. Excellent medical outcomes may result from either of these strategies, and, of course, a continuum exists between them. Some doctors may emphasize prevention, whereas others focus on treatment of disease. Also, when treating disease, some physicians may pursue a conservative course and others a more aggressive one. The important point is to be comfortable with your physician and his or her style. If you are to engage a doctor's training and knowledge in helping you be well, you must be completely honest about all aspects of your health and lifestyle. Above all, a primary care physician must be someone you trust to put you and your health concerns first.

With all the choices out there, where do you start? Here are some ideas. If you are in good health and need only general medical care, then perhaps the best strategy is to ask for recommendations from another physician you already know and respect. For example, if you are leaving a pediatric/adolescent practice, your current doctor may be an excellent reference for a primary care physician. It is also important to ask others. Find out which doctors your friends see and what they have to say about them. Go to the website of a prospective practice to learn about office hours, after-hours care, and what happens when the doctor is unavailable. You also can access public information on physicians. For example, the database of the Federation of State Medical Boards (www.fsmb.org) provides information on the professional qualifications of doctors (e.g., education and states in which they are licensed to practice) and any disciplinary actions by state medical boards against them. Visit the office, talk with the staff, and assess their courtesy, professionalism, and organization. Ask whether the practice has fully functional systems for maintaining electronic medical records (data pertaining to the services provided a patient at a particular care delivery organization, which owns this legal record) and electronic health records (a subset of data from various care delivery organizations that have treated a particular patient; the patient owns this record and can access it and append information).

Once you have narrowed your search for a primary care physician, how do you get in to visit a prospective doctor? The first step is to call the doctor's office and ask whether she or he is accepting new patients. If the answer is yes, then ask whether it would be possible to meet the doctor for an initial consultation. In some cases, you may have to pay for this consultation. Another strategy is to wait until you have a minor health problem, call the doctor's office, and ask whether you can see the doctor about it. If you are not satisfied with a physician, then continue your search until you find one to suit your needs.

1a.3 Getting the Most Out of an Appointment with Your Doctor

A visit to your doctor is going to be a short yet important interaction. Know ahead of time the length of your appointment, especially the duration of face-to-face time with your doctor. Keep in mind that most appointments last less than 20 minutes and might occur only once a year, as in an annual physical examination. By preparing for your visit in advance, you can make the most of the opportunity to learn from your physician and stay healthy.

Preparing for an Appointment

Before your visit, take time to make a list of medical questions and concerns; simple checklists are available to help you prepare for the appointment (Figure 1a.1). If some aspect of your physical or mental health is bothering you, then include it on the list. Prioritize the list so that your most serious two or three concerns are addressed. Along with your concerns, bring a list (or the actual containers) of any medications (prescribed and over-the-counter) that you are currently taking and the doses; include vitamins and supplements because they can interact with over-the-counter and prescription medications. Think about your personal medical history, including current medical conditions as well as past illnesses, medical procedures and surgeries, and your family's medical history. Make notes on any health challenges that either you or your immediate family members have experienced. Be sure to bring relevant documents, such as test results, records from other physicians, and insurance information. Be conservative about bringing documents from your personal research into your health concerns. This advice is not meant to discourage you from researching health issues on your own, but, rather, to warn you against bringing stacks of printouts to an appointment. Doctors need the freedom to perform their own independent assessment without being sidetracked by other information. Finally, you may want to ask a family member or friend to go with you to your appointment (Figure 1a.2). Although you may not want your companion in the examining room, having someone with you can be very helpful during the consultation phase of the appointment. Companions can provide support and take notes, both of which can result in more information being exchanged during the appointment and remembered afterward. Consistency is important, so bring the same family member or friend to your various appointments. Ideally, your companion should be the health care agent you have chosen to act on your behalf should you be unable to speak for yourself (see Section 1a.5).

Figure 1a.1 Completing a checklist, such as the one shown here, before your doctor's appointment can help you get the most out of your appointment.
From ParTNers for Health, State of Tennessee Group Insurance Program, www.partnersforhealthtn.gov

What to Expect during an Appointment

Typical preliminaries before a medical examination include recording weight, height, and blood pressure. These preliminaries take only a few minutes and are usually performed by staff. If the staff member doesn't tell you the results, be sure to ask for

Figure 1a.2 Many people find it helpful to have a friend or family member present when consulting with a physician.

them as they are recorded so that you will be prepared for discussion with the doctor.

Although every appointment is unique, most involve both consultation and examination. A typical pattern is to have a few minutes of discussion with your physician during which you explain the reason for your visit, followed by any examination that may be necessary, followed by a review of findings and the treatment plan, if needed. During discussions with your doctor, it is important to speak about your medical concerns as clearly, concisely, and directly as possible. For example, be specific when describing your symptoms and their time course: What symptoms are you experiencing, and when did they start? Have the symptoms improved or worsened? Many medical conditions can be difficult to discuss, but for maximum benefit you need to overcome shyness. Remember that your doctor is a professional who has probably heard similar stories. If you do not feel comfortable talking with your doctor, then you might have the wrong doctor.

During the consultation phase of your appointment, your primary care physician may recommend a particular laboratory test or screening procedure. Ask your doctor how the test or procedure will be performed, what information will be gained, what the risks are, and how accurate the test results will be. You should ask the doctor (or the doctor's staff, if time runs short) how and when you will receive the results and what to do if you don't receive them. It is not a good strategy to assume that "no news is good news," so take personal responsibility and follow up if test results do not arrive within a reasonable time.

Understanding Medications

During your appointment, the doctor may write a prescription for a new medication. Be sure to tell your doctor about any reactions you have had to medications in the past. Also, ask questions to learn as much as possible about your new prescription. For example, ask for the name of the new medication, and have the doctor write it down; be sure you can read the medication name written on the prescription that you will take to a pharmacist. Ask what the new medication is supposed to do and whether it might interact with any supplements or other medications (prescription or over-the-counter) that you are taking. Inquire about the mechanics of taking the medication, including how much to take, when to take it, and how long to take it. Find out about side effects and what to do if they occur. Some medications require you to avoid certain foods, drinks, or activities, and you should ask about this, too, as well as what to do if you miss a dose or accidentally take too large a dose. Ask what will happen if you don't take the medication. Finally, to save money, inquire whether a generic form of the medication is available.

When you pick up your medication from the pharmacy, make sure it is the medication prescribed by your doctor. If you have remaining questions about the new medication, then ask the pharmacist. Finally, take personal responsibility for reading and understanding drug labels, whether the medication is prescribed by your doctor or sold over the counter (Figure 1a.3). At the very least, read the label every time you open a new bottle of medication.

1a.4 Finding a Specialist and Getting a Second Opinion

Should you need a specialist, your primary care physician typically provides the referral. In addition, you can personally search online resources for information. For example, the database maintained by the American Board of Medical Specialties allows you to verify whether a certain physician is board certified, which means that he or she has completed specific education and training requirements in a particular area (for example, internal medicine), and passed an examination designed and administered by the specialty board. Another option is to check the for-profit WebMD site, which provides a directory of physicians, including specialists, when you type in your city and state or zip code. Included in the directory are physicians' names and contact information, areas of specialty, hospital affiliations, and the names of other physicians in their practice. Some listings provide the age and gender of the doctor as well as the medical school attended.

There are some key questions to ask when meeting with a specialist. If you have not personally researched the physician's background, then you may wish to find out whether he or she is board certified. If the doctor is to perform a certain procedure, then ask how often he or she has performed it in the past year—you want a doctor who has done it frequently. You might also ask how many of these procedures he or she has performed overall and what the success rate has been. Be sure to inquire about other treatment options and the benefits and risks of the proposed treatment.

Once a physician provides you with a diagnosis and treatment plan, you may wish to obtain a second opinion before starting treatment. This opinion, provided by another specialist, may confirm the first doctor's diagnosis and treatment plan or may suggest modifications. Seeking a second opinion provides reassurance that you have researched other options and offers additional opportunity for any remaining questions to be answered and concerns addressed. The doctor who provided your initial diagnosis and treatment plan can suggest a specialist for a second opinion, or you can personally search for one. To get a truly independent assessment, it is best to obtain a second opinion from a specialist not connected with your doctor; for example, find a doctor in a different practice. Additionally, the second doctor should examine you first and then look at records from your other physician. Most health insurance plans cover second opinions, and many plans require second opinions before paying for a major medical procedure. To be sure, check with your insurance provider. Even if you have to pay for a second opinion, getting one may still be very worthwhile.

what would YOU do? Your primary care physician refers you to a specialist, who wants to repeat an array of expensive medical tests just completed under the direction of your primary care physician. Your insurance company is willing to pay for this second round of tests. What would you do? Had your insurance company refused in advance to pay for these tests, what would you do? ∎

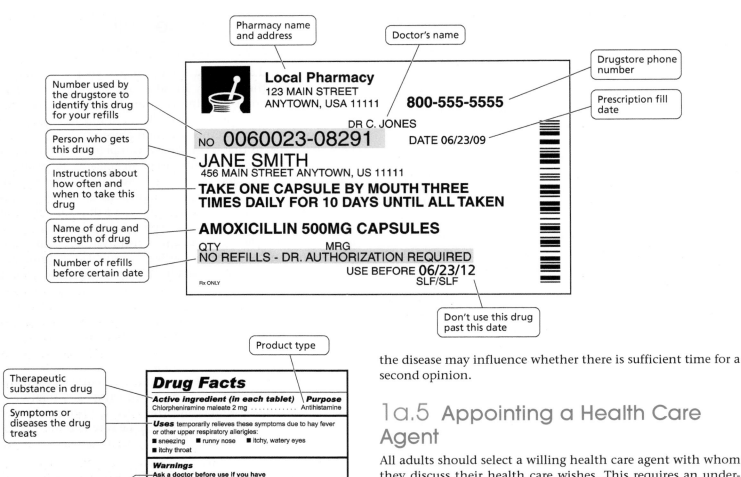

Figure 1a.3 Tips for reading drug labels: (a) prescription drug label, (b) over-the-counter drug label.

From the Office on Women's Health, U.S. Department of Health and Human Services, "How to Read Drug Labels," www.womenshealth.gov

Not every diagnosis requires a second opinion. You should seek one when a diagnosis is based on a test that does not always provide conclusive results and when suggested treatments are invasive (for example, surgery) or long term. The severity of the disease may influence whether there is sufficient time for a second opinion.

1a.5 Appointing a Health Care Agent

All adults should select a willing health care agent with whom they discuss their health care wishes. This requires an understanding of various treatment options so you can evaluate their costs and benefits, make informed decisions, and inform your agent of your wishes. Each state has its own laws regarding advance directives, which are legal documents that allow you to convey in advance your wishes for end-of-life care. Typically, though, any person at least 18 years old, other than your physician or an employee of the health care organization providing your care, can serve as your health care agent; an exception is made if the employee is a family member. You formalize the selection of your agent by completing a health care proxy form, copies of which should be provided to your agent, family members, loved ones, and primary care physician. The health care proxy form is a legal document, and health care providers are required to follow its instructions. You can update the form if necessary. Your agent, acting as your legal representative, will have the right to make health care decisions for you if your doctor decides you are unable to make them yourself. Such decisions include whether to have medical tests and treatments and when to start and stop treatments. It is difficult to predict medical situations, so it is best to be prepared in advance.

1a.6 Selecting a Hospital and Staying Safe

Should your treatment require hospitalization, a major step in your care is selecting the hospital. Choosing a hospital is a decision made with your doctor, so start by asking which hospital your doctor thinks is best for you and at which hospital (or hospitals) he or she can admit patients. Make sure that the hospitals suggested are covered by your health plan. Because it is important for you to be an active participant in the decision and to know as much as possible about the hospital where you will be treated, take time to learn about hospitals because they can vary greatly in patient populations and levels of experience with particular medical conditions. Some hospitals specialize in treating patients of a certain age group, such as children, and others specialize in treating certain medical conditions, such as cancer. Many hospitals, however, treat patients of all ages with diverse medical conditions. Next we offer some considerations when researching hospitals.

Accreditation Status

Checking the accreditation status of a hospital is an early and important step in the process of selecting a hospital. To determine whether they meet national standards of quality, most hospitals invite the Joint Commission to evaluate their staff, facilities and equipment, information management, medication management, infection control, and success in treating patients. Reviews are conducted at least once every three years to track improvements or declines in quality. Reports prepared by the Joint Commission include accreditation status (a six-level rating system, ranging from "Not accredited" to "Accredited with commendation"), areas evaluated and those needing improvement, and comparison to national results. By going to www.qualitycheck.org, you can find out the accreditation status of hospitals. Federal and state governments, nonprofit organizations, and private companies and organizations also offer report cards and other tools you can use to compare hospitals. For example, the U.S. Department of Health and Human Services offers Hospital Compare, an online resource that locates hospitals in the vicinity of the city, state, or zip code that you type in and then compares up to three hospitals of your choice on measures such as outcomes of care and surveys of patients' experiences. You can refine your comparison by specifying particular medical conditions and surgical procedures.

STOP and THINK

When some people first hear that they have a serious medical condition requiring inpatient treatment, they want to go to the best hospital, no matter how far it is from home. What challenges might distant inpatient care pose for a person?

Extent of Experience and Treatment Success

You should also choose your hospital based on the extent of its experience and the level of its success in treating your medical condition. Because hospitals that perform many of the same types of procedures typically have higher success rates, it is important to ask your doctor or the hospital about the number of patients who have undergone the procedure there. Also request information on patients' outcomes and satisfaction surveys. You should select a hospital where the procedure you need is performed frequently on large numbers of patients who do well after the procedure and highly rate their experience at the hospital.

Preventing Medical Errors

A 1999 report from the Institute of Medicine titled "To Err Is Human: Building a Safer Health System" raised public awareness of medical errors by estimating that between 44,000 and 98,000 people die each year in the United States as a result of medical errors in hospitals. A study published in 2013 in the *Journal of Patient Safety* estimated that between 210,000 and 400,000 Americans die each year from medical errors in hospitals. This new estimate makes medical errors the third leading cause of death in the United States, behind heart disease and cancer. Medical errors include incorrect or incomplete diagnosis or treatment and may involve lab tests, equipment, surgery, or medication (for example, a patient is given the wrong medication or given the correct medication but the wrong dose). At hospitals, communication failures during handoffs of patient care at shift changes are a major cause of errors: critical information may not be passed on, or incorrect information may be transferred. Medical errors can happen anyplace that you receive health care or medications. We focus on those in hospitals, but errors also can occur at doctors' offices and pharmacies and in your own home.

The best way to personally prevent errors is to be vigilant and informed about your health care. For example, when someone brings you a medication in the hospital, check that the medication is indeed meant for you and not someone else and that the medication and dose are correct (ask the nurse and read the label yourself). Also make sure that you are receiving the medication by the correct route (for example, orally versus intravenously) and at the right time interval (for instance, once every 12 hours). Almost 20% of medication doses in hospitals are given incorrectly; dispensing medications at the wrong time and omitting a dose are the most common mistakes. Be especially alert when your care has been handed off to a new set of health care workers (Figure 1a.4).

Figure 1a.4 At shift changes, patient handoffs at the bedside are more effective than when nurses exchange information about patients at nursing stations. Bedside handoffs reduce errors, allow patients and nurses to meet earlier in the process, and improve patients' satisfaction.

Throughout your hospital stay, information about your diagnosis and treatment should be communicated clearly among you, your hospital health care team, and your primary care physician. Communication is especially critical as your discharge time nears. Be sure that you understand all aspects of your discharge plan. Ideally, this written plan should include a list of follow-up appointments and tests, a medication regimen, a timetable for resuming normal activities, and steps to take if a problem arises. Hospitals can be confusing and stressful places, so having a friend or family member with you at the time your discharge plan is discussed can be very helpful. Once discharged, take personal responsibility, and comply with medication and other instructions.

1a.7 Researching Health Conditions on Your Own

In addition to learning about your health from your primary care physician and health care team (should you have a medical condition and be undergoing treatment), find other reliable sources of information. The Internet can provide information around the clock, but the information is not always accurate or unbiased. When using the Internet, be sure to scrutinize websites and avoid those selling products or making claims inconsistent with information from other sources. Verify that the person or group making the claims has the necessary scientific or medical training and expertise, and that the site is frequently updated. Reliable health information can most often be obtained from government agencies (for example, the National Institutes of Health) and nonprofit organizations (for example, the Mayo Clinic). Commercial websites often are less reliable and more biased. When investigating specific medical conditions, search for articles in the primary medical literature. Although reading articles in medical journals can appear daunting at first, give it a try because you may be able to understand enough of the information to ask your doctor about it.

LOOKING AHEAD

In this chapter, we discussed how to apply critical-thinking skills to keeping yourself healthy and getting involved in your health care. In Chapter 2, we focus on the basic chemical principles that help us understand how the human body is put together and how it functions. Like the material in this chapter, the information provided in Chapter 2 lays a foundation for discussions throughout the text.

CONSIDER THIS CASE

Sasha was experiencing severe headaches, fever, and a stiff neck. The health services at her college advised her to go to the ER of the local hospital for a spinal tap. During this procedure, cerebrospinal fluid (CSF; the fluid that bathes the brain and spinal cord) is withdrawn and assessed for evidence of infection, such as meningitis. After waiting for hours with a friend in the hectic ER, Sasha was brought to a nearby room, the spinal tap was finally performed, and she was instructed to wait for a few hours while her CSF sample was checked. Finally, a physician came and explained that her sample was negative for meningitis. Although she did not feel well or even fully recovered from the procedure, Sasha was so tired and stressed by the hospital environment, she just wanted to go back to her dorm. Once told she could go, she left quickly with her friend. When she returned to her dorm room, she didn't know whether it was okay to immediately lie down and sleep. The puncture site on her back hurt, and she wondered about taking a pain reliever.

- What critical step was missing from Sasha's care in the ER?
- What might Sasha have done differently to ensure better care?

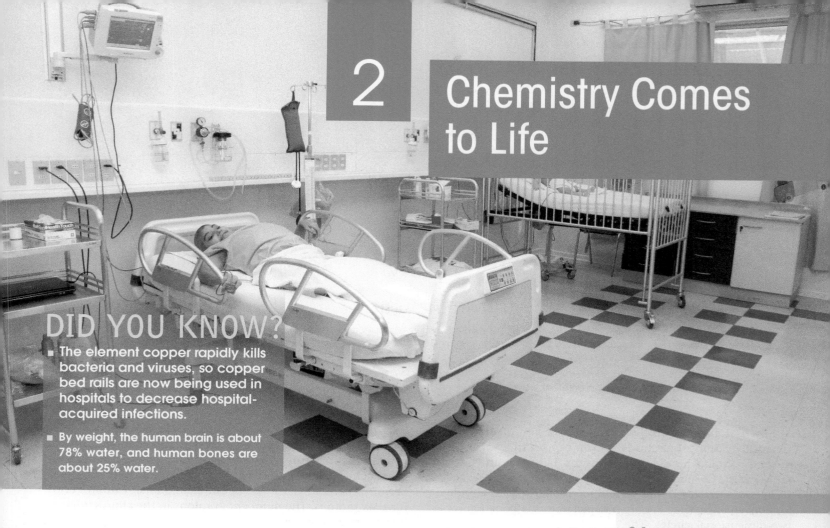

2 Chemistry Comes to Life

DID YOU KNOW?

- The element copper rapidly kills bacteria and viruses, so copper bed rails are now being used in hospitals to decrease hospital-acquired infections.

- By weight, the human brain is about 78% water, and human bones are about 25% water.

CHEMISTRY is the branch of science concerned with the composition and properties of substances, including the stuff our bodies are built from. In Chapter 1a, you learned that becoming an informed patient means knowing your basic medical history and understanding any treatments recommended and medications prescribed. In this chapter, we consider basic chemical concepts, such as the way atoms bond and the way molecules join to form the major molecules of life. By understanding fundamental concepts of chemistry, we gain insights into how our bodies work and how foods and medications affect our health. This chapter lays a foundation for discussions throughout the rest of the book.

2.1 The Nature of Atoms

The world around you contains an amazing variety of physical substances: the grass or concrete you walk on, the water you drink, the air you breathe, and even this book you are reading. All of these substances that make up our world are called matter. Fundamentally, **matter** is anything that takes up space and has mass. Commonly measured in grams or kilograms (or ounces and pounds), mass is a measure of how much matter is in an object. The three traditional states of matter are solids, liquids, and gases. All forms of matter are made up of atoms.

Atoms are units of matter that cannot be broken down into simpler substances by ordinary chemical means. Each atom is composed of even smaller, subatomic particles, such as protons, neutrons, and electrons. These subatomic particles are characterized by their location within the atom, their electrical charge, and their mass.

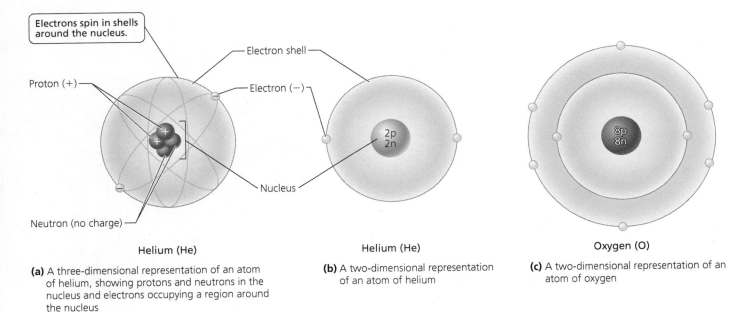

Helium (He)

(a) A three-dimensional representation of an atom of helium, showing protons and neutrons in the nucleus and electrons occupying a region around the nucleus

Helium (He)

(b) A two-dimensional representation of an atom of helium

Oxygen (O)

(c) A two-dimensional representation of an atom of oxygen

Figure 2.1 Atoms can be represented in different ways.

Each atom has a nucleus at its center and a surrounding spherical "cloud" of electrons. As you can see in Figure 2.1, the nucleus contains protons and neutrons. Electrons, in contrast, move around the nucleus and occur at certain energy levels called *shells*. Note that shells are three-dimensional spaces, although, for convenience, they are often depicted in textbook figures as two-dimensional circles. The shell closest to the nucleus can hold up to 2 electrons. The next shell out can hold up to 8 electrons. Atoms with more than 10 electrons have additional shells. Electrons have different amounts of energy; those with the most energy are found farthest from the nucleus. The number of electrons in the outermost shell determines an atom's chemical properties. As we will see, those atoms whose outermost shells are not full tend to interact with other atoms.

Neutrons, as their name implies, are neutral: they have no electrical charge. In contrast, protons have a positive charge, and electrons have a negative charge. The negatively charged electrons stay near the nucleus because they are attracted to the positively charged protons in it. Most atoms have the same number of positively charged protons and negatively charged electrons. As a result, they are "neutral," having no net charge. Table 2.1 summarizes the basic characteristics of protons, neutrons, and electrons.

Elements

An **element** is a pure form of matter containing only one kind of atom. You are probably familiar with many elements, such as gold, silver, iron, and oxygen. Earth, along with everything on

it or in its atmosphere, is made up of a little more than 100 elements. Only about 20 elements are found in the human body, which consists mostly of oxygen, carbon, hydrogen, and nitrogen. Each element consists of atoms containing a certain number of protons in the nucleus. For example, all carbon atoms have six protons. The number of protons in the atom's nucleus is called the *atomic number*.

The periodic table lists the elements and describes many of their characteristics (Figure 2.2). Note that each element has a name and a one- or two-letter symbol. The symbol for the element carbon is C, and that for chlorine is Cl. (The abbreviations are not always as intuitive; for example, the abbreviation for gold is Au, based on the Latin name *aurum* for the metal.) Besides an atomic number, each atom also has an *atomic mass* (or *mass number*). Each proton and neutron has an approximate mass of 1 atomic mass unit, or amu. The mass of an electron is so small that it is usually considered zero. Because electrons have negligible mass, and protons and neutrons each have an atomic mass of 1, the atomic mass for any atom equals the number of protons plus the number of neutrons. Oxygen has an atomic mass of 16, indicating that it has eight protons (we know this from its atomic number) and eight neutrons in its nucleus.

STOP and THINK

An atom of the element fluorine has an atomic mass of 19 and an atomic number of 9. How many protons and neutrons are in the nucleus of the fluorine atom? How many electrons surround the nucleus? Locate fluorine in the periodic table (Figure 2.2), and name two elements that you would expect to show the same kind of chemical reactivity as fluorine.

Isotopes and Radioisotopes

All the atoms of a particular element contain the same number of protons; they can, however, have different numbers of neutrons.

Table 2.1	Review of Subatomic Particles		
Particle	Location	Charge	Mass
Proton	Nucleus	1 positive unit	1 atomic mass unit
Neutron	Nucleus	None	1 atomic mass unit
Electron	Outside the nucleus	1 negative unit	Negligible

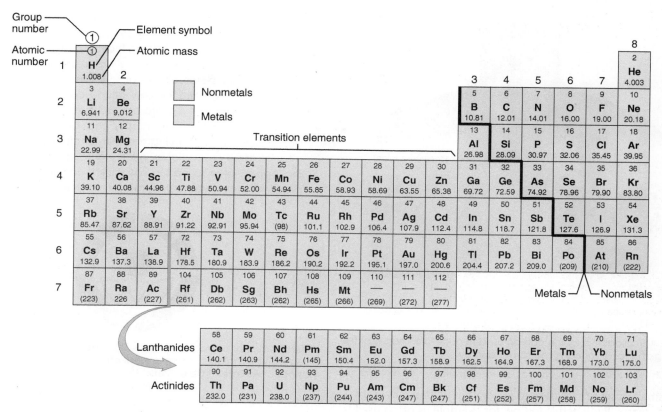

Figure 2.2 The periodic table provides the atomic symbol, mass, and number for each element. It also organizes elements into groups, members of which have the same number of electrons in their outer-most shell. For example, elements in group 3 have three electrons in their outermost shell. Number of electrons in the outermost shell tells us about chemical reactivity, so elements in the same group tend to behave in the same way.

Such differences result in atoms of the same element having slightly different atomic masses. Atoms that have the same number of protons but differ in the number of neutrons are called **isotopes.** More than 300 isotopes occur naturally on Earth. The element carbon, for example, has three isotopes. All carbon atoms have six protons in the nucleus. Most carbon atoms also have six neutrons, but some have seven or eight. The isotopes of carbon thus have atomic masses of 12, 13, and 14, respectively, depending on the number of neutrons in the nucleus. These isotopes are written ^{12}C (the most common form in nature), ^{13}C, and ^{14}C.

Radiation is energy moving through space. Examples include radio waves, light, heat, and the excess energy or particles given off by unstable isotopes as they break down. Some elements have both stable and unstable isotopes. Unstable, radiation-emitting isotopes are called **radioisotopes.** About 60 occur naturally, and many more have been made in laboratories.

Depending on the context, radiation can be dangerous (Figure 2.3) or useful (Figure 2.4). Absorption of harmful radiation may lead to damage to organs, such as the skin, and development of some cancers. In other cases, radiation may not produce any noticeable injury to the person who was exposed, but it may alter the hereditary material in the cells of the reproductive system, possibly causing defects in the individual's off-spring. For an example of the harmful effects of radiation and how to protect yourself from radiation that occurs naturally in the environment, see the Environmental Issue essay, *Radon Gas: A Killer That Can Be Stopped.*

In stark contrast to the harmful effects of radiation are its medical uses. Medical professionals use radiation for diagnosis and therapy. Perhaps the most familiar diagnostic use of radiation is x-ray imaging. A less common diagnostic procedure is the

Figure 2.3 Sunburn, perhaps the most common burn from radiation, is caused by overexposure to ultraviolet radiation from the sun's rays.

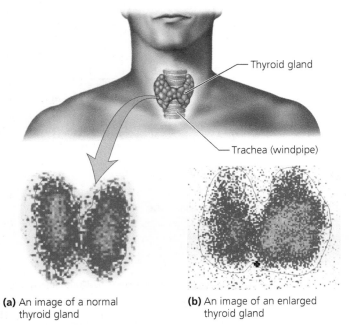

(a) An image of a normal thyroid gland

(b) An image of an enlarged thyroid gland

Figure 2.4 Radioactive iodine can be used to generate images of the thyroid gland for diagnosing metabolic disorders.

use of small doses of radiation to generate visual images of internal body parts. Radioactive iodine, for example, is often used to identify disorders of the thyroid gland. This gland, located in the neck, normally accumulates the element iodine, which it uses to regulate growth and metabolism. Small doses of iodine-131 (^{131}I), a radioactive isotope, can be given to a patient suspected of having metabolic problems. The radioactive iodine is taken up by the patient's thyroid gland and detected by medical instruments, as shown in Figure 2.4. The small amount of radioactive iodine used in imaging does not damage the thyroid gland or surrounding structures. However, larger doses can be used to kill thyroid cells when the gland is enlarged and overactive.

Radiation can also be used to kill cancer cells. These cells divide more rapidly and have higher rates of metabolic activity than do most normal cells. For these reasons, cancer cells are more susceptible to the destructive effects of radiation. Still, when medical professionals aim an outside beam of radiation at a tumor to kill the cancer cells inside it, they must also take steps to shield the surrounding healthy tissue. Sometimes a radiation source is placed within the body to treat a cancer. For example, one treatment for prostate cancer (the prostate gland is an accessory reproductive gland in males) involves placing radioactive seeds (pellets) directly in the prostate gland. Once in place, the seeds emit radiation that damages or kills nearby cancer cells. In most cases, the seeds are left in place, even though they stop emitting radiation within 1 year.

what would **YOU** do?

Irradiation is the process in which an item is exposed to radiation. Many foods today are intentionally irradiated to delay spoilage, increase shelf life, and remove harmful microorganisms, insect pests, and parasites. The food does not become radioactive as a result. Supporters of the practice note that test animals fed on irradiated food show no adverse effects. Opponents, however, point to the environmental risks of building and operating food irradiation plants and the lack of carefully controlled, long-term experiments verifying that irradiated food is safe for people of all ages and nutritional states. Several foods, including white potatoes, wheat flour, fresh meat and poultry, and fresh spinach and iceberg lettuce, can be irradiated in the United States. If the entire product is irradiated, then a distinctive logo (Figure 2.5) must appear on its packaging. If an irradiated food is an ingredient in another product, then it must be listed as irradiated in the ingredients statement, but the logo is not required. Do you think irradiating food is a safe practice? Would you eat irradiated food? ■

Figure 2.5 Logo for irradiated foods. This logo and words such as "Treated with radiation" must appear on the packaging of food that has been irradiated in its entirety.

2.2 Chemical Bonds and Compounds

Two or more elements may combine to form a new chemical substance called a **compound.** A compound's characteristics are usually different from those of its elements. Consider what happens when the element sodium (Na) combines with the element chlorine (Cl). Sodium is a silvery metal that explodes when it comes into contact with water. Chlorine is a deadly yellow gas. In combination, however, they form a crystalline solid called sodium chloride (NaCl)—plain table salt (Figure 2.6).

The atoms (or, as we will soon see, ions) in a compound are held together by chemical bonds. There are two types of chemical bonds: covalent and ionic. Recall that atoms have outer shells, which are the regions surrounding the nucleus where the electrons are most likely to be found. Figure 2.7 depicts the first two shells as concentric circles around the nucleus. A full innermost shell contains 2 electrons. A full second shell contains 8 electrons. Atoms with a total of more than 10 electrons have additional shells. When atoms form bonds, they lose, gain, or share the electrons in their outermost shell.

Covalent Bonds

A **covalent bond** forms when two or more atoms *share* electrons in their outer shells. Consider the compound methane (CH_4). Methane is formed by the sharing of electrons between one atom of carbon and four atoms of hydrogen. Notice in Figure 2.8a that the outer shell of an isolated carbon atom contains only four electrons, even though it can hold as many as eight. Also note that hydrogen atoms have only one electron, although the first shell can hold up to two electrons. A carbon atom can

(a) The element sodium is a solid metal.

(b) Elemental sodium reacts explosively with water.

(c) The element chlorine is a yellow gas.

(d) When the elements sodium and chlorine join, they form table salt, a compound quite different from its elements.

Figure 2.6 The characteristics of a compound are usually different from those of its elements.

fill its outer shell by joining with four atoms of hydrogen. At the same time, by forming a covalent bond with the carbon atom, each hydrogen atom fills its first shell. We see, then, that the covalent bonds between the carbon atom and hydrogen atoms of methane result in filled outer shells for all five atoms involved.

A **molecule** is a chemical structure held together by covalent bonds. Compounds are formed by two or more elements, so molecules that contain only one kind of atom are not considered compounds. For example, oxygen gas, which is formed by the joining of two oxygen atoms, is *not* a compound, but it *is* a molecule. Molecules are described by a formula that contains the symbols for all of the elements included in that molecule. If more than one atom of a given element is present in the molecule, a subscript is used to show the precise number of that kind of atom. For example, the molecular formula of sucrose (table sugar) is $C_{12}H_{22}O_{11}$, showing that one molecule

of sucrose contains 12 atoms of carbon, 22 atoms of hydrogen, and 11 atoms of oxygen. Numbers placed in front of the molecular formula indicate that more than one molecule is present. For example, three molecules of sucrose are described by the formula $3C_{12}H_{22}O_{11}$.

As shown in the methane molecule in Figure 2.8a, the bond between each of the four hydrogen atoms and the carbon atom consists of a single pair of electrons. A bond in which a single pair of electrons is shared is called a *single covalent bond;* in this example, the methane molecule contains four single covalent bonds. Sometimes, however, two atoms share two or three pairs of electrons. These bonds are called *double* and *triple covalent bonds,* respectively. For example, carbon dioxide, CO_2, produced by chemical reactions inside our cells, has double covalent bonds between the carbon atom and each of two oxygen atoms (Figure 2.8b). And the nitrogen atoms in nitrogen gas, N_2, are joined by triple covalent bonds (Figure 2.8c).

Covalent bonds in molecules are sometimes depicted by a structural formula. Notice in the box at the right of Figure 2.8a that one straight line is drawn between the carbon atom and each hydrogen atom in the structural formula for the methane molecule. The single line indicates a single covalent bond resulting from a pair of shared electrons. In the box to the right of Figure 2.8b, the double lines between the carbon and oxygen atoms in the carbon dioxide molecule indicate a double covalent bond, or two pairs of shared electrons. In Figure 2.8c, three lines drawn between the two nitrogen atoms in gaseous nitrogen depict a triple covalent bond, or three pairs of shared electrons.

Ionic Bonds

We have all heard the phrase "opposites attract" in reference to human relationships—and it is no different for ions. An **ion** is an atom or group of atoms that carries either a positive (+) or a negative (–) electrical charge. Electrical charges result from the *transfer* (as opposed to sharing) of electrons between atoms. Recall that a neutral atom has the same number of positively charged protons and negatively charged electrons. An atom that loses an electron has one more proton than electrons and therefore has a positive charge. An atom that gains an electron has one more electron than protons and has a negative charge. Oppositely charged ions are attracted to one another. An **ionic bond** results from the mutual attraction of oppositely charged ions.

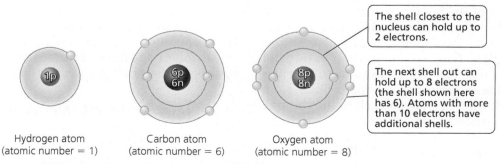

The shell closest to the nucleus can hold up to 2 electrons.

The next shell out can hold up to 8 electrons (the shell shown here has 6). Atoms with more than 10 electrons have additional shells.

Hydrogen atom (atomic number = 1)

Carbon atom (atomic number = 6)

Oxygen atom (atomic number = 8)

Figure 2.7 Atoms of hydrogen, carbon, and oxygen. Each of the concentric circles around the nucleus represents a shell occupied by electrons.

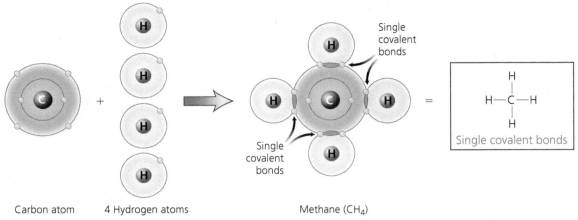

Carbon atom   4 Hydrogen atoms   Methane (CH_4)

(a) The molecule methane (CH_4) is formed by the sharing of electrons between one carbon atom and four hydrogen atoms. Because in each case one pair of electrons is shared, the bonds formed are single covalent bonds.

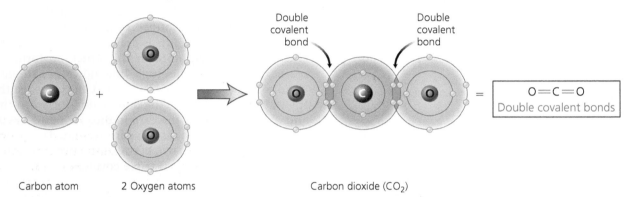

Carbon atom   2 Oxygen atoms   Carbon dioxide (CO_2)

(b) The oxygen atoms in a molecule of carbon dioxide (CO_2) form double covalent bonds with the carbon atom. In double bonds, two pairs of electrons are shared.

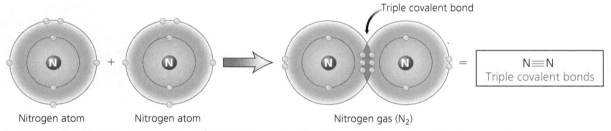

Nitrogen atom   Nitrogen atom   Nitrogen gas (N_2)

(c) The nitrogen atoms in nitrogen gas (N_2) form a triple covalent bond, in which three pairs of electrons are shared.

Figure 2.8 Covalent bonds form when atoms share electrons. Shown here are examples of single, double, and triple covalent bonds. For each example, the structural formula is given on the far right.

Ions form because of the tendency of atoms to attain a complete outermost shell. Consider, again, the atoms of sodium and chlorine that join to form sodium chloride. As shown in Figure 2.9, an atom of sodium has one electron in its outer shell. An atom of chlorine has seven electrons in its outer shell. Sodium chloride is formed when the sodium atom transfers the single electron in its outer shell to the chlorine atom. The sodium atom now has a full outer shell. This comes about because the sodium atom loses its third shell, making the second shell its outermost shell. The sodium atom, having lost an electron, has one more proton than electrons and therefore now has a positive charge (Na^+). The chlorine atom,

having gained an electron to fill its outer shell, has one more electron than protons and now has a negative charge (Cl^-). These oppositely charged ions are attracted to one another, and an ionic bond forms. Because they do not contain shared electrons, ionic bonds are weaker than covalent bonds.

2.3 The Role of Water in Life

Water is such a familiar part of our everyday lives that we often overlook its unusual qualities. Unique properties of water include its virtuosity as a dissolving agent, its high heat capacity, and its high heat of vaporization. Water's unusual qualities

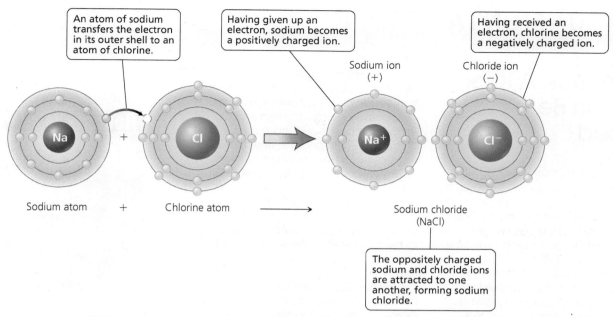

Figure 2.9 An ionic bond involves the transfer of electrons between atoms. Such a transfer creates oppositely charged ions that are attracted to one another.

can be traced to its *polarity* (tendency of its molecules to have positive and negative regions) and the hydrogen bonds between its molecules.

Polarity and Hydrogen Bonds

In covalently bonded molecules, electrons may be shared equally or unequally between atoms. When the sharing of electrons is unequal, different ends of the same molecule can have slight opposite charges. Unequal covalent bonds are called polar, and molecules with unevenly distributed charges are called polar molecules. In water (H_2O), for example, the electrons shared by oxygen and hydrogen spend more time near the oxygen atom than near the hydrogen atom. As a result, the oxygen atom has a slight negative charge; each hydrogen atom has a slight positive charge; and water molecules are polar

(Figure 2.10a). The hydrogen atoms of one water molecule are attracted to the oxygen atoms of other water molecules. The attraction between a slightly positively charged hydrogen atom and a slightly negatively charged atom nearby is called a **hydrogen bond.** In the case of water, the hydrogen bonding occurs between hydrogen and oxygen. However, sometimes hydrogen bonds form between hydrogen and atoms of other elements.

Hydrogen bonds are weaker than either ionic or covalent bonds. For this reason, we illustrate them by dotted lines rather than solid lines, as shown in Figure 2.10b. Even though individual hydrogen bonds are very weak, collectively they can be significant. Hydrogen bonds maintain the shape of proteins and our hereditary material, DNA, and they account for some of the unique physical properties of water.

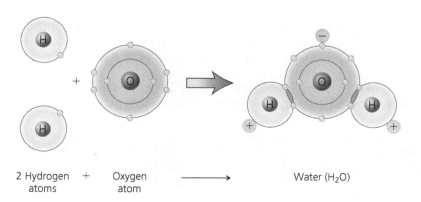

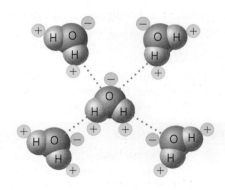

(a) Water is formed when an oxygen atom covalently bonds (shares electrons) with two hydrogen atoms. Because of the unequal sharing of electrons, oxygen carries a slight negative charge, and the hydrogen atoms carry a slight positive charge.

(b) The hydrogen atoms from one water molecule are attracted to the oxygen atoms of other water molecules. This relatively weak attraction (shown by dotted lines) is called a hydrogen bond.

Figure 2.10 The hydrogen bonds of water

ENVIRONMENTAL ISSUE

Radon Gas: A Killer That Can Be Stopped

Some lethal substances are obvious because you can see, smell, or taste them. Others are not, even when surrounding you in your own home. Such is the case for radon, a radioactive gas produced when the element uranium breaks down in rock, soil, or water. This invisible, odorless gas moves up through the soil, eventually seeping through cracks in the foundations of buildings. Once inside a building, radon may accumulate and reach harmful levels. The same techniques that help make a building energy efficient also tend to limit the exchange of air between the interior of a building and outside; as a result, modern, energy-efficient buildings can accumulate radon.

Although radon can enter any type of building, the greatest exposure threat usually occurs in homes because people typically spend more time in their home than in their school or workplace. Most radon enters buildings as gas from the soil, but radon can also enter a home through well water. The greatest risk from radon in water occurs when it is released into the air during showers or other household uses of water. The U.S. Environmental Protection Agency (EPA) estimates that 1 in 15 homes in the United States has an unacceptable level of radon, defined as 4 or more picocuries of radon per liter of air. (A picocurie is a measure of radioactivity that equals about 2.2 disintegrations of radioactive particles per minute.) Although radon levels vary from one part of the country to another, any home in any state can have a radon problem.

Radon is estimated to cause 21,000 lung cancer deaths each year in the United States. After cigarette smoking, radon is the next leading cause of lung cancer. Smoking combined with exposure to radon is particularly risky. Among environmental causes of cancer deaths, radon tops the list.

The EPA recommends that all homes be tested for radon, below the third floor. Residents can test for radon themselves, using a do-it-yourself kit available at most hardware stores (**Figure 2.A**). Alternatively, residents can hire a certified radon professional to do the testing. If testing reveals high levels of radon in a home, then a contractor trained to fix radon problems can install a venting system that pulls radon from beneath the house and releases it to the outside. New homes can be built with features to reduce radon levels; even so, testing should be performed to ensure that such construction techniques are effective.

Most Americans are unaware of the risks posed by radon. To address this, the EPA and other government agencies announced a Federal Radon Action Plan in 2011 to increase public awareness of radon, promote testing for radon in all homes, and offer financial incentives to fix

Figure 2.A Home radon-testing kits are available from the National Safety Council and are sold in many hardware and retail stores.

homes with high radon levels. Additionally, Healthy People 2020, a national 10-year initiative to improve the health of Americans, includes goals to reduce radon risks. These actions demonstrate that indoor radon exposure is a national public health issue deserving attention.

Questions to Consider

- If you live in a campus dormitory, would you be willing to pay more in fees to fix a newly discovered radon contamination problem in your building?
- States do not require the disclosure of radon risks during real estate transactions. Should radon testing be the responsibility of an individual buyer or renter?

Covalent bonds, ionic bonds, and hydrogen bonds are summarized in Table 2.2.

Properties of Water

Life depends on the properties of water. Many of these result from water's polarity and hydrogen bonding. For example, water molecules are cohesive, which means they cling together. Water is also adhesive, which means its molecules cling to other molecules. Let's consider some of the other properties that make water so vital to life.

Because of the polarity of its molecules, water interacts with many substances. This interactivity makes it an excellent

Table 2.2	Review of Chemical Bonds		
Type	Basis for Attraction	Strength	Example
Covalent	Sharing of electrons between atoms; the sharing between atoms may be equal or unequal	Strongest	CH_4 (methane)
Ionic	Transfer of electrons between atoms creates oppositely charged ions that are attracted to one another	Strong	NaCl (table salt)
Hydrogen	Attraction between a hydrogen atom with a slight positive charge and another atom (often oxygen) with a slight negative charge	Weak	Between a hydrogen atom on one water molecule and an oxygen atom on another water molecule

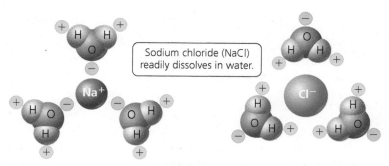

Figure 2.11 Water is an excellent solvent because of the polarity of its molecules. When a compound such as table salt (NaCl) is placed in water, it readily dissolves into independent ions.

solvent, easily dissolving both polar and charged substances. Ionic compounds, such as NaCl, dissolve into independent ions in water. The sodium ions and chloride ions separate from one another in water because the sodium ions are attracted to the negative regions of water molecules and the chloride ions are attracted to the positive regions (Figure 2.11). Because of its excellence as a solvent, and its cohesiveness, water serves as the body's main transport medium. As the liquid component of blood, it carries dissolved nutrients, gases, and wastes through the circulatory system. Metabolic wastes are excreted from the body in urine, another watery medium.

Because of its hydrogen bonds, water helps prevent dramatic changes in body temperature. About 67% of the human body is water (thus, if a person weighs 68 kg [150 lb], water makes up about 45 kg [100 lb] of the body weight). Because humans, as well as many other organisms, are made up largely of water, they are well suited to resist changes in body temperature and to keep a relatively stable internal environment. This ability comes from water's *high heat capacity,* which simply means that a great deal of heat is required to raise water's temperature. Hydrogen bonds hold multiple water molecules together, so a large amount of heat is required to break these bonds (a higher temperature corresponds to an increase in the movement of the molecules). Water in blood also helps redistribute heat within our bodies. Our fingers don't usually freeze on a frigid day because heat is carried to them by blood from muscles, where the heat is generated.

Another property of water that helps prevent the body from overheating is its *high heat of vaporization,* which means that a great deal of heat is required to make water evaporate (that is, change from a liquid to a gas). Water's high heat of vaporization is also due to its hydrogen bonds, which must be broken before water molecules can leave the liquid and enter the air. (These bonds, by the way, remain broken as long as water is in the gaseous phase known as *water vapor.*) Water molecules that evaporate from a surface carry away a lot of heat, cooling the surface. We rely on the evaporation of water in sweat to cool the body surface and prevent overheating. Sharp increases in body temperature, usually to 40°C (104°F) or higher, can cause heat stroke, a condition that can damage the brain and other organs. Exposure to hot environments for several days in the case of the very young (whose thermoregulatory abilities are not fully developed) or the very old (whose thermoregulatory abilities are declining) can cause heat stroke. Heat stroke can also occur

in anyone engaging in strenuous physical activity in a hot environment, especially if the person is not accustomed to the heat. The combination of heat and humidity is particularly dangerous because water vapor in the air can inhibit the evaporation of sweat, thereby preventing cooling.

It is clear that water is essential for human life and for the lives of many other organisms we share the planet with. Despite our reliance on water, we continue to pollute both seawater and freshwater. Equally alarming is the global shortage of freshwater, caused by the burgeoning human population and climate change. For one answer to the water shortage, see the Environmental Issue essay, *Toilet to Tap.*

Acids and Bases

Sometimes a water molecule dissociates, or breaks up, forming a positively charged hydrogen ion (H^+) and a negatively charged hydroxide ion (OH^-):

$$\text{H} \!-\! \text{O} \!-\! \text{H} \quad \longleftrightarrow \quad \text{H}^+ \quad + \quad \text{OH}^-$$

Water $\qquad\qquad$ Hydrogen $\qquad$ Hydroxide
$\qquad\qquad\qquad\quad$ ion $\qquad\qquad\quad$ ion

(Note that in equations describing chemical reactions, an arrow should be read as "yields.")

In any sample of water, the fraction of water molecules that are dissociated is extremely small, so water molecules are much more common in the human body than are H^+ and OH^-. In fact, the amount of H^+ in the body must be precisely regulated. Substances called acids and bases influence the concentration of H^+ in solutions.

Acids and bases are defined by what happens when they are added to water. An **acid** is anything that releases hydrogen ions (H^+) when placed in water. A **base** is anything that releases hydroxide ions (OH^-) when placed in water. Hydrochloric acid (HCl), for example, dissociates in water to produce hydrogen ions (H^+) and chloride ions (Cl^-). Because HCl increases the concentration of (H^+) in solution, it is classified as an acid. Sodium hydroxide (NaOH), by contrast, dissociates in water to produce sodium ions (Na^+) and hydroxide ions (OH^-). Because NaOH increases the concentration of OH^- in solution, it is classified as a base. The OH^- produced when NaOH dissociates reacts with H^+ to form water molecules and thus reduces the concentration of H^+ in solution. Therefore, acids increase the concentration of H^+ in solution, and bases decrease the concentration of H^+ in solution.

The pH Scale

We often want to know more than simply whether a substance is an acid or a base. For example, how strong an acid is battery acid? How strong a base is household ammonia? Questions like these can be answered by knowing the pH of these solutions and understanding the pH scale (Figure 2.12). The **pH** of a solution is a measure of hydrogen ion concentration. The **pH scale** ranges from 0 to 14; a pH of 7 is neutral (the substance does not increase H^+ or OH^-), a pH less than 7 is acidic, and a pH greater than 7, basic.

Usually, the amount of H^+ in a solution is very small. For example, the concentration of H^+ in a solution with a pH of 6 is 1×10^{-6} (or 0.000001) moles per liter (a mole, here, is not a small furry animal with a star-shaped nose but a unit of measurement

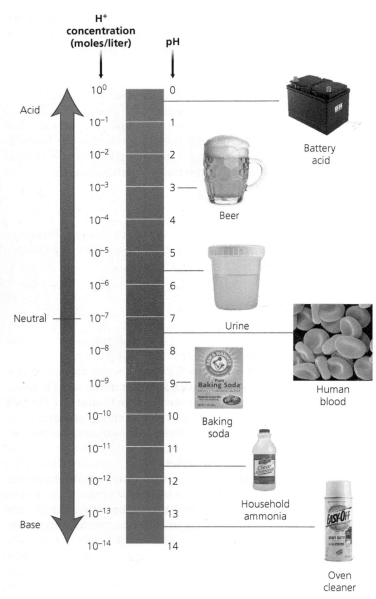

Table 2.3	Review of the Characteristics of Acids and Bases	
Characteristic	Acid	Base
Behavior in water	Releases H^+	Releases OH^-
pH	Less than 7	Greater than 7
Example	HCl (hydrochloric acid)	NaOH (sodium hydroxide)

Figure 2.12 The pH scale and the pH of some body fluids and other familiar substances

solution when concentrations of H^+ increase. Buffers add H^+ when concentrations of H^+ decrease. For example, an important buffering system that keeps the pH of blood at about 7.4 is the carbonic acid–bicarbonate system. When carbon dioxide is added to water it forms carbonic acid (H_2CO_3), which dissociates into hydrogen ions and bicarbonate ions (HCO_3^-):

$$CO_2 \ + \ H_2O \ \longleftrightarrow \ H_2CO_3 \ \longleftrightarrow \ H^+ \ + \ HCO_3^-$$

Carbon dioxide   Water   Carbonic acid   Hydrogen ion   Bicarbonate ion

Carbonic acid and bicarbonate have a buffering action because when levels of H^+ decrease in the blood, carbonic acid dissociates, adding H^+ to solution. When levels of H^+ increase in the blood, the H^+ combine with bicarbonate and are removed from solution. Such action is essential because even slight changes in the pH of blood—say, a drop from 7.4 to 7.0 or an increase to 7.8—can cause death in a few minutes.

In the human body, almost all biochemical reactions take place around pH 7 and are maintained at that level by powerful buffering systems. An important exception occurs in the stomach, where hydrochloric acid (HCl) produces pH values from about 1 to 3. In the stomach, HCl kills bacteria swallowed with food or drink and promotes the initial breakdown of proteins. These activities require an acid stomach, and the stomach has several ways of protecting itself from the acid (discussed in Chapter 15). However, sometimes stomach acid backs up into the esophagus, and "heartburn" is the uncomfortable result. Taking an antacid can ease the discomfort of heartburn. Antacids consist of weak bases that temporarily relieve the pain of stomach acid in the esophagus by neutralizing some of the hydrochloric acid.

The critical link between pH and life is illustrated by the impact of acid precipitation on our environment and health. *Acid precipitation* is usually defined as rain, snow, or fog with a pH lower than 5.6, the pH of natural precipitation. Burning of fossil fuels in cars, factories, and power plants is a major cause of acid precipitation. The sulfur dioxide and nitrogen oxides produced by these activities react with water in the atmosphere to form sulfuric acid (H_2SO_4) and nitric acid (HNO_3), which fall to Earth as rain, snow, or fog.

Acid precipitation has been linked to the decline of forests and to decreases in aquatic organisms, such as fishes and amphibians. Acid precipitation is harmful to human health, as well. The pollutants that cause acid precipitation form fine particles of sulfate and nitrate that are easily inhaled. Once inside us, they cause irritation and respiratory illnesses such as asthma and bronchitis. The good news is that power plants and automobile manufacturers have taken steps to lower emissions of sulfur dioxide and nitrogen oxides, leading to significant progress in reducing acid precipitation.

that indicates a specific number of atoms, molecules, or ions). Similarly, the concentration of H^+ in a solution with a pH of 5 is 1×10^{-5} (or 0.00001) moles per liter. Technically, pH is the negative logarithm of the concentration of H^+ in a solution. According to the pH scale, the lower the pH, the greater the acidity—or concentration of H^+—in a solution. Each reduction of pH by one unit represents a tenfold increase in the amount of H^+. So a solution with a pH of 5 is 10 times more acidic than a solution with a pH of 6. And a solution with a pH of 4 is 100 times more acidic than one with a pH of 6. Some characteristics of acids and bases, including their values on the pH scale, are summarized in Table 2.3.

Buffers

Most biological systems must maintain their fluids within a narrow range of pH values. Substances called **buffers** keep pH values from changing dramatically. Buffers remove excess H^+ from

2.4 Major Molecules of Life

Most of the molecules we have discussed so far have been small and simple. Many of the molecules of life, however, are enormous by comparison and have complex architecture. Some proteins, for example, are made up of thousands of atoms linked together in a chain that repeatedly coils and folds upon itself. Exceptionally large molecules, including many important biological molecules, are known as **macromolecules.**

Macromolecules that consist of many small, repeating molecular subunits linked in a chain are called **polymers. Monomers** are the small molecular subunits that form the building blocks of the polymer. We might think of a polymer as a pearl necklace, with each monomer representing a pearl. As we shall see, a protein is a polymer, or chain, of amino acid monomers linked together. And glycogen, the storage form of carbohydrates in animals, is a polymer of glucose monomers.

Polymers form through **dehydration synthesis** (sometimes called the *condensation reaction*). In this process, the reaction that bonds one monomer covalently to another releases a water molecule: one of the monomers donates OH, and the other donates H. The reverse process, called **hydrolysis,** which the body uses to break many polymers apart, requires the addition of water across the covalent bonds. The H from the water molecule attaches to one monomer, and the OH attaches to the adjoining monomer, thus breaking the covalent bond between the two. Hydrolysis plays a critical role in digestion. Most foods consist of polymers too large to pass from our digestive tract into the bloodstream and on to our cells. Thus, polymers are hydrolyzed into their component monomers, which can be absorbed into the bloodstream for transport throughout the body. Dehydration synthesis and hydrolysis are summarized in Figure 2.13.

Carbohydrates

The **carbohydrates,** known commonly as sugars and starches, provide fuel (energy) for the human body. Carbohydrates are compounds made entirely of carbon, hydrogen, and oxygen, with each molecule having twice as many hydrogen atoms as oxygen atoms. Sugars and starches can be classified by size into monosaccharides, oligosaccharides, and polysaccharides.

Monosaccharides **Monosaccharides,** also called simple sugars, are the smallest molecular units of carbohydrates. They contain from three to seven carbon atoms and can be classified by the number of carbon atoms they contain. A sugar that contains five carbons is *pentose;* one with six carbons is *hexose;* and so on. Glucose, fructose, and galactose are examples of six-carbon sugars. Monosaccharides can be depicted in several ways (Figure 2.14).

Oligosaccharides **Oligosaccharides** (*oligo* means "few") are chains of a few monosaccharides joined together by dehydration synthesis. A **disaccharide,** one type of oligosaccharide, is a double sugar that forms when two monosaccharides covalently bond to each other. The disaccharide sucrose (table sugar) consists of the monosaccharides glucose and fructose (Figure 2.15). Two glucose molecules form the disaccharide maltose, an important ingredient of beer. Another disaccharide is lactose, the principal carbohydrate of milk and milk products. The joining of glucose and galactose forms lactose.

Polysaccharides A **polysaccharide** (*poly* means "many") is a complex carbohydrate that forms when monosaccharides (most commonly glucose) join together in long chains. Most polysaccharides store energy or provide structure. In plants, the storage polysaccharide is **starch;** in animals, it is **glycogen,** a short-term energy source that can be broken down to release energy-laden glucose molecules. Humans store glycogen mainly in muscle and liver cells (Figure 2.16a).

Cellulose is a structural polysaccharide found in the cell walls of plants (Figure 2.16b). Humans lack the enzymes necessary to digest cellulose, so it passes unchanged through our digestive tract. (Enzymes are discussed later in this chapter.) Nevertheless, cellulose is an important form of dietary fiber (roughage) that helps fecal matter move through the large intestine. Including fiber in our diet may reduce the incidence of colon cancer.

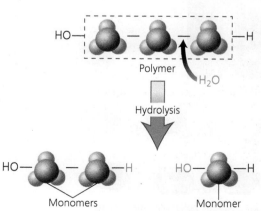

(a) Polymers are formed by dehydration synthesis, in which a water molecule is removed and two monomers are joined.

(b) Polymers are broken down by hydrolysis, in which the addition of a water molecule disrupts the bonds between two monomers.

Figure 2.13 Formation and breaking apart of polymers

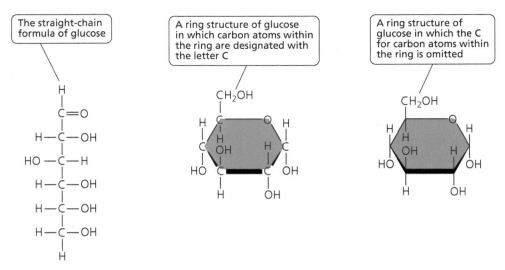

Figure 2.14 Monosaccharides are simple sugars, generally having a backbone of three to six carbon atoms. Many of these carbon atoms are also bonded to hydrogen (H) and a hydroxyl group (OH). In the fluid within our cells, the carbon backbone usually forms a ringlike structure. Here, three representations of the monosaccharide glucose ($C_6H_{12}O_6$) are shown.

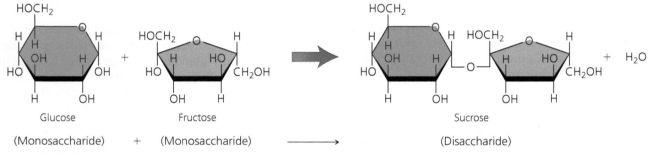

Glucose   Fructose   Sucrose

(Monosaccharide)   +   (Monosaccharide)   ⟶   (Disaccharide)

Figure 2.15 Disaccharides are built from two monosaccharides. Here, a molecule of glucose and one of fructose combine to form sucrose.

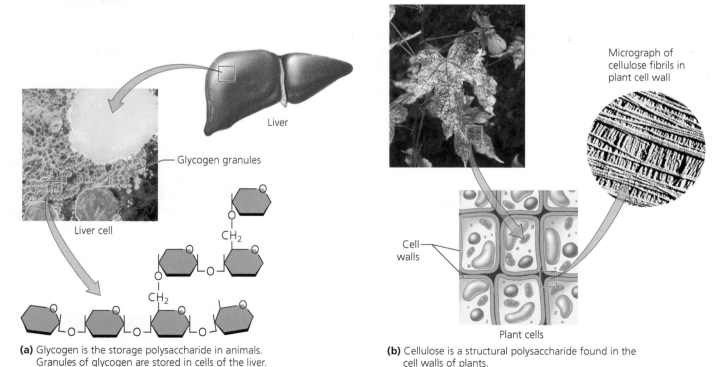

(a) Glycogen is the storage polysaccharide in animals. Granules of glycogen are stored in cells of the liver.

(b) Cellulose is a structural polysaccharide found in the cell walls of plants.

Figure 2.16 Polysaccharides may function in storage (for example, glycogen) or provide structure (for example, cellulose).

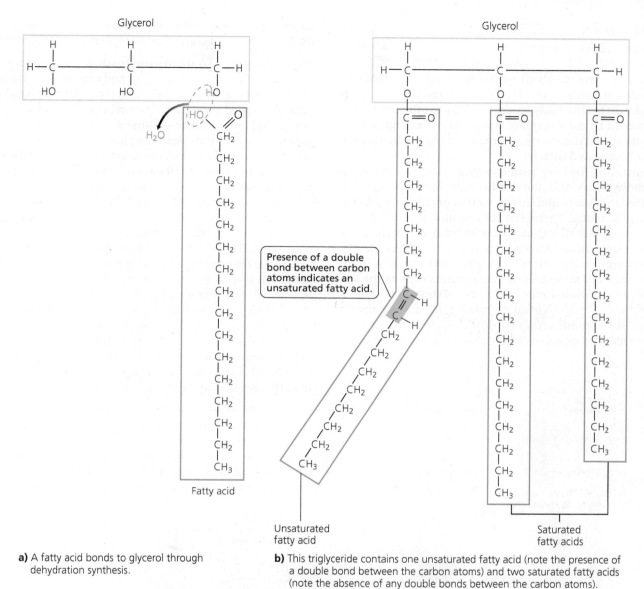

a) A fatty acid bonds to glycerol through dehydration synthesis.

b) This triglyceride contains one unsaturated fatty acid (note the presence of a double bond between the carbon atoms) and two saturated fatty acids (note the absence of any double bonds between the carbon atoms).

Figure 2.17 Triglycerides are composed of a molecule of glycerol joined to three fatty acids.

Q: Would the triglyceride shown in part (b) be a solid or a liquid at room temperature? Why?

Lipids

Lipids, such as fats, are compounds that do not dissolve in water. Lipids are nonpolar (having no electrical charges), whereas water is polar. Because of this difference, water shows no attraction for lipids and vice versa, so water and lipids do not mix. Three types of lipids that are important to human health are triglycerides, phospholipids, and steroids.

Triglycerides Fats and oils are **triglycerides,** compounds made of one molecule of glycerol and three fatty acids. **Fatty acids** are chains of carbon atoms also bonded to hydrogens and having the acidic group COOH at one end. The fatty acids bond to glycerol through dehydration synthesis (Figure 2.17a). Triglycerides are classified as saturated or unsaturated, depending on the presence or absence of double bonds between the carbon atoms in their fatty acids (Figure 2.17b). *Saturated fatty acids* have only single covalent bonds linking the carbon atoms. They are

described as "saturated with hydrogen" because their carbon atoms are bonded to as many hydrogen atoms as possible. Saturated fats are made from saturated fatty acids. Butter, a saturated fat, is solid at room temperature because its fatty acids can pack closely together. Fatty acids with one or more double bonds between carbon atoms are described as *unsaturated fatty acids*— that is, not saturated with hydrogen—because they could bond to more hydrogen atoms if the double bonds between their carbon atoms were broken. The double bonds cause "kinks" in the fatty acids and prevent molecules of unsaturated fat from packing tightly into a solid. Thus, unsaturated fats, such as olive oil, are liquid at room temperature. Sometimes hydrogens are added to unsaturated fats to stabilize them, with the goal of lengthening their shelf life, or to solidify them. For example, hydrogens are added to vegetable oil to make margarine. These partially hydrogenated fats are called *trans* fats and are found in many packaged snacks, such as cookies and potato chips.

STOP and THINK

What would hydrolysis of a fat yield?

Fats and oils provide about twice the energy per gram that carbohydrates or proteins do. This high energy density makes fat an ideal way for the body to store energy for the long term. Our bulk would be much greater if most of our energy storage consisted of carbohydrates or proteins, given their relatively low energy yield compared with fat.

In preparation for long-term energy storage, excess triglycerides, carbohydrates, and proteins from the foods we consume are converted into small globules of fat that are deposited in the cells of adipose tissue. There, the fat remains until our bodies need extra energy; at that time, our cells break down the fat to release the energy required to keep vital processes going. Besides long-term energy storage, fat serves a protective function in the body. Thin layers of fat surround major organs such as the kidneys, cushioning the organs against physical shock from falls or blows. Fat also functions as insulation and as a means of absorbing lipid-soluble vitamins from the intestines and transporting them in the bloodstream to cells. Despite the importance of fats

and oils to human health, in excess they can be dangerous, particularly to our circulatory system (discussed in Chapter 12a).

Phospholipids A **phospholipid** consists of a molecule of glycerol bonded to two fatty acids and a negatively charged phosphate group. Another small molecule of some kind—usually polar and called the variable group because it can vary from one phospholipid to another—is linked to the phosphate group. This general structure provides phospholipids with two regions having very different characteristics. As you will notice in Figure 2.18a, the region made up of fatty acids is nonpolar; it is described as a **hydrophobic,** or "water-fearing," tail. The other region, containing glycerol, phosphate, and the variable group (designated by the letter R), is polar, and it makes up the **hydrophilic,** or "water-loving," head. The tails, being hydrophobic, do not mix with water. The heads, being hydrophilic, interact readily with water. The hydrophilic heads and hydrophobic tails of phospholipids are responsible for the structure of plasma (cell) membranes. In cell membranes, phospholipids are arranged in a double layer, called a *bilayer* (Figure 2.18b), with the hydrophilic heads of each layer facing away from each other. That way, each surface of the membrane consists of hydrophilic heads in contact with the watery solutions inside and outside the cell. The hydrophobic tails of the two layers point toward each other and help hold the membrane together.

Steroids A **steroid** is a type of lipid made up of four carbon rings attached to molecules that vary from one steroid to the next. Cholesterol, one of the most familiar steroids, is a component of the plasma membrane and is also the foundation from which steroid hormones, such as estrogen and testosterone, are made (Figure 2.19). Cholesterol in our blood comes from two

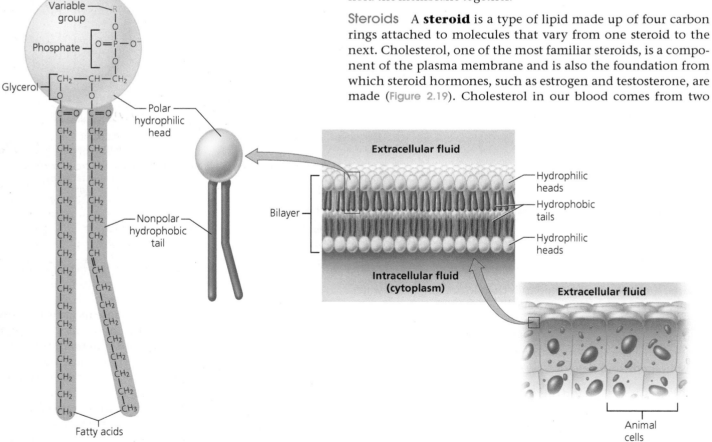

(a) A phospholipid consists of a variable group designated by the letter R, a phosphate, a glycerol, and two fatty acids. Because the variable group is often polar and the fatty acids nonpolar, phospholipids have a polar hydrophilic ("water-loving") head and a nonpolar hydrophobic ("water-fearing") tail.

(b) Within the phospholipid bilayer of the plasma membrane, the hydrophobic tails point inward and help hold the membrane together. The outward-pointing hydrophilic heads mix with the watery environments inside and outside the cell.

Figure 2.18 Structure of a phospholipid. Phospholipids are the main components of plasma membranes.

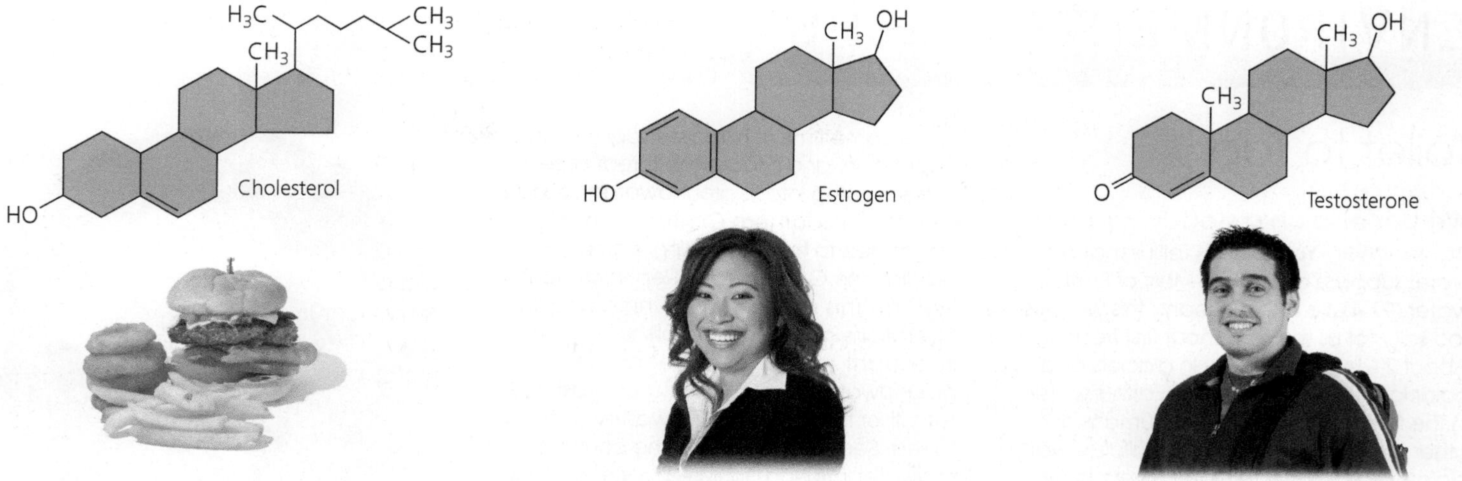

Figure 2.19 The steroid cholesterol is a component of cell membranes, and it is the substance used to make steroid hormones, such as estrogen and testosterone. All steroids have a structure consisting of four carbon rings. Steroids differ in the groups attached to these rings.

sources, our liver and our diet. A high level of cholesterol in the blood is considered a risk factor for heart disease (as described in Chapter 12a).

Proteins

A **protein** is a polymer made of one or more chains of amino acids. In many proteins, the chains are twisted, turned, and folded to produce complicated structures. Thousands upon thousands of different proteins are found in the human body, contributing to structural support, transport, movement, and regulation of chemical reactions. Despite their great diversity in structure and function, all proteins are made from a set of only 20 different amino acids.

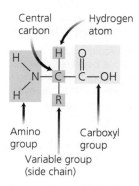

Figure 2.20 Structure of an amino acid. Amino acids differ from one another in the variable group they contain.

Amino acids **Amino acids** are the building blocks of proteins. They consist of a central carbon atom bound to a hydrogen atom (H), an amino group (NH_2), an acidic carboxyl group (COOH), and a variable group (sometimes called a side chain and designated by the letter R; Figure 2.20). Amino acids differ in their variable group. *Nonessential* amino acids are those that our bodies can synthesize. *Essential* amino acids are those that cannot be synthesized by our bodies and must be obtained from the foods we eat.

STOP and THINK
Which three elements are found in carbohydrates, fats, and proteins? Which additional element do proteins always contain?

The amino acids that form proteins are linked by special covalent bonds called peptide bonds, which are formed through dehydration synthesis. A peptide bond links the carboxyl group (COOH) of one amino acid to the amino group (NH_2) of the adjacent amino acid, as shown in Figure 2.21. Chains containing only a few amino acids are called **peptides.** *Di*peptides contain two amino acids, *tri*peptides contain three amino acids, and so on. Chains containing 10 or more amino acids are called **polypeptides.** The term *protein* is used for polypeptides with at least 50 amino acids.

Protein structure Proteins have four levels of structure: primary, secondary, tertiary, and quaternary (Figure 2.22). The **primary structure** of a protein is the particular sequence of amino acids.

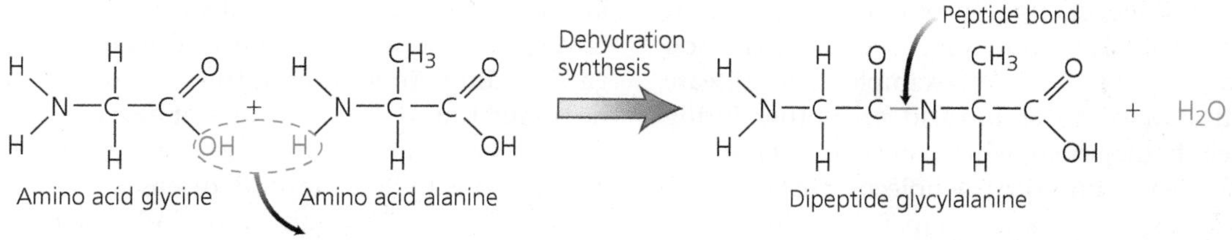

Figure 2.21 Formation of a peptide bond between two amino acids through dehydration synthesis. The carboxyl group (COOH) of one amino acid bonds to the amino group (NH_2) of the adjacent amino acid, releasing water.

ENVIRONMENTAL ISSUE

Toilet to Tap

We depend on a steady supply of freshwater. Yet, experts tell us that our water supply is dwindling. Most of Earth's water (97.4%) is in the oceans; this water is too salty for us to use without first treating it. About 2% is locked away in glaciers and polar ice. This leaves 0.6% of Earth's water, in the form of freshwater, for humans and other organisms to use. The available water is classified as surface water (rivers, lakes, reservoirs) and groundwater (water in porous rock layers below Earth's surface). For many years we have damaged our supplies of freshwater by redirecting the flow of rivers, constructing dams, draining wetlands, and extracting groundwater at rates that exceed its replacement (as part of the water cycle, groundwater is naturally replaced when water that falls as precipitation seeps into the ground). We will have an ever-greater impact on our water supply as the human population continues to grow. Additionally, climate change is predicted to intensify the water cycle and produce more extreme droughts and floods. Flooding caused by very heavy rainfall moves water quickly from the atmosphere back to the ocean, making it more difficult for us to store and use this valuable resource. The United Nations predicts that by 2030 half of the world's population will face water shortages.

Countries such as Singapore and Namibia have gained some measure of water security and independence by recycling wastewater for human consumption—in other words, changing sewage into safe drinkable water. Similar efforts are under way in the United States, particularly in California. Like many western states, California has been experiencing prolonged drought.

At the same time, it has a steadily growing population, and it faces the threat of seawater moving into its groundwater. Orange County, in Southern California, has responded to the impending water crisis by building the Groundwater Replenishment System. This new system, which began operations in 2008, accomplishes two very important things. First, it recharges the groundwater supply with treated wastewater rather than sending the wastewater out to sea. Second, it builds up the county's seawater intrusion barrier—a series of wells into which water is pumped to create an "underground water dam" that blocks seawater from entering the groundwater basin.

Here is how the system works. Industrial and household sewage is treated at the Orange County Sanitation District, as it has been in the past. The sewage, or primary effluent, undergoes several treatments designed to break down organic material and to remove particulate matter. After these treatments, the water, called secondary effluent, would normally be discharged to the ocean. But under the new system, at this point the treated wastewater enters the Advanced Water Purification Facility (AWPF). At the AWPF, the water undergoes a several-step purification process. About half of the water exiting the AWPF is injected into Orange County's seawater intrusion barrier. The other half is piped to a giant percolation pond, where it moves through gravel, sand, and clay into the groundwater supply, filtering naturally just as rainwater finds its way into groundwater. Eventually, this water will enter drinking well intakes. Hence, the water has been described as going from "toilet to tap" (Figure 2.B).

The end result of Orange County's Groundwater Replenishment System is water that meets or exceeds all existing

Figure 2.B The toilet-to-tap program replenishes groundwater supplies with reclaimed wastewater.

standards for drinking water. New wastewater recycling initiatives are under way in other parts of California, and in other states. Although some people may cringe at the thought of drinking water that has been recycled from sewage, it is a reality that we will have to accept as regional and global water supplies continue to tighten. In fact, the World Water Council predicts that recycling wastewater for human consumption will be routine in cities around the globe within 30 years.

Questions to Consider

- Would you be hesitant to drink water that has been recycled from sewage, even if it met current drinking water standards? If yes, what is the reason for your hesitation?
- Do you think that human ingenuity will always be able to produce the technology needed to avoid major environmental crises, such as a global shortage of freshwater?

This sequence, determined by the genes, dictates a protein's structure and function. Even slight changes in primary structure can alter a protein's shape and ability to function. The inherited blood disorder sickle-cell anemia provides an example. This disease results from the substitution of one amino acid for another during synthesis of the protein hemoglobin, which carries oxygen in our red blood cells. This single substitution in a molecule that contains hundreds of amino acids creates a misshapen protein, which alters the shape of red blood cells. Death can result when the oddly shaped cells clog the tiny vessels of the brain and heart (see Chapter 11).

The **secondary structure** of proteins consists of patterns known as helices and pleated sheets, which are formed by certain kinds of bends and coils in the chain, as a result of hydrogen bonding. Alterations in the secondary structure of a protein normally found on the surface of nerve cells can transform the protein into an infectious agent known as a *prion*. Prions have been implicated in several diseases, including Creutzfeldt-Jakob disease in humans and mad cow disease in cattle (see Chapter 13a).

The **tertiary structure** is the overall three-dimensional shape of the protein. Hydrogen, ionic, and covalent bonds

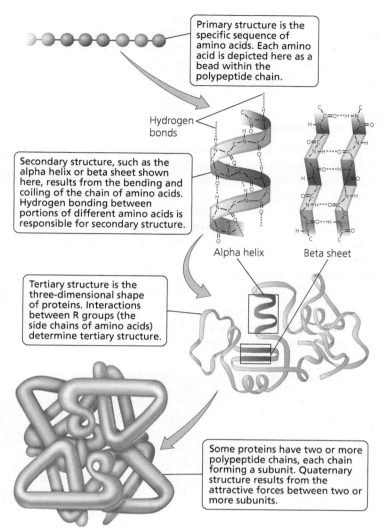

Primary structure is the specific sequence of amino acids. Each amino acid is depicted here as a bead within the polypeptide chain.

Hydrogen bonds

Secondary structure, such as the alpha helix or beta sheet shown here, results from the bending and coiling of the chain of amino acids. Hydrogen bonding between portions of different amino acids is responsible for secondary structure.

Alpha helix   Beta sheet

Tertiary structure is the three-dimensional shape of proteins. Interactions between R groups (the side chains of amino acids) determine tertiary structure.

Some proteins have two or more polypeptide chains, each chain forming a subunit. Quaternary structure results from the attractive forces between two or more subunits.

Figure 2.22 Levels of protein structure

between different side chains may all contribute to tertiary structure. Changes in the environment of a protein, such as increased heat or changes in pH, can cause the molecule to unravel and lose its three-dimensional shape. This process is called **denaturation.** Even a minor change in the shape of a protein can result in loss of function.

Finally, some proteins consist of two or more polypeptide chains. Each chain, in this case, is called a *subunit.* **Quaternary structure** results from the assembled subunits. The forces that hold the subunits in place are largely the attractions between oppositely charged variable groups.

Enzymes   Life is possible because of enzymes. Without them, most chemical reactions within our cells would occur far too slowly to sustain life. **Enzymes** are substances—almost always proteins—that speed up chemical reactions without being consumed in the process. Typically, reactions with enzymes proceed 10,000 to 1 million times faster than the same reactions without enzymes.

The basic process by which an enzyme speeds up a chemical reaction can be summarized by the following equation:

$$\text{E} + \text{S} \longrightarrow \text{ES} \longrightarrow \text{E} + \text{P}$$

| Enzyme | Substrate | Enzyme–substrate complex | Enzyme | Product |

❶ During an enzymatic reaction, the substance at the start of the process is called the *substrate*, and the substance at the end is called the *product* (Figure 2.23). For example, the enzyme maltase speeds up the reaction in which maltose is broken down into glucose. In this reaction, maltose is the substrate, and glucose is the product. Similarly, the enzyme sucrase speeds up the breakdown of sucrose (the substrate) into molecules of glucose and fructose (the products). From these examples you can see that an enzyme's name may resemble the name of its substrate. These particular examples are decomposition reactions, in which a substance is broken down into its component parts. Enzymes also increase the speed of many synthesis reactions.

❷ During reactions promoted by enzymes, the substrate binds to a specific location, called the **active site,** on the enzyme, to form an **enzyme–substrate complex.** This binding orients the substrate molecules so they can react.

❸ The substrate is converted to one or more products, which leave the active site, allowing the enzyme to bind to another substrate molecule (Figure 2.23). The entire process occurs

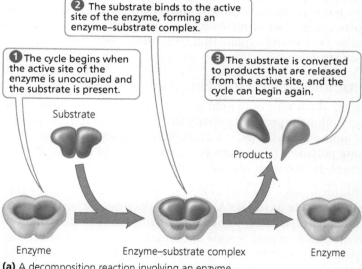

❷ The substrate binds to the active site of the enzyme, forming an enzyme–substrate complex.

❶ The cycle begins when the active site of the enzyme is unoccupied and the substrate is present.

❸ The substrate is converted to products that are released from the active site, and the cycle can begin again.

Substrate

Products

Enzyme   Enzyme–substrate complex   Enzyme

(a) A decomposition reaction involving an enzyme

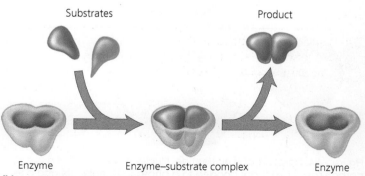

Substrates   Product

Enzyme   Enzyme–substrate complex   Enzyme

(b) A synthesis reaction involving an enzyme

Figure 2.23 The working cycle of an enzyme

very rapidly. One estimate suggests that a typical enzyme can convert about 1000 molecules of substrate into product every second.

Enzymes are very specific in their activity; each is capable of binding to and acting on only one or, at most, a few particular substrates. This specificity is due to the unique shape of each enzyme's active site. The enzyme's active site and the substrate fit together like pieces of a jigsaw puzzle.

Sometimes enzymes need *cofactors,* nonprotein substances that help them convert substrate to product. Some cofactors permanently reside at the enzyme's active site, whereas others bind to the active site at the same time as the substrate. Some cofactors are the organic (carbon-containing) substances we know as vitamins. Organic cofactors are called *coenzymes.* Other cofactors are inorganic (non-carbon-containing) substances, such as zinc or iron.

Enzyme deficiencies can affect our health. Lactase deficiency is one example. Lactase is the enzyme needed to digest the lactose in milk products, breaking it down to glucose and galactose. Infants and young children usually produce enough lactase, but many adults do not. For these adults, consumption of milk and milk products can lead to diarrhea, cramps, and bloating, caused by undigested lactose passing into the large intestine, where it feeds resident bacteria. The bacteria, in turn, produce gas and lactic acid, which irritate the bowels. The milk industry has responded to this problem (often called *lactose intolerance*) by marketing lactose-reduced milk. Tablets and caplets that contain the enzyme lactase are also available.

Nucleic Acids and Nucleotides

In our discussion of protein structure we mentioned that genes determine the protein's primary structure, which is the sequence of amino acids. Genes, our units of inheritance, are segments of long polymers called **deoxyribonucleic acid (DNA).** DNA is one of the two types of nucleic acids.

Nucleotides
The two nucleic acids in our cells are DNA and **ribonucleic acid (RNA).** Both are polymers of smaller units called **nucleotides,** joined into chains through dehydration synthesis. Every nucleotide monomer consists of a five-carbon (pentose) sugar bonded to one of five nitrogen-containing bases and at least one phosphate group (Figure 2.24). The five

nitrogen-containing bases are adenine, guanine, cytosine, thymine, and uracil. The bases cytosine, thymine, and uracil have a single ring made of carbon and nitrogen atoms; adenine and guanine have two such rings. The sequence of bases in DNA and RNA determines the sequence of amino acids in a protein. DNA, as we said earlier, is the nucleic acid found in genes. RNA, in various forms, converts the genetic information found in DNA into proteins.

DNA and RNA Key differences in the structures of RNA and DNA are summarized in Table 2.4. RNA is a single strand of nucleotides (Figure 2.25). The five-carbon sugar in RNA is ribose. The nitrogen-containing bases in RNA are cytosine (C), adenine (A), guanine (G), and uracil (U). In contrast, DNA is a double-stranded chain (Figure 2.26). Its two parallel strands, held together by hydrogen bonds between the nitrogen-containing bases, twist around one another to form a double helix. The five-carbon sugar in DNA is deoxyribose. The nitrogen-containing bases in DNA are adenine (A), thymine (T), cytosine (C), and guanine (G).

ATP At this moment within your cells, many molecules of the nucleotide **adenosine triphosphate (ATP)** are each splitting off a phosphate group. As the phosphate group splits off, energy

Table 2.4	Review of the Structural Differences between RNA and DNA	
Characteristic	RNA	DNA
Sugar	Ribose	Deoxyribose
Bases	Adenine, guanine, cytosine, uracil	Adenine, guanine, cytosine, thymine
Number of strands	One	Two; twisted to form a double helix

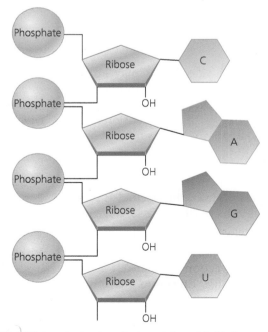

Figure 2.25 RNA is a single-stranded nucleic acid. It is formed by the linking together of nucleotides composed of the sugar ribose, a phosphate group, and the bases cytosine (C), adenine (A), guanine (G), and uracil (U).

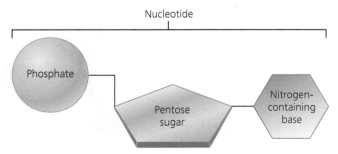

Figure 2.24 Structure of a nucleotide. Nucleotides consist of a five-carbon (pentose) sugar bonded to a phosphate molecule and one of five nitrogen-containing bases. Nucleotides are the building blocks of nucleic acids.

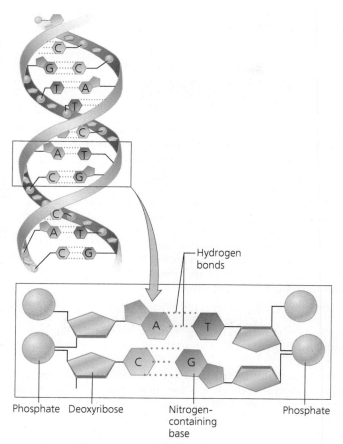

Figure 2.26 DNA is a nucleic acid in which two chains of nucleotides twist around one another to form a double helix. The two chains are held together by hydrogen bonds between the nitrogen-containing bases. Each nucleotide of DNA contains the sugar deoxyribose, a phosphate group, and one of the following four bases: adenine (A), thymine (T), cytosine (C), or guanine (G).

that the molecule stored by holding on to the phosphate group is released. Your cells trap that energy and use it to perform work. It is because of this activity that you are able to read this book. ATP consists of the sugar ribose, the base adenine, and three phosphate groups, attached to the molecule by phosphate bonds. It is formed from adenosine diphosphate (ADP) by covalent bonding of a phosphate group to the ADP in an energy-requiring reaction. The energy absorbed during the reaction is stored in the new phosphate bond. This high-energy phosphate bond is easily broken when the cell requires energy (**Figure 2.27**).

ATP is often described as the energy currency of cells. All energy from the breakdown of molecules, such as glucose, must be channeled through ATP before the body can use it.

LOOKING AHEAD

In Chapter 2, we learned about the major molecules of life. In Chapter 3, we see how these molecules contribute to cell structure and function.

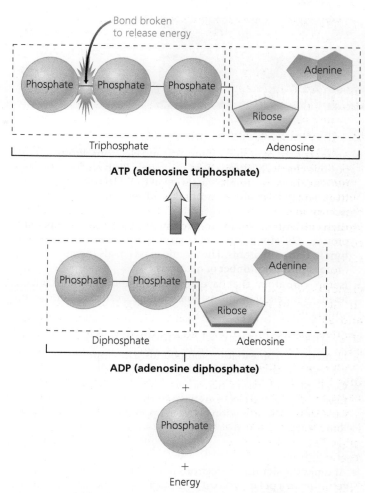

Figure 2.27 Structure and function of adenosine triphosphate (ATP). This nucleotide consists of the sugar ribose, the base adenine, and three phosphate groups. The phosphate bonds are unstable. When cells need energy, the last phosphate bond is broken, yielding adenosine diphosphate (ADP), a phosphate molecule, and energy.

CONSIDER THIS CASE

It is the first day of football practice, and the weather is hot and humid. The coaches have been working the players hard for half an hour when the head coach calls a 10-minute water break. Elijah, who has lived in the southern college town all his life, asks his friend Carter, who arrived back on campus only the day before from a more northern state, how he is holding up. Carter takes his helmet off, holds his head in his hands, and tries to answer, but his speech is slurred and he seems confused. Elijah helps his friend to the sideline and gets the team doctor.

- What might Carter be suffering from?
- What conditions likely contributed to Carter's state and why?

Chapter Review

MasteringBiology®

Highlighting the Concepts

2.1 The Nature of Atoms (pp. 21–24)

■ Atoms consist of protons, neutrons, and electrons. Protons have a positive charge. Neutrons have no charge. Both are found in the nucleus and have atomic masses equal to 1. Electrons have a negative charge, weigh almost nothing, and are found around the nucleus in shells.

■ Each element is made of atoms containing a certain number of protons. The atomic number of an element is the number of protons in one of its atoms. The atomic mass equals the number of protons plus the number of neutrons.

■ Isotopes are atoms that have the same number of protons but different numbers of neutrons. Some isotopes, called radioisotopes, emit radiation.

2.2 Chemical Bonds and Compounds (pp. 24–26)

■ Elements combine to form compounds. The atoms in a compound are held together by chemical bonds.

■ Covalent bonds form when atoms share electrons. Atoms that have lost or gained electrons have an electrical charge and are called ions. The attraction between oppositely charged ions is an ionic bond.

2.3 The Role of Water in Life (pp. 26–30)

■ At times the sharing of electrons in a covalent bond is unequal, resulting in a polar covalent bond and sometimes a polar molecule. Hydrogen bonds are weak attractive forces between the charged regions of polar molecules.

■ Water is an important component of the human body because of its polarity and hydrogen bonding. Its polarity makes water an excellent solvent. Its hydrogen bonds give water a high heat capacity and a high heat of vaporization.

■ Acids increase and bases decrease the concentration of H^+ in solution. The strengths of acids and bases are measured on the pH scale. Buffers prevent dramatic changes in pH.

2.4 Major Molecules of Life (pp. 31–39)

■ A polymer is a large molecule made of many smaller molecules, called monomers. Polymers form through dehydration synthesis and are broken apart by hydrolysis.

■ Carbohydrates are sugars and starches that provide fuel for the human body. Monosaccharides are the smallest monomers of carbohydrates. Polysaccharides are formed by large numbers of monosaccharides linked together.

■ Lipids, such as triglycerides, phospholipids, and steroids, are nonpolar molecules that do not dissolve in water. Triglycerides (fats and oils) function in long-term energy storage. Phospholipids and cholesterol are important components of plasma membranes.

■ Proteins contribute to structural support, transport, movement, and regulation of chemical reactions in the human body. They are polymers made from 20 different amino acids. Enzymes are proteins that speed up chemical reactions without being consumed in the process.

■ Deoxyribonucleic acid (DNA) and ribonucleic acid (RNA) are polymers of nucleotides. DNA carries hereditary information. RNA, in various forms, converts the genetic information found in DNA into proteins.

■ Adenosine triphosphate (ATP), the energy currency of cells, is a nucleotide made of the sugar ribose, the base adenine, and three phosphate groups. When cells require energy, one of the high-energy phosphate bonds is broken, and energy is released.

Recognizing Key Terms

chemistry *p. 21*
matter *p. 21*
atom *p. 21*
element *p. 22*
isotope *p. 23*
radioisotope *p. 23*
compound *p. 24*
covalent bond *p. 24*
molecule *p. 25*
ion *p. 25*
ionic bond *p. 25*
hydrogen bond *p. 27*
acid *p. 29*
base *p. 29*

pH *p. 29*
pH scale *p. 29*
buffer *p. 30*
macromolecule *p. 31*
polymer *p. 31*
monomer *p. 31*
dehydration synthesis *p. 31*
hydrolysis *p. 31*
carbohydrate *p. 31*
monosaccharide *p. 31*
oligosaccharide *p. 31*
disaccharide *p. 31*
polysaccharide *p. 31*
starch *p. 31*

glycogen *p. 31*
cellulose *p. 31*
lipid *p. 33*
triglyceride *p. 33*
fatty acid *p. 33*
phospholipid *p. 34*
hydrophobic *p. 34*
hydrophilic *p. 34*
steroid *p. 34*
protein *p. 35*
amino acid *p. 35*
peptide *p. 35*
polypeptide *p. 35*
primary structure *p. 35*

secondary structure *p. 36*
tertiary structure *p. 36*
denaturation *p. 37*
quaternary structure *p. 37*
enzyme *p. 37*
active site *p. 37*
enzyme–substrate complex *p. 37*
deoxyribonucleic acid (DNA) *p. 38*
ribonucleic acid (RNA) *p. 38*
nucleotide *p. 38*
adenosine triphosphate (ATP) *p. 38*

Reviewing the Concepts

1. Choose the *incorrect* statement:
   a. Electrons are found outside the nucleus at certain energy levels (shells).
   b. For any atom, the number of protons plus the number of electrons equals the atomic mass.
   c. The atomic number equals the number of protons in the nucleus.
   d. Electrons have negligible mass.

2. Covalent bonds
   a. form when two or more atoms share electrons.
   b. result from the mutual attraction of oppositely charged ions.
   c. form between a hydrogen atom on one water molecule and an oxygen atom on another water molecule.
   d. involve the transfer of electrons.

3. Acids
   a. have a pH of 7.
   b. with a pH of 3 have 100 times the amount of H^+ that acids with a pH of 4 have.
   c. increase the concentration of OH^+ in solution.
   d. release H^+ when added to water.

4. Choose the *incorrect* statement:
   a. Peptide bonds are formed through hydrolysis.
   b. Vitamins sometimes help an enzyme convert substrate to product.
   c. The primary structure of a protein is the precise sequence of amino acids.
   d. Quaternary structure results from attractive forces between the subunits of a protein.

5. Hydrogen bonds
   a. are stronger than either ionic or covalent bonds.
   b. form between a slightly positively charged hydrogen atom and a slightly negatively charged atom nearby.
   c. maintain the shape of proteins and DNA.
   d. b and c

6. Water
   a. is a nonpolar molecule and therefore an excellent solvent.
   b. has a high heat capacity and therefore helps maintain a constant body temperature.
   c. has a low heat of vaporization and therefore helps prevent overheating of the body.
   d. makes up about 25% of the human body.

7. Carbohydrates
   a. consist of chains of amino acids.
   b. supply our cells with energy.
   c. contain glycerol.
   d. function as enzymes.

8. Triglycerides
   a. have one molecule of glycerol and three fatty acids.
   b. are poor sources of energy.
   c. are saturated when there are two or more double bonds linking carbon atoms.
   d. are major components of plasma membranes.

9. Enzymes
   a. speed up chemical reactions and are consumed in the process.
   b. function only in decomposition reactions.
   c. are usually nonspecific and therefore capable of binding to many different substrates.
   d. have locations, known as active sites, to which the substrate binds.

10. Choose the *incorrect* statement:
    a. The base uracil is found in RNA but not in DNA.
    b. The two chains of RNA are held together by hydrogen bonds between the bases.
    c. Nucleotides are the monomers of nucleic acids.
    d. DNA molecules contain genes, which specify the sequence of amino acids in proteins.

11. Choose the *incorrect* statement:
    a. Most biochemical reactions in the human body occur around pH 7.
    b. Buffers prevent dramatic changes in pH.
    c. HCl is an important buffering system in the blood.
    d. Burning of fossil fuels causes acid rain.

12. Changes in temperature or pH can cause a protein to lose its three-dimensional shape and become nonfunctional. This process is called _____.

13. _____ are arranged in a double layer (bilayer) that forms the plasma membrane of cells.

Applying the Concepts

1. A friend eyes your lunch and begins to lecture you on the perils of high-fat foods. You decide to acknowledge the health risks of eating a high-fat diet but also point out to her the important roles that lipids play in your body. What will you say?

2. Bill claims that eating fruits and vegetables is overrated because humans lack the enzyme needed to digest cellulose and thus cellulose passes unchanged through our digestive tract. Is Bill correct that we gain nothing from eating food that contains cellulose?

3. For years your mother has been telling you to drink several large glasses of water each day. Having just read this chapter, you now understand the critical roles that water plays in your body. You vow to admit during your next phone call home that she has been right all along. Explain why dehydration might be dangerous.

4. Dental x-ray films are taken using small doses of radiation and are used to detect tooth decay, injuries to the roots of teeth, and problems with the bones supporting the teeth. A dental professional covers the patient with a lead apron that runs from the neck to the abdomen and then leaves the room to take the x-ray film. Why are such precautions necessary?

Finding and Evaluating Information

Nutrients include substances in food, such as fats and carbohydrates, that provide us with energy; proteins that form structures or enzymes in our bodies; and vitamins, minerals, and water. Whereas vitamins are organic compounds needed for growth and overall health, minerals are inorganic substances, some of which become components of enzymes or nucleic acids, or contribute to properly functioning nerves and muscles. Minerals consist of one or more elements. Nutritional supplements, such as multivitamins, often contain the minerals calcium, iron, and zinc. Below is a portion of an article about the use of nutritional supplements. The entire article can be found at: www.theatlantic.com/health/archive/2013/07/the-vitamin-myth-why-we-think-we-need-supplements/277947/

From Paul Offit, *Atlantic,* July 19, 2013

The Vitamin Myth: Why We Think We Need Supplements

Nutrition experts contend that all we need is what's typically found in a routine diet. Industry representatives, backed by a fascinating history, argue that foods don't contain enough, and we need supplements. Fortunately, many excellent studies have now resolved the issue.

On October 10, 2011, researchers from the University of Minnesota found that women who took supplemental multivitamins died at rates higher than those who didn't. Two days later, researchers from the Cleveland Clinic found that men who took vitamin E had an increased risk of prostate cancer. "It's been a tough week for vitamins," said Carrie Gann of ABC News.

These findings weren't new. Seven previous studies had already shown that vitamins increased the risk of cancer and heart disease and shortened lives. Still, in 2012, more than half of all Americans took some form of vitamin supplements.

1. Is sufficient detail provided about the studies showing negative health effects associated with taking nutritional supplements? If not, what additional information about the studies would you like to see included in the article?

2. Are the University of Minnesota and the Cleveland Clinic reliable sources of information? How could you find out? What particular factors make these sources reliable or unreliable?

3. Is the article balanced in its presentation of the advantages and disadvantages of taking nutritional supplements?

4. If you take nutritional supplements, do these three paragraphs from this article change your mind about taking them?

5. How many studies would you need to see before forming an opinion about nutritional supplements?

6. Where would you look to find other sources weighing the risks and benefits of taking supplements? Give some examples and explain why you chose them.

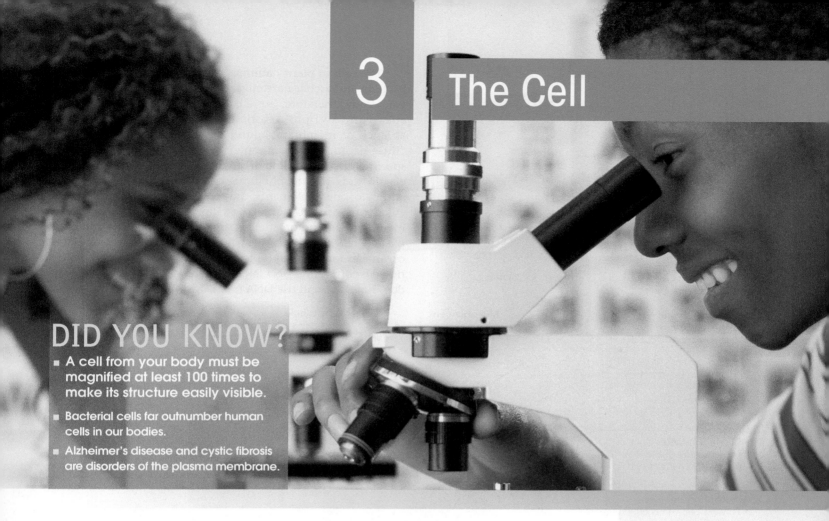

3 The Cell

IN CHAPTER 2, we learned about the major molecules of life, which are carbohydrates, lipids, proteins, and nucleic acids. In this chapter, we see how these molecules contribute to cell structure, direct activities of cells, and serve as sources of cellular energy. We first compare two basic types of cells— eukaryotic cells and prokaryotic cells. Then we explore how eukaryotic cells work by examining the structures shared by all cells in the human body. Finally, we explore the ways that cells obtain the energy they need to do their work of running the body.

3.1 Eukaryotic Cells Compared with Prokaryotic Cells

The **cell theory** is a fundamental organizing principle of biology that guides the way biologists think about living things. The cell theory states that (1) a cell is the smallest unit of life; (2) cells make up all living things, from unicellular to multicellular organisms; and (3) new cells can arise only from preexisting cells.

As we mentioned, there are two basic types of cells—eukaryotic cells and prokaryotic cells. **Prokaryotic cells** are structurally simpler and typically smaller than eukaryotic cells. They are limited to bacteria and another group of microscopic organisms called Archaea. You are probably already aware of bacteria, some of which inhabit your body. Many bacterial inhabitants are harmless, but others can cause illness (see Chapter 13a). Archaea may be less familiar to you. They include species that inhabit extreme environments such as the high-saline Great Salt Lake or the hot sulfur springs of Yellowstone National Park. Most prokaryotic cells are surrounded by a rigid cell wall, as shown in Figure 3.1.

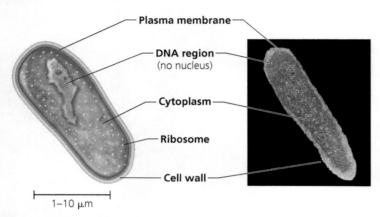

Plasma membrane

DNA region
(no nucleus)

Cytoplasm

Ribosome

Cell wall

1–10 μm

Figure 3.1 Prokaryotic cells, such as a bacterium, lack internal membrane-bound organelles.

The cells of plants, animals, and all other organisms except bacteria and archaea are eukaryotic. All the cells that make up your body, therefore, are eukaryotic. The difference between eukaryotic and prokaryotic cells relates to the presence or absence of membrane-bound organelles. An **organelle,** or "little organ," is a component within a cell that carries out specific functions. Some organelles have membranes, and others do not. Nonmembranous organelles, such as ribosomes and cytoskeletal elements, are found in both prokaryotic and eukaryotic cells. Unique to **eukaryotic cells,** however, are membrane-bound organelles, such as mitochondria and endoplasmic reticulum (Figure 3.2). Another of the membrane-bound organelles found in all typical eukaryotic cells is a well-defined nucleus containing DNA. Note that in prokaryotes, a membrane does not surround the DNA (refer, again, to Figure 3.1). Among

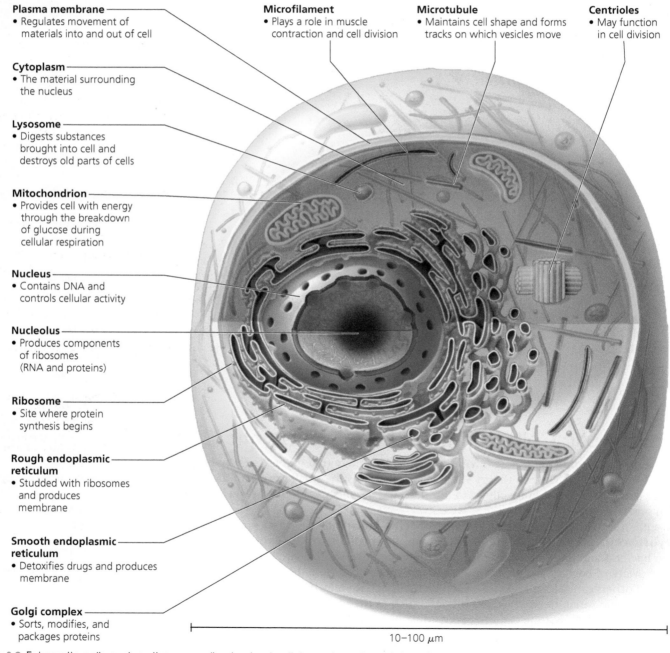

Plasma membrane
• Regulates movement of materials into and out of cell

Cytoplasm
• The material surrounding the nucleus

Lysosome
• Digests substances brought into cell and destroys old parts of cells

Mitochondrion
• Provides cell with energy through the breakdown of glucose during cellular respiration

Nucleus
• Contains DNA and controls cellular activity

Nucleolus
• Produces components of ribosomes (RNA and proteins)

Ribosome
• Site where protein synthesis begins

Rough endoplasmic reticulum
• Studded with ribosomes and produces membrane

Smooth endoplasmic reticulum
• Detoxifies drugs and produces membrane

Golgi complex
• Sorts, modifies, and packages proteins

Microfilament
• Plays a role in muscle contraction and cell division

Microtubule
• Maintains cell shape and forms tracks on which vesicles move

Centrioles
• May function in cell division

10–100 μm

Figure 3.2 Eukaryotic cells, such as the generalized animal cell shown here, have internal membrane-bound organelles.

Table 3.1	Review of Features of Prokaryotic and Eukaryotic Cells	
Feature	Prokaryotic Cells	Eukaryotic Cells
Organisms	Bacteria, archaea	Plants, animals, fungi, protists
Size	1–10 μm across	10–100 μm across
Membrane-bound organelles	Absent	Present
DNA form	Circular	Coiled, linear strands
DNA location	Cytoplasm	Nucleus
Internal membranes	Rare	Many
Cytoskeleton	Present	Present

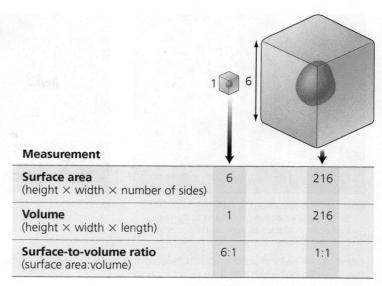

Measurement		
Surface area (height × width × number of sides)	6	216
Volume (height × width × length)	1	216
Surface-to-volume ratio (surface area:volume)	6:1	1:1

Figure 3.3 Cells must remain small because the ratio of surface area to volume decreases rapidly as cell size increases.

eukaryotes, plant cells have cell walls, but animal cells do not. Table 3.1 reviews the major differences between eukaryotic and prokaryotic cells.

3.2 Cell Size and Microscopy

Most eukaryotic and prokaryotic cells are so small that they are typically measured in micrometers (μm), which are equal to 1/1,000,000 meter (m). The small size of cells is dictated by a physical relationship known as the **surface-to-volume ratio.** As a cell gets larger, its surface area increases much more slowly than its volume (Figure 3.3). Nutrients enter a cell, and wastes leave a cell, at its surface. Consequently, a large cell would have difficulty moving all the nutrients it needs and all the wastes it produces across its inadequate surface and therefore would die. A small cell, in contrast, has sufficient surface for the uptake and removal of substances and would survive.

Because most cells are so small, you need a microscope to see them. Throughout this book you will find micrographs, which are photographs obtained using a microscope (Figure 3.4). Microscopic specimens can be imaged using beams of either light or electrons. Light microscopes, which are used in many classrooms, have the advantage of being relatively inexpensive

and simple to operate. Electron microscopes, though more complex and expensive, have the capacity to reveal finer details because the wavelength of an electron beam is smaller than the wavelengths of visible light. Whether light or electrons are used, the beam can be either transmitted through a thinly sliced specimen or bounced off the specimen's surface. Light microscopes, but not electron microscopes, allow observation of living cells.

Figure 3.4a is a light micrograph showing three striated muscle cells that have been stained with biological dyes to increase the contrast between different cellular components. The nuclei visible in this picture are colored dark purple because the dye has an affinity for acidic components in the cell, such as DNA. Figure 3.4b is a transmission electron micrograph that shows the structure of striated muscle cells in more detail than is possible using light to image the tissue. In this case, the contrast between different cellular components is produced by staining

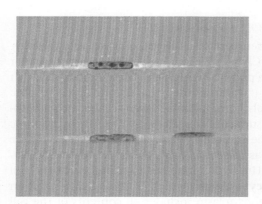

(a) Striated muscle cells viewed with a light microscope

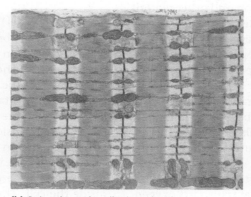

(b) Striated muscle cells viewed with a transmission electron microscope

(c) Striated muscle cells viewed with a scanning electron microscope

Figure 3.4 Micrographs are photographs taken through a microscope. Here, striated muscle cells have been photographed using three different types of microscope. Electron microscopes use beams of electrons to produce images with finer details than those viewed with light microscopes.

Q: If you wanted a detailed three-dimensional view of the surface of a human skin cell, which type of microscope would you use?

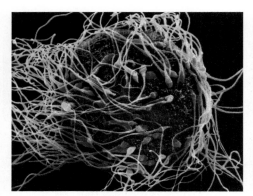

(a) A sperm is specialized to be highly mobile. In contrast, an egg is specialized to be large, immobile, and packed with material needed to initiate development.

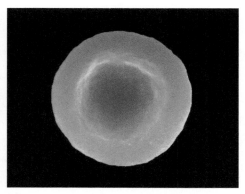

(b) A mature red blood cell, devoid of most organelles, is specialized for carrying oxygen.

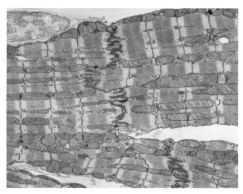

(c) A cardiac muscle cell is specialized for contraction and for propagating the signal for contraction.

Figure 3.5 A cell's structure reflects its specific function. These cell types from the human body illustrate the close tie between structure and function.

the tissue with heavy metals. Different components of the cells absorb different amounts of the metals. Components that readily absorb the metals differentially block the electron beam from passing through the sample. Figure 3.4c is a scanning electron micrograph produced by bouncing an electron beam off the surface of several striated muscle cells. The beam is scanned across the surface of the sample, and electrons that bounce off the surface are collected by a detector. For every point that is scanned, the number of electrons reaching the detector is used to calculate the relative brightness of that spot on the sample. This information is used to construct the image. Images produced with electron beams are not in color. The pictures shown in Figures 3.4b and 3.4c have been colored to highlight certain features, an improvement made possible by computer-assisted processing of images. Other micrographs in the text have also been colored.

3.3 Cell Structure and Function

The structure of a cell exquisitely reflects its functions. For example, few human cells are more specialized than sperm or eggs, the cells that carry genetic information and other materials needed to make a new individual of the next generation. A sperm is specialized for swimming to the egg and fertilizing it. As such, a sperm is streamlined and equipped with a whiplike tail. In the head of the sperm is an enzyme-containing sac that spills open to release enzymes that digest a path through the layers of cells surrounding the egg. In contrast, the egg is immobile and much larger than a typical cell because it is literally packed with nutrients and other materials needed to initiate development. A mature red blood cell is another example of a cell whose structure reflects its function. As the red blood cell matures, it extrudes its nucleus and most organelles, leaving more space for hemoglobin, the protein that transports oxygen. A mature red blood cell is thus an exception to the rule that eukaryotic cells have a well-defined nucleus and other membrane-bound organelles. Consider, also, a cardiac muscle cell. This cell is specialized for contraction and for propagating the signal for contraction from one muscle cell to the next. Thus it

is filled with contractile proteins and is joined to adjacent cells by specialized junctions that strengthen cardiac tissue and promote rapid conduction of impulses throughout the heart. In each of these cases, careful study of the cell's structure provides excellent clues to its function, and vice versa (Figure 3.5).

3.4 Plasma Membrane

We begin our examination of the cell at its outer surface—the **plasma membrane.** This remarkably thin outer covering controls the movement of substances both into and out of the cell. Because the concentrations of substances in a cell's interior are critically balanced, molecules and ions are not permitted to move randomly in and out.

Both prokaryotic and eukaryotic cells have a plasma membrane, but only eukaryotic cells also contain internal membranes that divide the cell into many compartments. Each compartment contains its own assortment of enzymes and is specialized for particular functions. In general, the principles described for the plasma membrane also apply to the membranes inside the cell.

Plasma Membrane Structure

The plasma membrane is made of lipids, proteins, and carbohydrates. Recall from Chapter 2 that phospholipids are the major components of the plasma membrane. These molecules, with their hydrophilic ("water-loving") heads and hydrophobic ("water-fearing") tails, form a double layer—called the *phospholipid bilayer*—at the surface of the cell (Figure 3.6). The hydrophilic heads facing outside the cell interact with the **extracellular fluid** (also known as *interstitial fluid*), which is the watery solution outside cells. The hydrophilic heads facing inside the cell interact with the **cytoplasm,** which is the jellylike solution inside the cell. The cytoplasm includes all contents of the cell between the plasma membrane and the nucleus. Within the phospholipid bilayer, the hydrophobic tails point toward each other and hold the plasma membrane together.

Interspersed in the phospholipid bilayer are proteins, as seen in Figure 3.6. Some proteins are embedded in the membrane,

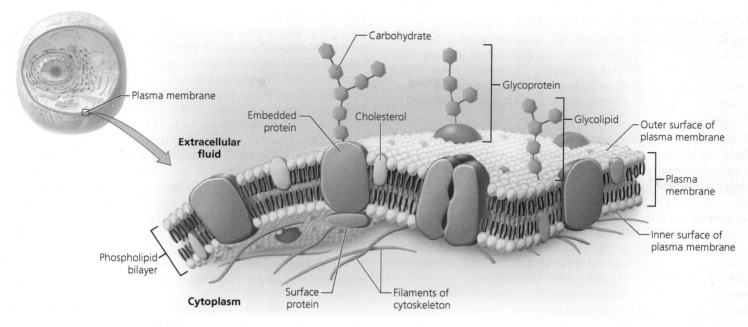

Figure 3.6 The structure of the plasma membrane of a cell according to the fluid mosaic model.

and some of these span the bilayer completely. Other proteins are simply attached to the inner or outer surface of the membrane. Molecules of cholesterol are also scattered throughout the bilayer, where they keep the membrane fluid and flexible.

As you can see in Figure 3.6, carbohydrates attach only to the outer surface of the plasma membrane. Most of these carbohydrates are attached to proteins, forming glycoproteins. Other carbohydrates are attached to lipids, forming glycolipids.

The structure of the plasma membrane is often described as a **fluid mosaic.** The proteins are interspersed among the lipid molecules like tiles of different colors within a mosaic. Many of the proteins are able to move sideways through the bilayer to some degree, giving the membrane its fluid quality.

Plasma Membrane Functions

The plasma membrane performs several vital functions for the cell. First, by imposing a boundary between the cell's internal and external environments, the plasma membrane maintains the cell's structural integrity. Second, the structure of the plasma membrane regulates the movement of substances into and out of the cell, permitting entry to some substances but not others. For this reason, the membrane is often described as being **selectively permeable.** You will read more about the transport of materials across the plasma membrane in the next section of this chapter.

The plasma membrane also functions in cell–cell recognition. Cells distinguish one type of cell from another by recognizing molecules—often glycoproteins—on their surface. Membrane glycoproteins differ from one species of organism to another and among individuals of the same species. Even different cell types within an individual have different membrane glycoproteins. This variation allows the body to recognize foreign invaders such as bacteria. The bacteria, in turn, "read" the

different surface molecules of your cells to settle preferentially on some kinds of cells but not others.

Another important function of the plasma membrane is communication between cells. Such communication relies on *receptors,* specialized proteins in the plasma membrane (or inside the cell) that bind particular substances that affect cell activities. For example, hormones secreted by one group of cells may bind to receptors in the plasma membranes of other cells. The receptors then relay a signal to proteins inside the cell, which transmit the message to other nearby molecules. Through a series of chemical reactions, the hormone's "message" ultimately initiates a response by the recipient cell, perhaps causing it to release a certain chemical.

Finally, the plasma membrane plays an important role in binding pairs or groups of cells together. **Cell adhesion molecules (CAMs)** extend from the plasma membranes of most cells and help attach the cells to one another, especially during the formation of tissues and organs in an embryo.

In summary, the functions of the plasma membrane are as follows:

- Maintain structural integrity of the cell
- Regulate movement of substances into and out of the cell
- Provide recognition between cells
- Provide communication between cells
- Stick cells together to form tissues and organs

STOP and THINK

Of the five functions of the plasma membrane, which might explain the difficulty of transplanting tissues and organs successfully from one person to another? Why would rejection of such transplants occur?

Movement across the Plasma Membrane

Recall that an important function of the plasma membrane is to control which substances move into and out of the cell. Substances cross the plasma membrane in several ways. These methods are described as either active (requiring the cell to expend energy) or passive (requiring no energy expenditure by the cell).

Simple diffusion   Some materials cross the plasma membrane passively through **simple diffusion,** the random movement of a substance from a region of higher concentration to a region of lower concentration. *Concentration* is the number of molecules of a substance in a particular volume, and a **concentration gradient** is a difference in the relative number of molecules or ions of a given substance in two adjacent areas. The end result of simple diffusion is an equal distribution of the substance in the two areas; in other words, diffusion tends to eliminate the concentration gradient. Consider what happens when someone is cooking bacon in the kitchen. At first, the smell of bacon is localized in the kitchen. Soon, however, the smell permeates adjoining rooms, too, as odor molecules move from where they are more concentrated (the kitchen) to where they are less concentrated (other parts of the house). Eventually the odor molecules are equally distributed, but they still move randomly in all directions. Likewise, when a substance diffuses across a membrane from a region of higher concentration to a region of lower concentration, the movement of its molecules does not stop once the concentration has equalized. Instead, the molecules continue to move randomly back and forth across the membrane. The rate of movement in each direction, however, is now the same. Substances such as carbon dioxide and oxygen diffuse through the plasma membrane of our cells (Figure 3.7).

Facilitated diffusion   Water-soluble substances are repelled by lipids, so they cannot move through the phospholipid bilayer by simple diffusion. If they are to cross a cell membrane, their transport must be assisted, or "facilitated," by certain proteins within the membrane. Some of these proteins, called carrier proteins, bind to a particular water-soluble substance. Such binding prompts a change in the protein's shape and has the effect of carrying the substance to the other side of the membrane. Other proteins form channels through which certain water-soluble substances can move. **Facilitated diffusion** is the movement of a substance from a region of higher concentration to a region of lower concentration with the aid of a membrane protein. Molecules of glucose enter fat cells by facilitated diffusion. In this example, a molecule of glucose in the extracellular fluid binds to a carrier protein in the plasma membrane, which helps to move the glucose molecule from outside to inside the fat cell (Figure 3.8). Facilitated diffusion does not require energy and is thus a form of passive transport.

Osmosis   **Osmosis** is a type of diffusion in which water moves across a plasma membrane or any other selectively permeable membrane from a region of higher water concentration to a region of lower water concentration. The movement of water occurs in response to a concentration gradient of a dissolved substance (solute). Consider what happens when a substance such as table sugar (our solute) is dissolved in water (our solvent) in a membranous bag through which water, but not sugar, can move. Keep in mind that when solute concentration is low, water concentration is high; and when solute concentration is high, water concentration is low. If the membranous bag is placed into a **hypertonic solution,** meaning a solution whose solute concentration is higher than that inside the bag, more

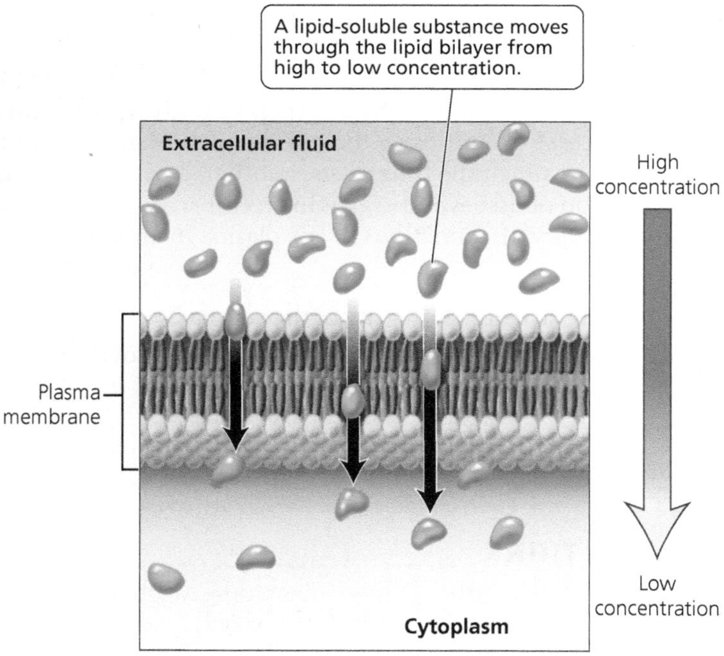

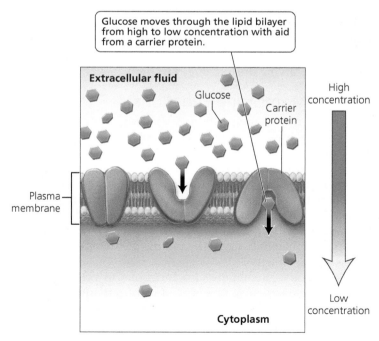

Figure 3.7 Simple diffusion is the random movement of a substance from a region of higher concentration to a region of lower concentration.

Figure 3.8 Facilitated diffusion is the movement through the plasma membrane of a substance from a region of higher concentration to a region of lower concentration with the aid of a membrane protein that acts as a channel or a carrier protein.

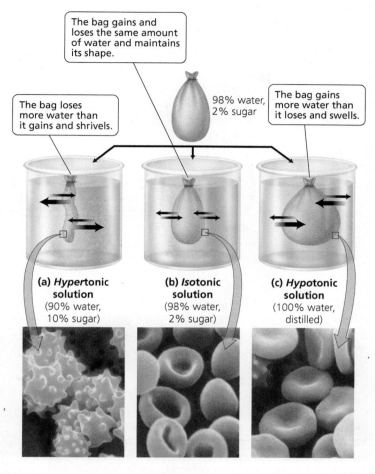

The bag gains and loses the same amount of water and maintains its shape.

The bag loses more water than it gains and shrivels.

98% water, 2% sugar

The bag gains more water than it loses and swells.

(a) *Hypertonic* solution
(90% water, 10% sugar)

(b) *Isotonic* solution
(98% water, 2% sugar)

(c) *Hypotonic* solution
(100% water, distilled)

Figure 3.9 Osmosis is the diffusion of water across a selectively permeable membrane. The drawings show what happens when a membranous bag through which water but not sugar can move is placed in solutions that are (a) hypertonic, (b) isotonic, or (c) hypotonic to the solution inside the bag. The width of the black arrows corresponds to the amount of water moving into and out of the bag. The photographs show what happens to red blood cells when placed in the three kinds of solutions. Red blood cells are normally shaped like flattened disks, as in part (b).

water moves out of the bag than in, causing the bag to shrivel (Figure 3.9a). If, however, the bag is placed into an **isotonic solution,** one with the same solute (sugar) concentration as inside the bag, there is no net movement of water in either direction, and the bag maintains its original shape (Figure 3.9b). When the bag is placed into a **hypotonic solution,** in which the concentration of solute is lower than that inside the bag, more water moves into the bag than out, causing the bag to swell and possibly burst (Figure 3.9c). Osmosis does not require energy and is thus a form of passive transport.

Red blood cells behave the same way the bag in our example does, as shown at the bottom of Figure 3.9. Red blood cells move through a fluid, called plasma. As the figure illustrates, the shape of red blood cells responds to different levels of solute concentration in plasma.

Active transport **Active transport** is a mechanism that moves substances across plasma membranes with the aid of a carrier protein and energy supplied by the cell (through the breakdown of ATP; see Chapter 2). So far in our discussion of movement across plasma membranes, we have described substances moving from regions of higher concentration to regions of lower concentration. However, in most cases of active transport, substances are moved from regions of lower concentration to higher concentration, as shown in Figure 3.10. This type of movement is described as going "against the concentration gradient" and occurs when cells need to concentrate certain substances. For example, the cells in our bodies contain higher concentrations of potassium ions (K^+) and lower concentrations of sodium ions (Na^+) than their surroundings. Through active transport, proteins in the plasma membrane help maintain these conditions, pumping potassium ions into the cell and sodium ions out of the cell. In this example, both potassium and sodium are moving from regions of lower concentration to regions of higher concentration.

Endocytosis Most small molecules cross the plasma membrane by simple diffusion, facilitated diffusion, or active transport. Large molecules, single-celled organisms such as bacteria,

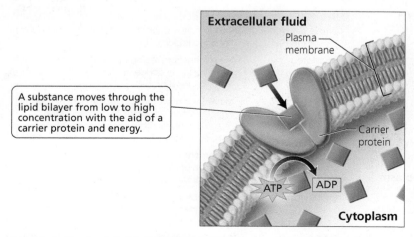
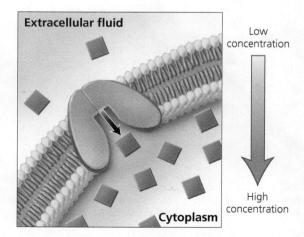

Extracellular fluid
Plasma membrane

A substance moves through the lipid bilayer from low to high concentration with the aid of a carrier protein and energy.

Carrier protein

ATP ADP

Cytoplasm

Extracellular fluid

Low concentration

High concentration

Cytoplasm

Figure 3.10 Active transport is the movement of molecules across the plasma membrane, often from an area of lower concentration to one of higher concentration, with help from a carrier protein and energy, usually in the form of ATP.

and droplets of fluid containing dissolved substances enter cells through endocytosis (Figure 3.11). In **endocytosis,** a region of the plasma membrane engulfs the substance to be ingested and then pinches off from the rest of the membrane; in this way it encloses the substance in a saclike structure called a **vesicle.** The vesicle then travels through the cytoplasm. Two types of endocytosis are phagocytosis ("cell eating") and pinocytosis ("cell drinking"). In **phagocytosis,** cells engulf large particles or bacteria (Figure 3.11a). In **pinocytosis,** they engulf droplets of fluid (Figure 3.11b), thus bringing all of the substances dissolved in the droplet into the cell.

Exocytosis   The process by which large molecules leave cells is **exocytosis** (Figure 3.12). In a cell that produces hormones, for example, the hormones are enclosed in membrane-bound vesicles that travel through the cell's cytoplasm toward the plasma

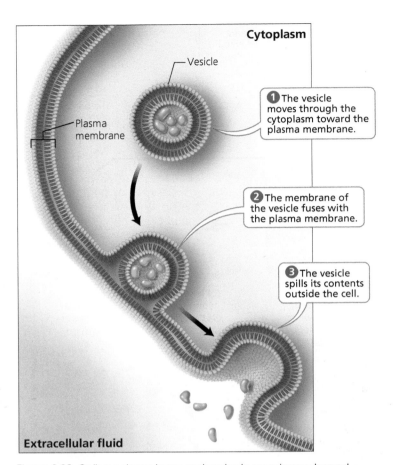

Figure 3.12 Cells package large molecules in membrane-bound vesicles, which then spill their contents by exocytosis.

membrane ❶. When the vesicle reaches the plasma membrane, the vesicle membrane fuses with the plasma membrane ❷. Then the vesicle opens up to release the hormone outside the cell ❸. Nerve cells also release chemicals by exocytosis.

Table 3.2 reviews the ways in which substances move across the plasma membrane.

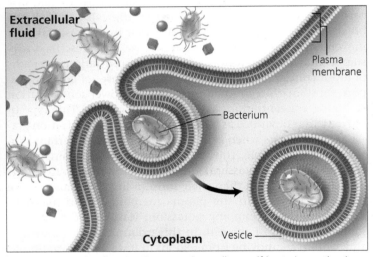

(a) Phagocytosis ("cell eating") occurs when cells engulf bacteria or other large particles.

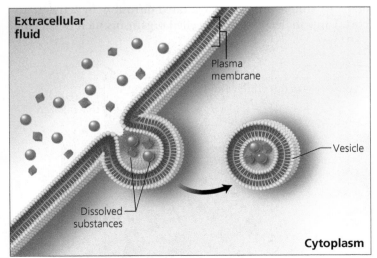

(b) Pinocytosis ("cell drinking") occurs when cells engulf droplets of extracellular fluid and the dissolved substances therein.

Figure 3.11 Endocytosis—phagocytosis or pinocytosis—occurs when a localized region of the plasma membrane surrounds a bacterium, large molecule, or fluid containing dissolved substances and then pinches inward to form a vesicle that moves into the cell.

Table 3.2	Review of Mechanisms of Transport across the Plasma Membrane
Mechanism	Description
Simple diffusion	Random movement from region of higher concentration to region of lower concentration
Facilitated diffusion	Movement from region of higher concentration to region of lower concentration with the aid of a carrier or channel protein
Osmosis	Movement of water from region of higher water concentration (lower solute concentration) to region of lower water concentration (higher solute concentration)
Active transport	Movement, often from region of lower concentration to region of higher concentration, with the aid of a carrier protein and energy, usually from ATP
Endocytosis	Process by which materials are engulfed by the plasma membrane and drawn into the cell in a vesicle
Exocytosis	Process by which a membrane-bound vesicle from inside the cell fuses with the plasma membrane and spills contents outside the cell

STOP and THINK

Participation in water-drinking contests can lead to water intoxication, which can be fatal when cells in the brain swell. Compare solute concentrations in the fluid outside and inside brain cells at the start of this condition. How do solute concentrations affect the movement of water? By what mechanism does water cross the plasma membrane?

3.5 Organelles

Inside the eukaryotic cell, the primary role of membranes is to create separate compartments where specific chemical processes critical to the life of the cell occur. The membrane-bound organelles distributed in the cells' cytoplasm have different functions—just like the different offices within a large company, some of which are responsible for production, some for purchasing, and others for shipping. The compartmentalization allows segregated combinations of molecules to carry out specific tasks (see Figure 3.2). Some organelles give directions for manufacturing cell products. Others make or modify the products or transport them. Still other organelles process energy or break down substances for use or disposal. Nonmembranous organelles also perform specific functions for the cell.

Nucleus

The cell **nucleus** contains almost all of the cell's genetic information (Figure 3.13). The DNA within the nucleus controls cellular structure and function because it contains a code for the production of proteins. All our cells contain the same genetic information. The characteristics of a particular cell—what makes it a muscle cell or a liver cell—are determined largely by the specific directions it receives from its nucleus.

A double membrane called the **nuclear envelope** surrounds the nucleus and separates it from the cytoplasm, as shown in Figure 3.13. Communication between the nucleus and cytoplasm occurs through openings in the envelope called **nuclear pores.** The traffic of selected materials across the nuclear envelope allows the contents of the cytoplasm to influence the nucleus and vice versa.

Genetic information within the nucleus is organized into **chromosomes,** threadlike structures made of DNA and associated proteins. The number of chromosomes varies from one species to another. For example, humans have 46 chromosomes (23 pairs), house mice have 40 chromosomes, and domestic dogs have 78. Individual chromosomes are visible with a light microscope during cell division, when they shorten and condense (Figure 3.14a). At all other times, however, the chromosomes are extended and not readily visible. In this dispersed state, the genetic material is called *chromatin* (Figure 3.14b). The chromatin and other contents of the nucleus constitute the *nucleoplasm.* We will discuss chromosomes and cell division in Chapter 19.

The **nucleolus,** a specialized region within the nucleus (see Figure 3.13), forms and disassembles during the course of the cell cycle (see Chapter 19). It is not surrounded by a membrane but is simply a region where DNA has gathered to produce a type of RNA called *ribosomal RNA (rRNA)*. Ribosomal RNA is a component of **ribosomes,** which are sites where protein synthesis begins. Ribosomes may be suspended in the cytoplasm (free ribosomes) or attached to the endoplasmic reticulum (bound ribosomes).

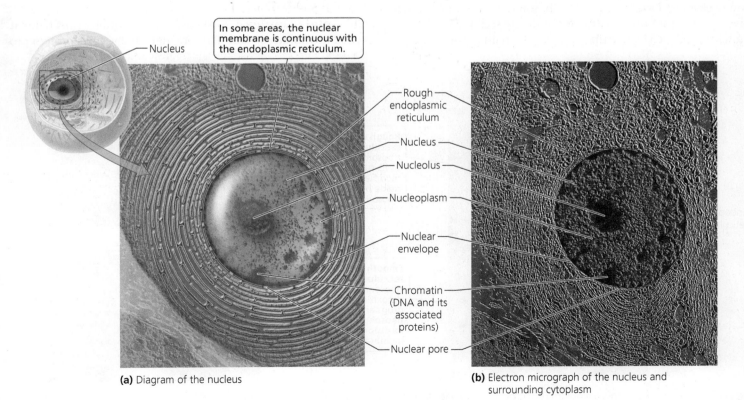

In some areas, the nuclear membrane is continuous with the endoplasmic reticulum.

Nucleus

Rough endoplasmic reticulum

Nucleus

Nucleolus

Nucleoplasm

Nuclear envelope

Chromatin (DNA and its associated proteins)

Nuclear pore

(a) Diagram of the nucleus

(b) Electron micrograph of the nucleus and surrounding cytoplasm

Figure 3.13 The nucleus contains almost all the genetic information of a cell.

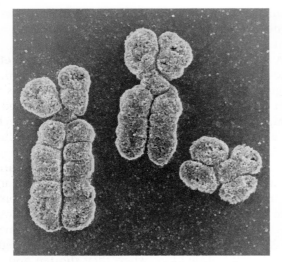

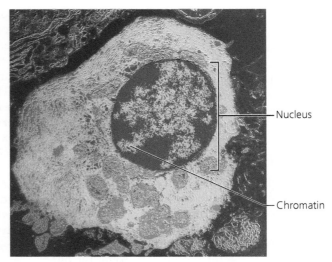

- Nucleus

- Chromatin

(a) Individual chromosomes are visible during cell division, when they shorten and condense.

(b) At all other times, the genetic material is dispersed and called chromatin.

Figure 3.14 Chromosomes are composed of DNA and associated proteins.

Endoplasmic Reticulum

The **endoplasmic reticulum (ER)** is part of an extensive network of channels connected to the nuclear envelope and certain organelles (Figure 3.15). In some regions, the ER is studded with ribosomes and because of this is called **rough endoplasmic reticulum (RER).** The amino acid chains made by the attached ribosomes are threaded through the RER's membrane to its internal spaces. There the chains are processed and modified, enclosed in vesicles formed from the RER membrane, and transferred to the Golgi complex (discussed shortly) for additional processing and packaging. Proteins made by ribosomes bound to ER will be incorporated into membranes or eventually secreted by the cell. Proteins produced by free ribosomes will remain in the cell.

Smooth endoplasmic reticulum (SER) lacks ribosomes. The SER (particularly in liver cells) detoxifies alcohol and other drugs. Typically, enzymes of SER modify the drugs to make them more water soluble and easier to eliminate from the body. Another function of SER is the production of phospholipids. These phospholipids, along with proteins from the RER, are used to make the RER membrane. Because the RER membrane is continually used to form vesicles for shipping, it must be replenished constantly.

Golgi Complex

The **Golgi complex** consists of a series of interconnected, flattened membranous sacs. This organelle is the cell's protein pro-

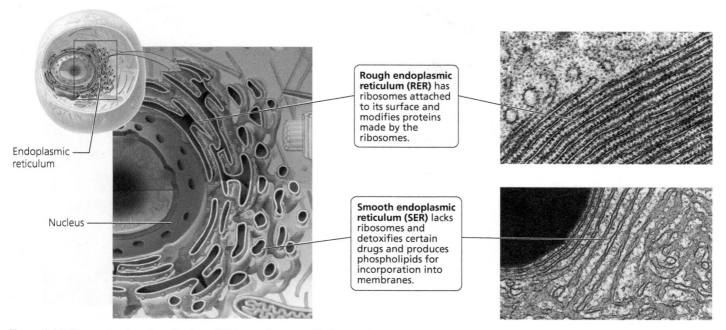

Endoplasmic reticulum

Nucleus

Rough endoplasmic reticulum (RER) has ribosomes attached to its surface and modifies proteins made by the ribosomes.

Smooth endoplasmic reticulum (SER) lacks ribosomes and detoxifies certain drugs and produces phospholipids for incorporation into membranes.

Figure 3.15 The endoplasmic reticulum (ER) is continuous with the nuclear membrane and consists of two regions: rough ER and smooth ER.

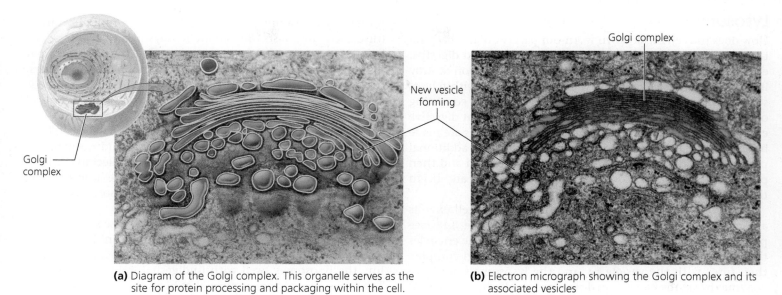

(a) Diagram of the Golgi complex. This organelle serves as the site for protein processing and packaging within the cell.

(b) Electron micrograph showing the Golgi complex and its associated vesicles

Figure 3.16 The Golgi complex

cessing and packaging center (Figure 3.16). Protein-filled vesicles from the RER arrive at the "receiving side" of the Golgi complex, fuse with its membrane, and empty their contents inside. The Golgi complex then chemically modifies many of the proteins as they move, by way of vesicles, from one membranous disk in the stack to the next. When the processing is finished, the Golgi complex sorts the proteins, much as a postal worker sorts letters, and sends them to their various destinations. Some of the proteins emerging from the "shipping side" are packaged in vesicles and sent to the plasma membrane for export from the cell or to become membrane proteins. Other proteins are packaged in lysosomes. Figure 3.17 summarizes the movement of protein-filled vesicles from the rough endoplasmic reticulum to the Golgi complex for processing and eventual release.

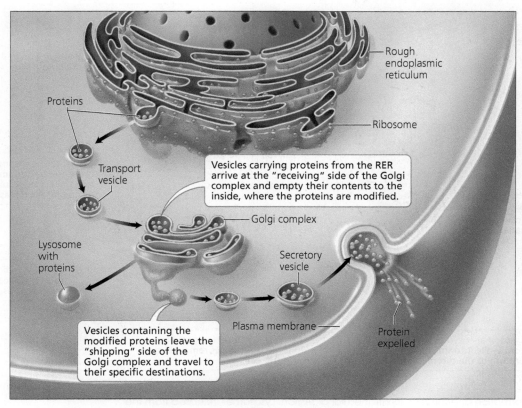

Figure 3.17 The route by which protein-filled vesicles from the rough endoplasmic reticulum travel to the Golgi complex for processing and eventual release.

Lysosomes

How does the cell break down worn-out parts or digest bacteria that it takes in by phagocytosis? If it simply released digestive enzymes into its cytoplasm, for example, it would soon destroy itself. Instead, intracellular digestion occurs mainly within lysosomes. **Lysosomes** are roughly spherical organelles consisting of a single membrane packed with about 40 different digestive enzymes. The enzymes and membranes of lysosomes are made by the RER and then sent to the Golgi complex for additional processing. Eventually, enzyme-filled lysosomes bud and then pinch off from the Golgi complex (see Figure 3.17) and begin their diverse roles in digestion within the cell.

Consider, for example, what happens when a cell engulfs a bacterium. You can follow this process in Figure 3.18 (see pathway on right). During phagocytosis ❶, a vesicle encircles the bacterium. A lysosome released from the Golgi complex then fuses with the vesicle ❷, and the lysosome's digestive enzymes break the bacterium down into smaller molecules ❸. These molecules diffuse out of the vesicle into the cytoplasm, where they can be used by the cell. Indigestible residues may be expelled from the cell by exocytosis ❹, or they may be stored indefinitely in vesicles inside the cell ❺.

Lysosomes also break down obsolete parts of the cell itself. Worn-out organelles and macromolecules are broken down into smaller components that can be reused (see Figure 3.18, pathway on left). For example, an organelle called a mitochondrion (discussed later) lasts only about 10 days in a typical liver cell before being engulfed by a lysosome ❶. After the worn-out mitochondrion is broken down, its component monomers, such as amino acids, are returned to the cytoplasm for reuse ❷. Such "housecleaning" keeps the cell functioning properly and promotes the recycling of essential materials.

The absence of a single kind of lysosomal enzyme can have devastating consequences. Molecules that would normally be broken down by the missing enzyme start to collect in the lysosomes and cause them to swell. Ultimately, the accumulating molecules interfere with cell function. These lysosomal storage diseases are inherited and progress with age.

Tay-Sachs disease is a lysosomal storage disease caused by the absence of the lysosomal enzyme hexosaminidase (Hex A), which breaks down lipids in nerve cells. When Hex A is missing, the lysosomes swell with undigested lipids. Infants with Tay-Sachs disease appear normal at birth but begin to deteriorate by about 6 months of age as abnormal amounts of lipid accumulate in the nervous system. By the age of 4 or 5, Tay-Sachs causes paralysis and death. At present there is no cure for this disease. However, a blood test is available to detect individuals who carry the gene for Tay-Sachs. Called *carriers*, these individuals do not have the disease but could pass the gene to their offspring.

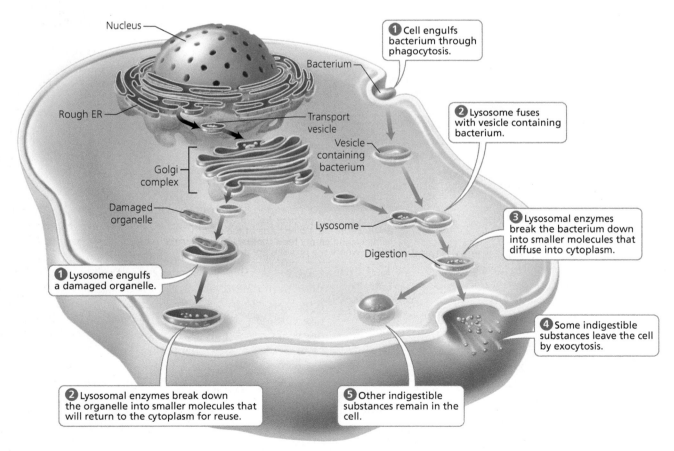

Figure 3.18 Lysosome formation and function in intracellular digestion. Lysosomes, released from the Golgi complex, digest a bacterium engulfed by the cell (see pathway on right). Lysosomes also digest obsolete parts of the cell itself (see pathway on left).

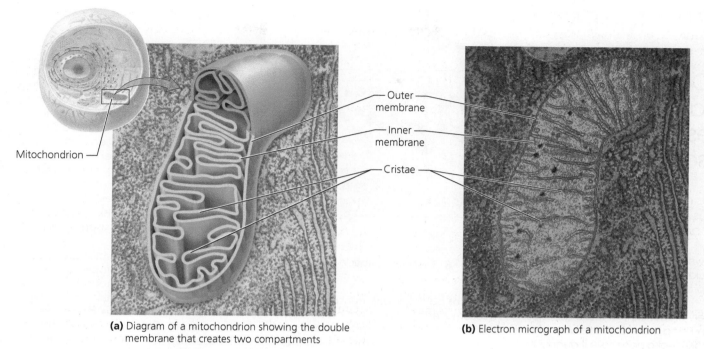

(a) Diagram of a mitochondrion showing the double membrane that creates two compartments

Outer membrane
Inner membrane
Cristae
Mitochondrion

(b) Electron micrograph of a mitochondrion

Figure 3.19 Mitochondria are sites of energy conversion in the cell.

what would YOU do? Imagine that you and your spouse want to start a family, but both of you are carriers of Tay-Sachs disease and could pass the gene to your children. The possible outcomes for any child you might conceive are as follows: the child may not have the gene for Tay-Sachs and may be healthy; or, the child may have the disease and die in early childhood; or, the child may be a carrier, as you are. Your parents urge adoption. Your spouse prefers not to adopt but to use prenatal screening to check whether your fetus has the disease. What would you do? On what would you base your choice? ■

Certain environmental factors cause disease by interfering with lysosomes. In the Environmental Issue essay, *The Deadly Interaction between Asbestos and Lysosomes*, we describe the impact of asbestos on health.

Mitochondria

Most cellular activities require energy. Energy is needed to transport certain substances across the plasma membrane and to fuel many of the chemical reactions that occur in the cytoplasm. Specialized cells such as muscle cells and nerve cells require energy to perform their particular activities. The energy that cells need is provided by **mitochondria** (singular, mitochondrion), the organelles where most of cellular respiration occurs. Cellular respiration, discussed later in the chapter, is a four-phase process in which oxygen and an organic fuel such as glucose are consumed and energy in the form of ATP is released. The first phase takes place in the cytoplasm. The remaining three phases occur in the mitochondria.

The number of mitochondria varies considerably from cell to cell and is roughly correlated with a cell's demand for energy. Most cells contain several hundred to thousands of mitochondria. Like the nucleus, but unlike other organelles, mitochondria

Table 3.3	Review of Major Organelles and Their Functions
Organelle	Function
Nucleus	Contains almost all the genetic information and influences cellular structure and function
Rough endoplasmic reticulum (RER)	Studded with ribosomes (sites where the synthesis of proteins begins); produces membrane
Smooth endoplasmic reticulum (SER)	Detoxifies drugs; produces membrane
Golgi complex	Sorts, modifies, and packages products of RER
Lysosomes	Digest substances imported from outside the cell; destroy old or defective cell parts
Mitochondria	Provide cell with energy through the breakdown of glucose during cellular respiration

are bounded by a double membrane (Figure 3.19). The inner and outer membranes create two separate compartments that serve as sites for some of the reactions in cellular respiration. The infoldings of the inner membrane of a mitochondrion are called *cristae,* and these are the sites of the last phase of cellular respiration. Finally, mitochondria contain ribosomes and a small percentage of a cell's total DNA (the rest is in the nucleus, as noted earlier). Mitochondria contain ribosomes and DNA because they are likely descendants of once free-living bacteria that invaded or were engulfed by ancient cells (see Chapter 22). Table 3.3 reviews the functions of organelles.

STOP and THINK

We have discussed the nucleus, endoplasmic reticulum (including rough and smooth), ribosomes, Golgi complex, lysosomes, and mitochondria. Assign each of these organelles to one of the following main functions within a cell: manufacturing, breakdown, or energy processing.

ENVIRONMENTAL ISSUE

The Deadly Interaction between Asbestos and Lysosomes

Asbestos represents a collection of six fibrous minerals that are strong, flexible, and resistant to heat and corrosion. Because of these properties, asbestos was used widely in construction—as an insulator on ceilings and pipes or to soundproof and fireproof the walls of schools.

The very properties that make asbestos an ideal building material—its fibrous nature and durability—also can make it deadly. For example, when fibers of asbestos insulation are dislodged, small, light particles become suspended in the air and can be inhaled into the lungs. Particles of asbestos are resistant to degradation and can remain in the lungs for life (Figure 3.A).

Inhalation of asbestos particles can cause lung cancer and mesothelioma, a form of cancer specific to the lining of the lungs and chest cavity (pleura) and the lining of the abdomen (peritoneum). Asbestosis, a third condition, is the most common disease caused by exposure to asbestos. It results from the dangerous interaction between asbestos and lysosomes. Cells responsible for cleaning the respiratory passages engulf small particles of asbestos inhaled into the lungs; lysosomes inside the cleaning cells then fuse with the vesicles containing the

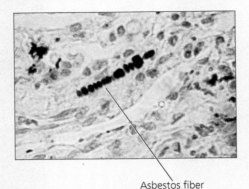

Figure 3.A An asbestos fiber in lung tissue.

asbestos particles. Unfortunately, the lysosomal enzymes cannot break down the asbestos particles. Instead, the particles destabilize the membranes of the lysosomes, causing massive release of enzymes, which destroy the cells of the respiratory tract. Irreversible scarring of lung tissue results, and eventually interferes with the exchange of gases in the lungs. People with asbestos-damaged lungs experience chronic coughing and shortness of breath. These symptoms become more severe over time and may cause death from impaired respiratory function.

At present, there is no effective treatment for asbestosis. The focus, therefore, has been on prevention. More than 50 countries have total bans on all forms of asbestos. In the United States, the use of asbestos for insulation and fireproofing, or for any new purposes, is banned. However, numerous asbestos-containing products are not banned, such as clothing

and cement shingles and pipes, and asbestos is still present in many buildings constructed before the insulation and fireproofing ban went into effect. In these buildings, it is generally recommended and often required that exposed asbestos be removed, enclosed by other building materials, or covered with a sealant. The sealing or removal of asbestos must be done by experts, because the greatest risk of asbestos exposure occurs when asbestos is handled improperly.

There is no question that asbestos causes serious health problems, yet it continues to be used around the globe. For example, Russia, China, and Brazil continue to produce, use, and export asbestos. Although India produces little or no asbestos, it is a major importer. The ongoing production and use of asbestos by these and other countries has caused some public health experts to call for a global ban.

Questions to Consider

- Cigarette smoking worsens diseases caused by exposure to asbestos. If a worker who smokes is exposed over many years to asbestos in the workplace and subsequently develops lung cancer, then who is responsible for his developing cancer? Is it the employer? Or does the worker bear some personal responsibility? What information would you consider when assessing responsibility?
- Should the United States totally ban asbestos? What impact might such a ban have on decisions by developing countries that are considering the risks and economics of asbestos use?

3.6 Cytoskeleton

Traversing the cytoplasm of the cell is a complex network of fibers called the **cytoskeleton.** The fibers are divided into three types: microtubules are the thickest; microfilaments are the thinnest; and intermediate filaments are the diverse group in between. Microtubules and microfilaments disassemble and reassemble, whereas intermediate filaments tend to be more permanent.

Microtubules are straight, hollow rods made of the protein tubulin. Some microtubules near the plasma membrane maintain cell shape. Microtubules also form tracks along which organelles or vesicles travel. Finally, microtubules play a role in the separation of chromosomes during cell division. A microtubule-organizing

center located near the nucleus contains a pair of **centrioles,** each composed of nine sets of three microtubules arranged in a ring (Figure 3.20). Centrioles function in cell division and in the formation of cilia and flagella.

Microtubules serve as the working parts of cilia (singular, cilium) and flagella (singular, flagellum). **Cilia** are numerous short extensions on a cell that move with the back-and-forth motion of oars. They are found, for example, on the surfaces of cells lining the respiratory tract (Figure 3.21a), where they sweep debris trapped in mucus away from the lungs. Smoking destroys these cilia and hampers cleaning of respiratory surfaces. A **flagellum** resembles a whip and moves in an undulating manner. Flagella are much longer than cilia. The only cell with a flagellum in humans is the sperm cell (Figure 3.21b).

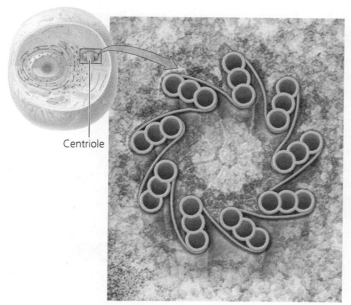

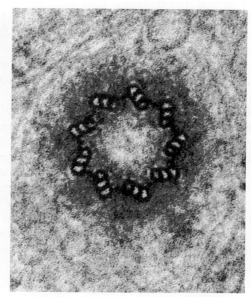

(a) Diagram of a centriole. Each centriole is composed of nine sets of triplet microtubules arranged in a ring.

(b) Electron micrograph showing the microtubules of a centriole

Figure 3.20 Centrioles play a role in cell division.

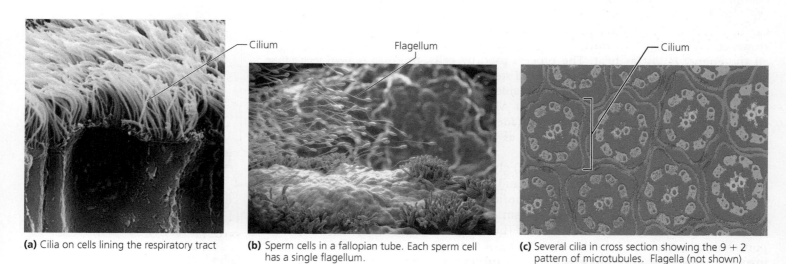

(a) Cilia on cells lining the respiratory tract

(b) Sperm cells in a fallopian tube. Each sperm cell has a single flagellum.

(c) Several cilia in cross section showing the 9 + 2 pattern of microtubules. Flagella (not shown) have a similar arrangement of microtubules.

Figure 3.21 Microtubules are responsible for the movement of cilia and flagella.

Cilia and flagella differ in length, number per cell, and pattern of movement. Nevertheless, they have a similar arrangement of microtubules, called a *9 + 2 pattern,* at their core. This arrangement consists of nine pairs of microtubules arranged in a ring with two microtubules at the center (Figure 3.21c).

Microfilaments are solid rods made of the protein actin. These fibers are best known for their role in muscle contraction, where they slide past thicker filaments made of the protein myosin. Also, during cell division, microfilaments form a band that contracts and pinches the cell in two.

Intermediate filaments are a diverse group of ropelike fibers that maintain cell shape and anchor certain organelles in place. Their protein composition varies from one type of cell to another.

3.7 Cellular Respiration and Fermentation in the Generation of ATP

Living requires work, and work requires energy. Logic tells us, therefore, that living requires energy.

We get our energy from the food we eat. Our digestive system (discussed in Chapter 15) breaks down complex macromolecules such as carbohydrates, proteins, and fats into their simpler components, such as glucose, amino acids, and fatty acids. These simpler molecules are then absorbed into the bloodstream and carried to our cells, where some of the energy stored in the molecules' chemical bonds is used to make ATP, the energy-rich molecule that our cells use to do their work. (Some energy is also given off as heat.) Although carbohydrates, proteins, and fats are all sources of cellular energy, we will focus on carbohydrates. Cells have two ways of breaking glucose molecules apart for energy: cellular respiration and fermentation. Cellular respiration requires oxygen; fermentation does not.

All the chemical reactions that take place in a cell constitute its **metabolism.** These chemical reactions are organized into metabolic pathways. Each pathway consists of steps in which a starting molecule is modified, eventually resulting in a particular product. Specific enzymes speed up each step of the pathway. Cellular respiration and fermentation are examples of *catabolic pathways*—pathways in which complex molecules, such as carbohydrates, are broken down into simpler compounds, releasing energy. *Anabolic pathways,* conversely, build complex molecules from simpler ones and consume energy.

Cellular Respiration

Cellular respiration is the oxygen-requiring pathway by which cells break down glucose. It is an elaborate series of chemical reactions whose final products are carbon dioxide, water, and energy. In a laboratory beaker, glucose and oxygen can be combined to produce those products in a single step. However, under those circumstances, the glucose burns, and all the energy is lost as heat. The process used by cells, in which glucose is broken down in a series of steps, enables the cells to obtain much of the energy in a usable form—specifically, as a high-energy chemical bond in ATP. Recall from Chapter 2 that ATP is formed from ADP (adenosine diphosphate) and phosphate (here, abbreviated as P) in a process that requires energy.

Cellular respiration has four phases: (1) glycolysis, (2) the transition reaction, (3) the citric acid cycle, and (4) the electron transport chain. All four phases occur continuously within cells. Glycolysis takes place in the cytoplasm of the cell. The transition reaction, the citric acid cycle, and the electron transport chain take place in mitochondria. Some of these phases involve a series of reactions in which the **products** from one reaction become the **substrates** (raw materials) for the next reaction. Also, the transfer of electrons from one atom or molecule to another is a key feature of the process our cells use to capture energy from fuel. As the electrons are passed along a chain of intermediate compounds, their energy is used to make ATP.

Blood brings oxygen and glucose to the cells of your body. Once oxygen enters your cells by simple diffusion, and glucose enters by facilitated diffusion, cellular respiration can begin.

Glycolysis   The first phase of cellular respiration, called **glycolysis** (*glyco,* sugar; *lysis,* splitting), begins with the splitting of glucose, a six-carbon sugar, into 2 three-carbon sugars. These three-carbon sugars are then converted into two molecules of **pyruvate** (Figure 3.22), another three-carbon

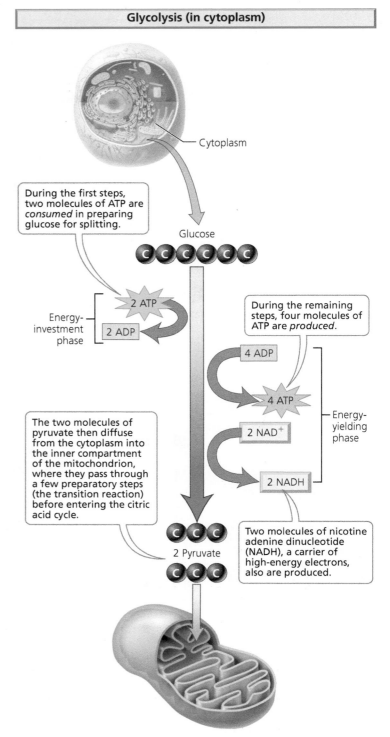

Glycolysis (in cytoplasm)

— Cytoplasm

During the first steps, two molecules of ATP are *consumed* in preparing glucose for splitting.

Glucose

Energy-investment phase — 2 ATP / 2 ADP

During the remaining steps, four molecules of ATP are *produced.*

4 ADP

4 ATP

2 NAD⁺

Energy-yielding phase

2 NADH

The two molecules of pyruvate then diffuse from the cytoplasm into the inner compartment of the mitochondrion, where they pass through a few preparatory steps (the transition reaction) before entering the citric acid cycle.

Two molecules of nicotine adenine dinucleotide (NADH), a carrier of high-energy electrons, also are produced.

2 Pyruvate

Figure 3.22 Glycolysis is a sequence of reactions in the cytoplasm. Glucose, a six-carbon sugar, is split into 2 three-carbon molecules of pyruvate.

compound. Glycolysis occurs in several steps, each requiring a different, specific enzyme. During the first steps, two molecules of ATP are consumed because energy is needed to prepare glucose for splitting. During the remaining steps, four molecules of ATP are produced, for a net gain of two ATP. Glycolysis also

Transition Reaction (in mitochondrion)

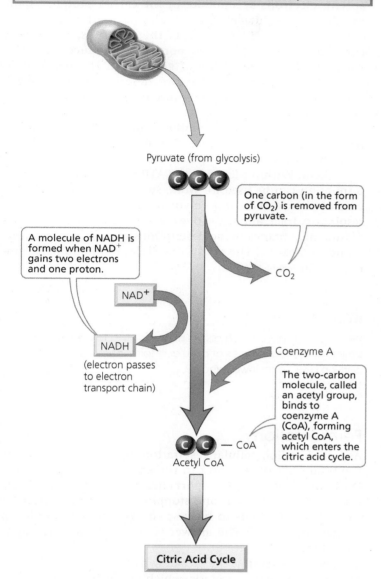

Pyruvate (from glycolysis)

One carbon (in the form of CO_2) is removed from pyruvate.

A molecule of NADH is formed when NAD^+ gains two electrons and one proton.

NAD^+

NADH

(electron passes to electron transport chain)

CO_2

Coenzyme A

The two-carbon molecule, called an acetyl group, binds to coenzyme A (CoA), forming acetyl CoA, which enters the citric acid cycle.

Acetyl CoA — CoA

Citric Acid Cycle

Figure 3.23 The transition reaction takes place inside the mitochondrion and links glycolysis and the citric acid cycle.

Citric Acid Cycle (in mitochondrion)

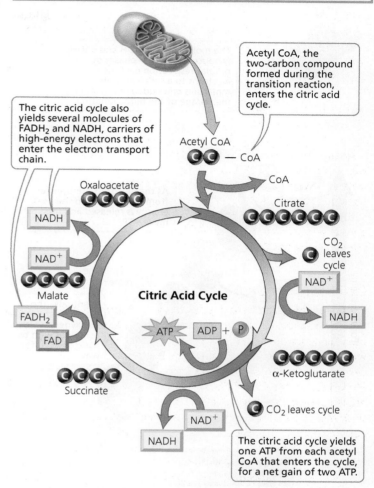

Acetyl CoA, the two-carbon compound formed during the transition reaction, enters the citric acid cycle.

Acetyl CoA — CoA

CoA

The citric acid cycle also yields several molecules of $FADH_2$ and NADH, carriers of high-energy electrons that enter the electron transport chain.

Oxaloacetate

NADH

NAD^+

Malate

$FADH_2$

FAD

Succinate

Citric Acid Cycle

ATP   ADP + P

Citrate

CO_2 leaves cycle

NAD^+

NADH

α-Ketoglutarate

CO_2 leaves cycle

NAD^+

NADH

The citric acid cycle yields one ATP from each acetyl CoA that enters the cycle, for a net gain of two ATP.

Figure 3.24 The citric acid cycle occurs inside the mitochondrion and yields two molecules of ATP and several molecules of NADH and $FADH_2$ per molecule of glucose.

produces two molecules of nicotine adenine dinucleotide (NADH), which are generated when electrons are donated to the coenzyme NAD^+. Coenzymes are organic molecules that help enzymes convert substrate to product. Glycolysis does not require oxygen and releases only a small amount of the chemical energy stored in glucose. Most of the energy remains in the two molecules of pyruvate. The pyruvate molecules move from the cytoplasm into the inner compartment of the mitochondrion.

Transition reaction   Once inside the inner compartment of the mitochondrion, pyruvate reacts with coenzyme A (CoA) in a reaction called the *transition reaction*. The transition reaction results in the removal of one carbon (in the form of carbon dioxide, CO_2) from each pyruvate (Figure 3.23). The resulting

two-carbon molecule, called an acetyl group, then binds to CoA to form acetyl CoA. Acetyl CoA is a high-energy fuel molecule that will enter the citric acid cycle. A molecule of NADH is also produced from each pyruvate.

Citric acid cycle   Still in the inner compartment of the mitochondrion, acetyl CoA reacts with a four-carbon compound in the first of a cyclic series of eight chemical reactions known as the **citric acid cycle,** named after the first product (citric acid, or citrate) formed along its route (Figure 3.24). The cycle is also called the *Krebs cycle*—after the scientist Hans Krebs, who described many of the reactions. Rather than considering each of the chemical reactions in the citric acid cycle, we will simply say that it completes the loss of electrons from glucose and yields two molecules of ATP (one from each acetyl CoA that enters the cycle) and several molecules of NADH and $FADH_2$ (flavin adenine dinucleotide). NADH and $FADH_2$ are carriers of high-energy electrons. The

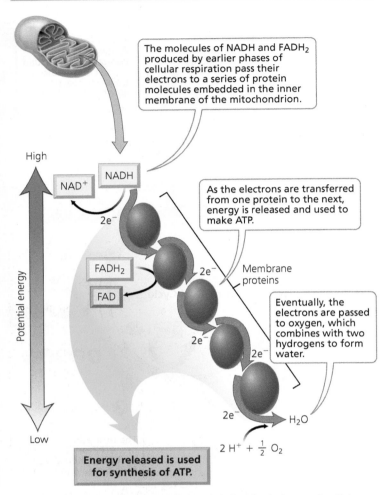

Electron Transport Chain (inner membrane of mitochondrion)

The molecules of NADH and FADH$_2$ produced by earlier phases of cellular respiration pass their electrons to a series of protein molecules embedded in the inner membrane of the mitochondrion.

High

Potential energy

NAD$^+$

NADH

2e$^-$

As the electrons are transferred from one protein to the next, energy is released and used to make ATP.

FADH$_2$

FAD

2e$^-$

Membrane proteins

2e$^-$

Eventually, the electrons are passed to oxygen, which combines with two hydrogens to form water.

2e$^-$

2e$^-$

Low

2e$^-$

H$_2$O

2 H$^+$ + $\frac{1}{2}$ O$_2$

Energy released is used for synthesis of ATP.

Figure 3.25 The electron transport chain is the final phase of cellular respiration. This phase yields 32 ATP molecules per molecule of glucose.

NADH and FADH$_2$ produced in glycolysis, in the transition reaction, and in the citric acid cycle enter the electron transport chain, the final phase of cellular respiration. The citric acid cycle also produces CO_2 as waste.

Electron transport chain   During the final phase of cellular respiration, the molecules of NADH and FADH$_2$ produced by earlier phases pass their electrons to a series of carrier proteins embedded in the inner membrane of the mitochondrion. These proteins are known as the **electron transport chain** (Figure 3.25). (Recall that the inner membrane of the mitochondrion is highly folded, providing space for thousands of sets of carrier proteins.) During the transfer of electrons from one protein to the next, energy is released and used to make ATP. Eventually, the electrons are passed to oxygen, the final electron acceptor, which then combines with two hydrogen ions to form water. Oxygen

has a critical role in cellular respiration. When oxygen is absent, electrons accumulate in the carrier proteins, halting the citric acid cycle and cellular respiration. But when oxygen is present, and accepts the electrons, respiration continues. The electron transport chain produces 32 molecules of ATP per molecule of glucose. In the Health Issue essay, *Mitochondrial Diseases*, we describe what happens when there is a deficiency of proteins in the electron transport chain.

Altogether, cellular respiration produces 36 molecules of ATP per molecule of glucose: 2 ATP from glycolysis, 2 ATP from the citric acid cycle, and 32 ATP from the electron transport chain. Within each cell, the ATP produced from cellular respiration can be used for work, such as contraction in the case of muscle cells, movement of cilia on cells lining the respiratory tract, and the active transport of substances across plasma membranes. Basic descriptions of each phase can be found in Table 3.4. The results of cellular respiration are summarized in Figure 3.26.

STOP and THINK . . . .

We inhale oxygen, which allows mitochondria to generate ATP. Which of the four phases of cellular respiration produce(s) the carbon dioxide that we exhale?

. . . .

Fermentation

As noted earlier, cellular respiration depends on oxygen as the final electron acceptor in the electron transport chain. Without oxygen, the transport chain comes to a halt, blocking the citric acid cycle and stopping cellular respiration. Is there a way for cells to harvest energy when molecules of oxygen are scarce? The answer is yes, and the pathway is fermentation.

Fermentation is the breakdown of glucose without oxygen. It begins with glycolysis, which occurs in the cytoplasm and does not require oxygen. From one molecule of glucose, glycolysis produces two molecules each of pyruvate, the electron carrier NADH, and ATP. The remaining fermentation reactions also take place in the cytoplasm, transferring electrons from NADH to pyruvate or a derivative of pyruvate. This transfer of electrons is critical because it regenerates NAD$^+$, which is essential for the production of ATP through glycolysis. Recall that in cellular respiration, oxygen is the final electron acceptor in the electron transport chain. In fermentation, it is pyruvate or a pyruvate derivative. Fermentation therefore nets only 2 molecules of ATP compared with the 36 molecules of ATP produced by cellular respiration (refer, again, to Figure 3.26). In short, fermentation is a very inefficient way for cells to harvest energy.

Lactic acid fermentation occurs in the human body. During strenuous exercise, the oxygen supply in our muscle cells runs low. Under these conditions, the cells increase lactic acid fermentation to ensure continued production

Phase	Location	Description	Main Products
Glycolysis	Cytoplasm	Several-step process by which glucose is split into 2 pyruvate	2 pyruvate 2 ATP 2 NADH
Transition reaction	Mitochondria	One CO_2 is removed from each pyruvate; the resulting molecules bind to CoA, forming 2 acetyl CoA	2 acetyl CoA 2 NADH
Citric acid cycle	Mitochondria	Cyclic series of eight chemical reactions by which acetyl CoA is broken down	2 ATP 2 $FADH_2$ 6 NADH
Electron transport chain	Mitochondria	Electrons from NADH and $FADH_2$ are passed from one protein to the next, releasing energy for ATP synthesis	32 ATP H_2O

Table 3.4   Review of Cellular Respiration

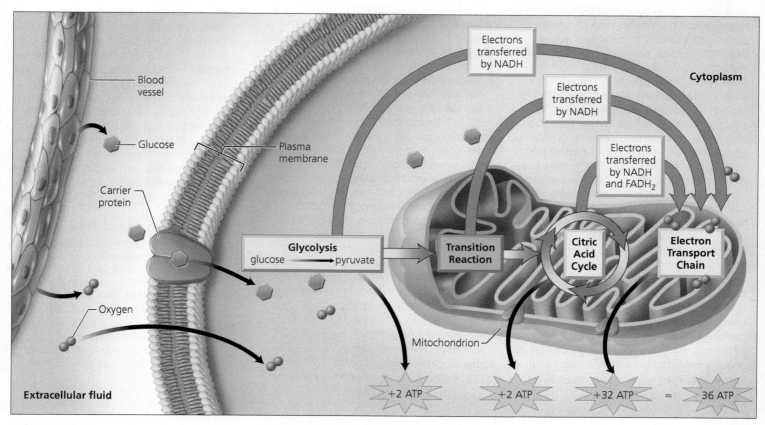

Figure 3.26 Summary of cellular respiration. Cellular respiration produces 36 ATP per molecule of glucose (2 ATP from glycolysis, 2 ATP from the citric acid cycle, and 32 ATP from the electron transport chain).

of ATP. The muscle pain we often experience after intense exercise is caused partly by the accumulation of lactic acid, a waste product of this type of fermentation. In time, the soreness disappears as the lactic acid moves into the bloodstream and is carried to the liver, where it is converted back to pyruvate.

LOOKING AHEAD

In Chapter 3, we learned about the basic structure of cells. In Chapter 4, we describe how specialized cells form tissues, organs, and organ systems.

HEALTH ISSUE

Mitochondrial Diseases

Outages in the electrical power grid can cause many services—air and rail transport, communications, water purification, heating and cooling—to slow and sometimes fail. A similar situation can happen in our bodies when mitochondria, our energy-processing organelles, fail. Mitochondria convert energy from food molecules into ATP for cells to use. Several steps of cellular respiration occur in mitochondria and require particular proteins to proceed. More than 40 illnesses, collectively known as *mitochondrial diseases*, result from deficiencies in the proteins that function in energy metabolism within mitochondria, including proteins that are part of the electron transport chain. When mitochondria fail to function properly, less energy is generated, cell function is compromised, and cell death can result. This, in turn, can affect tissues, organs, and organ systems. Mitochondrial diseases cause the most damage to parts of the body that need the most energy, such as the brain, heart, kidneys, and skeletal muscles.

Each year in the United States, an estimated 1000 to 4000 babies are born with mitochondrial diseases. Many physicians believe that mitochondrial diseases are underdiagnosed and misdiagnosed, so estimates may be low. These diseases are caused by mutations (changes) in DNA that encodes for proteins critical in energy metabolism within mitochondria. Some of these proteins are encoded by

mitochondrial DNA, but others are encoded by nuclear DNA and then imported into mitochondria. The mutations may be spontaneous or inherited. Children inherit nuclear DNA from their mother and father, but they inherit their mitochondrial DNA only from their mother. Recent research suggests a maternal age effect for mitochondrial DNA mutations: older mothers have more of these mutations, and so do their children. Environmental factors, such as infections and certain drugs, can also damage mitochondria.

People with a mitochondrial disease may experience fatigue and fail to gain weight. Symptoms of specific mitochondrial diseases are diverse because they reflect which cells and organs have compromised mitochondria. If cells in the brain are affected, then symptoms may include seizures, developmental delays, and dementia. Skeletal muscle cells with defective mitochondria can result in muscle weakness, cramps, and exercise intolerance. Sometimes multiple organ systems are affected. In addition, cells typically contain hundreds of mitochondria, so a single cell can have some mitochondria that are normal and others that are defective (i.e., carry a mutation). The health of cells (and the severity of disease symptoms) will depend on the relative proportions of normal and defective mitochondria. Symptoms may vary dramatically even among members of the same family with an inherited mutation in mitochondrial DNA. Some of a woman's eggs may have large proportions of defective mitochondria, while other eggs have mostly healthy mitochondria, so the severity of symptoms in the

children will depend on the proportion of defective mitochondria passed to them by their mother. Finally, depending on the particular disorder, the onset of symptoms can occur in infancy, childhood, or adulthood. Adult onset may occur in a person who was born with the genetic mutation but whose symptoms did not appear until an environmental trigger, such as a severe illness, brought them on.

Given variation in the number of organ systems affected and in the timing and severity of symptoms, it is difficult to predict the course of a mitochondrial disease. Indeed, some people may experience relatively good quality of life, while others may have severe symptoms and not survive childhood. There are no known cures for mitochondrial diseases, so medical professionals focus on alleviating symptoms and slowing disease progression. For example, a dietician may help patients to maintain or gain weight, and physical therapy might benefit patients whose skeletal muscles are affected. Patients are also advised to avoid energetically stressful situations, such as fasting or extreme cold.

Questions to Consider

- A woman has an inherited, adult-onset mitochondrial disease that was diagnosed only after she had two sons and a daughter. Her disease has been traced to a mutation in her mitochondrial DNA. Which, if any, of her children will inherit the mutation?
- What factors determine the extent of symptoms in any afflicted child? If all of her children have families of their own, which of her children will pass on the mutation?

CONSIDER THIS CASE

Bethany has been diagnosed with Pompe disease, which is a rare inherited disorder that progresses with age. Her physician explained to her that Pompe disease is characterized by the buildup of glycogen inside her cells, particularly her muscle cells. Glycogen, a storage polysaccharide, accumulates because she is missing the enzyme acid alpha-glucosidase, which normally breaks down glycogen into glucose. Glucose is a monosaccharide,

or simple sugar, that cells use for energy. In Bethany's condition, the accumulating glycogen interferes with cell function, ultimately causing muscle weakness.

- Is Pompe disease a mitochondrial disease or is it related to another organelle, and if so, which? Explain your answer.

Chapter Review

MasteringBiology®

Highlighting the Concepts

3.1 Eukaryotic Cells Compared with Prokaryotic Cells (pp. 43–45)

- Prokaryotic cells, unique to the Bacteria and Archaea, lack membrane-bound organelles. Eukaryotic cells, found in all other organisms, have membrane-bound organelles.

3.2 Cell Size and Microscopy (pp. 45–46)

- As a cell grows, its volume increases more than its surface area; therefore, a cell that is too large will encounter problems caused by inadequate surface area. For that reason, most cells are very small.
- Most cells can be seen only with a microscope. Whereas light microscopes use beams of light to image specimens, electron microscopes use beams of electrons.

3.3 Cell Structure and Function (p. 46)

- All eukaryotic cells have certain features in common, including a plasma membrane and membrane-bound organelles. Structural differences between eukaryotic cells often reflect differences in function.

3.4 Plasma Membrane (pp. 46–50)

- The plasma membrane is made of phospholipids arranged in a bilayer with proteins and molecules of cholesterol interspersed throughout and carbohydrates attached to the outer surface.
- The plasma membrane maintains the cell's integrity, regulates movement of substances into and out of the cell, functions in cell–cell recognition, promotes communication between cells, and binds cells together to form tissues and organs.

- Most small molecules cross the plasma membrane by simple diffusion, facilitated diffusion, or active transport. Water moves across by osmosis. Large molecules enter cells through endocytosis and leave by exocytosis.

3.5 Organelles (pp. 51–55)

- Membrane-bound organelles within eukaryotic cells include the nucleus, endoplasmic reticulum (rough and smooth), Golgi complex, lysosomes, and mitochondria. Ribosomes are non-membrane-bound organelles.

3.6 Cytoskeleton (pp. 56–57)

- The cytoskeleton, a complex network of fibers throughout the cytoplasm of the cell, consists of microtubules, microfilaments, and intermediate filaments.

3.7 Cellular Respiration and Fermentation in the Generation of ATP (pp. 57–61)

- Cells use two catabolic pathways—cellular respiration and fermentation—to break down the carbohydrate glucose and store its energy as ATP. Cellular respiration requires oxygen and usually yields 36 molecules of ATP per molecule of glucose. Fermentation does not require oxygen and yields 2 ATP.
- Cellular respiration has four phases—glycolysis, which occurs in the cytoplasm, and the transition reaction, the citric acid cycle, and the electron transport chain, all of which take place in mitochondria.

Recognizing Key Terms

cell theory *p. 43*
prokaryotic cell *p. 43*
organelle *p. 44*
eukaryotic cell *p. 44*
surface-to-volume ratio *p. 45*
plasma membrane *p. 46*
extracellular fluid *p. 46*
cytoplasm *p. 46*
fluid mosaic *p. 47*
selectively permeable *p. 47*
cell adhesion molecule (CAM) *p. 47*
simple diffusion *p. 48*
concentration gradient *p. 48*

facilitated diffusion *p. 48*
osmosis *p. 48*
hypertonic solution *p. 48*
isotonic solution *p. 49*
hypotonic solution *p. 49*
active transport *p. 49*
endocytosis *p. 50*
vesicle *p. 50*
phagocytosis *p. 50*
pinocytosis *p. 50*
exocytosis *p. 50*
nucleus *p. 51*
nuclear envelope *p. 51*
nuclear pore *p. 51*

chromosome *p. 51*
nucleolus *p. 51*
ribosome *p. 51*
endoplasmic reticulum (ER) *p. 52*
rough endoplasmic reticulum (RER) *p. 52*
smooth endoplasmic reticulum (SER) *p. 52*
Golgi complex *p. 52*
lysosome *p. 54*
mitochondrion *p. 55*
cytoskeleton *p. 56*
microtubule *p. 56*
centriole *p. 56*

cilia *p. 56*
flagellum *p. 56*
microfilament *p. 57*
intermediate filament *p. 57*
metabolism *p. 58*
cellular respiration *p. 58*
product *p. 58*
substrate *p. 58*
glycolysis *p. 58*
pyruvate *p. 58*
citric acid cycle *p. 59*
electron transport chain *p. 60*
fermentation *p. 60*
lactic acid fermentation *p. 60*

Reviewing the Concepts

1. Choose the *incorrect* statement:
   a. Phagocytosis and pinocytosis are two types of endocytosis.
   b. Phagocytosis requires a carrier protein.
   c. Nerve cells release chemicals by exocytosis.
   d. Cells engulf bacteria by phagocytosis.

2. Lysosomes
   a. function in extracellular digestion.
   b. produce phospholipids to incorporate into membranes.
   c. have a double membrane.
   d. function in intracellular digestion.

3. Choose the *incorrect* statement:
   a. Cellular respiration requires oxygen.
   b. Glycolysis occurs in both cellular respiration and fermentation.
   c. Cellular respiration yields more ATP per molecule of glucose than does fermentation.
   d. Fermentation occurs in mitochondria.

4. Prokaryotic cells
   a. rarely have a cell wall.
   b. are usually larger than eukaryotic cells.
   c. lack internal membrane-enclosed organelles.
   d. have linear strands of DNA within a nucleus.

5. The plasma membrane
   a. is selectively permeable.
   b. contains lipids that function in cell–cell recognition.
   c. has cell adhesion molecules that prevent cells from sticking together.
   d. is made of nucleic acids.

6. Facilitated diffusion is
   a. the random movement of a substance from a region of higher concentration to a region of lower concentration.
   b. the movement of water across the plasma membrane.
   c. the movement of molecules across the plasma membrane against a concentration gradient with the aid of a carrier protein and energy supplied by the cell.
   d. the movement of a substance from a region of higher concentration to a region of lower concentration with the aid of a membrane protein.

7. Almost all the genetic information of a cell is found in the
   a. endoplasmic reticulum.
   b. Golgi complex.
   c. nucleus.
   d. mitochondria.

8. Ribosomes
   a. are found on smooth endoplasmic reticulum.
   b. are sites where protein synthesis begins.
   c. process and modify proteins.
   d. break down foreign invaders and old organelles.

9. Mitochondria
   a. process energy for cells.
   b. lack ribosomes and DNA.
   c. are bounded by a single membrane.
   d. function in cell digestion.

10. Microtubules
    a. are found in eukaryotic cilia and flagella.
    b. are made of the protein actin.
    c. play a role in muscle contraction.
    d. pinch a cell in two during cell division.

11. Glycolysis
    a. occurs in the mitochondria.
    b. requires oxygen.
    c. splits glucose into pyruvate.
    d. nets 32 molecules of ATP per molecule of glucose.

12. _____is the jellylike solution within a cell that contains everything between the nucleus and the plasma membrane.

13. _____is the final electron acceptor in the electron transport chain.

14. Our muscle cells may switch from cellular respiration to _____ when oxygen is low.

Applying the Concepts

1. Given what you know about the composition of the plasma membrane, would you expect an anesthetic to be soluble or insoluble in lipids? Explain your answer.

2. Would you expect to find more mitochondria in muscle cells or bone cells? Explain your answer.

3. Explain what causes "smoker's cough."

Finding and Evaluating Information

Probiotics include living bacteria (prokaryotes) and yeast (eukaryotes). These microorganisms are present in healthy digestive tracts. They also can be found in certain foods (for example, yogurt) and supplements. Below is an excerpt from an article from WebMD on probiotics and human health. The article also includes information on common probiotics (*Lactobacillus* and *Bifidobacterium*), the conditions probiotics are used to treat (irritable bowel syndrome, inflammatory bowel disease, infectious diarrhea, and diarrhea caused by antibiotics), and how to safely use probiotics.
   The entire article can be found at: http://www.webmd.com/digestive-disorders/features/what-are-probiotics

How Do They Work?

Researchers are trying to figure out exactly how probiotics work. Here are some of the ways they may keep you healthy:

When you lose "good" bacteria in your body (like after you take antibiotics, for example), probiotics can help replace them.

They can lower the amount of "bad" bacteria in your system that can cause infections or other problems.

They can help balance your "good" and "bad" bacteria to keep your body working like it should.

1. What is your reaction to the sentence, "Researchers are trying to figure out exactly how probiotics work"?

2. Based on the information provided, would you consider taking supplements with probiotics or eating foods that contained probiotics?

3. Where would you look to find other sources about probiotics? Give some examples and explain why you chose them.

Body Organization and Homeostasis

4

DID YOU KNOW?

- Skin is the largest organ in the human body.

- By age 70, the average person has shed about 105 pounds of skin, at the rate of 600,000 particles every hour and about 1.5 pounds each year.

- People who use indoor tanning salons are at a much higher risk of developing skin cancer than people who have never tanned indoors.

IN THE PREVIOUS CHAPTER, we learned about cells. This chapter begins by describing the variety of cells and their functions. It then describes the body's organization at four levels: cells, tissues, organs, and organ systems. It looks at the functions of the skin as an organ system and discusses how all the body's systems interact to maintain relatively constant internal conditions, when they can, at every organizational level.

4.1 From Cells to Organ Systems

Think for a moment about the multitude of functions taking place in your body at this very instant. Your heart is beating. Your lungs are taking in oxygen and eliminating carbon dioxide. Your eyes are forming an image of these words, and your brain is thinking about them. Your body can carry out these functions and more because its cells are specialized to perform specific tasks. But cell specialization is only the beginning. Specialized cells are organized into tissues, organs, and organ systems.

Tissues

A **tissue** is a group of cells of similar type that work together to serve a common function. Human tissues come in four primary types: epithelial tissue, connective tissue, muscle tissue, and nervous tissue. **Epithelial tissue** covers body surfaces, lines body cavities and organs, and forms glands. **Connective tissue** serves as a storage site for fat, plays an important role in immunity, and provides the body and its organs with protection and support. **Muscle tissue** is responsible for body movement and for movement of substances through the body. **Nervous tissue** conducts nerve impulses from one part of the body to another. As you read this chapter, you learn more about each of these types of tissue.

Epithelial tissue   All epithelial tissues share two characteristics: a free surface and a basement membrane. The free surface may be specialized for protection, secretion, or absorption. The **basement membrane** is a noncellular layer that binds the epithelial cells to underlying connective tissue and helps the epithelial tissue resist stretching.

The three basic shapes of epithelial cells are suited to their functions. **Squamous** (skway´-mus) **epithelium** is made up of flattened, or scale-like, cells. These cells form linings—in the blood vessels or lungs, for instance—where their flattened shape allows oxygen and carbon dioxide to diffuse across the lining easily. In blood vessels, the smooth surface of the lining reduces friction. **Cuboidal epithelium** is made up of cube-shaped cells. Cuboidal cells are found in many glands and in the lining of kidney tubules, where they provide some protection and are specialized for secretion and absorption. **Columnar epithelium,** consisting of elongated, column-shaped cells, is specialized for absorption and secretion. The small intestine is lined with columnar cells. These, like many examples of columnar cells, have numerous small, fingerlike folds on their exposed surfaces, which greatly increase the surface area for absorption. The goblet cells of this lining produce mucus to ease the passage of food and protect the cells of the lining.

Squamous, cuboidal, and columnar epithelium can be either simple (a single layer of cells) or stratified (multiple layers of cells). Stratified epithelium often serves a protective role, because its multiple layers provide additional thickness that makes it more difficult for molecules to pass through. Table 4.1 and Figure 4.1 summarize the types of epithelial tissue.

A **gland** is epithelial tissue that secretes a product. **Exocrine glands** secrete their products into ducts leading to body surfaces, cavities, or organs. Examples of exocrine glands include the glands that produce digestive enzymes, the milk glands, and the oil and sweat glands of the skin. **Endocrine glands** (covered in more depth in Chapter 10) lack ducts and secrete their products, hormones, into spaces just outside the cells. Ultimately, hormones diffuse into the bloodstream and are carried throughout the body.

Connective tissue   Connective tissue has many forms and functions. Sometimes described as the body's glue, its most common role is to bind (tendons and ligaments) and support the other tissues (cartilage and bone). However, certain connective tissues specialize in transport (blood) and energy storage (adipose tissue). Connective tissue is the most abundant and widely distributed tissue in the body.

All connective tissues contain cells embedded in an extracellular **matrix.** This matrix consists of protein fibers and a noncellular material called ground substance. The **ground substance** may be solid (as in bone), fluid (as in blood), or gelatinous (as in cartilage). It is secreted by the connective tissue cells themselves or by other cells nearby. Whereas all other types of tissue consist primarily of cells, connective tissue is made up mostly of its matrix. The cells are distributed in the matrix much like pieces of fruit suspended in a gelatin dessert.

The connective-tissue matrix contains three types of protein fibers in proportions that depend on the type of connective tissue. **Collagen fibers** are strong and ropelike and can withstand pulling because of their great tensile strength. **Elastic fibers** contain random coils and can stretch and recoil like a spring. They are common in structures where great elasticity is needed, including the skin, lungs, and blood vessels. **Reticular fibers** are thin strands of collagen[1] that branch extensively, forming interconnecting networks suitable for supporting soft tissues (for example, they support the liver and spleen).

All three types of protein fibers—collagen, elastic, and reticular—are produced by cells called **fibroblasts** in the connective tissue. Fibroblasts also repair tears in body tissues. For example, when skin is cut, fibroblasts move to the area of the wound and produce collagen fibers that help close the wound, cover the damage, and provide a surface upon which the outer layer of skin can grow back.

There are two broad categories of connective tissue—connective tissue proper (loose and dense connective tissue) and specialized connective tissue (cartilage, bone, and

[1]Reticular fibers have the same subunits as collagen fibers, but they are assembled into a slightly different kind of structure.

Table 4.1	Review of Epithelial Tissue			
Shape	Number of Layers	Example Locations	Functions	
Squamous (flat, scale-like cells)	Simple (single layer)	Lining of heart and blood vessels, air sacs of lungs	Allows passage of materials by diffusion	
	Stratified (more than one layer)	Linings of mouth, esophagus, and vagina; outer layer of skin	Protects underlying areas	
Cuboidal (cube-shaped cells)	Simple	Kidney tubules, secretory portion of glands and their ducts	Secretes; absorbs	
	Stratified	Ducts of sweat glands, mammary glands, and salivary glands	Protects underlying areas	
Columnar	Simple	Most of digestive tract (stomach to anus), air tubes of lungs (bronchi), excretory ducts of some glands, uterus	Absorbs; secretes mucus, enzymes, and other substances	
	Stratified	Rare; urethra, junction of esophagus and stomach	Protects underlying areas, secretes	

SIMPLE EPITHELIUM

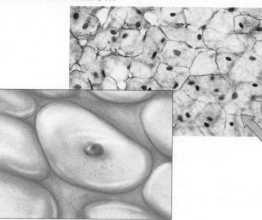

Simple squamous
- One layer of flattened cells
- Located in air sacs of lungs, heart and blood vessel linings
- Allows exchange of nutrients, gases, and wastes

Simple cuboidal
- One layer of cube-shaped cells
- Located in linings of kidney tubules and glands
- Functions in absorption and secretion

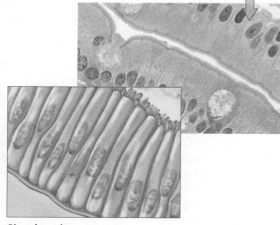

Simple columnar
- One layer of tall, slender cells
- Located in lining of gut and respiratory tract
- Functions in absorption and secretion

STRATIFIED EPITHELIUM

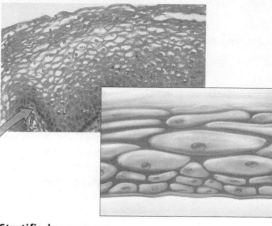

Stratified squamous
- Several layers of flattened cells
- Located on surface of skin, lining of mouth, esophagus, and vagina
- Provides protection against abrasion, infection, and drying out

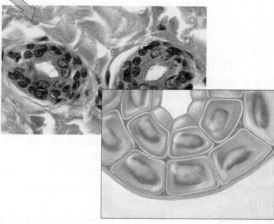

Stratified cuboidal
- Usually two layers of cube-shaped cells
- Located in ducts of mammary glands, sweat glands, and salivary glands
- Functions in protection

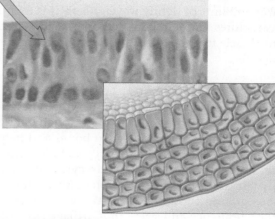

Stratified columnar
- Several layers of tall, slender cells
- Rare, located in urethra (tube through which urine leaves the body)
- Functions in protection and secretion

Figure 4.1 Types of epithelial tissue. These are named for the shape of the cell and the number of cell layers.

Table 4.2 Review of Connective Tissue		
Type	Example Locations	Functions
Connective tissue proper		
Loose, areolar	Between muscles, surrounding glands, wrapping small blood vessels and nerves	Wraps and cushions organs
Loose, adipose (fat)	Under skin, around kidneys and heart	Stores energy, insulates, cushions organs
Dense	Tendons, ligaments	Attaches bone to bone (ligaments) or bone to muscle (tendons)
Specialized connective tissue		
Cartilage (semisolid)	Nose (tip); rings in respiratory air tubules; external ear	Provides flexible support, cushions
Bone (solid)	Skeleton	Provides support and protection (by enclosing) and levers for muscles to act on
Blood (fluid)	Within blood vessels	Transports oxygen and carbon dioxide, nutrients, hormones, and wastes; helps fight infections

blood). Table 4.2 and Figure 4.2 group the many types of connective tissue and summarize the characteristics of each type. The characteristics of any specific connective tissue are determined more by its matrix than by its cells.

Connective tissue proper Loose and dense connective tissues differ in the ratio of cells to extracellular fibers. **Loose connective tissue** contains many cells but has fewer and more loosely woven fibers than are seen in the matrix of dense connective tissue (Figure 4.2). One type of loose connective tissue, **areolar** (ah-ree´-o-lar) **connective tissue,** functions as a universal packing material between other tissues. Its many cells are embedded in a gelatinous matrix that is soft and easily shaped. Areolar connective tissue is found, for example, between muscles, where it permits one muscle to move freely over another. It also anchors the skin to underlying tissues and organs.

The second type of loose connective tissue is **adipose** (ad´-ë-pos) **tissue;** it contains cells that are specialized for fat storage. Most of the body's long-term energy stores are fat. Fat also serves as insulation and, around certain organs, as a shock absorber.

Dense connective tissue forms strong bands because of its large amounts of tightly woven fibers. It is found in ligaments (structures that join bone to bone), tendons (structures that join muscle to bone), and the dermis (layer of skin below the epidermis).

Specialized connective tissue Specialized connective tissue, as shown in Figure 4.2, comes in three types: cartilage, bone, and blood. **Cartilage** (kär´-tl-ij) is tough but flexible. It serves as cushioning between certain bones and helps maintain the structure of certain body parts, including the ears and the nose. The cells in cartilage (chondrocytes) sit within spaces in the matrix called *lacunae.* The protein fibers and somewhat gelatinous ground substance of cartilage are responsible for the tissue's resilience and strength. Cartilage lacks blood vessels and nerves, so nutrients reach cartilage cells by diffusion from nearby capillaries. Because this process is fairly slow, cartilage heals more slowly than bone, which is a tissue with a rich blood supply.

The human body has three types of cartilage:

- *Hyaline cartilage,* the most abundant, provides support and flexibility. It contains numerous cartilage cells in a matrix of collagen fibers and a bluish white, gel-like ground substance. Known commonly as gristle, hyaline cartilage is found at the ends of long bones (look carefully at your next drumstick), where it allows one bone to slide easily over another. It also forms part of the nose, ribs, larynx, and trachea.

- *Elastic cartilage* is more flexible than hyaline cartilage because of the large amounts of wavy elastic fibers in its matrix. Elastic cartilage is found in the external ear, where it provides strength and elasticity.

- *Fibrocartilage* contains fewer cells than either hyaline or elastic cartilage. Like hyaline cartilage, its matrix contains collagen fibers. Fibrocartilage forms a cushioning layer in the knee joint as well as the outer part of the shock-absorbing disks between the vertebrae of the spine. It is made to withstand pressure.

Bone, in combination with cartilage and other components of joints, makes up the skeletal system. To many people's surprise, bone is a living, actively metabolizing tissue with a good blood supply that promotes prompt healing. Bone has many functions: protection and support for internal structures; movement, in conjunction with muscles; storage of lipids (in yellow marrow), calcium, and phosphorus; and production of blood cells (in red marrow). The matrix secreted by bone cells is hardened by calcium, enabling bones to provide rigid support. Collagen fibers in bone also lend it strength. You will read more about the structure and function of bones in Chapter 5.

Blood is a specialized connective tissue consisting of a liquid matrix, called *plasma,* in which so-called formed elements (cells and cell fragments known as platelets) are suspended (Figure 4.2). The "fibers" in blood are soluble proteins, visible only when the blood clots. An important function of blood is to transport various substances, many of which are dissolved in the plasma. One kind of formed element, the *red blood cell,* transports oxygen to cells and also carries some of the carbon dioxide away from cells. The other two kinds of formed elements are *white blood cells,* which help fight infection, and *platelets,* which assist in clotting. Both white blood cells and

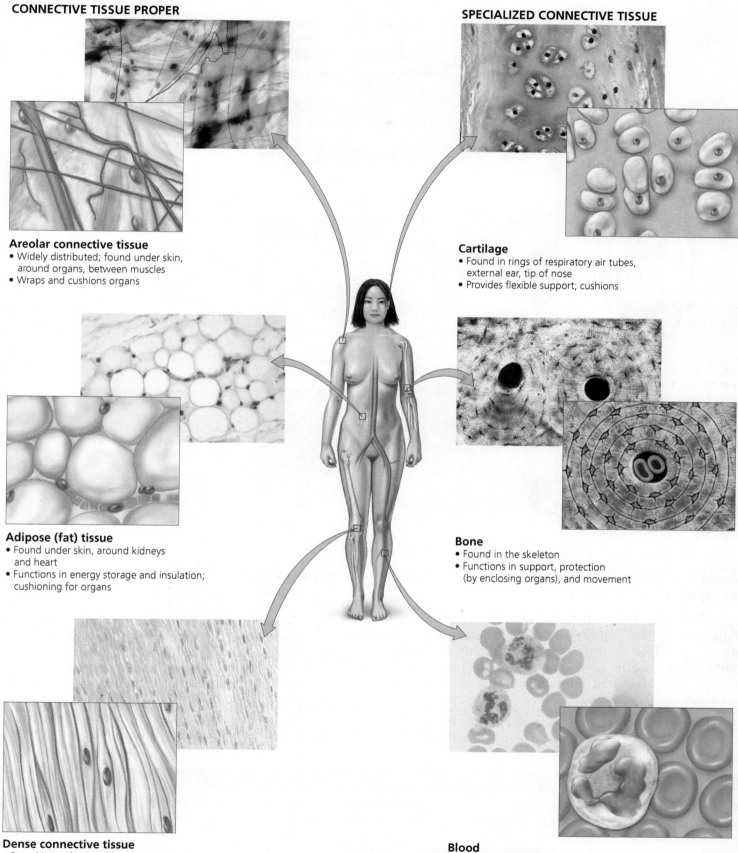

CONNECTIVE TISSUE PROPER

Areolar connective tissue
• Widely distributed; found under skin, around organs, between muscles
• Wraps and cushions organs

Adipose (fat) tissue
• Found under skin, around kidneys and heart
• Functions in energy storage and insulation; cushioning for organs

Dense connective tissue
• Found in tendons and ligaments
• Forms strong bands that attach bone to muscle or bone to bone

SPECIALIZED CONNECTIVE TISSUE

Cartilage
• Found in rings of respiratory air tubes, external ear, tip of nose
• Provides flexible support; cushions

Bone
• Found in the skeleton
• Functions in support, protection (by enclosing organs), and movement

Blood
• Found within blood vessels
• Transports nutrients, gases, hormones, wastes; fights infections

Figure 4.2 Types of connective tissue.

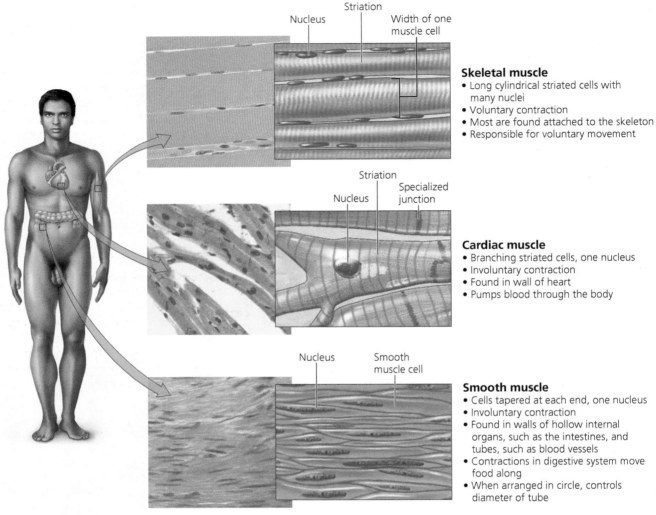

Figure 4.3 Types of muscle tissue

Skeletal muscle
- Long cylindrical striated cells with many nuclei
- Voluntary contraction
- Most are found attached to the skeleton
- Responsible for voluntary movement

Cardiac muscle
- Branching striated cells, one nucleus
- Involuntary contraction
- Found in wall of heart
- Pumps blood through the body

Smooth muscle
- Cells tapered at each end, one nucleus
- Involuntary contraction
- Found in walls of hollow internal organs, such as the intestines, and tubes, such as blood vessels
- Contractions in digestive system move food along
- When arranged in circle, controls diameter of tube

platelets help protect the body. You will read more about blood in Chapter 11.

Muscle tissue Muscle tissue is composed of muscle cells (called *muscle fibers*) that contract when stimulated. As shown in Figure 4.3, there are three types of muscle tissue: skeletal, cardiac, and smooth. Their characteristics are summarized in Table 4.3. You will read more about muscle tissue in Chapters 6 and 12.

- **Skeletal muscle tissue** is so named because it is usually attached to bones. When skeletal muscle tissue contracts,

therefore, it usually moves a part of the body. Because skeletal muscle is under conscious control, it is described as *voluntary muscle.* Skeletal muscle cells are long, cylinder-shaped cells, each containing several nuclei. In addition, skeletal muscle cells have striations, which are alternating light and dark bands visible under a light microscope. The striations are caused by the orderly arrangement of the contractile proteins actin and myosin, which interact to cause muscle contraction.

- **Cardiac muscle tissue** is found only in the walls of the heart, where its contractions are responsible for pumping blood to the rest of the body. Cardiac muscle contractions

Table 4.3	Review of Muscle Tissue		
Type	Description	Example Locations	Functions
Skeletal	Long, cylindrical cells; multiple nuclei per cell; obvious striations	Muscles attached to bones	Provides voluntary movement
Cardiac	Branching, striated cells; one nucleus; specialized junctions between cells	Wall of heart	Contracts and propels blood through the circulatory system
Smooth	Cells taper at each end; single nucleus; arranged in sheets; no striations	Walls of digestive system, blood vessels, and tubules of urinary system	Propels substances or objects through internal passageways

are not under conscious control; we cannot *make* them contract by thinking about them. Thus, cardiac muscle is considered *involuntary muscle*. Cardiac muscle cells resemble branching cylinders and have striations and typically only one nucleus. Special junctions at the plasma membranes of these cells strengthen cardiac tissue and promote rapid conduction of impulses throughout the heart.

■ **Smooth muscle tissue** is involuntary and is found in the walls of blood vessels and airways, where its contraction reduces the flow of blood or air. Smooth muscle is also found in the walls of organs such as the stomach, intestines, and bladder, where it aids in mixing and propelling food through the digestive tract and in eliminating wastes. The cells of smooth muscle tissue taper at each end, contain a single nucleus, and lack striations.

Nervous tissue   The final major type of tissue, nervous tissue, makes up the nervous system: brain, spinal cord, and nerves. Nervous tissue consists of two general cell types, neurons and accessory cells called neuroglia (Figure 4.4). **Neurons** generate and conduct nerve impulses, which they conduct to other neurons, muscle cells, or glands. Although neurons come in many shapes and sizes, most have three parts—the cell body, dendrites, and an axon. The cell body houses the nucleus and most organelles. Dendrites are highly branched processes that provide a large surface area for the reception of signals from other neurons. A neuron generally has one axon, a long extension that usually conducts impulses away from the cell body. Far more numerous than neurons, the **neuroglia** (or, more simply, *glial cells*) support, insulate, and protect neurons. They increase the rate at which impulses are conducted by neurons and provide neurons with nutrients from nearby blood vessels. Recent studies indicate that glial cells communicate with one another and with neurons. You will read more about nervous tissue in Chapters 7 and 8.

Cell Junctions

In many tissues, especially epithelial tissue, the cell membranes have structures for forming attachments between adjoining cells. Three kinds of junctions are found between cells: tight junctions, adhesion junctions, and gap junctions. Each type of junction suits the function of the tissue. In **tight junctions** (Figure 4.5a), the membranes of neighboring cells are attached so securely that they form a leakproof seal. Tight junctions are found in the linings of the urinary tract and intestines, where secure seals between cells prevent urine or digestive juices from passing through the epithelium. Less rigid than tight junctions, **adhesion junctions** (also called desmosomes; Figure 4.5b) resemble rivets holding adjacent tissue layers together. The plasma membranes of adjacent cells do not actually touch but are instead bound together by intercellular filaments attached to a thickening in the membrane. Thus, the cells are connected but can still slide slightly relative to one another. Adhesion junctions are common in tissues that must withstand stretching, such as the skin and heart muscle. **Gap junctions** (Figure 4.5c) connect the cytoplasm of adjacent cells through small holes, allowing certain small molecules and ions to flow directly from one cell into the next. In heart and smooth muscle cells, gap junctions help synchronize electrical activity and thus contraction.

Organs and Organ Systems

An **organ** is a structure composed of two or more different tissues that work together to perform a specific function. Organs themselves do not usually function as independent units but instead form part of an **organ system**—a group of organs with a common function. For example, organs such as the trachea, bronchi, and lungs constitute the respiratory system. The common function of these organs is to bring oxygen into the body and remove carbon dioxide. The human body includes 11 major organ systems.

what would YOU do?   When organs fail to function properly, the result can be illness and death. Certain organs can be transplanted from a living or a deceased donor. Most commonly, living donors give a kidney, but parts of lung, liver, and pancreas can now be donated. Would you consider being a living donor? If so, would you be willing to donate to a stranger? Are you willing to donate your organs after death? If so, have you signed an organ donor card and made your wishes known to family? ■

Body Cavities Lined with Membranes

Most of our organs are suspended in internal body cavities. These cavities have two important functions. First, they help protect the vital organs from being damaged when we walk or jump. Second, they allow organs to slide past one another and change shape. Sliding and changing shape are important when

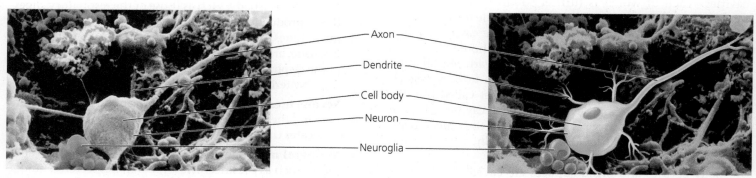

Figure 4.4 Neurons and neuroglia

Axon
Dendrite
Cell body
Neuron
Neuroglia

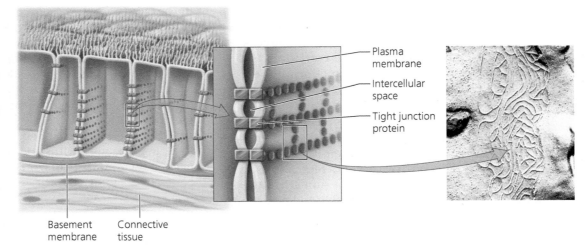

(a) Tight junction
- Creates an impermeable junction that prevents the exchange of materials between cells
- Found between epithelial cells of the digestive tract, where they prevent digestive enzymes and microorganisms from entering the blood

Plasma membrane

Intercellular space

Tight junction protein

Basement membrane Connective tissue

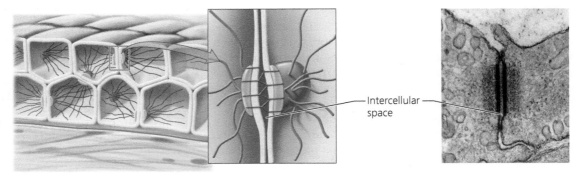

(b) Adhesion junction
- Holds cells together despite stretching
- Found in tissues that are often stretched, such as the skin and the opening of the uterus

Intercellular space

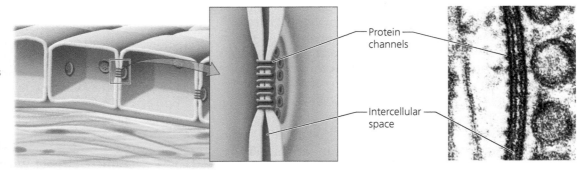

(c) Gap junction
- Allows cells to communicate by allowing small molecules and ions to pass from cell to cell
- Found in epithelia in which the movement of ions coordinates functions, such as the beating of cilia; found in excitable tissue such as heart and smooth muscle

Protein channels

Intercellular space

Figure 4.5 Specialized cell junctions

the lungs fill with air, the stomach fills with food, or the urinary bladder fills with urine, or when our bodies bend or stretch.

There are two main body cavities—the ventral and dorsal cavities—each of which is further subdivided. The ventral (toward the abdomen) cavity is divided into the *thoracic* (chest) *cavity* and the *abdominal cavity*. The thoracic cavity is subdivided again into the pleural cavities, which house the lungs, and the pericardial cavity, which holds the heart. The abdominal cavity contains the digestive system, the urinary system, and the reproductive system. A muscle sheet called the diaphragm separates the thoracic and abdominal cavities. The dorsal (toward the back) cavity is subdivided into the *cranial cavity,* which encloses the brain, and the *spinal cavity,* which houses the spinal cord.

Body cavities and organ surfaces are covered with membranes—sheets of epithelium supported by connective tissue.

Membranes form physical barriers that protect underlying tissues. The body has four types of membranes.

- **Mucous membranes** line passageways that open to the exterior of the body, such as those of the respiratory, digestive, reproductive, and urinary systems. Some mucous membranes, including the mucous membrane of the small intestine, are specialized for absorption. Others, like those of the respiratory system, for instance, secrete mucus that traps bacteria and viruses that could cause illness.

- **Serous membranes** line the thoracic and abdominal cavities and the organs within them. They secrete a fluid that lubricates the organs within these cavities.

- **Synovial membranes** line the cavities of freely movable joints, such as the knee. These membranes secrete a fluid that lubricates the joint, easing movement.

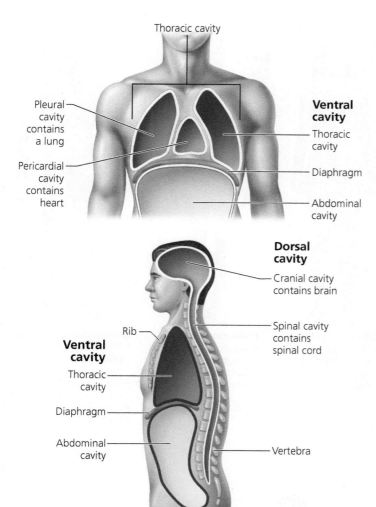

Figure 4.6 Body cavities. The internal organs are suspended in body cavities that protect the organs and allow them to slide past one another as the body moves. Ventral means "toward the abdomen," and dorsal means "toward the back."

■ **Cutaneous membrane,** or skin, covers the outside of the body. Unlike other membranes, it is thick, relatively waterproof, and comparatively dry.

The cavities of the human body are shown in Figure 4.6. We will consider the structure and function of the skin in the next section. Details about the structure and functions of the other organ systems, shown and described in Figure 4.7, are presented in subsequent chapters.

4.2 Skin: An Organ System

We have all been told that "beauty is only skin deep," but our skin does much more than just make us attractive. The skin and its derivatives—hair, nails, sweat glands, and oil glands—are sometimes called the **integumentary system** (an *integument* is an outer covering). It is considered an organ system because

the skin and its derivatives function together to provide many services for the body.

Skin Functions

A major function of our skin is protection. It serves as a physical barrier that shields the contents of the body from invasion by foreign bacteria and other harmful particles, from ultraviolet (UV) radiation, and from physical and chemical insult. Besides offering this somewhat passive form of protection, skin contains cells called *macrophages* that have a more active way of fighting infection, as we will see in Chapter 13.

The skin has many other functions, as well. For example, because its outermost layer of cells contains the water-resistant protein keratin, the skin plays a vital role in preventing excessive water loss from underlying tissues. It plays a part in temperature regulation, too. Although we perspire (imperceptively) through our skin almost constantly, during times of strenuous exercise or high environmental temperatures our sweat glands become active and increase their output of perspiration dramatically. The evaporation of this perspiration from the skin's surface helps rid the body of excess heat. Later we will see how changes in the flow of blood to the skin help regulate body temperature. The skin even functions in the production of vitamin D. Modified cholesterol molecules in the skin's outer layer are converted to vitamin D by UV radiation. The vitamin D then travels in the bloodstream to the liver and kidneys, where it is chemically modified to assume its role in stimulating the absorption of calcium and phosphorus from the food we eat.

In addition, the skin contains structures for detecting temperature, touch, pressure, and pain stimuli. These receptors—components of the nervous system—help keep us informed about conditions in our external environment. Keep these many functions of the integumentary system in mind as you read on about the structure of the skin and its derivatives.

Skin Layers

On most parts of your body, the skin is less than 5 mm (less than a quarter of an inch) thick, yet it is one of your largest organs. It represents about one-twelfth of your body weight and has a surface area of 1.5 to 2 m^2 (1.8 to 2.4 yd^2).

The skin has two principal layers, as shown in Figure 4.8. The thin, outer layer, the **epidermis,** forms a protective barrier against environmental hazards. The inner layer, the **dermis,** contains blood vessels, nerves, sweat and oil glands, and hair follicles. Beneath the skin is a layer of loose connective tissue called the *hypodermis,* or *subcutaneous layer,* which anchors the skin to the tissues of other organ systems that lie beneath.

The epidermis The outermost layer of skin, the epidermis, is itself composed of several layers of epithelial cells. The outer surface of epidermis, the part you can touch, is made up of dead skin cells. Thus, when we look at another person, most of what we see on the person's surface is dead. These dead cells are constantly being shed, at a rate of about 30,000 to 40,000 each minute. In fact, much of the dust in any room consists of dead skin cells. When you go swimming or soak in the bathtub for a long time, the dead cells on your skin's surface absorb water and

Integumentary system
- Protects underlying tissues
- Provides skin sensation
- Helps regulate body temperature
- Synthesizes vitamin D

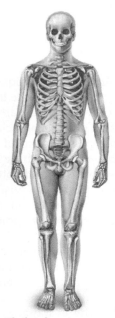

Skeletal system
- Attachment for muscles
- Protects organs
- Stores calcium and phosphorus
- Produces blood cells

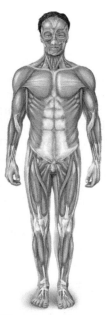

Muscular system
- Moves body and maintains posture
- Internal transport of fluids
- Generation of heat

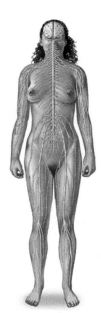

Nervous system
- Regulates and integrates body functions via neurons

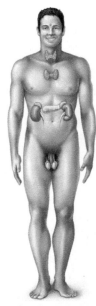

Endocrine system
- Regulates and integrates body functions via hormones

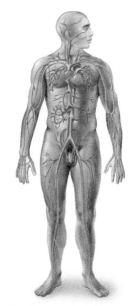

Cardiovascular system
- Transports nutrients, respiratory gases, wastes, and heat
- Transports immune cells and antibodies
- Transports hormones
- Regulates pH

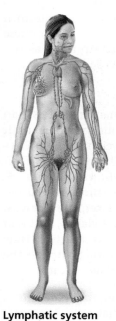

Lymphatic system
- Returns tissue fluids to bloodstream
- Protects against infection and disease

Respiratory system
- Exchanges respiratory gases with the environment

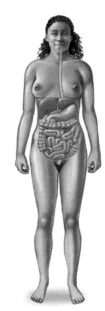

Digestive system
- Physical and chemical breakdown of food
- Absorbs, processes, stores food

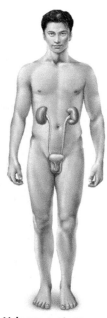

Urinary system
- Maintains constant internal environment through the excretion of nitrogenous waste

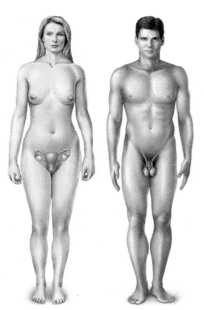

Reproductive system
- Produces and secretes hormones
- Produces and releases egg and sperm cells
- Houses embryo/fetus (females only)
- Produces milk to nourish offspring (females only)

Figure 4.7 Major organ systems of the human body.

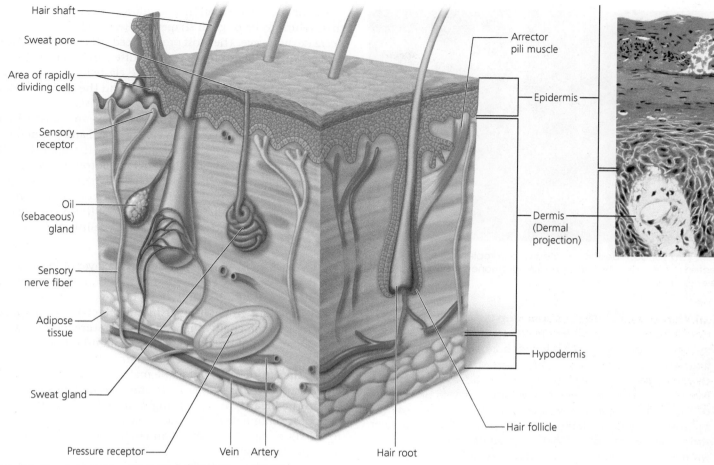

Figure 4.8 Structures of the skin and underlying hypodermis.

swell, causing the skin to wrinkle. This is particularly noticeable where the layer of dead cells is thickest, such as on the palms of the hands and soles of the feet.

The skin does not get thinner as the dead cells are shed, because they are continuously replaced from below. The deepest layer of epidermis contains rapidly dividing cells. As new cells are produced in this layer, older cells are pushed toward the surface. On their way, they flatten and die because they no longer receive nourishment from the dermis. Along this death route, keratin—a tough, fibrous protein—gradually replaces the cytoplasmic contents of the cells. It is keratin that gives the epidermis its protective properties. About 2 weeks to a month pass from the time a new cell is formed to the time it is shed.

Drugs that must be continuously administered are often given across the skin (transdermally) using a drug-containing patch that adheres to the skin (Figure 4.9). Although the epidermis is a water-resistant protective barrier, lipid-soluble materials are able to cross the lipid cell membranes of the cells of the epidermis. Thus, if you dissolve a drug in a lipid solvent, it can cross the epidermis, diffuse into the underlying connective tissue, and be absorbed into the blood. Today, transdermal drug administration is commonly used to provide hormones for birth control or for treating menopausal symptoms, or to provide nicotine to ease the urge to smoke while trying to quit, and to give antiemetics to stop nausea from motion sickness.

Figure 4.9 A transdermal patch continuously delivers a drug across the skin. Here, a cigarette smoker uses a nicotine patch to help quit smoking.

Figure 4.10 Tattoos—designs created when droplets of ink are injected into the dermis—are essentially permanent because, unlike the epidermis, the dermis is not shed.

what would YOU do? To speed up the movement of a drug from a transdermal patch to the patient's blood supply, the patch is prepared with a higher concentration of the drug than would be found in a pill. In transdermal patches that deliver hormones for birth control, the blood levels of hormones may also be higher than would result with birth control pills. During the past few years, several young women using a transdermal patch for birth control have had heart attacks or strokes; some have died. Contraceptive patches come with warning labels informing women of these increased risks. Do you think that women or their families should be able to sue the patch manufacturer for their losses? ∎

The dermis Over most parts of the body, the dermis is a much thicker layer than the epidermis. The dermis lies just beneath the epidermis and consists primarily of connective tissue. In addition, it contains blood vessels, hair follicles, oil glands, the ducts of sweat glands, sensory structures, and nerve endings. Unlike the epidermis, the dermis does not wear away. This durability explains why tattoos—designs created when tiny droplets of ink are injected into the dermal layer—are permanent (Figure 4.10). Because the dermis is laced with nerves and sensory receptors, getting a tattoo hurts. In the past, the only way to remove a tattoo was by surgical means, such as "shaving" (abrading) of the skin. Today, laser treatments that destroy the pigments of the tattoo can often be used for tattoo removal.

Blood vessels are present in the dermis but not in the epidermis. Nutrients reach the epidermis by passing out of dermal blood vessels and diffusing through tissue fluid into the layer above. Such tissue fluid is probably quite familiar to you. Where skin is traumatized by, for example, a burn or an ill-fitting shoe rubbing against your heel, this fluid accumulates between the epidermis and dermis, separating the layers and forming blisters.

The lower layer of the dermis consists of dense connective tissue containing collagen and elastic fibers, a combination that allows the skin to stretch and then return to its original shape. The resilience of our skin also decreases as we age. The most pronounced effects begin in the late forties, when collagen fibers start to stiffen and decrease in number and elastic fibers thicken and lose elasticity. These changes, combined with reductions in moisture and the amount of fat in the hypodermis, lead to wrinkles and sagging skin.

Certain wrinkles, such as frown lines, are caused by the contraction of facial muscles. A controversial and popular treatment for these wrinkles is to inject Botox, the toxin from the bacterium that causes botulism. When Botox is injected into facial muscles, they become temporarily paralyzed. The muscle contractions that form the wrinkles cannot occur, and the skin smoothes out. The muscles regain the ability to contract over the next several months, however, and the injection has to be repeated (Figure 4.11).

The hypodermis The **hypodermis,** a layer of loose connective tissue just below the epidermis and dermis, is not usually considered part of the skin. It does, however, share some of the skin's functions, including cushioning blows and helping to prevent extreme changes in body temperature, because it contains about half of the body's fat stores. In infants and toddlers, this layer of fat that lies under the skin—often called baby fat—covers the entire body, but as we mature, some of the fat stores are redistributed. In women, subcutaneous fat tends to accumulate in the breasts, hips, and thighs. In both sexes, it has a tendency to accumulate in the abdominal hypodermis, contributing to the all-too-familiar potbelly, and in the sides of the lower back, forming "love handles."

Liposuction, a procedure for vacuuming fat from the hypodermis, is a way to reshape the body. The physician makes a small incision in the skin above the area of unwanted fat, inserts a fine tube, and moves the tube back and forth to loosen the fat cells, which are then sucked into a container. Liposuction is not a way to lose a lot of weight, because only a small amount of fat—not more than a few pounds—can be removed. However, it is a way of sculpting the body and removing bulges. Furthermore, because liposuction removes the cells that store the fat, fat does not usually return to those areas. The procedure is generally safe, but it is not risk free. In some patients, it has produced blood clots that traveled to the lungs, causing death. People who are considering liposuction should choose their doctor carefully.

There are several newer, noninvasive and FDA-approved procedures that can remove fat from problem areas such as the

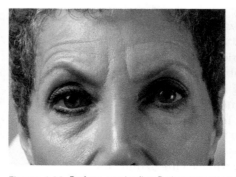

Figure 4.11 Before and after Botox injections.

abdomen, thighs, or back. These procedures use freezing, laser, ultrasound, or radio frequencies to kill fat cells. The body removes the dead cells over the next few days to months through natural processes. Although they can't remove as much fat as liposuction, these procedures can remove half an inch from one's waistline after a single half hour treatment, and the same area can be treated several times.

Skin Color

Two interacting factors produce skin color: (1) the quantity and distribution of pigment and (2) blood flow. The pigment, called **melanin,** is produced by cells called **melanocytes** at the base of the epidermis. These cells, with their spiderlike extensions, produce two kinds of melanin: a yellow-to-red form and the more common black-to-brown form. The melanin is then taken up by surrounding epidermal cells, thus coloring the entire epidermis.

All people have about the same number of melanocytes. Differences in skin color are due to differences in the form of melanin produced and the size and number of pigment granules. A person's genetic makeup determines the combination of the yellowish red or the brown form of melanin produced.

Circulation also influences skin color. When well-oxygenated blood flows through vessels in the dermis, the skin has a pinkish or reddish tint that is most easily seen in light-skinned people. Intense embarrassment can increase the blood flow, causing the rosy color to heighten, particularly in the face and neck. This response, known as blushing, is impossible to stop. Other intense emotions may cause color to disappear temporarily from the skin. A sudden fright, for example, can cause a rapid drop in blood supply, making a person pale. Skin color may also alter in response to changing levels of oxygen in the blood. Compared to well-oxygenated blood, which is ruby red, poorly oxygenated blood is a much deeper red that gives the skin a bluish appearance. Poor oxygenation is what causes the lips to appear blue in extremely cold conditions. When it is cold, your body shunts blood away from the skin to the body's core, which conserves heat and keeps vital organs warm. This shunting reduces the oxygen supply to the blood in the small vessels near the surface of the skin. The oxygen-poor blood seen through the thin skin of the lips makes them look blue. When you do not get enough sleep, the amount of oxygen in your blood may be slightly lower than usual, causing the color to darken. In some people, the darker color of blood is visible through the thin skin under their eyes as dark circles.

Tanning is a change in skin color from exposure to the sun. Melanocytes respond to the UV radiation in sunlight by increasing the production of melanin. This is a protective response, because melanin absorbs some UV radiation, preventing it from reaching the lower epidermis and the dermis. The skin requires some UV radiation for the production of vitamin D, but too much can be harmful. See the Health Issue essay, *Fun in the Sun*?

Hair, Nails, and Glands

The epidermis gives rise to many seemingly diverse structures: hair, nails, oil glands, sweat glands, and teeth. We will now consider the first four of these in view of their structure and roles in everyday life. (Teeth are discussed in Chapter 15.)

Hair   Hair usually grows all over the body, except on a few areas such as the lips, palms of the hands, and soles of the feet. What functions do these dead cells serve? An important one is protection. Hair on the scalp shields the head from UV radiation. Hair in the nostrils and external ear canals prevents particles and bugs from entering. Likewise, eyebrows and eyelashes help keep unwanted particles and glare (and perspiration and rain) out of the eyes. Hair also has a sensory role: receptors associated with hair follicles are sensitive to touch.

A hair consists of a shaft and a root (see Figure 4.8). The shaft projects above the surface of the skin, and the root extends below the surface into the dermis or hypodermis, where it is embedded in a structure called the *hair follicle*. Nerve endings surround the follicle and are so sensitive to touch that we are aware of even slight movements of the hair shaft. (Try to move just one hair without feeling it.) Each hair is also supplied with an oil gland that opens onto the follicle and supplies the hair with an oily secretion that makes it soft and pliant. In the dermis, a tiny smooth muscle called the *arrector pili* is attached to the hair follicle. Contraction of this muscle—which pulls on the follicle, causing the hair to stand up—is associated with fear and with cold. The tiny mound of flesh that forms at the base of the erect hair is sometimes called a goose bump.

Nails   Nails protect the sensitive tips of fingers and toes. Like hair, nails are modified skin tissue hardened by the protein keratin. Although the nail itself is dead and lacks sensory receptors, it is embedded in tissue so sensitive that we detect even the slightest pressure of an object on the nail. In this way, nails serve as sensory "antennas." They also help us manipulate objects, as when we undo a tight knot in a shoelace.

Glands   Three types of glands—oil, sweat, and wax—are found in the skin. Although all three types develop from epidermal cells, they differ in their locations, structures, and functions.

Oil (sebaceous) **glands** are found virtually all over the body except on the palms of the hands and soles of the feet. They secrete sebum, an oily substance made of fats, cholesterol, proteins, and salts. The secretory part of these glands is located in the dermis, as shown in Figure 4.8. Sebum lubricates hair and skin and contains substances that inhibit growth of certain bacteria. Sometimes, however, the duct of an oil gland becomes blocked, causing sebum to accumulate and disrupt the gland's proper function. Then, bacteria can invade the gland and hair follicle, resulting in a condition called acne. See the Health Issue essay, *Acne: The Miseries and Myths*.

As their name implies, **sweat glands** produce sweat, which is largely water plus some salts, lactic acid, vitamin C, and metabolic wastes such as urea. Although some wastes are eliminated through sweating, the principal function of sweat is to help regulate body temperature by evaporating from the skin surface. Wax glands are modified sweat glands found in the external ear canal. As their name implies, they produce wax, which protects the ear by trapping small particles.

HEALTH ISSUE

Fun in the Sun?

A beach crowded with people on a sunny day is hardly a scene we would equate with disfigurement and death. Nonetheless, that is a connection we should make, because skin cancers are increasing at an alarming rate, largely the result of our exposure to the sun.

The ultraviolet (UV) radiation of sunlight causes the melanocytes of the skin to increase their production of the pigment melanin, which absorbs UV radiation before it can damage the genetic information of deeper layers of cells. Unfortunately, this protective buildup of melanin is not instantaneous. In skin cancer, UV radiation alters the genetic material in skin cells so that the cells grow and divide uncontrollably, forming a tumor. Some experts fear that the rates of skin cancer will increase dramatically if the ozone layer, which blocks some of the UV radiation before it reaches Earth, continues to become thinner (the ozone layer is discussed in Chapter 24). Three types of skin cancer are caused by overexposure to the sun (Figure 4.A):

- *Basal cell carcinoma*, the most common form of skin cancer, arises in the rapidly dividing cells of the deepest layer of epidermis.

- *Squamous cell carcinoma*, the second most common form of skin cancer, arises in the newly formed skin cells as they flatten and move toward the skin surface.

- *Melanoma* is the least common and most dangerous type of skin cancer. It arises in melanocytes, the pigment-producing cells of the skin. Unlike basal or squamous cell carcinomas, melanomas, when left untreated, often metastasize (spread rapidly) throughout the body, first infiltrating the lymph nodes and later the vital organs. The survival rate in persons whose melanoma is found before it has metastasized is about 90% but drops to about 14% if the cancerous cells have spread throughout the body.

You can catch melanomas at an early stage if you carefully examine your skin while applying the ABCD mnemonic of the American Cancer Society:

A—stands for "asymmetry." Most melanomas are irregular in shape.

B—stands for "border." Melanomas often have a diffuse, unclear border.

C—stands for "color." Melanomas usually have a mottled appearance and contain colors such as brown, black, red, white, and blue.

D—stands for "diameter." Growths with a diameter of more than 5 mm (about 0.2 in.) are threatening.

The best way to prevent skin cancer is to avoid prolonged exposure to the sun. If you must be out in the sun, wear a hat, long sleeves, and sunglasses. Use a sunscreen with a sun protection factor (SPF) of at least 15. Apply your sunscreen about 45 minutes before going out into the sun, allowing time for the skin to absorb it so that it is less likely to wash away with perspiration. Use sunscreen even when it is overcast, because UV rays can penetrate the clouds. Reapply it after swimming.

Always remember that sunscreens are not foolproof. Most block the higher-energy portion of the sun's UV radiation, known as UV-B, while providing only limited protection against the lower-energy portion, called UV-A. Whereas UV-B causes skin to burn, recent research suggests that exposure to UV-A weakens the body's immune system, possibly impairing its ability to fight melanoma. Ironically, by providing protection from sunburn, sunscreens have had the potentially devastating effect of enabling people to spend more time in the sun, possibly increasing their risk of developing melanoma.

Avoid tanning salons. For many years, tanning salons claimed to use "safe" wavelengths of UV radiation because they did not use skin-reddening UV-B. But these "safe" wavelengths are actually UV-A. Given the apparent link between UV-A and increased risk of melanoma, the potential danger of these "safe" wavelengths is now obvious.

Questions to Consider

- Do you think that tanning salons should be required to explain the dangers of UV-A to the public?

- Some physicians are now warning that excessive use of sunscreen can lower the body's ability to produce enough vitamin D, which can lead to osteoporosis (a loss of bone density). What steps might you take to balance the risk of developing skin cancer with the risk of vitamin D deficiency?

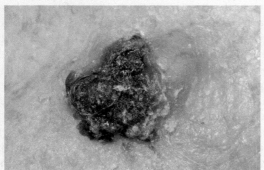

(a) Basal cell carcinoma

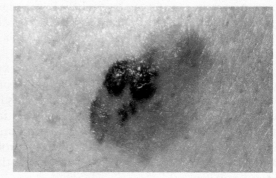

(b) Squamous cell carcinoma

(c) Melanoma

Figure 4.A Three skin cancers

HEALTH ISSUE

Acne: The Miseries and Myths

Acne and adolescence go hand in hand. In fact, about four out of five teenagers have acne, a skin condition that will probably annoy, if not distress, them well into their twenties and possibly beyond.

Simple acne is a condition that affects hair follicles associated with oil glands. During the teenage years, oil glands increase in size and produce larger amounts of oily sebum. These changes are prompted, in both males and females, by increasing levels of "male" hormones called *androgens* in the blood; the androgens are secreted by the testes, ovaries, and adrenal glands. The changes thus induced in the activity and structure of oil glands set the stage for acne. It should come as no surprise, then, that acne occurs most often on areas of the body where oil glands are largest and most numerous: the face, chest, upper back, and shoulders.

Acne is the inflammation that results when sebum and dead cells clog the duct where the oil gland opens onto the hair follicle (**Figure 4.B**). A follicle obstructed by sebum and cells is called a whitehead. Sometimes the sebum in plugged follicles mixes with the skin pigment melanin, forming a blackhead. Thus, melanin, not dirt or bacteria, lends the dark color to these blemishes. The next stage of acne is pimple formation, beginning with the development of a red, raised bump, often with a white dot of pus at the center. The bump occurs when obstructed follicles rupture and spew their contents into the surrounding epidermis. Such ruptures may occur naturally by the general buildup of sebum and cells or may be induced by squeezing the area. The sebum, dead cells, and bacteria that thrive on them then cause a small infection—a pimple or pustule—that will usually heal within a week or two without leaving a scar.

There are many misconceptions about the causes of acne. Eating nuts, chocolate, pizza, potato chips, or any of the other "staples" of the teenage diet does not cause acne. Also, acne is not caused by poor hygiene. Follicles plug from below, so dirt or oil on the skin surface is not responsible. (Most doctors do, however, recommend washing the face two or three times a day with hot water to help open plugged follicles.)

Questions to Consider

- Why do you think that there are so many misconceptions about the causes of acne?
- If a new medication for acne were marketed, how would you decide whether to use it?

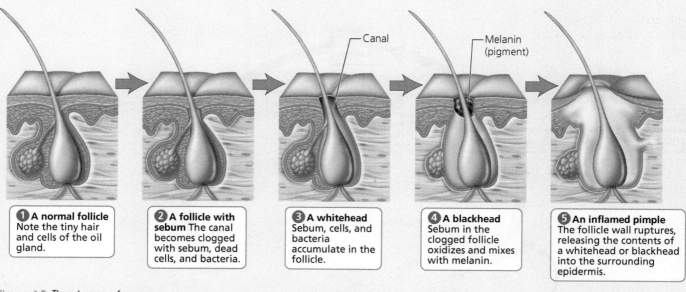

❶ **A normal follicle** Note the tiny hair and cells of the oil gland.

❷ **A follicle with sebum** The canal becomes clogged with sebum, dead cells, and bacteria.

❸ **A whitehead** Sebum, cells, and bacteria accumulate in the follicle.

❹ **A blackhead** Sebum in the clogged follicle oxidizes and mixes with melanin.

❺ **An inflamed pimple** The follicle wall ruptures, releasing the contents of a whitehead or blackhead into the surrounding epidermis.

Figure 4.B The stages of acne

4.3 Homeostasis

To remain healthy, the organ systems of the body must constantly adjust their functioning in response to changes in the internal and external environments. We have already learned that the body's organ systems are interdependent, working together to provide the basic needs of all cells—water, nutrients, oxygen, and a normal body temperature. Just as city dwellers breathe the same air and drink the same city water, the cells of the body are surrounded by the same extracellular fluid. Changes in the makeup of that fluid will affect every cell.

One advantage of our body's multicellular, multi-organ-system organization is its ability to provide a controlled environment for the cells. Although conditions outside the body sometimes vary dramatically, our organ systems interact to maintain relatively stable conditions within. This ability to maintain a relatively stable internal environment despite changes in the surroundings is called **homeostasis** (meaning "to stay the same"). But conditions within the body never stay the same. As internal conditions at any level vary, the body's processes must shift to counteract the variation. Homeostatic mechanisms do not maintain absolute internal constancy, but they do dampen fluctuations around a set point to keep internal conditions within a certain range. Thus, homeostasis is not a static state but a dynamic one.

Illness can result if homeostasis fails. We see this in diabetes, a condition in which either the pancreas does not produce enough of the hormone insulin or the body cells are unable to use insulin. Normally, as a meal is digested and nutrients are absorbed into the bloodstream, the rising level of glucose in the blood stimulates the pancreas to release insulin. The general effect of insulin is to lower the blood level of glucose, returning it to a more desirable value. Without insulin, blood glucose can rise to a point that causes damage to the eyes, kidneys, nerves, and blood vessels. A healthy diet, exercise, medication, and sometimes insulin injections can help people with diabetes regulate their blood glucose level.

Homeostasis depends on communication within the body. The nervous and endocrine systems are the two primary means of communication. The nervous system can bring about quick responses to changes in internal and external conditions. The endocrine system produces hormones, which bring about slower and longer-lasting responses to change.

STOP and **THINK**
When you exercise, your breathing rate, blood pressure, and heart rate increase. Is this a violation of homeostasis?

Negative Feedback Mechanisms

Homeostasis is maintained primarily through **negative feedback mechanisms**—corrective measures that slow or reverse a variation from the normal value of a factor, such as blood glucose level or body temperature, and return the factor to its normal value. When the normal value is reached, the corrective measures cease; the normal value is the feedback that turns off the response. (In contrast, a positive feedback mechanism causes a change that promotes continued change in the same direction. Positive feedback mechanisms, which are described in Chapter 10, do not promote homeostasis.)

Homeostatic mechanisms have three components (Figure 4.12).

❶ A *receptor* detects change in the internal or external environment. A receptor, in this context, is a sensor that monitors the environment. When the receptor detects a change in some factor or event—some variable—it sends that information to the control center, the second of the three components.

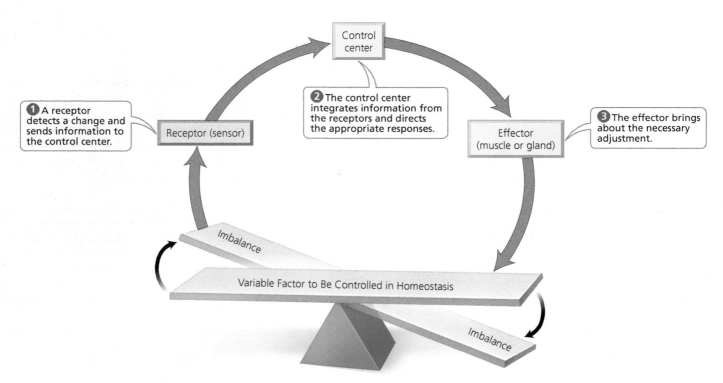

Figure 4.12 The components of a homeostatic control system maintained by negative feedback mechanisms

Q: Stable blood calcium levels are important to many physiological processes. Calcitonin is a hormone from the thyroid gland that lowers blood calcium levels. Parathyroid hormone from the parathyroid glands is a hormone that raises blood calcium levels. Describe a negative feedback relationship involving these hormones as effectors that would maintain homeostasis by keeping blood calcium levels stable.

② A *control center* determines the factor's set point—the level or range that is normal for the factor in question. The control center integrates information coming from all the pertinent receptors and selects an appropriate response. In most of the body's homeostatic systems, the control center is located in the brain.

③ An *effector,* often a muscle or gland, carries out the selected response.

Consider how a negative feedback mechanism controls the temperature in your home during frigid winter months. A thermostat in the heating system serves as both the temperature-sensing receptor and the control center. If it senses that the temperature inside your home has fallen below a certain programmed set point, the thermostat turns on the heating system (the effector). When the thermostat senses that the internal temperature has returned to the set point, it turns the heating system off. Thus, the temperature fluctuates around the set point but remains within a certain range. Now, let's apply these principles to see how homeostatic mechanisms regulate body temperature.

Hypothalamus and Body Temperature

The body's temperature control center is located in a region of the brain called the *hypothalamus.* Its set point is approximately 37°C (98.6°F), although it differs slightly from one person to the next. Body temperature must not vary too far from this mark, because even small temperature changes have dramatic effects on metabolism. Temperature is sensed at the body's outer surface by skin receptors and deep inside the body by receptors that sense the temperature of the blood. The hypothalamus receives input from both types of receptor. If the input indicates that body temperature is below the set point, the brain initiates mechanisms to increase heat production and conserve heat. When the input indicates that body temperature is above the set point, the brain initiates mechanisms that promote heat loss.

Let's consider what happens when we find ourselves in an environment where the temperature is above our set point, say, 38°C (100.4°F). Thermoreceptors in the skin detect heat and activate nerve cells that send a message to the hypothalamus, which then sends nerve impulses to the sweat glands to increase their secretions. As the secretions (perspiration) evaporate and body temperature drops below 37°C (98.6°F), the signals from the brain to the sweat glands are discontinued. In this homeostatic system, the thermoreceptors in the skin are the receptors, the hypothalamus is the control center, and the sweat glands are the effectors. The system is a negative feedback mechanism because it produces an effect (cooling of the skin) that is relayed (feeds back) to the control center, shutting off the corrective mechanism when the desired change has been produced.

Other mechanisms that the brain may activate to lower body temperature include dilation of blood vessels in the dermis and relaxation of the arrector pili muscles attached to the hair follicles. The former response releases more heat to the surrounding air and explains the flushed appearance we get during strenuous exercise. The latter keeps damp, cooling hair lying close to the skin. The brain may also initiate behavioral responses to a high body temperature, such as seeking shade or removing a sweatshirt.

STOP and **THINK**........................
As people age, the activity of their sweat glands declines. How does this explain why public authorities are less concerned about children than about the elderly developing a heat-related illness during a heat wave?

Now let's consider what happens when body temperature drops below the set point. Subtle drops in body temperature are detected largely by thermoreceptors in the skin, which send a message to the hypothalamus in the brain. The brain then sends nerve impulses to sweat glands, ordering a decrease in their activity, as well as messages to vessels in the dermis, telling them to constrict. This constriction reduces blood flow to the extremities, conserving heat for the internal organs and giving credence to the saying, "cold hands, warm heart." Another response to decreasing body temperature is contraction of arrector pili muscles, causing hairs to stand on end and thereby trapping an insulating layer of air near the body. This response, known as *piloerection,* is less effective in humans than in more heavily furred animals. The body also responds to cooling by increasing metabolic activity to generate heat and by the repeated contraction of skeletal muscles, known as shivering. Finally, behavioral responses, such as folding one's arms across one's chest, may be called upon to help combat a drop in body temperature. See Figure 4.13 for a summary of body temperature regulation.

Sometimes the mechanisms for lowering higher-than-normal temperatures fail, resulting in potentially deadly *hyperthermia*—abnormally elevated body temperature. Commonly called *heat stroke,* hyperthermia is marked by confusion and dizziness. If the core temperature reaches about 42°C (107°F), the heartbeat becomes irregular, oxygen levels in the blood drop, the liver ceases to function, and unconsciousness and death soon follow. Few people can survive core temperatures of 43°C (110°F).

If the body's temperature drops too far—to 35°C (95°F) or below—a condition called *hypothermia* results, disrupting nervous system function and temperature-regulating mechanisms. People suffering from hypothermia usually become giddy and confused at first. When their temperature drops to 33°C (91.4°F), they lose consciousness. Finally, at a body temperature of 30°C (86°F), blood vessels are completely constricted and temperature-regulating mechanisms are fully shut down. Death soon follows. Hypothermia can be treated if detected early enough. In severe cases, dialysis machines may be used to artificially warm the blood and pump it back into the body.

STOP and **THINK**........................
Frostbite is damage to tissues exposed to cold temperatures. Given what you know about the body's response to cold temperature, why are fingers and toes particularly susceptible to frostbite?

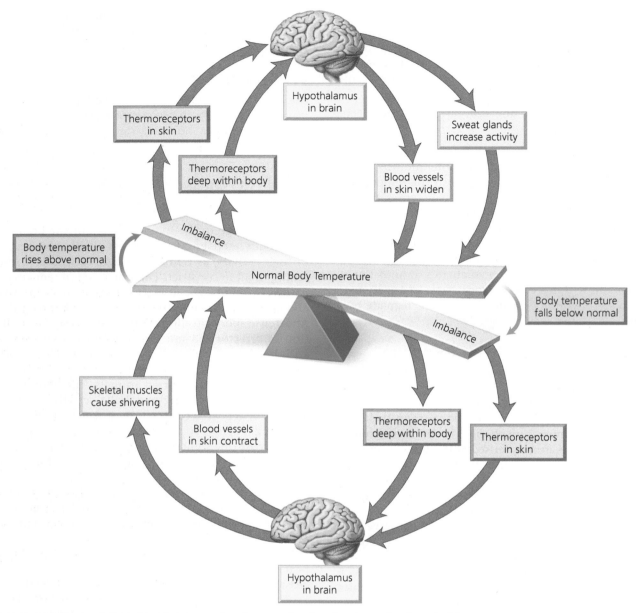

Figure 4.13 Homeostatic regulation of body temperature by negative feedback mechanisms. In this homeostatic control system, thermoreceptors are the sensors; the hypothalamus is the control center; and sweat glands, blood vessels in the skin, and skeletal muscles are the effectors.

LOOKING AHEAD

In this chapter, we saw how cells form tissues, tissues form organs, and organs form organ systems. Next we will explore each organ system, beginning with Chapter 5, "The Skeletal System."

CONSIDER THIS CASE

Firefighters entered the burning apartment and rescued Eunho, a 19-year-old woman. In the ambulance, Depak, one of the EMTs, assessed her condition. He reported to Emma, another EMT, that most of Eunho's burns were minor and involved only the upper layers of epidermis. However, her right leg had some second-degree burns, in which the damage extended into the upper region of the dermis. Unfortunately, Eunho's right arm suffered third-degree burns, in which damage extended through the epidermis and dermis to underlying tissue. When the EMTs asked Eunho what she was feeling, she cried, "I have excruciating pain in my right leg."

- Considering skin structure, why would Eunho experience more pain in her right leg than in her right arm, even though the damage to the arm was greater?
- Given your knowledge of skin functions, what would you predict to be the immediate medical concerns for a patient with third-degree burns?

Chapter Review

MasteringBiology®

Highlighting the Concepts

4.1 From Cells to Organ Systems (pp. 65–73)

■ Tissues are groups of cells that work together to perform a common function. The human body has four main types of tissue: epithelial tissue (covers body surfaces, forms glands, and lines internal cavities and organs); connective tissue (acts as storage site for fat, plays a role in immunity and in transport, and provides protection and support); muscle tissue (generates movement); and nervous tissue (coordinates body activities through initiation and transmission of nerve impulses).

■ All connective tissues contain cells in an extracellular matrix composed of protein fibers and ground substance. The types of connective tissue are connective tissue proper (loose and dense connective tissue) and specialized connective tissue (cartilage, bone, and blood).

■ Blood consists of formed elements (red blood cells, white blood cells, and platelets) suspended in a liquid matrix (plasma). The protein fibers are normally dissolved in the plasma and play a role in blood clotting. Red blood cells transport oxygen and carbon dioxide; white blood cells aid in fighting infections; and platelets function in blood clotting.

■ Muscle tissue is composed of muscle fibers that contract when stimulated, generating a mechanical force. There are three types of muscle tissue: skeletal, cardiac, and smooth. Skeletal muscle tissue is usually attached to bone, is voluntary, has cross-striations visible under a microscope, and has several nuclei in each cell. Cardiac muscle tissue is found in the walls of the heart, is involuntary, has cross-striations, and usually contains only one nucleus in each cell. Smooth muscle tissue is in the walls of blood vessels, airways, and organs. It is involuntary and lacks striations. A smooth muscle cell tapers at each end and has a single nucleus.

■ Nervous tissue consists of cells called neurons and accessory cells called neuroglia. Neurons convert stimuli into nerve impulses that they conduct to glands, muscles, or other neurons. Neuroglia increase the rate at which impulses are conducted by neurons and provide neurons with nutrients from nearby blood vessels. Neuroglial cells can communicate with one another and with neurons.

■ Three types of specialized junctions hold tissues together. Tight junctions prevent the passage of materials through the boundaries where cells meet. Adhesion junctions link cells by intercellular filaments attached to thickenings in the plasma membrane. Gap junctions have small pores that allow physical and chemical communication between cells.

■ An organ is a structure that is composed of two or more different tissues and has a specialized function.

■ Two or more organs that participate in a common function are collectively called an organ system. The human body has 11 major organ systems.

■ Internal organs are located in body cavities. There are two main body cavities: (1) the dorsal cavity, which is subdivided into the cranial cavity, where the brain is located, and the spinal cavity, where the spinal cord is located; and (2) the ventral cavity, which is subdivided into the thoracic (chest) cavity and the abdominal cavity. The thoracic cavity is further divided into the pleural cavities, which contain the lungs, and the pericardial cavity, which contains the heart. Membranes line body cavities and spaces within organs.

4.2 Skin: An Organ System (pp. 73–78)

■ The integumentary system includes the skin and its derivatives, such as hair, nails, and sweat and oil glands. It protects underlying tissues from abrasion and dehydration; regulates body temperature; synthesizes vitamin D; detects stimuli associated with touch, temperature, and pain; and initiates body defense mechanisms.

■ The skin has two layers. The outermost layer, or epidermis, is composed of epithelial cells that die and wear away. The dermis, just below, is a much thicker, nondividing layer composed of connective tissue and containing nerves, blood vessels, and glands. Below the dermis is the hypodermis, a layer of loose connective tissue that anchors the skin to underlying tissues.

■ The epidermis is a renewing barrier. Cells produced in the deepest layer are pushed toward the skin surface, flattening and dying as they move away from the blood supply of the dermis, and replace their cytoplasmic contents with keratin.

■ Skin color is partially determined by melanin, a pigment released by melanocytes at the base of the epidermis and taken up by neighboring cells on their way to the surface. Blood flow and blood oxygen content also influence skin color.

■ Hair is a derivative of skin. The primary function of hair is protection.

■ Nails are modified skin tissue hardened by keratin. They protect the tips of our fingers and toes and help us grasp and manipulate small objects.

■ Oil and sweat glands are derivatives of skin. Sebum, the oily substance secreted by oil glands, lubricates the skin and hair, prevents desiccation, and inhibits the growth of certain bacteria.

4.3 Homeostasis (pp. 79–81)

■ Homeostasis is the relative internal constancy maintained at all levels of body organization. It is a dynamic state, with small fluctuations occurring around a set point, and is sustained primarily through negative feedback mechanisms.

■ Homeostatic mechanisms consist of receptors, a control center, and effectors.

Recognizing Key Terms

tissue *p. 65*
epithelial tissue *p. 65*
connective tissue *p. 65*
muscle tissue *p. 65*

nervous tissue *p. 65*
basement membrane *p. 66*
squamous epithelium *p. 66*
cuboidal epithelium *p. 66*

columnar epithelium *p. 66*
gland *p. 66*
exocrine gland *p. 66*
endocrine gland *p. 66*

matrix *p. 66*
ground substance *p. 66*
collagen fibers *p. 66*
elastic fibers *p. 66*

Reviewing the Concepts

1. The four basic tissue types in the body are
   a. simple, cuboidal, squamous, columnar.
   b. neural, epithelial, muscle, connective.
   c. blood, nerves, bone, cartilage.
   d. fat, cartilage, muscle, neural.

2. A gland is composed of _____ tissue.
   a. epithelial
   b. connective
   c. muscle
   d. nervous

3. The lining of the intestine is composed primarily of
   a. epithelial cells.
   b. muscle cells.
   c. connective tissue cells.
   d. nerve cells.

4. Which of the following is *not* a function of epithelia?
   a. providing physical protection
   b. storing energy reserves
   c. producing specialized secretions
   d. absorption

5. _____ glands secrete hormones into the blood via tissue fluids.
   a. Endocrine
   b. Mixed
   c. Exocrine
   d. Unicellular

6. Which cells form disks that cushion the vertebrae?
   a. bone
   b. muscle
   c. epithelium
   d. cartilage

7. Which of the following is an example of dense connective tissue?
   a. tendon
   b. blood
   c. adipose (fat) tissue
   d. cartilage at the tip of the nose

8. Which type of tissue gets its characteristics from a matrix rather than cells?
   a. epithelial tissue
   b. muscle tissue
   c. connective tissue
   d. nerve tissue

9. Functions of connective tissue include
   a. establishing a structural framework for the body.
   b. transporting fluids and dissolved materials.
   c. storing energy reserves.
   d. all of the above

10. Which type of muscle cell propels substances or objects through internal passageways?
   a. skeletal
   b. cardiac
   c. smooth
   d. striated

11. Which type of junction allows cells to communicate by letting small molecules and ions pass from cell to cell?
   a. tight
   b. adhesion
   c. gap

12. Which is *not* a function of the integumentary system?
   a. production of blood cells
   b. protection of underlying tissues
   c. synthesis of vitamin D
   d. regulation of body temperature

13. Which type of membrane lines passageways that open to the exterior of the body?
   a. mucous
   b. serous
   c. synovial
   d. cutaneous

14. The effector in a negative feedback loop produces changes that
   a. are opposite to the change produced by the initial stimulus.
   b. increase the effect of the initial stimulus.
   c. are not related to the initial stimulus.

Applying the Concepts

1. Thor, a ski champion at his college, tore the cartilage in his knee in a ski accident. He asked the doctor whether he would be ready to compete in a month. Why would you expect the doctor's answer to be "No"?

2. Hannah has the flu. As her fever rises, she gets the chills. She shivers and covers herself in extra blankets. She takes some acetaminophen, and her fever breaks. As her body temperature returns to normal, she throws off the blankets, looks flushed, and perspires. Use the mechanisms of body temperature control to explain what is happening as Hannah's fever rises and falls.

3. Ehlers-Danlos syndrome (EDS) is a group of disorders caused by defects in genes that disrupt the production of collagen, which is a chief component of connective tissue. Explain why symptoms of EDS include joints that extend beyond their normal range and stretchy, saggy skin.

Finding and Evaluating Information

An important function of skin is to be a protective barrier against infectious organisms. Cleanliness is important to the skin's ability to perform this function, and hand sanitizers are a popular way to achieve cleanliness. But are all sanitizers created equal? Below are excerpts from R. Babeluk et al., "Hand hygiene—evaluation of three disinfectant hand sanitizers in a community setting."[1] The entire article can be found at: www.plosone.org/article /info%3Adoi%2F10.1371%2Fjournal.pone.0111969

> This study involved "sixty undergraduate students . . . (who had) no prior training in hand hygiene and were therefore believed to be representative of the general (non-healthcare) population. . . . The 60 volunteers were briefed to attend the two testing sessions at the University, using public transport. They were also asked to contaminate their hands by touching typical everyday surfaces (i.e. hand rails, door handles, vending machines, money) with both hands prior to testing.

> "On arrival at the University laboratory, a swab of each subject's left palm and finger tips was taken and cultured on agar plates to determine a maximum spectrum of microbes present. This provided the base line for the testing.

> "The volunteers were randomized into three groups of 20, each group was allocated one of the three hand sanitizers."

[1]R. Babeluk et al., "Hand hygiene—evaluation of three disinfectant hand sanitizers in a community setting," *PLoS One 9* [2014]: e111969.

The participants then cleaned their hands with the assigned sanitizer. Their hands were swabbed and the swabs were plated as before.

"Before disinfection . . . there was no significant difference between the groups in the bacterial load detected on hands." Following disinfection, "there was a significant overall reduction in bacteria following hand disinfection with all three products."

Two of the three sanitizers "led to a satisfactory bacterial reduction." The researchers conclude that there "are significant differences in efficacy between products that have been certified in accordance with the applicable European standards, compared to the non-certified product. The two certified products achieved superior outcomes compared to the non-certified product."

1. Is the conclusion in the paper valid based on the experimental design and results?

2. It is often difficult to determine the truth behind claims made in the media. For cleaning hands, is hand washing with soap superior to using hand sanitizers? Which hand sanitizers are most effective? Does use of these sanitizers lead to the development of antibiotic-resistant bacteria? Do these products contain toxic ingredients? Use reliable sources of information (books, newspapers, magazines, journals, or trustworthy websites) to find answers to these questions so you can make an informed decision on whether to use hand sanitizers. Create a list of guidelines for the use of hand sanitizers. Cite your sources.

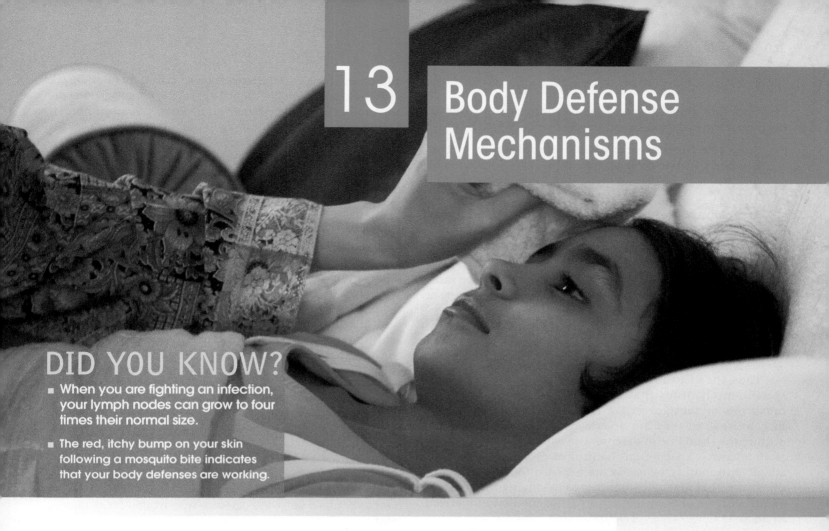

13 Body Defense Mechanisms

DID YOU KNOW?

- When you are fighting an infection, your lymph nodes can grow to four times their normal size.

- The red, itchy bump on your skin following a mosquito bite indicates that your body defenses are working.

IN THE PREVIOUS TWO CHAPTERS, we learned about the structure and function of the cardiovascular and lymphatic systems. We considered white blood cells and their roles in body defenses. In this chapter, we study how the body reacts to the invasion of disease-causing organisms and substances that it perceives as threats. We see that three lines of defense are present. We also learn that the body can acquire long-lasting resistance to a microbe by becoming ill or by being immunized. Finally, we consider some potential problems caused by the immune system.

13.1 The Body's Defense System

Your body generally defends you against anything that it does not recognize as being part of or belonging inside you. Common targets of your defense system include organisms that cause disease or infection and body cells that have turned cancerous.

The bacteria, viruses, protozoans, fungi, parasitic worms, and prions (infectious proteins) that cause disease are called **pathogens** (discussed further in Chapter 13a). Note that this term does not apply to most of the microorganisms we encounter. Many bacteria, for example, are actually beneficial. Some bacteria flavor our cheese and produce foods, such as yogurt, beer, and pickles; others help rid the planet of corpses through decomposition, thereby recycling nutrients to support new life; and some help keep other, potentially harmful bacteria in check within our bodies.

Cancerous cells also threaten our well-being. A cancer cell was once a normal body cell, but because of changes in its genes, it can no longer regulate its own division. If left unchecked, these renegade cells can multiply until they take over the body, upsetting its balance, choking its pathways, and ultimately causing great pain and sometimes death.

13.2 Three Lines of Defense

The body has three strategies for defending against foreign organisms and molecules or cancer cells.

1. **Keep the foreign organisms or molecules out of the body in the first place.** This is accomplished by the first line of defense—*chemical and physical surface barriers.*

2. **Attack any foreign organism or molecule or cancer cell inside the body.** The second line of defense consists of *internal cellular and chemical defenses* that become active if the surface barriers are penetrated.

3. **Destroy a specific type of foreign organism or molecule or cancer cell inside the body.** The third line of defense is the *adaptive immune response,* which destroys *specific* targets (usually disease-causing organisms) and remembers those targets so that a quick response can be mounted if they enter the body again.

Thus, the first and second lines of defense consist of nonspecific mechanisms that are effective against *any* foreign organisms or substances. We are born with these defense mechanisms, so they are described as *innate responses.* We acquire the third line of defense, the *immune response,* which is an adaptive, specific mechanism of defense. We acquire adaptive immunity when we are exposed to chemicals and organisms that are not recognized as belonging in the body. The three lines of defense against pathogens are summarized in **Figure 13.1.**

First Line of Innate Defense: Physical and Chemical Barriers

The skin and mucous membranes that form the first line of defense are physical barriers that help keep foreign substances from entering the body (**Figure 13.2**). In addition, they produce several protective chemicals.

Physical barriers   Like a suit of armor, unbroken skin helps shield the body from pathogens by providing a barrier to foreign substances. A layer of dead cells forms the tough outer layer of skin. These cells are filled with the fibrous protein keratin, which waterproofs the skin and makes it resistant to the disruptive toxins (poisons) and enzymes of most would-be invaders. Some of the strength of this barrier results from the tight connections binding the cells together. What is more, the dead cells are continuously shed and replaced, at the rate of about a

million cells every 40 minutes. As dead cells flake off, they take with them any microbes that have somehow managed to latch on. Another physical barrier, the mucous membranes lining the digestive and respiratory passages, produces sticky mucus that traps many microbes and prevents them from fully entering the body. The cells of the mucous membranes of the upper respiratory airways have cilia—short, hairlike structures that beat constantly. This beating moves the contaminated mucus to the throat. We eliminate the mucus in the throat by swallowing, coughing, or sneezing.

Chemical barriers   The skin also provides chemical protection against invaders. Sweat and oil produced by glands in the skin wash away microbes. Moreover, the acidity of the secretions slows bacterial growth, and the oils contain chemicals that kill some bacteria.

Other chemical barriers include the lining of the stomach, which produces hydrochloric acid and protein-digesting enzymes that destroy many pathogens. Beneficial bacteria in a woman's vagina create an acidic environment that discourages the growth of some pathogens. The acidity of urine slows bacterial growth. (Urine also works as a physical barrier, flushing microbes from the lower urinary tract.) Saliva and tears contain an enzyme called *lysozyme* that kills some bacteria by disrupting their cell walls.

STOP and THINK
Harmful bacteria within the digestive system often cause diarrhea. How might this be a protective response of the body?

Second Line of Innate Defense: Defensive Cells and Proteins, Inflammation, and Fever

The second line of defense consists of nonspecific internal defenses against any pathogen that breaks through the physical and chemical barriers and enters the body. This second line of defense includes defensive cells and proteins, inflammation, and fever (**Table 13.1**).

Defensive cells   Specialized "scavenger" cells called **phagocytes** (*phag–,* to eat; *–cyte,* cell) engulf pathogens, damaged tissue, or dead cells by the process of phagocytosis (Chapter 3). This class of white blood cells serves not only as the front-line soldiers in the body's internal defense system but also as janitors that clean up debris. When a phagocyte encounters a foreign particle,

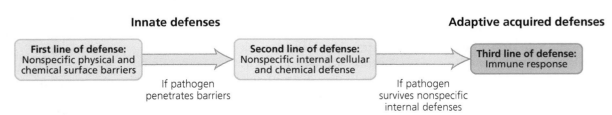

Figure 13.1 The body's three lines of defense against pathogens

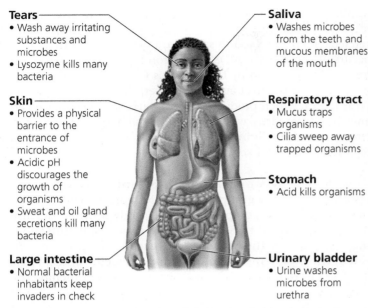

Tears
- Wash away irritating substances and microbes
- Lysozyme kills many bacteria

Skin
- Provides a physical barrier to the entrance of microbes
- Acidic pH discourages the growth of organisms
- Sweat and oil gland secretions kill many bacteria

Large intestine
- Normal bacterial inhabitants keep invaders in check

Saliva
- Washes microbes from the teeth and mucous membranes of the mouth

Respiratory tract
- Mucus traps organisms
- Cilia sweep away trapped organisms

Stomach
- Acid kills organisms

Urinary bladder
- Urine washes microbes from urethra

Figure 13.2 The body's first line of defense consists of physical and chemical barriers that serve as innate, nonspecific defenses against any threats to our well-being. Collectively, they prevent many invading organisms and substances from entering the body or confine them to a local region, kill them, remove them, or slow their growth.

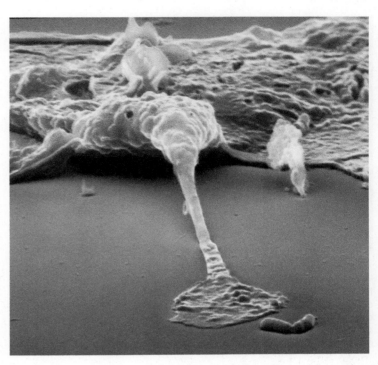

Figure13.3 A macrophage ingesting a bacterium (the rod-shaped structure). The bacterium will be pulled inside the cell within a membrane-bound vesicle and quickly killed.

cytoplasmic extensions flow from the phagocytic cell, bind to the particle, and pull it inside the cell. Once inside the cell, the particle is enclosed within a membrane-bound vesicle and quickly destroyed by digestive enzymes.

The body has several types of phagocytes. One type, the *neutrophil,* arrives at the site of attack before the other types of white blood cells and immediately begins to consume the pathogens, especially bacteria, by phagocytosis. Other white blood cells (monocytes) leave the vessels of the circulatory system and enter the tissue fluids, where they develop into large **macrophages** (*macro–,* big; *–phage,* to eat). Macrophages have hearty and less discriminating appetites than neutrophils do, and they attack and consume virtually anything that is not recognized as belonging in the body—including viruses, bacteria, and damaged tissue (Figure 13.3).

A second type of white blood cell, the *eosinophil,* attacks pathogens that are too large to be consumed by phagocytosis, such as parasitic worms. Eosinophils get close to the parasite and discharge enzymes that destroy the organism. Macrophages then remove the debris.

Natural killer cells   A third type of white blood cell, the **natural killer (NK) cell,** roams the body in search of abnormal cells and quickly orchestrates their death. In a sense, NK cells function as the body's police walking a beat. They are not seeking a specific villain. Instead, they respond to any suspicious character, including a cell whose cell membrane has been altered by the addition of proteins that are unfamiliar to the NK cell. The prime targets of NK cells are cancerous cells and cells infected with viruses. Cancerous cells routinely form but are

Table 13.1	The Second Line of Defense—Innate, Nonspecific Internal Defenses	
Defense	Example	Function
Defensive cells	Phagocytic cells, such as neutrophils and macrophages	Engulf invading organisms
	Eosinophils	Kill parasites
	Natural killer cells	Kill many invading organisms and cancer cells
Defensive proteins	Interferons	Slow the spread of viruses in the body
	Complement system	Stimulates histamine release; promotes phagocytosis; kills bacteria; enhances inflammation
Inflammation	Widening of blood vessels and increased capillary permeability, leading to redness, heat, swelling, and pain	Brings in defensive cells and speeds healing
Fever	Abnormally high body temperature	Slows the growth of bacteria; speeds up body defenses

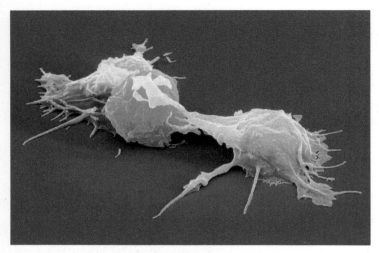

Figure 13.4 Natural killer, or NK, cells (shown in orange) attacking a leukemia cell (shown in red). NK cells patrol the body, bumping and touching other cells as they go. When NK cells contact a cell with an altered cell surface, such as a cancer or virus-infected cell, a series of events is immediately initiated. The NK cell attaches to the target cell and releases proteins that create pores in the target cell, making the membrane leaky and causing the cell to burst.

quickly destroyed by NK cells and prevented from spreading (Figure 13.4).

As soon as it touches a cell with an abnormal surface, the NK cell attaches to the abnormal cell and delivers a "kiss of death" in the form of proteins that create many pores in the target cell. The pores make the target cell "leaky," so that it can no longer maintain a constant internal environment and eventually bursts.

Defensive proteins The second line of defense also includes defensive proteins. We will discuss two types of defensive proteins: interferons, which slow viral reproduction, and the complement system, which assists other defensive mechanisms.

Interferons A cell that has been infected with a virus can do little to help itself. But cells infected with a virus can help cells that are not yet infected. Before certain virally infected cells die, they secrete small proteins called **interferons** that act to slow the spread of viruses already in the body. Thus, interferons interfere with viral activity.

Interferons function in a manner somewhat similar to a fire alarm in a public building, which both summons firefighters to extinguish the fire and warns occupants to take the necessary precautions. Interferons also mount a two-pronged attack. First, they help rid the body of virus-infected cells by attracting macrophages and NK cells that destroy the infected cells immediately. Second, interferons warn cells that are not yet infected with the virus to take protective action. When released, interferons diffuse to neighboring cells and stimulate them to produce proteins that prevent viruses from replicating in those cells. Because viruses cause disease by replicating inside body cells, preventing replication curbs the disease. Interferons help protect uninfected cells from *all* strains of viruses, not just the one responsible for the initial infection.

Pharmaceutical preparations of interferons have proved effective against certain cancers and viral infections. Interferons

inhibit cell division of cancer cells. For instance, interferons are often successful in combating a rare form of leukemia (hairy cell leukemia) and Kaposi's sarcoma, a type of cancer that often occurs in people with AIDS. Interferon has also been approved for treating infection by the hepatitis C virus, which can lead to cirrhosis of the liver and liver cancer; the human papilloma virus (HPV), which produces genital warts and cervical cancer; and the herpes virus, which causes genital herpes. When interferons are taken during the first attack of multiple sclerosis, recurrences are less likely.

Complement system The **complement system,** or simply *complement,* is a group of at least 20 proteins whose activities enhance, or complement, the body's other defense mechanisms. Until these proteins are activated by infection, they circulate in the blood in an inactive state. Once activated, these proteins enhance both nonspecific and specific defense mechanisms. The effects of complement include the following:

■ **Destruction of pathogen.** Complement can act *directly* by ❶ punching holes in a target cell's membrane (Figure 13.5) so that ❷ the cell is no longer able to maintain a constant internal environment. Just as when NK cells secrete proteins that make a target cell's membrane leaky, ❸ water enters the cell, causing it to burst.

■ **Enhancement of phagocytosis.** Complement enhances phagocytosis in two ways. First, complement proteins attract macrophages and neutrophils to the site of infection to remove the foreign cells. Second, one of the complement proteins binds to the surface of the microbe, making it easier for macrophages and neutrophils to "get a grip" on the intruder and devour it.

■ **Stimulation of inflammation.** Complement also causes blood vessels to widen and become more permeable. These changes provide increased blood flow to the area and increased access for white blood cells.

Inflammation When body tissues are injured or damaged, a series of events called the **inflammatory response,** or *inflammatory reaction,* occurs. This response destroys invaders and helps repair and restore damaged tissue. The four cardinal signs of inflammation that occur at the site of a wound are redness, heat (or warmth), swelling, and pain. These signs announce that certain cells and chemicals have combined efforts to contain infection, clean up the damaged area, and heal the wound. Let's consider the causes of the cardinal signs and how they are related to the benefits of inflammation.

■ **Redness.** Redness occurs because blood vessels dilate (widen) in the damaged area, causing blood flow in this area to increase. The dilation is caused by **histamine,** a substance also released during allergic reactions (discussed later in the chapter). Histamine is released by small, mobile connective tissue cells called **mast cells** in response to chemicals from damaged cells.

The increased blood flow to the site of injury delivers phagocytes, blood-clotting proteins, and defensive proteins, including complement and antibodies. At the same time,

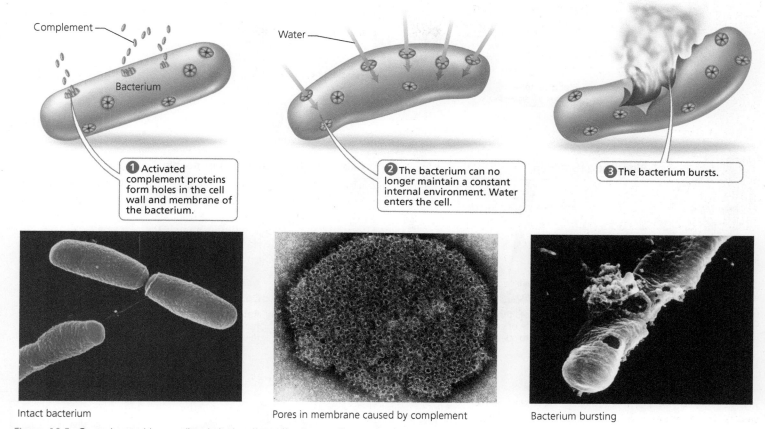

① Activated complement proteins form holes in the cell wall and membrane of the bacterium.

② The bacterium can no longer maintain a constant internal environment. Water enters the cell.

③ The bacterium bursts.

Intact bacterium

Pores in membrane caused by complement

Bacterium bursting

Figure 13.5 Complement has a direct destructive effect on pathogens.

the increased blood flow washes away dead cells and toxins produced by the invading microbes.

- **Heat.** The increased blood flow also elevates the temperature in the area of injury. The elevated temperature raises the metabolic rate of the body cells in the region and speeds healing. Heat also increases the activities of phagocytic cells and other defensive cells.

- **Swelling.** The injured area swells because histamine also makes capillaries more permeable, or leakier, than usual. Fluid seeps into the tissues from the bloodstream, bringing with it many beneficial substances. Blood-clotting factors enter the injured area and begin to wall off the region, thereby helping to protect surrounding areas from injury and preventing excessive loss of blood. The seepage also increases the oxygen and nutrient supply to the cells. If the injured area is a joint, swelling can hamper movement—an effect that might seem to be an inconvenience, but that actually permits the injured joint to rest and recover.

- **Pain.** Several factors cause pain in an inflamed area. For example, the excessive fluid leaking into the tissue presses on nerves and contributes to the sensation of pain. Some soreness might be caused by bacterial toxins, which can kill body cells. Injured cells also release pain-causing chemicals, such as prostaglandins. Pain usually prompts a person to protect the area to avoid additional injury.

Because of the wider blood vessels and increased capillary permeability that bring about the inflammatory response, phagocytes begin to swarm to the injured site, attracted by chemicals released when tissue is damaged. Within minutes, the neutrophils squeeze through capillary walls into the fluid around cells and begin engulfing pathogens, toxins, and dead body cells. Soon macrophages arrive and continue the body's counterattack for the long term. Macrophages are also important in cleaning debris, such as dead body cells, from the damaged area. As the recovery from infection continues, certain body fluids, dead cells (including microbes), body tissue cells, and phagocytes may begin to ooze from the wound as pus (Figure 13.6).

Fever A *fever* is an abnormally high body temperature. Fevers are caused by *pyrogens* (*pyro–,* fire; *–gen,* producer), chemicals that raise the "thermostat" in the brain (the hypothalamus) to a higher set point. Bacteria release toxins that sometimes act as pyrogens. It is interesting, however, that the body produces its own pyrogens as part of its defensive strategy. Regardless of the source, pyrogens have the same effect on the hypothalamus, raising the set point so that physiological responses, such as shivering, are initiated to elevate body temperature (as discussed in Chapter 4). Thus, we have the chills while the fever is rising. When the set point is lowered, the fever breaks, and physiological responses such as perspiring reduce the body temperature until it reaches the new set point.

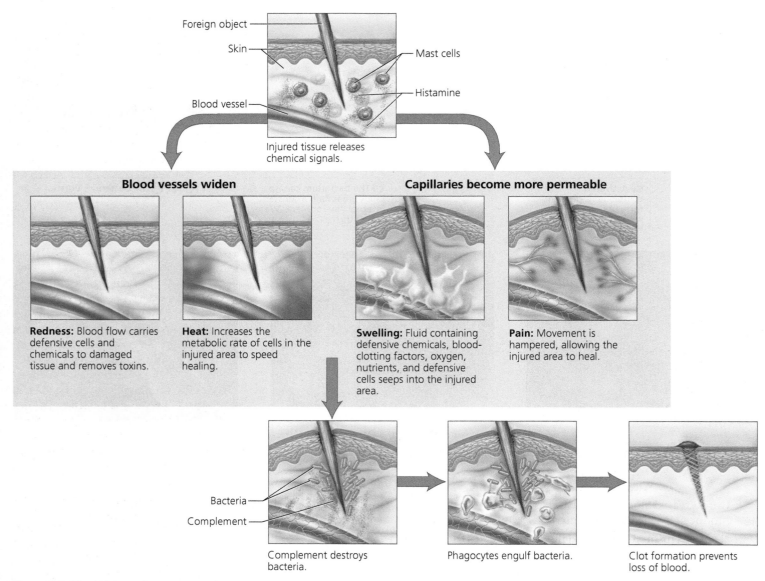

Foreign object

Skin

Mast cells

Histamine

Blood vessel

Injured tissue releases chemical signals.

Blood vessels widen

Redness: Blood flow carries defensive cells and chemicals to damaged tissue and removes toxins.

Heat: Increases the metabolic rate of cells in the injured area to speed healing.

Capillaries become more permeable

Swelling: Fluid containing defensive chemicals, blood-clotting factors, oxygen, nutrients, and defensive cells seeps into the injured area.

Pain: Movement is hampered, allowing the injured area to heal.

Bacteria

Complement

Complement destroys bacteria.

Phagocytes engulf bacteria.

Clot formation prevents loss of blood.

Figure 13.6 The inflammatory response is a general response to tissue injury or invasion by foreign microbes. It serves to defend against pathogens and to clear the injured area of pathogens and dead body cells, allowing repair and healing to occur. The four cardinal signs of inflammation are redness, heat, swelling, and pain.

A mild or moderate fever helps the body fight bacterial infections by slowing the growth of bacteria and stimulating body defense responses. Bacterial growth is slowed because a mild fever causes the liver and spleen to remove iron from the blood, and many bacteria require iron to reproduce. Fever also increases the metabolic rate of body cells; the higher rate speeds up defensive responses and repair processes. However, a very high fever over 40.6°C (105°F), is dangerous. It can inactivate enzymes needed for biochemical reactions within body cells.

Third Line of Defense: Adaptive Immune Response

When the body's first and second lines of defense fail to stop a pathogen, cancer cell, or foreign molecule from entering the body, the third line of defense, the **adaptive immune response,** takes over. The adaptive immune response provides the specific responses and memory needed to target the invader. The organs of the lymphatic system (see Chapter 12) are important components of the immune system because they produce the various cells responsible for immunity. The immune system is not an organ system in an anatomical sense. Instead, the immune system is defined by its *function*: recognizing and destroying specific pathogens or foreign molecules.

An adaptive immune response has certain important characteristics. First, it is directed at a particular pathogen. For example, the adaptive immune responses of a child infected with measles recognize the measles virus as a foreign substance (not belonging in the body) and then act to immobilize, neutralize, or destroy it. An effective immune response will enable the child to recover from the illness. Second, the adaptive immune response has memory. If the same child is again exposed to the same pathogen years later, the immune system remembers the pathogen and attacks it so quickly and vigorously that the child will not become ill with measles a second time.

13.3 Distinguishing Self from Nonself

To defend against a foreign organism or molecule, the body must be to able distinguish it from a body cell and recognize it as foreign. This ability depends on the fact that each cell in your body has special molecules embedded in the plasma membrane that label the cell as *self*. These molecules serve as flags declaring the cell as a "friend." The molecules are called **MHC markers,** named for the *major histocompatibility complex* genes that code for them. The self labels on your cells are different from those of any other person (except an identical twin) as well as from those of other organisms, including pathogens. The immune system uses these labels to distinguish what is part of your body from what is not (Figure 13.7). It doesn't attack cells that are recognized as self.

A nonself substance or organism that triggers an immune response is an **antigen.** Because an antigen is not recognized as belonging in the body, the immune system directs an attack against it. Typically, antigens are large molecules, such as proteins, polysaccharides, or nucleic acids. Often, antigens are found on the surface of an invader—embedded in the plasma membrane of an unwelcome bacterial cell, for instance, or part of the protein coat of a virus. However, pieces of invaders and chemicals secreted by invaders, such as bacterial toxins, can also serve as antigens. Each antigen is recognized by its shape.

Certain white blood cells, called lymphocytes, are responsible for both the specificity and the memory of the adaptive

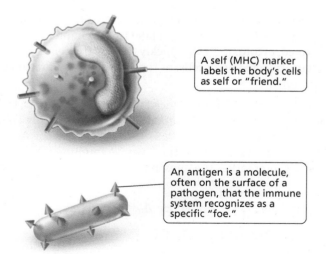

A self (MHC) marker labels the body's cells as self or "friend."

An antigen is a molecule, often on the surface of a pathogen, that the immune system recognizes as a specific "foe."

Figure 13.7 All nucleated cells in the body have molecular MHC markers on their surface that label them as self. Foreign substances, including potential disease-causing organisms, have molecules on their surfaces that are not recognized as belonging in the body. Foreign molecules that are capable of triggering an adaptive immune response are called antigens.

immune response. There are two principal types of lymphocytes: **B lymphocytes,** or more simply *B cells,* and **T lymphocytes,** or *T cells.* Both types form in the bone marrow, but they mature in different organs of the body. It is thought that B cells mature in the bone marrow. The T cells mature in the thymus gland, which overlies the heart.

As T lymphocytes mature, they develop the ability to distinguish cells that belong in the body from those that do not. T cells must be able to recognize the specific MHC self markers of that person and *not* respond vigorously to cells bearing that MHC self marker. T cells that do respond to cells with those self markers are destroyed. Once they are mature, T lymphocytes circulate through the body, bumping into other cells and checking to be sure those cells have the correct self (MHC) marker. Cells with proper MHC markers are passed by.

In addition, both T and B lymphocytes are programmed during development to recognize one particular type of antigen. This recognition is the basis of the specificity of the adaptive immune response. Each lymphocyte develops its own particular receptors—molecules having a unique shape—on its surface. Thousands of *identical* receptor molecules pepper the surface of each lymphocyte, and they are unlike the receptor molecules on other lymphocytes. When an antigen fits into a lymphocyte's receptors, much like a key into a lock, the body's defenses target that particular antigen. Because of the tremendous diversity of receptor molecules, each type occurring on a different lymphocyte, a few of the billions of lymphocytes in your body are able to respond to each of the thousands of different antigens that you will be exposed to in your lifetime. Thus lymphocytes are prepared to respond to each antigen when it is first encountered.

How do we build an effective force of lymphocytes to defend against a particular antigen? When an antigen is detected, B cells and T cells bearing receptors able to respond to that particular invader are stimulated to divide repeatedly, forming two lines of cells. One line of descendant cells is made up of **effector cells,** which carry out the attack on the enemy. Effector cells generally live for only a few days. Thus, after the invader has been eliminated from the body, the number of effector cells declines. The other line of descendant cells is composed of **memory cells,** long-lived cells that "remember" that particular invader and mount a rapid, intense response to it if it should ever appear again. The quick response of memory cells is the mechanism that prevents you from getting ill from the same pathogen twice.

13.4 Antibody-Mediated Responses and Cell-Mediated Responses

An analogy can be made between the body's adaptive immune defenses and a nation's military defense system. The military has scouts who look for invaders. If an invader is found, the scout alerts the commander of the military forces and provides an exact description of the enemy. The scout must also provide the appropriate password so that the commander knows he or she is not a spy planting misinformation. The body also has scouts, called macrophages, that are part of the nonspecific defenses. Macrophages roam the tissues, looking for any invader. The cells that act as the immune system's commander are a subset of T cells called helper T cells. When macrophages properly alert helper T cells, they respond by calling out the body's specific defensive forces, and the adaptive immune responses begin.

A nation's military may have two (or more) branches. For example, it may consist of an army and a navy. Specialized to respond in slightly different ways to enemy invasion, each branch is armed with certain types of weapons. Either branch can be activated to combat a particular threat, say, little green people with purple hair. The navy may be called into action if the enemy is encountered at sea, whereas the army will come to the defense if the enemy is on land.

The body, similarly, has two types of specific defenses. These specific defenses recognize and destroy the same antigens, but they do so in different ways.

- *Antibody-mediated immune responses* defend primarily against antigens found traveling freely in intercellular and other body fluids—for example, toxins or extracellular pathogens such as bacteria or free viruses. The warriors of this branch of immune defense are the effector B cells (also called *plasma cells*), and their weapons are Y-shaped proteins called *antibodies,* which neutralize and remove potential threats from the body. Antibodies are programmed to recognize and bind to the antigen posing the threat; they

Table 13.3 Steps in the Adaptive Immune Response

Step 1: Threat	Foreign cell or molecule enters the body.
Step 2: Detection	■ Macrophage detects foreign cell or molecule and engulfs it.
Step 3: Alert	■ Macrophage puts antigen from the pathogen on its surface and finds the helper T cell with correct receptors for that antigen. ■ Macrophage presents antigen to the helper T cell. ■ Macrophage alerts the helper T cell that there is an invader that "looks like" the antigen. ■ Macrophage activates the helper T cell.
Step 4: Alarm	■ Helper T cell activates both lines of defense to fight that specific antigen.
Step 5: Building specific defenses (clonal selection)	■ Antibody-mediated defense—B cells are activated and divide to form plasma cells that secrete antibodies specific to the antigen. ■ Cell-mediated defense—T cells divide to form cytotoxic T cells that attack cells with the specific antigen.
Step 6: Defense	■ Antibody-mediated defense—antibodies specific to the antigen eliminate the antigen. ■ Cell-mediated defense—cytotoxic T cells cause cells with the antigen to burst.
Step 7: Continued surveillance	■ Memory cells formed when helper T cells, cytotoxic T cells, and B cells were activated remain to provide swift response if the antigen is detected again.
Step 8: Withdrawal of forces	■ Once the antigen has been destroyed, suppressor T cells shut down the immune response to that antigen.

Table 13.2 Cells Involved in the Adaptive Immune Response

Cell	Functions
Macrophage, dendritic cell, or B cell	**An antigen-presenting cell** ■ Engulfs and digests pathogen or invader ■ Places a piece of digested antigen on its plasma membrane ■ Presents the antigen to a helper T cell ■ Activates the helper T cell
T Cells Helper T cell	**The "on" switch for both lines of immune response** ■ Helper T cells activate B cells and T cells
Cytotoxic T cell (effector T cell)	**Responsible for cell-mediated immune responses** ■ Destroys cellular targets, such as infected body cells, bacteria, and cancer cells
Suppressor T cell	**The "off" switch for both lines of immune responses** ■ Suppresses the activity of the B cells and T cells after the foreign cell or molecule has been successfully destroyed
B Cells	**Involved in antibody-mediated responses** ■ When activated by helper T cells, the B cell divides to form plasma cells and memory cells
Plasma cell	**Effector in antibody-mediated response** ■ Secretes antibodies specific to extracellular antigens, such as toxins, bacteria, and free viruses
Memory cells	**Responsible for memory of immune system** ■ Generated by B cells or any type of T cell during an immune response ■ Enable quick and efficient response on subsequent exposures of the antigen ■ May live for years

help eliminate the antigen from the body. We discuss how this works in greater detail later in the chapter.

- *Cell-mediated immune responses* protect against cellular pathogens or abnormal cells, including body cells that have become infected with viruses or other pathogens and cancer cells. The lymphocytes responsible for cell-mediated immune responses are a type of T cell called *cytotoxic T cell* (discussed at greater length later in the chapter). Once activated, cytotoxic T cells quickly destroy the cellular pathogen, infected body cells, or cancerous cells by causing them to burst.

Now that we have introduced the various defenders, let's see how they work together to produce your body's highly effective adaptive immune response. Table 13.2 summarizes the functions of the cells participating in the adaptive immune response, and Table 13.3 summarizes the steps in the adaptive immune response.

13.5 Steps of the Adaptive Immune Response

Although the cell-mediated immune response and the antibody-mediated immune response use different mechanisms to defend against pathogens or foreign molecules (nonself), the general steps in these responses are the same (Figure 13.8).

❶ **Threat** The adaptive immune response begins when a molecule or organism (an antigen) lacking the self (MHC)

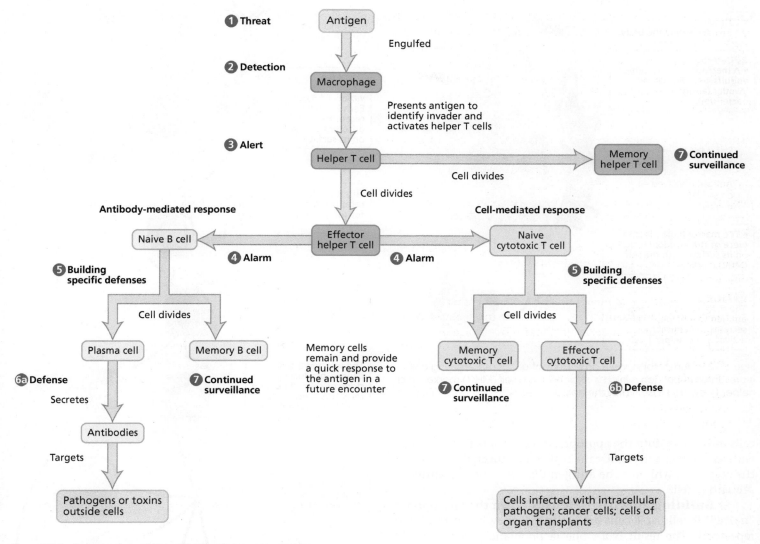

Figure 13.8 An overview of the adaptive immune response

Q: Why are helper T cells critical to the adaptive immune response?

marker manages to evade the first two lines of defense and enters the body (Figure 13.9).

❷ **Detection** Recall that macrophages are phagocytic cells that roam the body, engulfing any foreign material or organisms they may encounter. Within the macrophage, the engulfed material is digested into smaller pieces.

❸ **Alert** The macrophage then alerts the immune system's commander, a helper T cell, that an antigen is present. The macrophage accomplishes this task by transporting some of the digested pieces to its own surface, where they bind to the MHC self markers on the macrophage membrane. On the one hand, the self marker acts as a secret password that identifies the macrophage as a "friend." On the other hand, the antigen bound to the self marker functions as a kind of wanted poster, telling the lymphocytes that there is an invader and revealing how the invader can be identified. The displayed antigens trigger the adaptive immune response. Thus, the macrophage is an important type of **antigen-presenting cell (APC).** (B cells and dendritic

cells—cells with long extensions found in lymph nodes—are two other kinds of antigen-presenting cells.)

The macrophage presents the antigen to a **helper T cell,** the kind of T cell that serves as the main switch for the entire adaptive immune response. However, the macrophage must alert the *right* kind of helper T cell—a helper T cell bearing receptors that recognize the specific antigen being presented. These specific helper T cells constitute only a tiny fraction of the entire T cell population. Finding the right helper T cell is like looking for a needle in a haystack. The macrophage wanders through the body until it literally bumps into an appropriate helper T cell. The encounter most likely occurs in one of the lymph nodes, because these bean-shaped structures, discussed in Chapter 12, contain huge numbers of lymphocytes of all kinds. When the antigen-presenting macrophage meets the appropriate helper T cell and binds to it, the macrophage secretes a chemical that activates the helper T cell.

❹ **Alarm** Within hours, an activated helper T cell begins to secrete its own chemical messages. The helper T cell's message

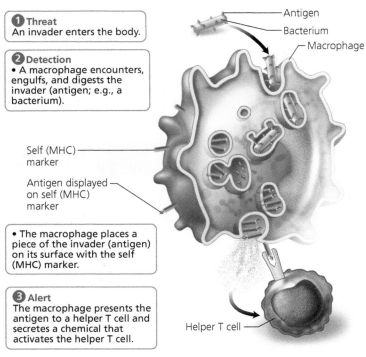

1 Threat
An invader enters the body.

Antigen
Bacterium
Macrophage

2 Detection
• A macrophage encounters, engulfs, and digests the invader (antigen; e.g., a bacterium).

Self (MHC) marker

Antigen displayed on self (MHC) marker

• The macrophage places a piece of the invader (antigen) on its surface with the self (MHC) marker.

3 Alert
The macrophage presents the antigen to a helper T cell and secretes a chemical that activates the helper T cell.

Helper T cell

Figure 13.9 A macrophage is an important antigen-presenting cell. It presents the antigen, which is attached to a self (MHC) marker, to a helper T cell, and it activates the helper T cell.

calls into active duty the appropriate B cells and T cells—those with receptors that recognize the particular antigen that triggered the response, which is the antigen displayed by the antigen-presenting cell.

5 Building Specific Defenses When the appropriate "naive"[1] B cells or T cells are activated, they begin to divide repeatedly. The result is a clone (a population of genetically identical cells) that is specialized to protect against the particular target antigen.

The process by which this highly specialized clone is produced, called **clonal selection,** underlies the entire adaptive immune response (Figure 13.10). We have seen that each lymphocyte is equipped to recognize an antigen of a specific shape. Any antigen that enters the body will be recognized by only a few lymphocytes at most. By binding to the receptors on a lymphocyte's surface, an antigen *selects* a lymphocyte that was preprogrammed during its maturation with receptors able to recognize that particular antigen. That particular lymphocyte is then stimulated to divide and produces a clone of millions of identical cells able to recognize that same antigen.

The following analogy may be helpful for understanding clonal selection. Consider a small bakery with only sample cookies on display. A customer chooses a particular cookie and places an order for many cookies of that type. The cookies are then prepared especially for that person. The sample cookies do not take a lot of space, so a wide selection can be on display for other customers to select. The baker does not waste energy making cookies that have not been specifically requested. Your

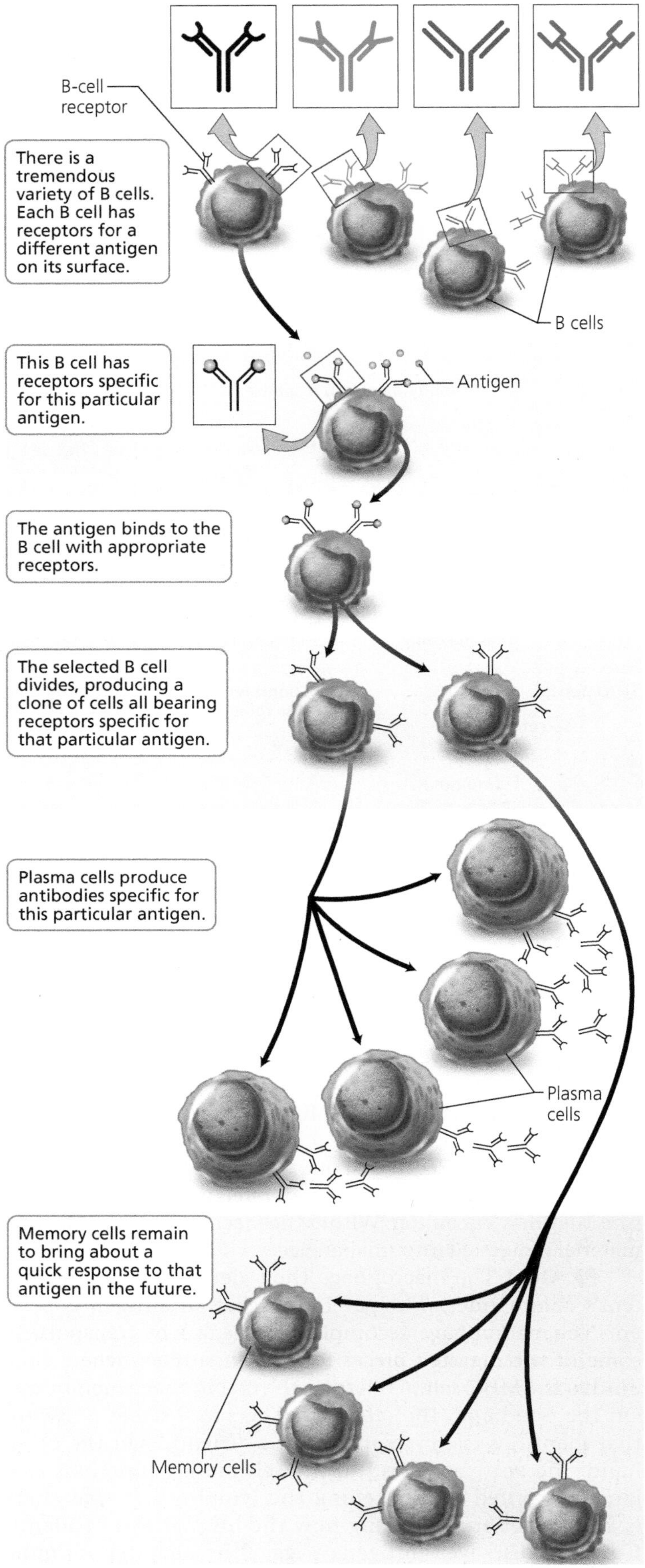

[1]A "naive" cell is one that has been programmed to respond to a particular antigen but has not been previously activated to respond.

B-cell receptor

There is a tremendous variety of B cells. Each B cell has receptors for a different antigen on its surface.

B cells

This B cell has receptors specific for this particular antigen.

Antigen

The antigen binds to the B cell with appropriate receptors.

The selected B cell divides, producing a clone of cells all bearing receptors specific for that particular antigen.

Plasma cells produce antibodies specific for this particular antigen.

Plasma cells

Memory cells remain to bring about a quick response to that antigen in the future.

Memory cells

Figure 13.10 Clonal selection is the process by which an adaptive immune response to a specific antigen becomes amplified. This figure shows clonal selection of B cells, but a similar process occurs with T cells.

body prepares samples of many kinds of lymphocytes; a given lymphocyte responds to only one antigen. When an antigen selects the appropriate lymphocyte, the body produces many additional copies of the lymphocyte chosen by that particular antigen.

STOP and THINK

Helper T cells are a primary target of HIV, the human immunodeficiency virus that leads to AIDS. Why does the virus's preference for the helper T cell impair the immune system more than if another type of lymphocyte were targeted?

We have already mentioned that when building specific defenses, the body produces two types of cells: memory cells and effector cells. Before turning to the role of memory cells, let's look more closely at exactly *how* the effector cells protect us.

6a Defense—The Antibody-Mediated Response In the **antibody-mediated immune response,** activated B cells divide. The effector cells they produce through clonal selection, which are called **plasma cells,** secrete antibodies into the bloodstream to defend against antigens free in the blood or bound to a cell surface (Figure 13.11). **Antibodies** are Y-shaped proteins that recognize a specific antigen by its shape. Each antibody is specific for one particular antigen. The specificity results from the shape of the proteins that form the tips of the Y (Figure 13.12). Because of their shapes, the antibody and antigen fit together like a lock and a key. Each antibody can bind to two identical antigens, one at the tip of each arm on the Y.

Antibodies can bind only to antigens that are free in body fluids or attached to the surface of a cell. Their main targets are toxins and extracellular microbes, including bacteria, fungi, and protozoans. Antibodies help defend against these pathogens in several ways that can be remembered with the acronym PLAN:

- **Precipitation.** The antigen–antibody binding causes antigens to clump together and precipitate (settle out of solution), enhancing phagocytosis by making the antigens easier for phagocytic cells to capture and engulf.

- **Lysis (bursting).** Certain antibodies activate the complement system, which then pokes holes through the membrane of the target cell and causes it to burst.

- **Attraction of phagocytes.** Antibodies also attract phagocytic cells to the area. Phagocytes then engulf and destroy the foreign material.

- **Neutralization.** Antibodies bind to toxins and viruses, neutralizing them and preventing them from causing harm.

There are five classes of antibodies, each with a special role to play in protecting against invaders. Antibodies are also called **immunoglobulins** (Ig), and each class is designated with a letter: IgG, IgA, IgM, IgD, and IgE. As you can see in Table 13.4, the antibodies of some classes exist as single Y-shaped molecules (monomers); in one class they exist as two attached molecules (dimers); and in one class they exist as five attached molecules (pentamers) radiating outward like the spokes of a wheel.

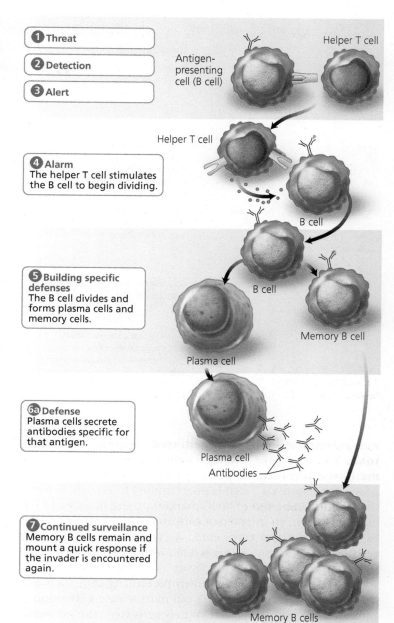

1 Threat
2 Detection
3 Alert

4 Alarm
The helper T cell stimulates the B cell to begin dividing.

5 Building specific defenses
The B cell divides and forms plasma cells and memory cells.

6a Defense
Plasma cells secrete antibodies specific for that antigen.

7 Continued surveillance
Memory B cells remain and mount a quick response if the invader is encountered again.

Helper T cell
Antigen-presenting cell (B cell)
Helper T cell
B cell
B cell
Memory B cell
Plasma cell
Plasma cell
Antibodies
Memory B cells

Figure 13.11 Antibody-mediated immune response

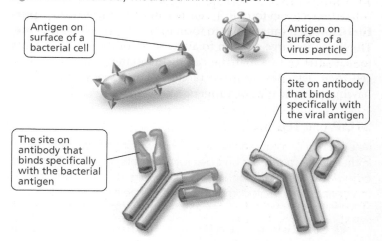

Antigen on surface of a bacterial cell

Antigen on surface of a virus particle

The site on antibody that binds specifically with the bacterial antigen

Site on antibody that binds specifically with the viral antigen

Figure 13.12 An antibody is a Y-shaped protein designed to recognize an antigen having a specific shape. The shape of the tips of the Y in the antibody molecule allows a specific antigen to be recognized.

Table 13.4 Classes of Antibodies

Class	Structure	Location	Characteristics	Protective Functions
IgG	Monomer	Blood, lymph, and intestines	Most abundant of all antibodies in body; involved in primary and secondary immune responses; can pass through placenta from mother to fetus and provides passive immune protection to fetus and newborn	Enhances phagocytosis; neutralizes toxins; triggers complement system
IgA	Dimer or monomer	Present in tears, saliva, and mucus as well as in secretions of gastrointestinal system and excretory systems; present in breast milk	Levels decrease during stress, raising susceptibility to infection	Prevents pathogens from attaching to epithelial cells of surface lining
IgM	Pentamer	Attached to a B cell, where it acts as a receptor for antigens; free in blood and lymph	First Ig class released by plasma cell during primary response	Powerful agglutinating agent (10 antigen-binding sites); activates complement
IgD	Monomer	Surface of many B cells; blood and lymph	Life span of about 3 days	Thought to be involved in recognition of antigen and in activating B cells
IgE	Monomer	Secreted by plasma cells in skin, mucous membranes of gastrointestinal and respiratory systems	Binds to surface of mast cells and basophils	Involved in allergic reactions by triggering release of histamine and other chemicals from mast cells or basophils

6b Defense—The Cell-Mediated Response The **cytotoxic T cells** are the effector T cells responsible for the **cell-mediated immune response** that destroys antigen-bearing cells. Each cytotoxic T cell is programmed to recognize a particular antigen bound to MHC markers on the surface of a cellular pathogen, an infected or cancerous body cell, or on cells of a tissue or organ transplant. A cytotoxic T cell becomes activated to destroy a target cell when two events occur simultaneously, as shown in Figure 13.13. First, the cytotoxic T cell must encounter an antigen-presenting cell, such as a macrophage. Second, a helper T cell must release a chemical to activate the cytotoxic T cell. When activated, the cytotoxic T cell divides, producing memory cells and effector cytotoxic T cells.

An effector cytotoxic T cell releases chemicals called **perforins,** which cause holes to form in the target cell membrane. The holes are large enough to allow some of the cell's contents to leave the cell so that the cell disintegrates. The cytotoxic T cell then detaches from the target cell and seeks another cell having the same type of antigen.

STOP and THINK
Rejection of an organ transplant occurs when the recipient's immune system attacks and destroys the cells of the transplanted organ. Why would this attack occur? Would the cell-mediated or the antibody-mediated immune response be most involved?

7 Continued Surveillance The first time an antigen enters the body, only a few lymphocytes can recognize it. Those lymphocytes must be located and stimulated to divide in order to produce an army of lymphocytes ready to eliminate that particular antigen. As a result, the *primary response*, the one that occurs during the body's first encounter with a particular antigen, is relatively slow. A lapse of several days occurs before the antibody concentration begins to rise, and the concentration does not peak until 1 to 2 weeks after the initial exposure to the antigen (Figure 13.14).

Following subsequent exposure to the antigen, the *secondary response* is strong and swift. Recall that when naive B cells and T cells are stimulated to divide, they produce not only effector cells that actively defend against the invader, but also memory cells. These memory B cells, memory cytotoxic T cells, and memory helper T cells live for years or even decades. As a result, the number of lymphocytes programmed to respond to that particular antigen is much greater than it was before the first exposure. When the antigen is encountered again, each of those memory cells divides and produces new effector cells and additional memory cells specific for that antigen. Therefore, the number of effector cells rises quickly during the secondary response and within 2 or 3 days reaches a higher peak than it did during the primary response.

Withdrawal of Forces As the immune system begins to conquer the invading organism and the level of antigens declines, another type of T cell, the **suppressor T cell,** releases chemicals that dampen the activity of both B cells and T cells. Suppressor T cells turn off the adaptive immune response when the antigen no longer poses a threat. This may be a mechanism that prevents the immune system from overreacting and harming healthy body cells.

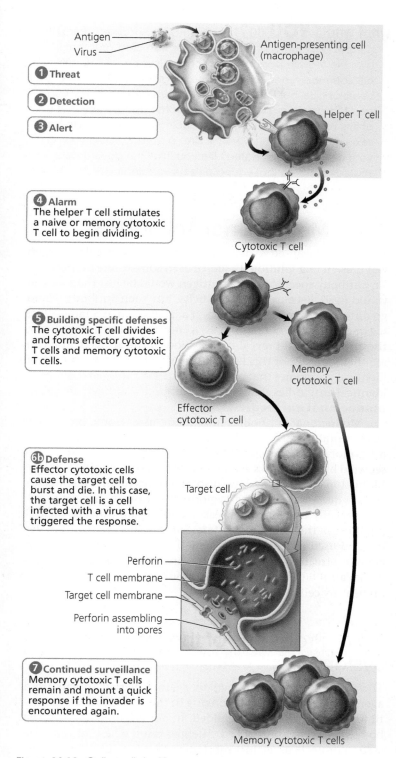

④ **Alarm**
The helper T cell stimulates a naive or memory cytotoxic T cell to begin dividing.

Cytotoxic T cell

⑤ **Building specific defenses**
The cytotoxic T cell divides and forms effector cytotoxic T cells and memory cytotoxic T cells.

Memory cytotoxic T cell

Effector cytotoxic T cell

⑥ᵇ **Defense**
Effector cytotoxic cells cause the target cell to burst and die. In this case, the target cell is a cell infected with a virus that triggered the response.

Target cell

Perforin
T cell membrane
Target cell membrane
Perforin assembling into pores

⑦ **Continued surveillance**
Memory cytotoxic T cells remain and mount a quick response if the invader is encountered again.

Memory cytotoxic T cells

Antigen
Virus

① **Threat**
② **Detection**
③ **Alert**

Antigen-presenting cell (macrophage)

Helper T cell

Figure 13.13 Cell-mediated immune response

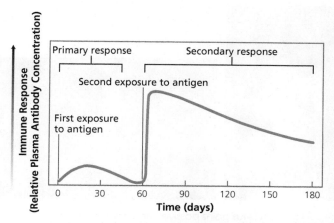

Figure 13.14 The primary and secondary immune responses. In the primary response, which occurs after the first exposure to an antigen, there is a delay of several days before the concentration of circulating antibodies begins to increase. It takes 1 to 2 weeks for the antibody concentration to peak because the few lymphocytes programmed to recognize that particular antigen must be located and activated. (The T cells show a similar pattern of response.) The secondary response following a subsequent exposure to an antigen is swifter and stronger than the primary response. The difference is due to the long-lived memory cells produced during the primary response; these are a larger pool of lymphocytes programmed to respond to that particular antigen.

known as *immunization*), a procedure that introduces a harmless form of an antigen into the body to stimulate adaptive immune responses against that antigen. Today, some vaccines, such as the vaccine for hepatitis B, are prepared using yeasts that are genetically modified to produce a protein from the pathogen. Because only the protein (antigen) is injected, rather than the actual virus, the vaccine can't cause disease. In some kinds of vaccination—those for whooping cough and typhoid fever, for instance—the microbe is killed before the vaccine is prepared. Other vaccines must be made from live organisms in order to be effective. In these cases, the microbes are first weakened so that they can no longer cause disease. The microbes are weakened by transferring them repeatedly in tissue culture, which allows unpredictable mutations to occur. Still other vaccines, including the one against smallpox, are prepared from microbes that cause related but milder diseases.

Because it leads to the production of memory cells, active immunity—occurring naturally or via vaccination—is relatively long-lived. The first dose of a vaccine causes the primary immune response, and antibodies and some memory cells are generated. In certain cases, especially when inactivated antigens are used in the vaccine, the immune system may "forget" its encounter with the antigen after a time. A booster is administered periodically to make sure the immune system does not forget. The booster results in a secondary immune response and enough memory cells to provide for a quick response should a potent form of that pathogen ever be encountered.

Vaccinations have saved millions of lives. In fact, they have been so effective in preventing diseases such as whooping cough and tetanus that many people mistakenly think those diseases have been eliminated. However, most of the diseases

13.6 Active and Passive Immunity

There are two types of immunity. In **active immunity,** the body actively defends itself by producing memory B cells and T cells following exposure to an antigen. Active immunity happens naturally whenever a person gets an infection. Fortunately, active immunity can also develop through *vaccination* (also

Figure 13.15 (a) A fetus gains passive immunity from antibodies produced by the mother that pass through the placenta. (b) Breast milk also contains maternal antibodies.

that vaccines prevent still exist, so vaccinations are still important. For example, measles was declared to be eliminated in 2000, but several outbreaks in the United States in 2015 resulted in 164 cases of measles. The frequency of whooping cough also increased dramatically in 2014. Children should be immunized (given vaccines) on a recommended schedule. (The safety of vaccinations is addressed in Chapter 18a.)

Passive immunity is protection that results when a person receives antibodies produced by another person or animal. For instance, some antibodies produced by a pregnant woman can cross the placenta and give the growing fetus some immunity. These maternal antibodies remain in the infant's body for as long 3 months after birth, at which point the infant is old enough to produce his or her own antibodies. Antibodies in breast milk also provide passive immunity to nursing infants, especially against pathogens that might enter through the intestinal lining (Figure 13.15). The mother's antibodies are a temporary yet critical blanket of protection, because most of the pathogens that would otherwise threaten the health of a newborn have already been encountered by the mother's immune system.

People can acquire passive immunity medically by being injected with antibodies produced in another person or animal. In this case, passive immunity is a good news–bad news situation. The good news is that the effects are immediate. Gamma globulin, for example, is a preparation of antibodies used to protect people who have been exposed to diseases such as hepatitis B or who are already infected with the microbes that cause tetanus, measles, or diphtheria. Gamma globulin is often given to travelers before they visit a country where viral hepatitis is common. The bad news is that the protection is short-lived. The borrowed antibodies circulate for 3 to 5 weeks before being destroyed in the recipient's body. Because the recipient's immune system was not stimulated to produce memory cells, protection disappears with the antibodies.

STOP and THINK

The viruses that cause influenza (the flu) mutate rapidly, so the antigens in the protein coat continually change. Why does this characteristic make it difficult to develop a flu vaccine that will be effective for several consecutive years?

what would YOU do? There is now a vaccine against the human papilloma virus, a sexually transmitted virus that is also the most important cause of cervical cancer. Health officials recommend the vaccine for girls and boys 11 or 12 years of age, but it can be given to girls as young as 9 years and to women as old as 26 years. Some people fear that use of this vaccine will encourage vaccinated teenagers to be sexually active. If you were (or are) a parent, would you have your daughter vaccinated? Do you think the government should mandate that young girls be vaccinated?

13.7 Monoclonal Antibodies

Suppose you wanted to determine whether a particular antigen was present in a solution, tissue, or even somewhere in the body. An antibody specific for that antigen would be just the tool you would need. Because of its specificity, any such antibody would go directly to the target antigen. If a label (such as a radioactive tag or a molecule that fluoresces) were attached to the antibody, the antibody could reveal the location of the antigen. You can see that for a test of this kind, it is desirable to have a supply of identical antibodies that react with a specific antigen. Groups of identical antibodies that bind to one specific antigen are called **monoclonal antibodies.**

Monoclonal antibodies have many uses. Home pregnancy tests contain monoclonal antibodies produced to react with a hormone (human chorionic gonadotropin; see Chapter 18) secreted by membranes associated with the developing embryo. Monoclonal antibodies have also proved useful in screening for certain diseases, including Legionnaire's disease, hepatitis, certain sexually transmitted diseases, and certain cancers, including those of the lung and prostate. Some monoclonal antibodies are also used in cancer treatment. The radioactive material or chemical treatment to combat the cancer is attached to a monoclonal antibody that targets the tumor cells but has little effect on healthy cells.

13.8 Problems of the Immune System

The immune system protects us against myriad threats from agents not recognized as belonging in the body. However, sometimes the defenses are misguided. In autoimmune disease, the body's own cells are attacked. Allergies result when the immune system protects us against substances that are not harmful. Tissue rejection following organ transplant is also caused by the immune system (see the Health Issue essay, *Rejection of Organ Transplants*).

Autoimmune Disorders

Autoimmune disorders occur when the immune system fails to distinguish between self and nonself and attacks the tissues or organs of the body. If the immune system can be called the body's military defense, then autoimmune disease is the equivalent of friendly fire.

HEALTH ISSUE

Rejection of Organ Transplants

Each year, tens of thousands of people receive a gift of life in the form of a transplanted kidney, heart, lungs, liver, or pancreas. Although these transplants seem almost commonplace today, they have been performed for only about 30 years. Before organ transplants could be successful, physicians had to learn how to prevent the effector T cells of the immune system from attacking and killing the transplanted tissue because it lacked appropriate self markers. When transplanted tissue is killed by the host's immune system, we say that the transplant has been rejected.

The success of a transplant depends on the similarity between the host tissues and the transplanted tissues. The most successful transplants are those in which tissue is taken from one part of a person's body and transplanted to another part. In cases of severe burns, for example, healthy skin from elsewhere on the body can replace badly burned areas of skin.

Another way to increase the likelihood that a transplant will be accepted is to use cells from the person's body to grow the transplant in a laboratory. Today, it is possible to grow some organs—urinary bladders, for instance—in the laboratory. Cells are taken from the defective organ and grown in tissue culture. When there are enough cells, they are placed on a three-dimensional model of the organ. Then the cell-covered mold is incubated until the new organ is formed. We discuss laboratory-grown organs in more detail in Chapter 19a.

Because identical twins are nearly genetically identical, their cells have the same self markers, and organs can be transplanted from one twin to another with little fear of tissue rejection. But few of us have an identical twin. The next best source of tissue for a transplant, and the most common, is a person whose cell surface markers closely match those of the host. Usually the transplanted tissue comes from a person who has recently died. Typically, the donor is someone who is brain-dead, but whose heart is kept beating by life-support equipment. Some organs—primarily kidneys—can be harvested from someone who has died and whose heart has stopped beating. In some cases, living people can donate organs; one of two healthy kidneys can be donated to a needy recipient, as can sections of liver.

Unfortunately, the waiting list of patients in need of an organ from a suitable donor has outpaced the supply. Some researchers believe that in the future, organs from nonhuman animals may fill the gap between the supply of organs and the demand. So far, however, attempts to transplant animal organs into people have failed. The biggest obstacle is hyperacute rejection. Within minutes to hours after transplant, the animal organ dies because its blood supply is choked off by the human immune system. Today, researchers are hopeful that genetic modification of animals for organ transplants will reduce the chances of rejection.

Other dangers may remain, even if the rejection problem is solved. Animals carry infectious agents that are harmless to their hosts but that might "jump species" and then gain the ability to spread from the transplant recipient to another person. If that were possible, we would have to ask whether it is ethical to expose a third party to risk.

Questions to Consider

- If you were a tissue match for someone who needed a kidney or a bone marrow transplant, how would you decide whether to be a donor?
- Do you think that family members who are a tissue match should be obligated to donate a kidney or bone marrow?
- Do you think that people should be able to buy a kidney or bone marrow from a suitable donor?

As we have seen, during their development, lymphocytes are programmed to attack a specific foreign antigen while still tolerating self antigens. The body usually destroys lymphocytes that do not learn to make this distinction. Unfortunately, some lymphocytes that are primed to attack self antigens escape destruction. These cells are like time bombs ready to attack the body's own cells at the first provocation. For example, if these renegade lymphocytes are activated by a virus or bacterium, they may direct their attack against healthy body cells as well as the invading organism.

Autoimmune disorders are often classified as organ-specific or non-organ-specific. As the name implies, organ-specific autoimmune disorders are directed against a single organ. Organ-specific autoimmune disorders are usually caused by T cells that have gone awry. The thyroid gland, for example, is attacked in *Hashimoto's thyroiditis*. Type 1 diabetes is an autoimmune disorder in which the pancreatic cells that produce insulin are attacked (see Chapter 10a). In contrast, non-organ-specific autoimmune disorders are generally caused by antibodies produced by B cells gone awry and tend to have effects throughout the body. In *systemic lupus erythematosus,* for instance, connective tissue is attacked. Because connective tissue can be found throughout the body, almost any organ can be affected. Lupus can cause skin lesions or rashes, most notably a butterfly-shaped rash centered on the nose and spreading to both cheeks. It may affect the heart (pericarditis), joints (arthritis), kidneys (nephritis), or nervous system (seizures).

A number of autoimmune disorders occur because portions of disease-causing organisms resemble proteins found on normal body cells. If the immune system mistakes the body's antigens for the foreign antigens, it may attack them. For instance, the body's attack on certain streptococcal bacteria that cause a sore throat may result in the production of antibodies that target not only the streptococcal bacteria but also similar molecules that are found in the valves of the heart and joints. The result is an autoimmune disorder known as *rheumatic fever.*

Treatment of autoimmune disorders is usually two-pronged. First, any deficiencies caused by the disorder are corrected. Second, drugs are administered to depress the immune system.

Allergies

An **allergy** is an overreaction by the immune system to an antigen, in this case called an *allergen*. The immune response in an allergy is considered an overreaction because the allergen itself usually is not harmful to the body. The most common allergy is hay fever—which, by the way, is not caused by hay and does not cause a fever. *Hay fever* is more correctly known as *allergic rhinitis* (*rhin–*, nose; *–itis,* inflammation of). The symptoms of hay fever—sneezing and nasal congestion—occur when an allergen is inhaled, triggering an immune response in the respiratory system. Mucous membranes of the eyes may also respond, resulting in red, watery eyes. Common causes of hay fever include pollen, mold spores, animal dander, and the feces of dust mites—microscopic creatures that are found throughout your home (Figure 13.16). The same allergens, however, can trigger asthma. During an asthma attack, the small airways in the lung (bronchioles) constrict, making breathing difficult. In food allergies, the immune response occurs in the digestive system and may cause nausea, vomiting, abdominal cramps, and diarrhea. Food allergies can also produce hives, a skin condition in which patches of skin temporarily become red and swollen.

❶ An immediate allergic response begins when a person is exposed to an allergen and a primary immune response is launched (Figure 13.17). ❷ Soon, plasma cells churn out the antibody IgE, which binds to either basophils or mast cells. In subsequent exposures to that allergen, ❸ the allergen binds to IgE antibodies on the surface of basophils or mast cells and causes granules within the cells to release their contents: histamine.

❹ The next time the allergen enters the body, ❺ the allergen combines with IgE attached to mast cells and greater quantities of histamine are released. ❻ Histamine then causes swelling, redness, and other symptoms of an allergic response. ❼ The blood vessels widen, increasing blood flow and producing redness. At the same time, the blood vessels become leaky, allowing fluid to flow from the vessels into spaces between tissue cells, swelling the tissues. Histamine also causes the release of large amounts of mucus, so the nose begins to run. In addi-

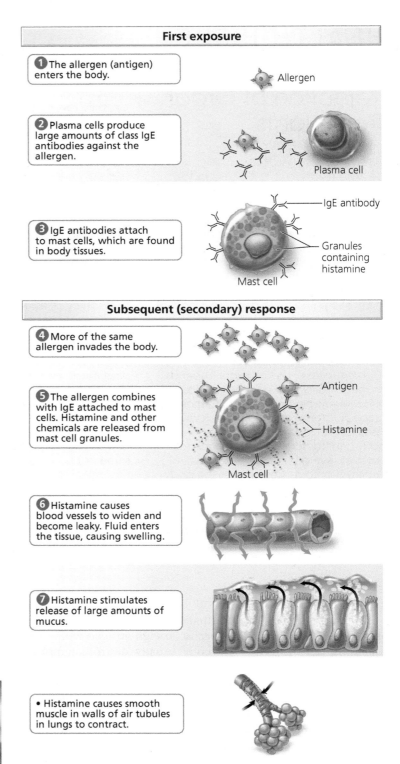

First exposure

❶ The allergen (antigen) enters the body.

Allergen

❷ Plasma cells produce large amounts of class IgE antibodies against the allergen.

Plasma cell

❸ IgE antibodies attach to mast cells, which are found in body tissues.

IgE antibody

Granules containing histamine

Mast cell

Subsequent (secondary) response

❹ More of the same allergen invades the body.

❺ The allergen combines with IgE attached to mast cells. Histamine and other chemicals are released from mast cell granules.

Antigen

Histamine

Mast cell

❻ Histamine causes blood vessels to widen and become leaky. Fluid enters the tissue, causing swelling.

❼ Histamine stimulates release of large amounts of mucus.

• Histamine causes smooth muscle in walls of air tubules in lungs to contract.

Figure 13.17 Steps in an allergic reaction

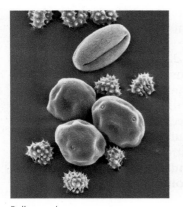

Pollen grains

Dust mite

Figure 13.16 Common causes of allergies are pollen grains and the feces of dust mites, such as the mite shown here.

tion, histamine can cause smooth muscles of internal organs to contract. Thus, if the allergen is in the respiratory system, histamine can trigger an asthma attack by making the air tubules contract.

If the allergen moves from the area where it entered the body, these effects can be widespread. The result can be *anaphylactic shock,* an extreme allergic reaction that occurs within minutes after exposure to the substance a person is allergic to. It can cause pooling of blood in capillaries, which leads to dizziness, nausea, and sometimes unconsciousness as well as extreme difficulty in breathing. Anaphylactic shock can be fatal, but most people survive. Allergies that are common triggers of anaphylactic shock include certain foods; medicines, including antibiotics such as penicillin; and insect stings, especially stings from bees, wasps, yellow jackets, and hornets.

People with allergies often know which substances cause their problems. When the culprits are not known, doctors can identify them using a crude but effective technique in which small amounts of suspected allergens are injected into the skin. If the person is allergic to one of the suspected allergens, a red welt will form at the site of injection.

If you know you have an allergy, the simplest way to avoid the miseries of an allergic reaction is to avoid exposure to the substances that cause problems. During pollen season, spend as much time as possible indoors, using an air conditioner to filter pollen out of the incoming air. Unfortunately, spores from molds growing in air conditioners and humidifiers are also common triggers of allergies. Some common allergy-causing foods—for instance, strawberries or shellfish—may be easy to avoid. Others, such as peanut oil, can show up in some unlikely dishes, including stew, chili, baked goods, or meat patties.

Certain drugs may reduce allergy symptoms. As their name implies, antihistamines block the effects of histamine. Antihistamines are most effective if they are taken before the allergic reaction begins. Unfortunately, allergies tend to become less susceptible to antihistamines over time, and most antihistamines cause drowsiness, which can impair performance on the job or in school and can make driving a car extremely hazardous. Doctors often prescribe epinephrine auto-injectors (EpiPens) for people with extreme allergies. These devices auto-

matically administer the correct dose of epinephrine to stop an allergic response. The epinephrine constricts blood vessels and keeps blood pressure from dropping dangerously low.

Some allergies can be treated by gradually desensitizing the person to the offending allergens. Allergy shots containing gradually increasing amounts of a known allergen are injected into the person's bloodstream. During this treatment, the allergen causes the production of another class of antibodies—IgG. Afterward, when the allergen enters the body, IgG antibodies bind to it and prevent it from binding to IgE antibodies on mast cells and triggering an allergic reaction.

LOOKING AHEAD

In this chapter, we learned about the mechanisms that protect us against harmful organisms and substances. In the next chapter, we consider some infectious organisms that cause disease.

CONSIDER THIS CASE

Rashon has leukemia, a cancer in which the number of white blood cells increases dramatically. The doctors decide that a bone marrow transfer might help by replacing defective bone stem cells with healthy ones. His girlfriend offered to be a donor, but the doctors chose his brother instead.

- Why did the doctors choose Rashon's brother instead of his girlfriend?
- Why might Rashon be given drugs to suppress his immune system after the transplant?

Chapter Review   MasteringBiology®

Highlighting the Concepts

13.1 The Body's Defense System (p. 239)
- The targets of the body's defense system include anything that is not recognized as belonging in the body, such as disease-causing organisms and cancerous cells. These foreign agents that cause illness are called pathogens.

13.2 Three Lines of Defense (pp. 240–245)
- The first line of defense is innate—nonspecific physical barriers, such as skin and mucous membranes, and chemical barriers, such as sweat, oil, tears, and saliva, all of which prevent entry of pathogens.
- The second line of innate defense consists of defensive cells and proteins, inflammation, and fever. Defensive cells include

phagocytes, eosinophils, and natural killer cells. Two types of defensive proteins are antiviral interferons and complement proteins, which cause cells to burst.
- The inflammatory response occurs as a result of tissue injury or invasion by foreign microbes. It begins when mast cells in the injured area release histamine, which increases blood flow by dilating blood vessels to the region and by increasing the permeability of capillaries there. Increased blood flow causes redness and warmth in the region. Fluid leaking from the capillaries produces swelling.
- Fever, an abnormally high body temperature, helps the body fight invading microbes by enhancing several body defense mechanisms and slowing the growth of many pathogens.

■ The third line of defense, the adaptive immune response, targets specific pathogens. The immune system has memory.

13.3 Distinguishing Self from Nonself (p. 245)

■ All body cells are labeled with proteins called major histocompatibility complex (MHC) proteins, which serve as self markers. Cells that lack self markers (MHC) are considered nonself and are attacked. A nonself substance or organism triggers an immune response and is called an antigen.

■ Lymphocytes are white blood cells that are responsible for immune responses. Both B lymphocytes (B cells) and T lymphocytes (T cells) develop in the bone marrow. The B cells are thought to mature in the bone marrow, but the T cells mature in the thymus gland. During maturation, B cells and T cells develop receptors on their surfaces that allow each of those cells to recognize an antigen of a different shape.

■ When an antigen is detected, B cells and T cells with receptors that respond to that antigen divide repeatedly, forming effector cells that destroy the antigen and forming memory cells that remain in the body over years or even decades to provide a quick response on subsequent exposure to that antigen.

13.4 Antibody-Mediated Responses and Cell-Mediated Responses (pp. 245–246)

■ The antibody-mediated immune response and the cell-mediated immune response simultaneously defend against the same antigen.

13.5 Steps of the Adaptive Immune Response (pp. 246–250)

■ Macrophages are an example of antigen-presenting cells. They are phagocytic cells that engulf any foreign material or organism they encounter. After engulfing the material, the macrophage places a part of the destroyed substance on its own surface to serve as an antigen that alerts lymphocytes to the presence of an invader and reveals what the invader looks like. Macrophages also have molecular (MHC) markers on their membranes that identify them as belonging in the body, that is, as self.

■ A macrophage then presents the antigen to a helper T cell, which serves as the main switch to the entire immune response. When this encounter occurs, the macrophage secretes a chemical that activates the helper T cell. The helper T cell, in turn, secretes a chemical that activates the appropriate B cells and T cells (those specific for the antigen that the macrophage engulfed).

■ B cells are responsible for antibody-mediated immune responses, which defend against antigens that are free in body fluids, including bacteria, free virus particles, and toxins. When called into action by a helper T cell, a B cell divides repeatedly, forming two lines of descendant cells: effector cells that transform into plasma cells and memory B cells. Plasma cells secrete Y-shaped proteins called antibodies into the bloodstream. Antibodies bind to the particular antigen and inactivate it or help remove it from the body.

■ Cytotoxic T cells are responsible for cell-mediated immune responses, which are effective against cellular threats, including infected body cells and cancer cells. When a T cell is activated, it divides, forming two lines of descendant cells: effector cells, called cytotoxic T cells, and memory T cells. Cytotoxic T cells secrete perforins that poke holes in the foreign or infected cell, causing it to burst and die.

■ After the first encounter with a particular antigen, the primary response is initiated, which may take several weeks to become effective against the antigen. However, because of memory cells, a subsequent exposure to the same antigen triggers a quicker response, called a secondary response.

■ Suppressor T cells dampen the activity of B cells and T cells when antigen levels begin to fall.

13.6 Active and Passive Immunity (pp. 251–252)

■ In active immunity, the body actively participates in forming memory cells to defend against a particular antigen. Active immunity may occur when an antigen infects the body, or it may occur through vaccination, a procedure that introduces a harmless form of an antigen into the body.

■ Passive immunity results when a person receives antibodies that were produced by another person or animal. Passive immunity is short-lived.

13.7 Monoclonal Antibodies (p. 252)

■ Monoclonal antibodies are identical antibodies that bind to a specific antigen. They are useful in research and in the diagnosis and treatment of diseases.

13.8 Problems of the Immune System (pp. 252–255)

■ Autoimmune disorders occur when the immune system mistakenly attacks the body's own cells.

■ An allergy is a strong immune response against an antigen (called an allergen). An allergy occurs when the allergen binds to IgE antibodies on the surface of mast cells or basophils, causing them to release histamine. Histamine, in turn, produces the redness, swelling, itching, and other symptoms of an allergic response.

Recognizing Key Terms

pathogen *p. 239*
phagocyte *p. 240*
macrophage *p. 241*
natural killer (NK) cells *p. 241*
interferon *p. 242*
complement system *p. 242*
inflammatory response *p. 242*

histamine *p. 242*
mast cell *p. 242*
adaptive immune response *p. 244*
MHC marker *p. 245*
antigen *p. 245*
B lymphocyte *p. 245*
T lymphocyte *p. 245*
effector cell *p. 245*
memory cell *p. 245*

antigen-presenting cell (APC) *p. 247*
helper T cell *p. 247*
clonal selection *p. 248*
antibody-mediated immune response *p. 249*
plasma cell *p. 249*
antibody *p. 249*
immunoglobulin *p. 249*
cytotoxic T cell *p. 250*

cell-mediated immune response *p. 250*
perforins *p. 250*
suppressor T cells *p. 250*
active immunity *p. 251*
passive immunity *p. 252*
monoclonal antibody *p. 252*
autoimmune disorders *p. 252*
allergy *p. 254*

Reviewing the Concepts

1. Indicate the *correct* statement:
   a. An antibody is specific to one particular antigen.
   b. Antibodies are held within the cell that produces them.
   c. Antibodies are produced by macrophages.
   d. Antibodies can be effective against viruses that are inside the host cell.

2. What is an antigen?
   a. a cell that produces antibodies
   b. a receptor on the surface of a lymphocyte that recognizes invaders
   c. a memory cell that causes a quick response to an invader when it is encountered a second time
   d. a large molecule on the surface of an invader that triggers an immune response

3. Which of the following pairings of cell type and function is *incorrect*?
   a. helper T cell—serves as "main switch" that activates both the cell-mediated immune responses and the antibody-mediated immune responses
   b. cytotoxic T cell—presents antigen to the helper T cell
   c. macrophage—roams the body looking for invaders, which are engulfed and digested when they are found
   d. suppressor T cell—shuts off the immune response when the invader has been removed

4. When the doctors say they are looking for a suitable donor for a kidney transplant, they are looking for someone
   a. whose tissues have self markers similar to those of the recipient.
   b. who lacks antibodies to the recipient's tissues.
   c. who has suppressor T cells that will suppress the immune response against the donor kidney.
   d. who lacks macrophages.

5. The piece of the antigen displayed on the surface of a macrophage
   a. stimulates the suppressor T cells to begin dividing.
   b. attracts other invaders to the cell, causing them to accumulate and making it easier to kill the invaders.
   c. informs the other cells in the immune system of the exact nature of the antigen they should be looking for (what the antigen "looks like").
   d. has no function in the immune response.

6. A cytotoxic T cell could attack all of the following *except*
   a. transplants of foreign tissue.
   b. cells infected with viruses.

   c. cancerous cells.
   d. viruses that are free in the bloodstream.

7. Which of the following is *not* a function of the inflammatory response?
   a. preventing the injurious agent from spreading to nearby tissue
   b. replacing injured tissues with connective tissue
   c. disposing of cellular debris and pathogens
   d. setting the stage for repair processes

8. In clonal selection of B cells, which substance is responsible for determining which cells will eventually become cloned?
   a. antigen
   b. interferon
   c. antibody
   d. complement

9. Innate immune system defenses include which of the following?
   a. B cells
   b. T cells
   c. plasma cells
   d. phagocytosis

10. Fever
    a. is a higher-than-normal body temperature that is always dangerous.
    b. decreases the metabolic rate of the body to conserve energy.
    c. results from the actions of chemicals that reset the body's thermostat to a higher setting.
    d. causes the liver to release large amounts of iron, which seems to inhibit bacterial replication.

11. The lymphocytes that develop and mature in the bone marrow are the
    a. B cells
    b. macrophages
    c. natural killer cells
    d. T cells

12. A cell that kills any unrecognized cell in the body and is part of the nonspecific body defenses is a(n) _____.

13. _____ is a chemical released by mast cells and basophils that produces most of the symptoms of an allergy.

14. Antibodies are produced by _____.

15. _____ are important antigen-presenting cells.

Applying the Concepts

1. After being exposed to the hepatitis B virus, Barbara goes to the doctor and asks to be vaccinated against it. Instead, the doctor gives her an injection of gamma globulin (a preparation of antibodies). Why wasn't she given the vaccine?

2. More than 100 viruses can cause the common cold. How does this fact explain why you can catch a cold from Raymond immediately after recovering from a cold you caught from Jessica?

3. HIV is a virus that kills helper T cells. This virus is not the direct cause of death in people who are infected with it. Instead, people

die of diseases caused by organisms that are common in the environment. Explain why HIV-infected persons are susceptible to these diseases.

4. Ira finds a deer tick attached to the back of his leg. He knows that deer ticks can transmit the bacterium that causes Lyme disease and that untreated Lyme disease can cause arthritis and fatigue. He immediately goes to the doctor to get tested, which would involve drawing blood to look for antibodies to the bacterium. The doctor refuses to test Ira for Lyme disease. Why?

Finding and Evaluating Information

In this chapter, we learned about allergies. We saw that following first exposure to an allergen, plasma cells produce IgG antibodies that are specific for that allergen, which bind either basophils or mast cells. This binding causes the cells to release histamine. In turn, histamine produces the redness and swelling we identify as allergy symptoms.

We also considered anaphylactic shock, an extreme, potentially fatal allergic response. In anaphylactic shock, blood collects in capillaries, causing extremely low blood pressure. Air tubules constrict and make breathing difficult. Anaphylactic shock occurs within minutes after a subsequent exposure to the triggering allergen.

You can read the entire study here: J. Ching et al., "Peanut and fish allergy due to platelet transfusion in a child," *Canadian Medical Association Journal* [April 7, 2015] 187(6); doi:10.1503/cmaj.141407

According to a report in the *Canadian Medical Association Journal,* children can develop allergies after blood transfusions. The report presents the case of an 8-year-old boy who was given a blood transfusion as part of treatment for brain cancer. Less than 2 weeks after the transfusion, the boy, who had no known food allergies previously, went into anaphylactic shock after eating salmon. The emergency room personnel noted that his blood pressure was low. The doctors treated the boy with antihistamines and advised him to carry an EpiPen (an epinephrine injector). Four days later, the boy ate a chocolate peanut butter cup. His lips swelled and he vomited. An allergy test revealed that the boy was allergic to fish and nuts. The boy's oncologist called the center that supplied the blood for transfusion and learned that the donor had food allergies to fish, shellfish, and nuts. The doctor concluded that IgG antibodies in the donor's plasma triggered food allergies in the recipient. Within a few months, the allergies ended, because the boy's blood no longer contained IgG antibodies.

1. Based on the evidence cited in the case report, do you think that the doctor's conclusion about the cause of the allergies is valid? Why or why not?

2. Use at least three reliable sources to find some other possible negative responses to a blood transfusion. Cite your sources.

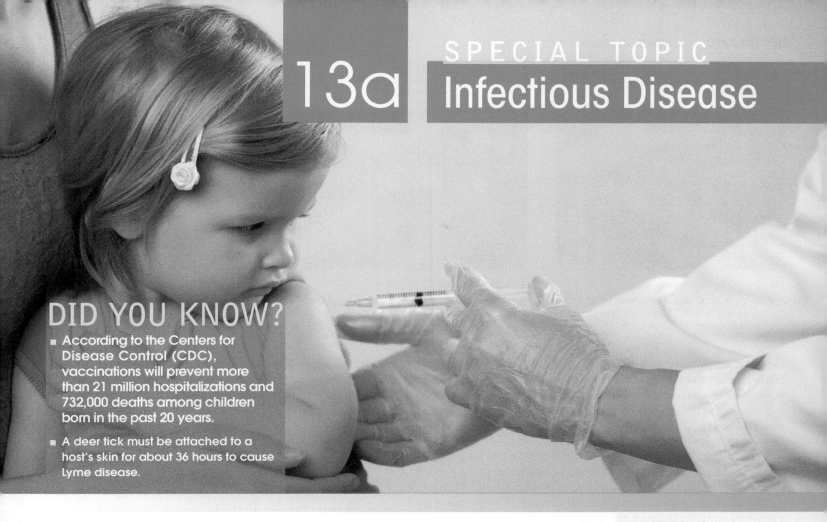

DID YOU KNOW?

- According to the Centers for Disease Control (CDC), vaccinations will prevent more than 21 million hospitalizations and 732,000 deaths among children born in the past 20 years.

- A deer tick must be attached to a host's skin for about 36 hours to cause Lyme disease.

IN THE PREVIOUS CHAPTER, we learned about the ways our bodies protect us against pathogens. In this chapter, we discuss the most important categories of pathogens, the disease-causing organisms introduced in Chapter 13. We explore how pathogens cause harm, how they are transmitted from person to person, and how they are studied so that steps may be taken to hold them in check.

13a.1 Pathogens

As we explained in Chapter 13, *pathogens* are disease-causing organisms. There are different types of pathogens and a wide range of differences within each type. As a result, each pathogen has specific effects on the body, and some pathogens are a greater menace than others. In this chapter, we look at bacteria, viruses, protozoans, fungi, parasitic worms, and prions. We consider the general means these different types of pathogens use to attack the body and cause symptoms. Keep in mind, however, as we do so, that some of the symptoms are caused not by the pathogen itself but by the immune responses our body uses to protect us (Chapter 13).

Virulence is the relative ability of a pathogen to cause disease. Factors contributing to this ability include how easily the pathogen invades tissues and the degree and type of damage it does to body cells. An organism that always causes disease—the typhoid bacterium, for instance—is highly virulent. In contrast, the yeast *Candida albicans,* which *sometimes* causes disease, is moderately virulent.

Bacteria

Bacterial cells differ from the cells that make up our bodies. Recall from Chapter 3 that our bodies are made up of eukaryotic cells, which contain a nucleus and membrane-bound organelles. Bacteria, in

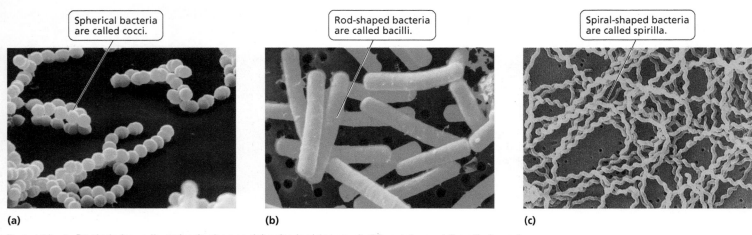

Figure 13a.1 Bacteria have three basic shapes: (a) spherical (coccus), (b) rod-shaped (bacillus), and (c) corkscrew-shaped (spirillum). All bacteria are prokaryotic cells, meaning that they lack a nucleus and membrane-bound organelles.

contrast, are prokaryotes, which means they lack a nucleus and other membrane-bound organelles. Nearly all bacteria have a semirigid cell wall composed of a strong mesh of peptidoglycan, a type of polymer consisting of sugars and amino acids. The cell wall endows most types of bacteria with one of three common shapes: a sphere (a spherical bacterium is called a *coccus*), which can occur singly, in pairs, or in chains; a rod (called a *bacillus*), which usually occurs singly; or a spiral or corkscrew shape (such bacteria are called *spirilla*) (Figure 13a.1).

Bacteria can reproduce rapidly. This rapid growth rate is a matter of concern because the greater the number of bacteria, the greater harm they can potentially do. Rapid reproduction is possible because bacteria reproduce asexually in a type of cell division called *binary fission*. In binary fission, the bacterial genetic material (DNA) is copied, the cell is pinched in half, and each new cell contains a complete copy of the original genetic material. Under ideal conditions, certain bacteria can divide every 20 minutes. Thus, if every descendant lived, a single bacterium could result in a massive infection of trillions of bacteria within 24 hours. If a percentage of the descendant bacteria die before dividing, the population of bacteria will begin to grow more slowly than does a population in which all descendants survive, but the populations will eventually have the same growth rate.

Bacteria have defenses or other adaptive mechanisms that affect their virulence. Some bacteria have long, whiplike structures known as *flagella* that allow them to move and spread through tissues to new areas where they can cause infection. Bacteria may also have filaments, called *pili,* that help them attach to the cells they are attacking. Outside the bacterial cell, there is often a capsule that provides a means of adhering to a surface and prevents scavenger cells of the immune system (phagocytes; see Chapter 13) from engulfing them.

Beneficial bacteria Many bacteria are beneficial. For instance, certain bacteria are important in food production, especially of dairy products such as cheese and yogurt. Other bacteria have a significant role in the environment, serving as decomposers or driving the cycling of nitrogen, carbon, and phosphorus between organisms and the environment (see Chapter 23). Yet other

bacteria are useful in genetic engineering (see Chapter 21). Some bacteria are normal residents in the body that keep potentially harmful microorganisms in check, and bacteria in our intestines produce vitamin K.

Bacterial enzymes and toxins Destructive enzymes and toxins (poisons) are among the offensive mechanisms that certain bacteria use to spread and to attack. Some of these bacteria secrete enzymes that directly damage tissue and cause lesions, allowing the bacteria to push through tissues like a bulldozer. An example is *Clostridium,* the bacterium that causes gas gangrene, a condition in which tissue dies because its blood supply is shut off. The bacterium secretes an enzyme that dissolves the material holding muscle cells together, permitting the bacteria to spread with ease. When this bacterium digests muscle cells for energy, a gas is produced that presses against blood vessels and shuts off the blood supply. In addition, *Clostridium* causes anemia by secreting an enzyme that bursts red blood cells.

Most bacteria, however, do their damage by releasing toxins into the bloodstream or the surrounding tissues. If the toxins enter the bloodstream, they can be carried throughout the body and disturb body functions.

The disease symptoms depend on which body tissues are affected by the toxin. Thus, the bacteria that cause various types of food poisoning have different effects. *Staphylococcus* is often the culprit responsible for contaminating poultry, meat and meat products, and creamy foods such as pudding or salad dressing. These bacteria multiply when food is undercooked or unrefrigerated. The toxins they produce stimulate cells in the immune system to release chemicals that result in inflammation, vomiting, and diarrhea. Another type of food poisoning is caused by *Salmonella,* often encountered in undercooked contaminated chicken or eggs. In this case, the toxin causes changes in the permeability of intestinal cells, leading to diarrhea and vomiting. One type of *Escherichia coli* (*E. coli*) food poisoning is often caused by contaminated meat, particularly ground meat. Besides vomiting and diarrhea, *E. coli* toxin can cause kidney failure in children and the elderly. The toxin that causes botulism, a type of food poisoning often brought on by eating improperly canned food, is one of the most toxic substances known. Produced by the bacterium *Clostridium botulinum,* it interferes with nerve functioning, especially motor nerves that cause muscle contraction. Death occurs because muscle paralysis prevents breathing. If enough is consumed, this toxin is almost always fatal.

Antibiotics   Fortunately, bacteria can be killed. As we learned in Chapter 13, the human body has its own array of defenses against foreign invaders. But when the body needs outside help, we can call on *antibiotics,* chemicals that inhibit the growth of microorganisms. Antibiotics work to reduce the number of bacteria or slow the growth rate of the population, allowing time for body defenses to conquer the bacteria. Some antibiotics kill bacteria directly by preventing the synthesis of bacterial cell walls, causing them to burst. Recall that our body cells lack cell walls (see Chapter 3). Thus, our cells are unaffected by antibiotics that target cell walls. Some antibiotics block protein synthesis by bacteria but do so without interfering with protein synthesis in human body cells. This selective action is possible because the structure of ribosomes, the organelles on which proteins are synthesized, is slightly different in bacteria and humans.

When antibiotics were introduced during the 1940s, they were considered miracle drugs. For the first time, a cure was available for such devastating bacterial diseases as pneumonia, bacterial meningitis, tuberculosis, and cholera. Today, there are more than 160 antibiotics. These lifesaving drugs have become so commonplace that we take them for granted.

Unfortunately, antibiotics are losing their power. Infections that were once easy to cure with antibiotics can now turn deadly as bacteria gain resistance to the drugs. Several bacterial species capable of causing life-threatening illnesses have produced strains that are resistant to every antibiotic available today.[1]

Contradictory as it may seem, the use of antibiotics can actually increase antibiotic resistance in a strain of bacteria. When a strain of bacteria is exposed to an antibiotic, the bacteria that are susceptible die. The more resistant bacteria, however, may survive and multiply. If the bacteria are exposed to the antibiotic again, the selection process is repeated. With each exposure to the drug, the resistant bacteria gain a stronger foothold. Making matters worse, antibiotics kill beneficial bacteria along with harmful ones. Normally, the beneficial bacterial strains help keep the harmful strains in check. Loss of the "good" bacteria can allow the harmful ones to dominate.

The overuse and misuse of antibiotics are largely to blame for the resistance problem. Prescribing antibiotics for illnesses that are viral, such as a cold or flu, is an example of overuse. Antibiotics have no effect on viruses, so they are unnecessary for treating such illnesses. Patients misuse antibiotics when they stop taking their medicine as soon as they feel better, instead of completing the full course of treatment. By stopping too early, they may be leaving the bacteria with greater resistance alive. Hospitals use antibiotics heavily, so it is not surprising that they are breeding grounds for antibiotic-resistant bacteria. The resistant bacteria

survive, outgrow susceptible strains, and spread from person to person. Indeed, most infections by antibiotic-resistant bacteria occur in hospitals. An example is *Staphylococcus aureus,* which can cause many types of infections, including blood poisoning, pneumonia, skin infections, heart infections, and nervous system infections. The strain of *S. aureus* called MRSA (methicillin-resistant *Staphylococcus aureus*) is actually resistant to many antibiotics. For many years, MRSA existed only in hospitals, but it is now found in the community at large. In the past several years, outbreaks of MRSA have occurred in public places, including schools, locker rooms, fitness centers, and doctors' offices. For a time, vancomycin was the only antibiotic that remained effective against MRSA. Unfortunately, a vancomycin-resistant *S. aureus* (VRSA) strain has arisen. An antibiotic-resistant strain of another bacterium, *Clostridium difficile* (often called "C. diff"), is more dangerous than other strains, because it produces more toxin. Outbreaks of *C. difficile* are spreading in health care facilities, such as hospitals and nursing homes, because antibiotics are used heavily there. Hospital-acquired *C. difficile* infections cause 18,000 to 20,000 deaths a year in the United States, mostly among the elderly.

More than 40% (by mass) of the antibiotics used in the United States are given to livestock to promote growth and ensure health. Farmers also spray crops with antibiotics to control or prevent bacterial infections in the crops. These practices also contribute to antibiotic resistance, and the antibiotic-resistant bacteria can then infect humans. For this reason, the U.S. Food and Drug Administration (FDA) has recently banned the use of antibiotics in animal feed.

What can you do to slow the spread of drug-resistant bacteria? Use antibiotics responsibly. Do not insist on a prescription for antibiotics against your doctor's advice. Take antibiotics exactly as prescribed, and be sure to complete the recommended treatment. Also, reduce your risk of getting an infection that might require antibiotic treatment: wash your hands frequently, rinse fruits and vegetables before eating them, and cook meat thoroughly.

Viruses

Viruses are responsible for many human illnesses. Some viral diseases, such as the common cold, are usually not very serious. Other viral diseases, such as yellow fever, can be deadly.

Most biologists do not consider a virus to be a living organism because, on its own, it cannot perform any life processes (see Chapter 1 for a review on the basic characteristics of life). To copy itself, a virus must enter a host cell. The virus exploits the host cell's nutrients and metabolic machinery to make copies of itself that then infect other host cells.

Viruses are much smaller than bacteria. A virus consists of a strand or strands of genetic material, either DNA or RNA, surrounded by a coat of protein, called a capsid. The genetic material carries the instructions for making new viral proteins. Some of these proteins become structural parts of the new viruses. Some of them serve as enzymes that help carry out biochemical functions important to the virus. Some are regulatory proteins, such as the proteins that trigger specific viral genes to become active under certain sets of conditions or the proteins that convert the host cell into a virus-producing factory.

[1]Bacteria resistant to all antibiotics available today include some strains of *Staphylococcus aureus* (which cause skin infection and pneumonia), *Mycobacterium tuberculosis* (the cause of tuberculosis), *Enterococcus faecalis* (which causes intestinal infections), and *Pseudomonas aeruginosa* (which causes many types of infections).

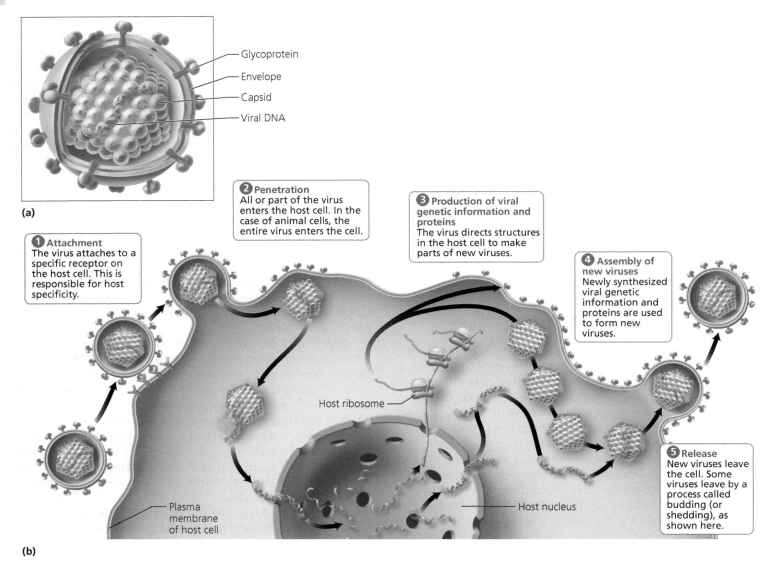

(a)

(b)

Figure 13a.2 (a) The structure of a typical virus. A coat, called a capsid, made of protein surrounds a core of genetic information made of DNA or RNA. Some viruses have an outer membranous layer, called the envelope, from which glycoproteins project. (b) Steps in viral replication.

Q: Which part of a virus would have to change for it to be able to infect a new type of tissue?

Some viruses have an envelope, an outer membranous layer studded with glycoproteins. In some viruses, the envelope is actually a bit of plasma membrane from the previous host cell that became wrapped around the virus as it left the host cell. The envelope of certain other viruses—those in the herpes family, for instance—comes from a previous host cell's nuclear membrane. In any case, the virus produces the glycoproteins on the envelope. Some glycoproteins are important for attachment of the virus to the host cell.

A virus can replicate (make copies of itself) only when its genetic material is inside a host cell. Figure 13a.2 illustrates the general steps in the replication of viruses that infect animal cells:

❶ **Attachment.** The virus gains entry by binding to a receptor (a protein or other molecule of a certain configuration) on the host cell surface. Such binding is possible because the viral surface has molecules of a specific shape (glycoproteins or capsids) that fit the host's receptors. The host cell receptors play a

role in normal cell functioning. However, a molecule on the surface of the virus has a shape that is similar to the chemical that would normally bind to the receptor. Viruses generally attack only certain kinds of cells in certain species, because a particular virus can infect only cells bearing a receptor the virus can bind to. For example, the virus that causes the common cold infects only cells in the respiratory system, and the virus that causes hepatitis infects only liver cells.

❷ **Penetration.** After a virus has bound to a receptor on a host cell, the entire virus enters the host cell, often by phagocytosis by the host cell. Once inside, the virus loses its capsid, leaving only its genetic material intact.

❸ **Production of viral genetic information and proteins.** Viral genes then direct the host cell machinery to make thousands of copies of viral DNA or RNA. Next, viral genes direct the synthesis of viral proteins, including coat proteins and enzymes.

❹ Assembly of new viruses. Copies of the viral DNA (or RNA) and viral proteins then assemble to form new viruses.

❺ Release. Some viruses leave the cell through *budding,* or shedding. In this process, the newly formed viruses push through the host cell's plasma membrane and become wrapped in this membrane, which forms an envelope. Budding need not kill the host cell. Other virus types do not acquire an envelope but rather cause the host cell membrane to rupture, releasing the newly formed viruses and killing the host cell.

Viruses can cause disease in several ways, as summarized in Table 13a.1. Some viruses produce disease when they kill the host cells or cause the cells to malfunction. The host cell dies when viruses leave it so rapidly that it lyses (bursts). In such cases, disease symptoms will depend on which cells are killed. However, if viruses are shed slowly, the host cell may remain alive and continue to produce new viruses. Slow shedding causes *persistent infections* that can last a long time. Some viruses can produce *latent infections,* in which the viral genes remain in the host cell for an extended period without harming the cell. At any time, however, the virus can begin replicating and cause cell death as new viruses are released.

An example of a virus that can act in all of these ways is the herpes simplex virus that causes fever blisters ("cold sores") on the mouth. The virus is spread by contact (discussed shortly) and enters the epithelial cells of the mouth, where it actively replicates. Rapid shedding kills the host cells, resulting in fever blisters. Slow shedding may not cause outward signs of infection, but the virus can still be transmitted. When the blisters are gone, the virus remains in a latent form within nerve cells without producing symptoms. However, stress can activate the virus. It then follows nerves to the skin and begins actively replicating, causing new blisters in the same region of the mouth.

Certain viruses can also cause cancer. Some do this when they insert themselves into the host chromosome near a gene that regulates cell division and, in so doing, alter the functioning of that gene. Still other viruses bring cancer-causing genes with them into the host cell.

Unfortunately, viruses are not as easy to destroy as bacteria. It is difficult to attack viruses inside their host cells without killing the host cell itself. Most attempts to develop antiviral drugs have failed for this reason. Nonetheless, some drugs are now available to slow viral growth, and others are being developed. Most of the antiviral drugs available today, including those against the herpes virus and HIV, work by blocking one of the steps necessary for viral replication. As mentioned in Chapter 13, interferons are proteins produced by virus-infected cells that protect neighboring cells from all strains of viruses. Interferons are not as useful as originally hoped, but they have been used for certain viral infections, including hepatitis C and the human papilloma virus that causes genital warts.

Because of these obstacles to treatment, the best way to fight viral infections is to prevent them with vaccines (discussed in Chapter 13).

STOP and THINK

How do the structure and replication cycle of viruses explain why antibiotics are not effective against viral diseases?

Protozoans

Protozoans are single-celled eukaryotic organisms with a well-defined nucleus. They can cause disease by producing toxins or by releasing enzymes that prevent host cells from functioning normally. Protozoans are responsible for many diseases, including malaria, sleeping sickness, amebic dysentery, and giardiasis. Giardiasis is a diarrheal disease that can last for weeks. Outbreaks of giardiasis occur frequently in the United States, most of them resulting from water supplies contaminated with human or animal feces. Even clear and seemingly clean lakes

Table 13a.1	Possible Effects of Animal Virus on Cells
Lytic infection	Rapid release of new viruses from infected cell causes cell death. Symptoms of the disease depend on which cells are killed.
Persistent infection	Slow release of new viruses allows the cell to remain alive and continue to produce new viruses for a prolonged period.
Latent infection Primary infection Latent period Secondary infection	Delay between infection and symptoms. Virus is present in the cell without harming the cell. Symptoms begin when the virus starts to actively replicate, and new viruses exiting the host cell can cause cell death.
Transformation to cancerous cell	Certain viruses insert their genetic information into host cell chromosomes. Some carry oncogenes (cancer-causing genes) that are active in the host cell. Some disrupt the functioning of the host cell's genes that regulate cell division, causing the cell to become cancerous.

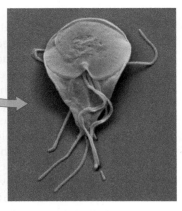

Figure 13a.3 *Giardia* is a protozoan commonly found in lakes and streams used as sources of drinking water, even those in pristine areas. It causes severe diarrhea that lasts for weeks and can be especially dangerous for children.

and streams in the wilderness can contain *Giardia* (Figure 13a.3). Fortunately, drugs are available to treat protozoan infections. Some of these drugs work by preventing protozoans from synthesizing proteins.

Fungi

Like the protozoans, fungi are also eukaryotic organisms with a well-defined nucleus in their cells. Some fungi exist as single cells. Others are organized into simple multicellular forms, with not much difference among the cells. There are more than 100,000 species of fungi, but fewer than 0.1% cause human ailments. Fungi obtain food by infiltrating the bodies of other organisms—dead or alive—secreting enzymes to digest the food, and absorbing the resulting nutrients. If the fungus is growing in or on a human, body cells of the human are digested, causing disease symptoms. Some fungi cause serious lung infections, such as histoplasmosis and coccidioidomycosis. Other, less threatening fungal infections occur on the skin and include athlete's foot and ringworm. Most fungal infections can be cured. Fungal cell membranes have a slightly different composition from those of human cells. As a result, the membrane is a point of vulnerability. Some antifungal drugs work by altering the permeability of the fungal cell membrane. Others interfere with membrane synthesis by fungal cells. Fungal infections of the skin, hair, and nails can be combated with a drug that prevents the fungal cells from dividing.

Parasitic Worms

Parasitic worms are multicellular animals that benefit from a close, prolonged relationship with their hosts while harming, but usually not killing, their hosts. They include flukes, tapeworms, and roundworms, such as hookworms and pinworms. They can cause illness by releasing toxins into the bloodstream, feeding off blood, or competing for food with the host. Parasitic worms cause many serious human diseases, including ascariasis, schistosomiasis, and trichinosis.

Ascariasis is caused by a large roundworm, *Ascaris,* that is about the size of an earthworm. People become infected with *Ascaris* when they consume food or drink contaminated with *Ascaris* eggs. The eggs develop into larvae (immature worms) in the per-

son's intestine. The larvae then penetrate the intestinal wall, enter the bloodstream, and travel to the lungs. After developing further, the worms are coughed up and swallowed, thus returning to the intestine. Within 2 to 3 months, they mature into male and female worms, which live for about 2 years. During those years, female worms can produce more than 200,000 eggs a day.

As much as 25% of the world population is infected with *Ascaris,* particularly in tropical regions. Up to 50% of the children in some parts of the United States (mostly rural areas in the Southeast) are infected. Many people with ascariasis have no symptoms. However, the worms can cause lung damage and severe malnutrition. When many worms are present, they can block or perforate the intestines, leading to death.

Prions

Prions (pree´-ons) are infectious particles of proteins—or, more simply, infectious proteins. They are misfolded versions of a harmless protein normally found on the surface of nerve cells. If a prion is present, it somehow causes the host protein to change its shape to the abnormal form. Prions cause a group of diseases called *transmissible spongiform encephalopathies (TSEs),* which are associated with degeneration of the brain. The misshapen proteins clump together and accumulate in the nerve tissue of the brain. These clumps of prions may damage the plasma membrane or interfere with molecular traffic. Spongelike holes develop in the brain, causing death.

Transmissible spongiform encephalopathies are progressive and fatal. Prions cannot be destroyed by heat, ultraviolet light, or most chemical agents. Currently, there is no treatment for any disease they cause. Several of the TSEs are animal infections, notably mad cow disease, scrapie in sheep, and chronic wasting disease (CWD), which affects deer and elk.

Prions also cause a human neurological disorder called *Creutzfeldt-Jakob disease (CJD).* Indeed, the prion responsible for mad cow disease is thought to cause one form of CJD. The incubation period for CJD can be months to decades. Symptoms include sensory and psychiatric problems. Once the symptoms begin, death usually occurs within a year.

what would YOU do? Mad cow disease is spread in cattle when they consume contaminated food. There are laws to prevent feeding cattle food that might be contaminated. When violations of the laws occur, who should be held responsible: the food manufacturers or the farmers?

13a.2 Spread of a Disease

Obviously, you catch a disease when the pathogen enters your body. But how do diseases travel from person to person or enter the body in the first place? The answer to this question varies with the type of pathogen.

- **Direct contact.** One means of transmission is direct contact of an infected person with an uninfected person, as might occur when shaking hands, hugging and kissing, or being sexually intimate. For example, sexually transmitted diseases (STDs)—including chlamydia, gonorrhea, syphilis, genital herpes, and human papilloma virus (HPV)—are spread when a susceptible body surface touches an infected

Figure 13a.4 Pathogens can be spread through the air in droplets of moisture when an infected person sneezes or coughs.

✹ Actual size

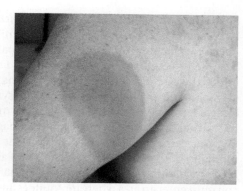

Figure 13a.5 A tiny tick, the deer tick, is a vector that transmits the bacterium responsible for Lyme disease. One characteristic sign of Lyme disease is a red bull's-eye rash surrounding the tick bite. The rash gradually increases in diameter.

body surface (see Chapter 17a). The organisms that cause STDs generally cannot remain alive outside the body for very long, so direct intimate contact is necessary. A few disease-causing organisms—HIV and the bacterium that causes syphilis, for instance—can spread across the placenta from a pregnant woman to her growing fetus.

■ **Indirect contact.** Indirect contact, the transfer from one person to another without their touching, can spread other diseases. Most respiratory infections, including the common cold, are spread by indirect contact (see Chapter 14). When an infected person coughs or sneezes, airborne droplets of moisture full of pathogens are carried through the air (Figure 13a.4). The infected droplets may be inhaled or land on nearby surfaces. When another person touches an affected surface, the organisms are transmitted. In this way, droplet infection spreads pathogens on contaminated inanimate objects, including doorknobs, drinking glasses, and eating utensils.

■ **Contaminated food or water.** Certain diseases are transmitted in contaminated food or water (see also Chapter 15a). You have read that spoiled food can cause food poisoning. Another disease transmitted by food or water is hepatitis A, an inflammation of the liver caused by a certain virus. *Legionella,* the bacterium that causes a severe respiratory infection known as Legionnaire's disease, is a common inhabitant of the water in condensers of large air conditioners and cooling towers. The disease-causing bacteria are spread through tiny airborne water droplets. Coliform bacteria come from the intestines of humans and are, therefore, an indicator of fecal contamination of water. Their numbers are monitored in drinking and swimming water. To be safe, drinking water should not have any coliform bacteria.

■ **Animal vectors.** Another means of transmission is by *vector,* an animal that carries a disease from one host to another. The most common vector-borne disease in the United States is Lyme disease. It is caused by a bacterium transmitted by the deer tick (the vector), which is about the size of the head of a pin (Figure 13a.5). The tick larva picks up the infectious agent when it bites and sucks blood from an infected

animal. When the tick subsequently feeds on a human or other mammalian host, the bacteria gradually move from the tick's gut to its salivary glands and then are passed to its victim. The incubation period, during which there are no symptoms, can be as long as 6 to 8 weeks. Early symptoms include a headache, backache, chills, and fever. Often, a rash resembling a bull's-eye develops, with an intense red center and border. Over a period of weeks, the circle increases in diameter. Weeks to months later, unless the disease is treated promptly, pain, swelling, and arthritis may develop. Cardiovascular and nervous system problems may follow the arthritis.

Mosquitoes transmit the West Nile virus, which can cause both meningitis (inflammation of the meninges, the protective coverings of the central nervous system) and encephalitis (brain inflammation; Figure 13a.6). The first reported cases of West Nile virus in North America were in New York City in 1999. Since then, the disease has spread to nearly every state. The virus can infect certain vertebrates, including humans, horses, birds, and occasionally dogs and cats. Testing mosquitoes and dead birds,

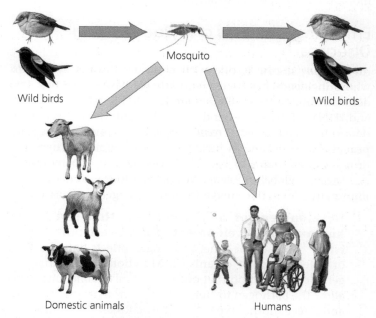

Wild birds

Mosquito

Wild birds

Domestic animals

Humans

Figure 13a.6 The mosquito is the vector that transmits West Nile virus.

especially crows and starlings, for the virus is one way to track its spread. Because the symptoms are similar to those of the flu (fever, headache, and muscle and joint pain) many people who become infected are unaware of it—and most infected people under the age of 50 have few symptoms or none at all. However, older people have weaker immune systems. If they become infected, they are more likely to develop meningitis or encephalitis, either of which can cause brain damage, paralysis, or death.

You can protect yourself from West Nile virus and other mosquito-borne viral infections such as Eastern equine encephalitis by avoiding wet and humid places that harbor mosquitoes. If you must enter an area where mosquitoes are likely to be, wear light-colored clothing that covers your body, and use insect repellent.

■ **Intravenous Drug Use** Intravenous drug use can transmit disease when two people, one of whom is infected, share a needle. IV drug use is epidemic in some parts of the United States, especially the Northeast. The CDC fears that rates of HIV and hepatitis C—two diseases that are transmitted through needle sharing in IV drug use—will increase dramatically in the coming years. Indeed, in Indiana, an outbreak of HIV linked to injection of prescription painkillers began in 2015. Eighty percent of the HIV-positive drug users also had hepatitis C.

13a.3 Infectious Diseases as a Continued Threat

An *epidemic* is a large-scale outbreak of an infectious disease. The most notorious epidemics—bubonic plague, cholera, diphtheria, and smallpox—have happened in the distant past, although new outbreaks may occur sporadically. However, outbreaks of serious new diseases continue to present problems. For example, the tick-borne Powassan virus first appeared in 2015. Symptoms of infection are similar to, but worse than, those of Lyme disease. It currently has no cure or treatment. We discuss other modern-day plagues elsewhere in the text.

Emerging Diseases and Reemerging Diseases

An *emerging disease* is one with clinically distinct symptoms whose incidence has increased, particularly over the past two decades. Among these diseases are HIV, SARS, H1H5 influenza, and H1N1 influenza. Other diseases thought to have been conquered have reemerged. A *reemerging disease* is one that has reappeared after a decline in incidence. For example, because new drug-resistant strains of bacteria have emerged, tuberculosis is once again a global problem. We consider four factors that play important roles in the emergence and reemergence of disease.

1. **Development of new organisms that can infect humans and development of drug-resistant organisms.** Most of the time, a pathogen infects only one type or a few types of organisms. Mutations are changes in genetic information that occur randomly. Some mutations allow the pathogen to "jump species" from its original host and infect another type of organism. Recall that a virus can penetrate a cell only if the virus has the appropriate molecule

on its surface—one that will fit into a receptor on the host cell. Another mechanism that could allow an animal virus to infect humans is *antigenic shift*, the mixing of genetic information of an animal virus and a human virus, which might occur if both viruses infected the same cell. This is how the H1N1 virus that causes swine flu developed: a person passed human influenza A viruses to a pig with influenza A. When the viruses infected the same cell, pieces of the viruses' genetic material were mixed and created a new strain of virus.

Pathogens can also undergo changes in their response to drugs. We have seen that certain bacteria have acquired resistance to antibiotics, for example. As a result, some diseases that were once easily cured by antibiotics are now much more difficult to treat. Improper antibiotic treatment during the reemergence of tuberculosis (TB) has led to antibiotic-resistant strains of TB that, in turn, make TB more difficult to treat. Infections with multi-drug-resistant strains of *Mycobacterium tuberculosis,* the bacterium that causes TB, are increasing at an alarming rate. The World Health Organization coined a new term to describe drug resistance in a new strain of the tuberculosis bacterium— *XDR,* which stands for *extensively drug resistant.* The new XDR strain causes a tuberculosis infection that is nearly impossible to treat.

what would YOU do? The number of people with drug-resistant TB is rising, especially in poorer countries. Inadequate treatment is one reason for this rise. When new drugs to combat drug-resistant strains become available, they are extremely expensive. People in poor countries cannot afford the drugs, and cases of XDR increase, which puts us all at risk. Clearly, it would be globally beneficial to decrease the prevalence of XDR tuberculosis by using effective drugs. Who do you think should foot the bill?

2. **Environmental change.** Changes in local climate—the annual amount of rainfall and the average temperature—can affect the distribution of organisms and change the size of the geographic region where certain organisms can live. Global warming makes the redistribution of pathogens a growing concern.

3. **Population growth.** Another important factor in the emergence or reemergence of diseases is the increase in the human population in association with the development and growth of cities. Swelling human populations in cities cause people to move out of the city into surrounding areas, creating suburbs. If the surrounding areas were previously undeveloped, the move brings more people into contact with animals and insects that might carry infectious organisms. Indeed, wild animals serve as reservoirs for more than 100 species of pathogens that can affect humans. The development of suburbs also destroys populations of predators, such as foxes and bobcats. In some regions of New York, the loss of predators has led to an increase in the numbers of tick-carrying mice and a rise in the incidence of Lyme disease.

Figure 13a.7 Air travel is one reason that new diseases can spread rapidly.

Population density and mobility also enable infectious diseases to spread more easily today than in the past. Densely populated cities allow diseases to begin spreading quickly, and air travel enables them to spread over great distances (Figure 13a.7).

4. **Failure to vaccinate.** Vaccination has completely or nearly completely eliminated 14 infectious diseases (diphtheria, *Haemophilus influenzae* infection, hepatitis A and B, measles, mumps, whooping cough, pneumococcal disease, polio, rubella, congenital rubella, smallpox, tetanus, and chickenpox), but the failure of parents to vaccinate their children has allowed recent outbreaks of several of these diseases. For example, although measles was declared to be eliminated in the United States in 2000, in 2015 vaccination gaps allowed measles to spread to 166 persons in 19 states.

Global Trends in Emerging Infectious Diseases

Emerging infectious diseases are a concern because of economic costs and public health issues. These diseases are not evenly distributed throughout the world. The most important factors determining where new infectious diseases will emerge are (1) the rate of human population growth and the density of the human population, and (2) the number of species of wild mammals. Most pathogens responsible for emerging infectious diseases are spread to humans by animals—wildlife, pets and livestock, and vectors. As we have seen, the development of drug resistance in some pathogens has also led to emergent infectious diseases.

Epidemiology

Epidemiology is the study of patterns of disease, including rate of occurrence, distribution, and control. Most diseases can be described as having one of the following four patterns:

- *Sporadic diseases* occur only occasionally at unpredictable intervals. They affect a few people within a restricted area.
- *Endemic diseases* are always present in a population and pose little threat. The common cold provides an example.

- An *epidemic disease* occurs suddenly and spreads rapidly to many people. Outbreaks of smallpox and cholera are examples of epidemics.
- A *pandemic* is a global outbreak of disease. HIV/AIDS is considered to be a pandemic.

Epidemiologists are "disease detectives" who try to determine why a disease is triggered at a particular time and place. The first step in answering this question is to verify that there is indeed a disease outbreak, defined as more than the expected number of cases of individuals with similar symptoms in a given area. Next, epidemiologists try to identify what causes the disease; whether it can be transmitted to other people; and, if it can be, how the disease is transmitted. To identify the cause of an infectious disease, epidemiologists try to isolate the same infectious agent from all people showing symptoms of the condition. They also try to identify factors—including age, sex, race, personal habits, and geographic location—shared by people with symptoms of the condition. These factors might provide a clue as to whether the condition can be transmitted and how.

LOOKING AHEAD

In this chapter, we considered infectious diseases—the pathogens that cause them, the methods by which they spread, reasons for emerging and reemerging diseases, and the epidemiologists who track the causes. In Chapter 14, we examine the respiratory system, which brings life-giving oxygen into the body and rids the body of carbon dioxide.

CONSIDER THIS CASE

Casey and her roommate were very excited that spring semester was coming to a close. Finals were over and it was the first very warm day of the year, so they decided to celebrate by sharing a sundae at their favorite ice cream shop in town. The next morning they visited Health Services because they were both vomiting and had diarrhea, and their muscles ached. The doctor discovered they had a fever. A stool sample revealed that they had listeriosis, a foodborne bacterial infection that kills one in five people infected. The doctor asked them for a list of all the foods and drinks they had consumed in the previous 3 days and the places where the items were obtained. The dining commons was cleared because they were the only two students affected. However, several other people in the neighborhood had similar symptoms. Over the next few weeks, clusters of people scattered across the country were sickened by *Listeria* organisms.

- Why did the doctor test a stool sample?
- Why did the doctor ask for a list of the foods and drinks the students consumed during the previous days and the locations at which they were consumed?
- What do you think was the source of the food poisoning?
- Why would there be outbreaks across the country?

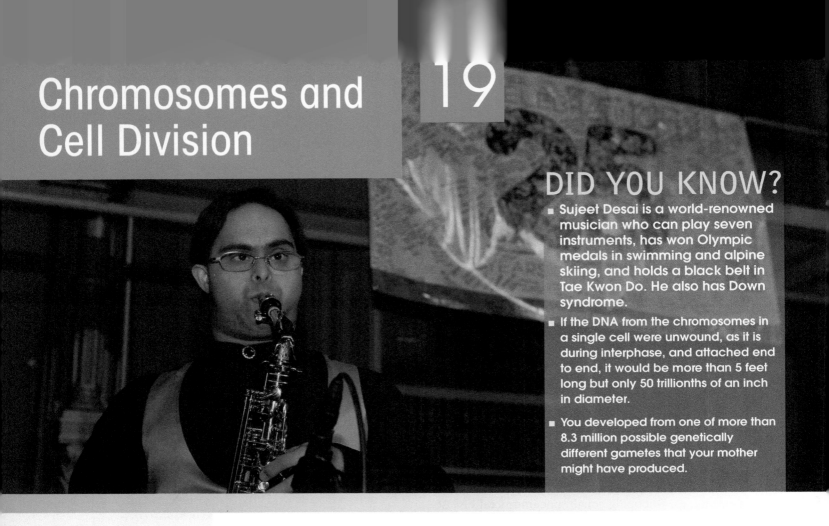

Chromosomes and Cell Division

19

DID YOU KNOW?

- Sujeet Desai is a world-renowned musician who can play seven instruments, has won Olympic medals in swimming and alpine skiing, and holds a black belt in Tae Kwon Do. He also has Down syndrome.

- If the DNA from the chromosomes in a single cell were unwound, as it is during interphase, and attached end to end, it would be more than 5 feet long but only 50 trillionths of an inch in diameter.

- You developed from one of more than 8.3 million possible genetically different gametes that your mother might have produced.

IN THE PREVIOUS FEW CHAPTERS, we considered reproduction and development. In this chapter, we examine the role of two types of cell division, mitosis and meiosis, in the human life cycle. We consider the physical basis of heredity—the chromosomes—and how the chromosomes are parceled out during mitosis and meiosis. We finish the chapter by examining why it is important for each cell to have the correct number of chromosomes.

19.1 Two Types of Cell Division

We begin life as a single cell called a *zygote,* formed by the union of an egg and a sperm. By adulthood, our bodies consist of trillions of cells. What happened in the intervening years? How did we go from a single cell to the multitude of cells that make up the tissues of a fully functional adult? The answer is cell division, which happened over and over again as we grew. Even in adults, many cells continue to divide for growth and repair of body tissues. With very few exceptions, each of those cells carries the same genetic information as its ancestors. The type of nuclear division that results in identical body cells is called *mitosis.*

In Chapter 17, you learned that males and females produce specialized reproductive cells known as gametes (eggs or sperm). You'll recall that *meiosis* is a special type of nuclear division that gives rise to gametes. In females, meiosis occurs in the ovaries and produces eggs. In males, meiosis occurs in the testes and produces sperm. Meiosis is important because through it the gametes end up with half the amount of genetic information (half the number of chromosomes) in the original cell. When the nuclei of an egg and sperm unite (fertilization), the chromosome number is restored to that of the original cell. As a result, the number of chromosomes in body cells remains constant from one generation to the next.

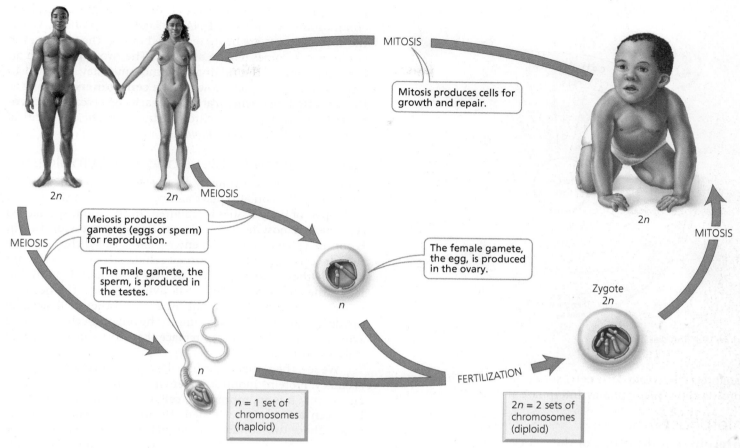

MITOSIS

Mitosis produces cells for growth and repair.

2n

2n

MEIOSIS

MEIOSIS

Meiosis produces gametes (eggs or sperm) for reproduction.

The male gamete, the sperm, is produced in the testes.

The female gamete, the egg, is produced in the ovary.

n

n

2n

MITOSIS

Zygote
2n

FERTILIZATION

n = 1 set of chromosomes (haploid)

2*n* = 2 sets of chromosomes (diploid)

Figure 19.1 The human life cycle

The roles of mitosis (which produces new body cells) and meiosis (which forms gametes) are summarized in the diagram of the human life cycle in Figure 19.1. You will learn more about both mitosis and meiosis later in this chapter.

19.2 Form of Chromosomes

A **chromosome** is a tightly coiled combination of a DNA molecule (which contains genetic information for the organism) and specialized proteins called *histones*. Chromosomes are found in the cell nucleus. The information contained in the DNA molecules in chromosomes directs the development and maintenance of the body. The histones combined with the DNA are for support and control of gene activity. A **gene** is a specific segment of the DNA that directs the synthesis of a protein, which in turn plays a structural or functional role within the cell. By coding for a specific protein, a gene determines the expression of a particular characteristic, or trait. Each chromosome in a human cell contains a specific assortment of genes. Like beads on a string, genes are arranged in a fixed sequence along the length of specific chromosomes.

In the human body, **somatic cells**—that is, all cells except eggs or sperm—have 46 chromosomes. Those 46 chromosomes are actually 23 pairs of chromosomes. One member of each pair came from the mother's egg, and another member of each pair came from the father's sperm. Thus, each cell contains 23

homologous chromosome pairs, a pair being two chromosomes (one from the mother and one from the father) with genes for the same traits. Homologous pairs are called *homologues* for short. Any cell with two of each kind of chromosome is described as being **diploid** (annotated as **2n**, with *n* representing the number of each kind of chromosome). In diploid cells, then, genes also occur in pairs. The members of each gene pair are located at the same position on homologous chromosomes.

One of the 23 pairs of chromosomes consists of the **sex chromosomes** that determine whether a person is male or female. There are two types of sex chromosomes, X and Y. A person who has two X chromosomes is described as XX and is genetically female; a person who has an X and a Y chromosome is described as XY and is genetically male. The other 22 pairs of chromosomes are called the **autosomes.** The autosomes determine the expression of most of a person's inherited characteristics.

19.3 The Cell Cycle

In **mitosis,** one nucleus divides into two daughter nuclei containing the same number and kinds of chromosomes. But mitosis is only one phase during the life of a dividing cell. The entire sequence of events that a cell goes through, from its origin in the division of its parent cell through its own division into two

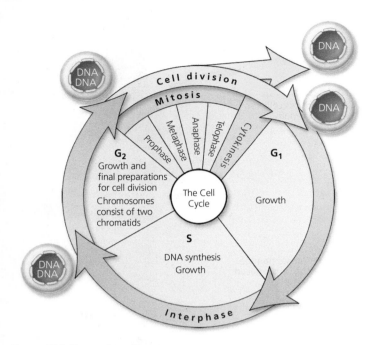

Figure 19.2 The cell cycle

daughter cells, is called the **cell cycle** (Figure 19.2). The cell cycle consists of two major phases: interphase and cell division.

Interphase

Interphase is the period of the cell cycle between cell divisions. It accounts for most of the time that elapses during a cell cycle. During active growth and divisions (depending on the type of cell), an entire cell cycle might take about 16 to 24 hours to complete, and only 1 to 2 hours are spent in division. Interphase is not a "resting period," as once thought. Instead, interphase is a time when the cell carries out its functions and grows. If the cell is going to divide, interphase is a time of intense preparation for cell division. During interphase, the DNA and organelles are duplicated. These preparations ensure that when the cell divides, each of its resulting cells, called *daughter cells,* will receive the essentials for survival.

Interphase consists of three parts: G_1 (first "gap"), S (DNA synthesis), and G_2 (second "gap"). All three parts of interphase are times of cell growth, characterized by the production of organelles and the synthesis of proteins and other macromolecules. There are, however, some events specific to certain parts of interphase:

- G_1: A time of major growth before DNA synthesis begins
- S: The time during which DNA is synthesized (replicated)
- G_2: A time of growth after DNA is synthesized and before mitosis begins

The details of DNA synthesis (replication) are described in Chapter 21. Our discussion in this chapter introduces some basic terminology pertaining to the cell cycle.

Throughout interphase, the genetic material is in the form of long, thin threads that are often called *chromatin* (Figure 19.3). They twist randomly around one another like tangled strands of yarn. In this state, DNA can be synthesized (replicated), and

genes can be active. At the start of interphase, during G_1, each chromosome consists of a DNA molecule and proteins. When the chromosomes are being replicated during the S phase, the chromosome copies remain attached. The two copies, each an exact replicate of the original chromosome, stay attached to one another at a region known as the **centromere.** As long as the replicate copies remain attached, each copy is called a **chromatid.** The two attached chromatids are genetically identical and are referred to as *sister chromatids.*

Division of the Nucleus and the Cytoplasm

Body cells divide continually in the developing embryo and fetus. Such division also plays an important role in the growth and repair of body tissues in children. In the adult, specialized cells, such as most nerve cells, lose their ability to divide. Late in G_1 of interphase, these cells enter what is called the G_0 stage: they are carrying out their normal cellular activities but do not divide. Other adult cells, such as liver cells, stop dividing but retain the ability to undergo cell division should the need for tissue repair and replacement arise. Still other cells actively divide throughout life. For example, the ongoing cell division of skin cells in adults serves to replace the enormous numbers of cells worn off each day.

We see, then, that the cell cycle requires precise timing and accuracy. Proteins monitor the environment within the cell to ensure that it is appropriate for cell division and that the DNA has been accurately replicated. Healthy cells will not divide unless these two conditions are met. However, as we will see in Chapter 21a, cancer cells escape this regulation and divide uncontrollably.

The division of body cells (after interphase) consists of two processes that overlap somewhat in time. The first process, division of the nucleus, is called *mitosis.* The second is *cytokinesis,* the division of the cytoplasm that occurs toward the end of mitosis (Figure 19.4).

19.4 Mitosis: Creation of Genetically Identical Diploid Body Cells

For the purpose of discussion, mitosis is usually divided into four stages: prophase, metaphase, anaphase, and telophase. Keep in mind, however, that mitosis is a dynamic process. It continues through the stages without stopping. The major events of each stage are depicted in Figure 19.5, p. 398.

- **Prophase.** Mitosis begins with **prophase,** a time when changes occur in the nucleus as well as the cytoplasm. In the nucleus, the chromatin condenses and forms chromosomes as DNA wraps around histones. The DNA then loops and twists to form a tightly compacted structure (see Figure 19.3). When DNA is in this condensed state, it cannot be replicated, and gene activity is shut down. In this condensed state, the sister chromatids are easier to separate without breaking. At about this time, the nuclear membrane also begins to break down.

  Outside the nucleus, in the cytoplasm, the mitotic spindle forms. The mitotic spindle is made of microtubules associated with the centrioles (see Chapter 3). During

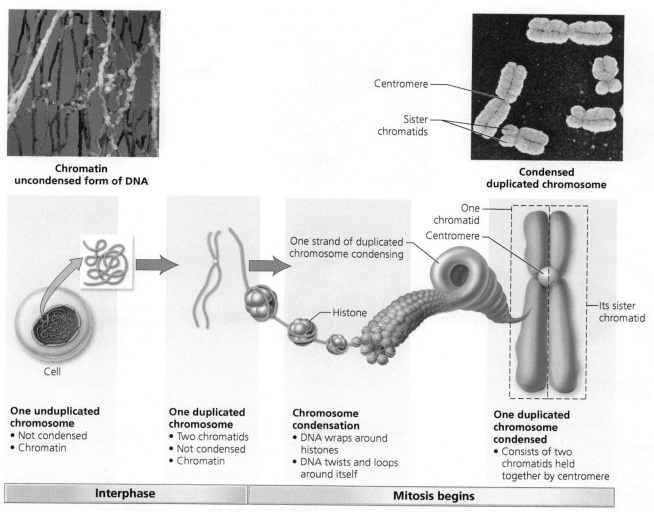

Figure 19.3 Changes in chromosome structure due to DNA replication during interphase and preparation for nuclear division in mitosis

Q: Describe the difference in the structure of a chromosome between the start of interphase and the end of interphase.

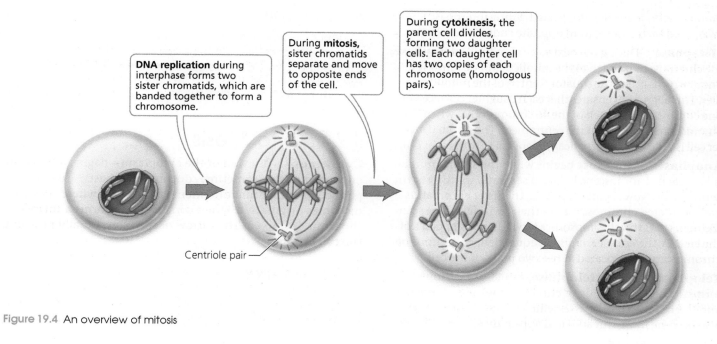

Figure 19.4 An overview of mitosis

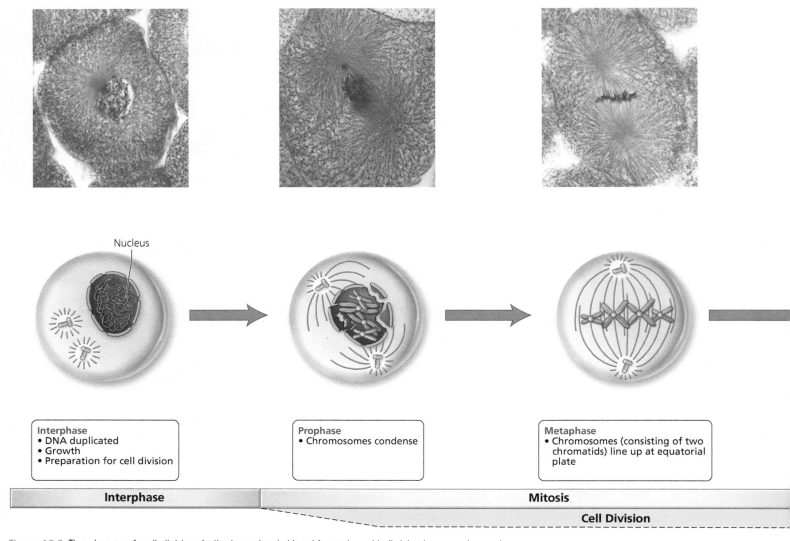

Figure 19.5 The stages of cell division (mitosis and cytokinesis) captured in light micrographs and depicted in schematic drawings

prophase, the centrioles, duplicated during interphase, move away from each other toward opposite ends of the cell.

- **Metaphase.** During the next stage of mitosis, **metaphase,** the chromosomes attach to the mitotic spindles, forming a line at what is called the equator (center) of the mitotic spindles. This alignment ensures that each daughter cell receives one chromatid from each of the 46 chromosomes when the chromosomes separate at the centromere. Thus, each daughter cell is a diploid cell genetically identical to the parent cell.

- **Anaphase.** **Anaphase** begins when the sister chromatids of each chromosome begin to separate, splitting at the centromere. Now separate entities, the sister chromatids are considered chromosomes in their own right. The spindle fibers pull the chromosomes toward opposite poles of the cell. By the end of anaphase, equivalent collections of chromosomes are located at the two poles of the cell.

- **Telophase.** During **telophase,** a nuclear envelope forms around each group of chromosomes at each pole, and the mitotic spindle disassembles. The chromosomes also become more threadlike in appearance.

STOP and **THINK**

Cancer cells divide frequently and without end. One type of drug used in cancer chemotherapy inhibits the formation of spindle fibers. Why can this be an effective anticancer treatment?

19.5 Cytokinesis

Cytokinesis—division of the cytoplasm—begins toward the end of mitosis, sometime during telophase. During this period, a band of microfilaments in the area where the chromosomes originally aligned contracts and forms a furrow, as shown in Figure 19.6. The furrow deepens, eventually pinching the cell in two.

STOP and **THINK**

What would happen if a cell completed mitosis but did not complete cytokinesis?

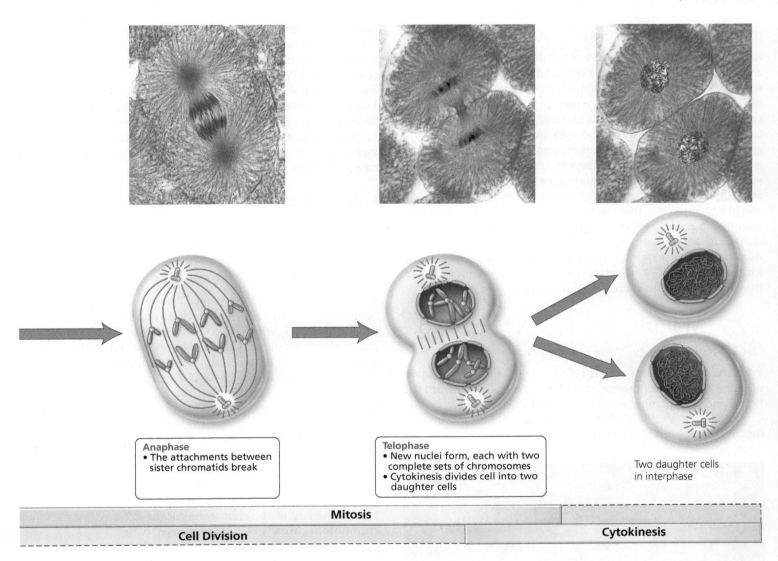

Anaphase
- The attachments between sister chromatids break

Telophase
- New nuclei form, each with two complete sets of chromosomes
- Cytokinesis divides cell into two daughter cells

Two daughter cells in interphase

Mitosis

Cell Division

Cytokinesis

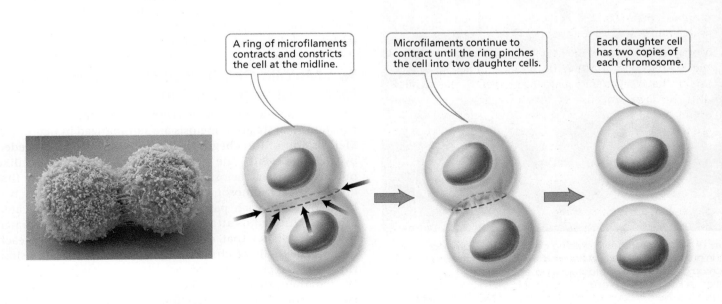

A ring of microfilaments contracts and constricts the cell at the midline.

Microfilaments continue to contract until the ring pinches the cell into two daughter cells.

Each daughter cell has two copies of each chromosome.

Figure 19.6 Cytokinesis is the division of the cytoplasm to form two daughter cells.

19.6 Karyotypes

As we have seen, a major feature of cell division is the shortening and thickening of the chromosomes. In this state, the chromosomes are visible with a light microscope and can be used for diagnostic purposes, such as when potential parents want to check their own chromosomal makeup for defects. One often-used method takes white blood cells from a blood sample and grows them for a while in a nourishing medium. The culture then is treated with a drug that destroys the mitotic spindle, thus preventing separation of the chromosomes and halting cell division at metaphase. Next the cells are preserved from decay, stained, and photographed so that the images of the chromosomes can be arranged in pairs based on physical characteristics, such as location of the centromere and overall length. The chromosomes are numbered from largest to smallest, in an arrangement called a **karyotype** (Figure 19.7). Karyotypes can be checked for irregularities in number or structure of chromosomes.

19.7 Meiosis: Creation of Haploid Gametes

We have seen that the somatic cells contain a homologous pair of each type of chromosome, one member of each pair from the father and one member of each pair from the mother.

Recall that a cell with homologous pairs of chromosomes is described as being diploid, $2n$. The gametes—eggs or sperm—differ

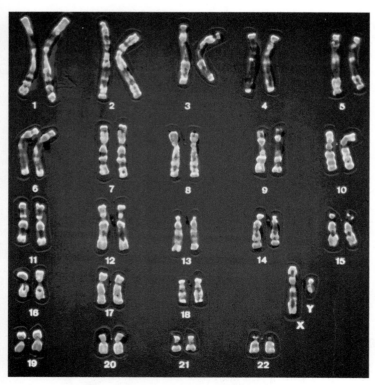

Figure 19.7 Chromosomes in dividing cells can be examined for defects in number or structure. A karyotype is constructed by arranging the chromosomes from photographs based on size and centromere location. A karyotype is prepared just prior to cell division, so each chromosome here is duplicated and consists of two chromatids.

from somatic cells in that they are **haploid,** indicated by n, meaning that they have only one member of each homologous pair of chromosomes. As you read earlier in the chapter, gametes are produced by a type of cell division called **meiosis,** which is actually two divisions that result in up to four haploid daughter cells. When a sperm fertilizes an egg, a new cell—the zygote—is created. Because the egg and sperm both contribute a set of chromosomes to the zygote, it is diploid. After many mitotic cell divisions, a zygote and its descendant cells can eventually develop into a new individual.

Functions of Meiosis

Meiosis serves two important functions in sexual reproduction:

- Meiosis keeps the number of chromosomes in a body cell constant from generation to generation.
- Meiosis increases genetic variability in the population.

Meiosis keeps the number of chromosomes in a body cell constant over generations because it creates haploid gametes (sperm and eggs) with only one member of each homologous pair of chromosomes. If gametes were produced by mitosis, they would be diploid; each sperm and egg would contain 46 chromosomes instead of 23. Then, if a sperm containing 46 chromosomes fertilized an egg with 46 chromosomes, the zygote would have 92 chromosomes. The zygote of the next generation would have 184 chromosomes, having been formed by an egg and sperm that each contained 92 chromosomes. The next generation would have 368 chromosomes in each cell, and the next one 736—and so on. You can see that the chromosome number would quickly become unwieldy and, more importantly, alter the amount of genetic information in each cell. As we will see toward the end of the chapter, even one extra copy of a single chromosome usually causes an embryo to die.

Meiosis also increases genetic variability in the population. Later in this chapter we consider the mechanisms by which it accomplishes this increase. Genetic variability is important because it provides the raw material through which natural selection can act, leading to the changes described collectively as evolution. The relationship between genetic variability and evolution is discussed in Chapter 22.

Two Meiotic Cell Divisions: Preparation for Sexual Reproduction

First, let's consider how meiosis keeps the chromosome number constant. The stages in meiosis are summarized in Figure 19.8. Meiosis and mitosis begin the same way. Both are preceded by the same event—the replication of chromosomes. Unlike mitosis, however, meiosis involves *two* divisions. In the first division, the chromosome number is reduced because the two homologues of each pair of chromosomes (each replicated into two chromatids attached by a centromere) are separated into two cells so that each cell has one member of each homologous pair of chromosomes. In the second division, the replicated chromatids of each chromosome are separated. We see, then, that meiosis begins with one diploid cell and, two divisions later, produces four haploid cells. The orderly

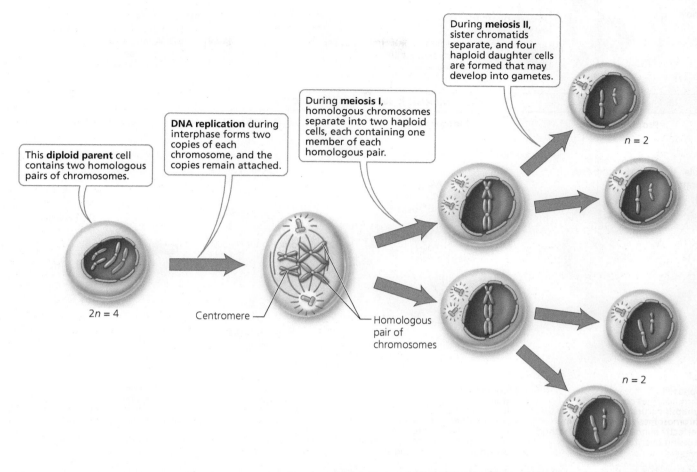

This **diploid parent** cell contains two homologous pairs of chromosomes.

DNA replication during interphase forms two copies of each chromosome, and the copies remain attached.

During **meiosis I**, homologous chromosomes separate into two haploid cells, each containing one member of each homologous pair.

During **meiosis II**, sister chromatids separate, and four haploid daughter cells are formed that may develop into gametes.

2*n* = 4

Centromere

Homologous pair of chromosomes

n = 2

n = 2

Figure 19.8 Overview of meiosis. Meiosis reduces the chromosome number from the diploid number to the haploid number. Meiosis involves two cell divisions.

movements of chromosomes during meiosis ensure that each haploid gamete produced contains one member of each homologous pair of chromosomes. Although not shown in the summary figure, each of the two meiotic divisions has four stages similar to those in mitosis: prophase, metaphase, anaphase, and telophase.

Meiosis I The first meiotic division—meiosis I—produces two cells, each with 23 chromosomes. Note that the daughter cells do not contain a random assortment of any 23 chromosomes. Instead, each daughter cell contains one member of each homologous pair, with each chromosome consisting of two sister chromatids.

It is important that each daughter cell receive one of each kind of chromosome during meiosis I. If one of the daughter cells had two of chromosome 3 and no chromosome 6, it would not survive. Although 23 chromosomes would still be present, part of the instructions for the structure and function of the body (chromosome 6) would be missing. The separation of homologous chromosomes occurs reliably during meiosis I because, during prophase I (the *I* indicates this phase takes place during meiosis I), members of homologous pairs line up next to one another by a phenomenon called **synapsis** ("bringing together"). For example, the chromosome 1 that was originally

from your father would line up with the chromosome 1 originally from your mother. Paternal chromosome 2 would pair with maternal chromosome 2, and so on. During metaphase I, matched homologous pairs become positioned at the midline of the cell and attach to spindle fibers. The pairing of homologous chromosomes helps ensure that the daughter cells will receive one member of each homologous pair. Consider the following analogy. By pairing your socks before putting them in a drawer, you are more likely to put matching socks on your feet than if you randomly pulled out two socks.

Next, during anaphase I, the members of each homologous pair of chromosomes separate, and each homologue moves to opposite ends of the cell. During telophase I, cytokinesis begins, resulting in two daughter cells, each with one member of each chromosome pair. Each chromosome in each daughter cell still consists of two replicated sister chromatids. Telophase I is followed by *interkinesis,* a brief interphase-like period. Interkinesis differs from mitotic interphase in that no replication of DNA takes place during interkinesis.

Meiosis II During the second meiotic division—meiosis II—each chromosome lines up in the center of the cell independently (as occurs in mitosis), and the sister chromatids (attached replicates) making up each chromosome separate. Separation of

Interphase

Centriole pairs — DNA

Premeiotic Interphase
- DNA replicates
- Copies remain attached to one another by centromere
- Each copy is called a chromatid

Interkinesis
- A brief interphase-like period
- No DNA replication occurs during interkinesis
- DNA is chromatin

Meiosis I: Separates Homologues

Prophase I **Metaphase I** **Anaphase I** **Telophase I and Cytokinesis**

Spindle apparatus

Synapsis Sister chromatids

Homologues separate

Centromere

Prophase I
- Chromosomes condense
- Synapsis occurs (homologous chromosomes pair and become perfectly aligned with one another)
- Crossing over takes place

Metaphase I
- Homologous pairs of chromosomes line up at the midline of the cell
- Spindle fiber from one pole attaches to one member of each pair while spindle fiber from opposite pole attaches to the homologue

Anaphase I
- Homologous pairs of chromosomes separate and move to opposite ends of the cell
- Each homologue still consists of two chromatids

Telophase I
- One member of each homologous pair is at each pole
- Cytokinesis occurs and forms two haploid daughter cells
- Each chromosome still consists of two chromatids

Two important sources of genetic variation

Recombination due to crossing over occurs during prophase I. Parts of nonsister chromatids are exchanged.

Independent assortment occurs during metaphase I. Maternal and paternal members of homologous pairs align randomly at the equatorial plate, so when they separate during meiosis they form a random combination of maternal and paternal chromosomes in the daughter cells.

Meiosis II: Separates Sister Chromatids

Prophase II **Metaphase II** **Anaphase II** **Telophase II and Cytokinesis**

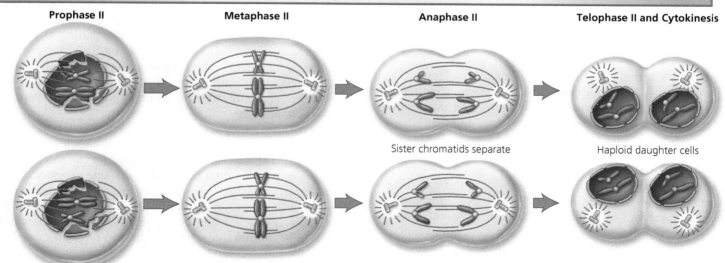

Sister chromatids separate

Haploid daughter cells

Prophase II
- Chromosomes condense again
- Occurs in both daughter cells

Metaphase II
- Chromosomes line up at the midline of the cell

Anaphase II
- Centromeres of sister chromatids separate
- Chromatids of each pair are now called chromosomes
- Chromosomes move to opposite poles

Telophase II
- One complete set of chromosomes is located at each pole
- Cytokinesis occurs in both daughter cells, forming four haploid daughter cells

Figure 19.9 Stages of meiosis

the sister chromatids occurs in both daughter cells that were produced in meiosis I. This event results in four cells, each containing one of each kind of chromosome. The events of meiosis II are similar to those of mitosis, except that only 23 chromosomes are lining up independently in meiosis II compared with the 46 chromosomes aligning independently in mitosis. Figure 19.9 depicts the events of meiosis. Table 19.1 and Figure 19.10 compare mitosis and meiosis.

Subsequent changes in the shape and functioning of the four haploid cells result in functional gametes. In males, one diploid cell can result in four functional sperm. In contrast, in females, meiotic divisions of one diploid cell result in only one functional egg and up to three nonfunctional cells called *polar*

Table 19.1	Mitosis and Meiosis Compared
Mitosis	**Meiosis**
Involves one cell division	Involves two cell divisions
Produces two diploid cells	Produces up to four haploid cells
Occurs in somatic cells	Occurs only in ovaries and testes during the formation of gametes (egg and sperm)
Results in growth and repair	Results in gamete (egg and sperm) production
No exchange of genetic material	Parts of chromosomes are exchanged in crossing over
Daughter cells are genetically similar	Daughter cells are genetically dissimilar

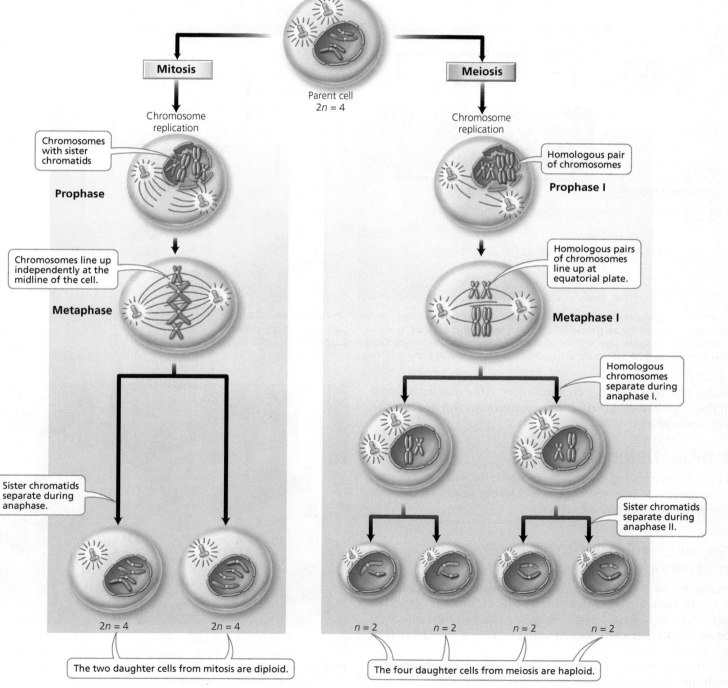

Figure 19.10 A comparison of meiosis and mitosis

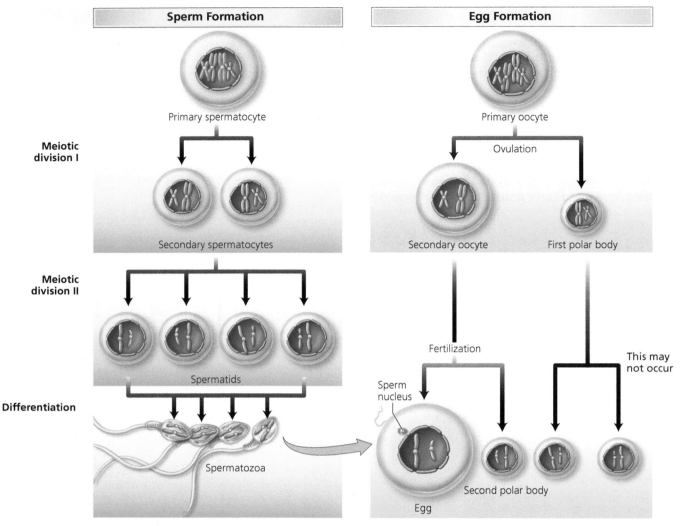

Figure 19.11 Comparison of spermatogenesis and oogenesis. Meiosis results in haploid cells that differentiate into mature gametes. Spermatogenesis produces four sperm cells that are specialized to transport the male's genetic information to the egg. Oogenesis produces up to three polar bodies and one ovum that is packed with nutrients to nourish the early embryo.

bodies. As a result, the egg contains most of the nutrients found in the original diploid cell, and these nutrients will nourish the early embryo (Figure 19.11).

STOP and THINK

If you were examining dividing cells under a microscope, how could you determine whether a particular cell was in metaphase of mitosis or metaphase I of meiosis?

Genetic Variability: Crossing Over and Independent Assortment

At the moment of fertilization, when the nuclei of an egg and a sperm fuse, a new, *unique* individual is formed. Although certain family characteristics may be passed along, each child bears his or her own assortment of genetic characteristics (Figure 19.12).

Genetic variation arises largely because of the shuffling of maternal and paternal forms of genes during meiosis. One way

Figure 19.12 Each child inherits a unique combination of maternal and paternal genetic characteristics due to the shuffling of chromosomes that occurs during meiosis. This photograph shows Eric and Mary Goodenough with their four sons: Derick, Stephen, David, and John.

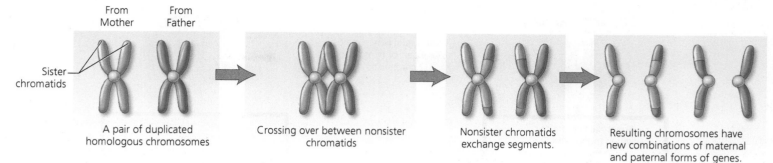

Figure 19.13 Crossing over. During synapsis, when the homologous chromosomes of the mother and the father are closely aligned, corresponding segments of nonsister chromatids are exchanged. Each of the affected chromatids has a mixture of maternal and paternal genetic information.

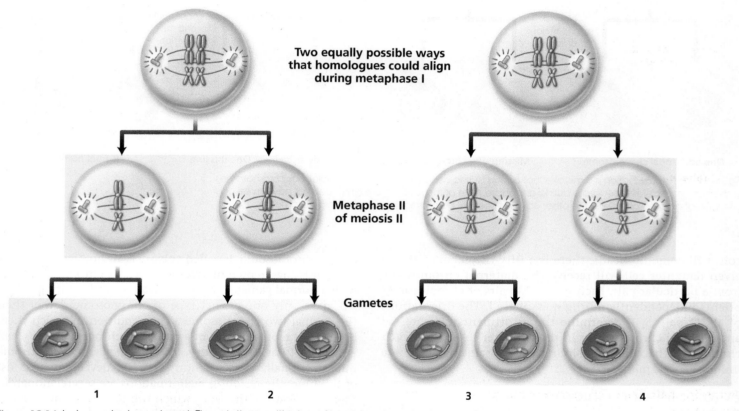

Figure 19.14 Independent assortment. The relative positioning of homologous maternal and paternal chromosomes with respect to the poles of the cell is random. The members of each homologous pair orient independently of the other pairs. Notice that with only two homologous pairs, there are four possible combinations of chromosomes in the resulting gametes.

this mixing occurs is through a process called **crossing over,** in which corresponding pieces of chromatids of maternal and paternal homologues (nonsister chromatids) are exchanged during synapsis when the homologues are aligned side by side. After crossing over, the affected chromatids have a mixture of DNA from the two parents. Because the homologues align gene by gene during synapsis, the exchanged segments contain genetic information for the same traits. However, because the genes of the mother and those of the father may direct different expressions of the trait—attached or unattached earlobes, for

instance—the chromatids affected by crossing over have a novel combination of genes. Thus, crossing over increases the genetic variability of gametes (Figure 19.13).

Independent assortment is a second way that meiosis provides for the shuffling of genes between generations (Figure 19.14). Recall that the homologous pairs of chromosomes line up at the equator (midpoint) of the mitotic spindles during metaphase I. However, the orientation of the members of the pair is random with respect to which member is closer to which pole. Thus, like the odds that a flipped

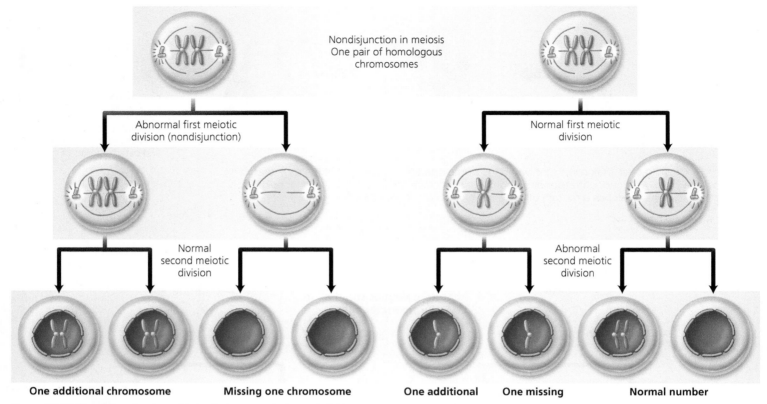

Figure 19.15 Nondisjunction is a mistake that occurs during cell division in which homologous chromosomes or sister chromatids fail to separate during anaphase. One of the resulting daughter cells will have three of one type of chromosome, and the other daughter cell will be missing that type of chromosome.

coin will come up heads, there is a fifty-fifty chance that a given daughter cell will receive the maternal chromosome from a particular pair. Each of the 23 pairs of chromosomes orients independently during metaphase I. The orientations of all 23 pairs will determine the assortments of maternal and paternal chromosomes in the daughter cells. Thus, each child (other than identical siblings) of the same parents has a unique genetic makeup.

Extra or Missing Chromosomes

Most of the time, meiosis is a precise process that results in the even distribution of chromosomes to gametes. But meiosis is not foolproof. A pair of chromosomes or sister chromatids may adhere so tightly to one another that they do not separate during anaphase. As a result, both go to the same daughter cell, and the other daughter cell receives none of this type of chromosome (Figure 19.15). The failure of homologous chromosomes to separate during meiosis I or of sister chromatids to separate during meiosis II is called **nondisjunction.**

What happens if nondisjunction creates a gamete with an extra or a missing chromosome and that gamete is then united with a normal gamete during fertilization? The resulting zygote will have an excess or deficit of chromosomes. For instance, if the abnormal gamete has an extra chromosome, the resulting zygote will have three of one type of chromosome and two of the rest. This condition, in which there are three representatives

of one chromosome, is called **trisomy.** If, however, a gamete that is missing a representative of one type of chromosome joins with a normal gamete during fertilization, the resulting zygote will have only one of that type of chromosome, rather than the normal two chromosomes. The condition in which there is only one representative of a particular chromosome in a cell is referred to as **monosomy.** The imbalance of chromosome numbers usually causes abnormalities in development. Most of the time, the resulting malformations are severe enough to cause the death of the fetus, which will result in a miscarriage. Indeed, in about 70% of miscarriages, the fetus has an abnormal number of chromosomes.

When a fetus inherits an abnormal number of certain chromosomes—for instance, chromosome 21 or the sex chromosomes—the resulting condition is usually not fatal (see the Ethical Issue essay, *Trisomy 21*, p. 408). The upset in chromosome balance does, however, cause a specific syndrome. (A *syndrome* is a group of symptoms that generally occur together.)

Like autosomes, sex chromosomes may fail to separate during anaphase. This error can occur during either egg or sperm formation. A male is chromosomally XY, so when the X and Y separate during anaphase, equal numbers of X-bearing and Y-bearing sperm are produced. However, if nondisjunction of the sex chromosomes occurs during sperm formation, half of the resulting sperm will carry both X and Y chromosomes, whereas the other resulting sperm will not

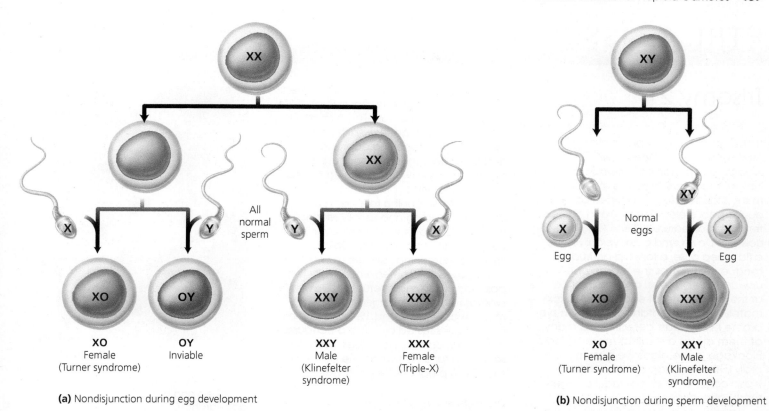

Figure 19.16 The sex chromosomes may fail to separate during formation of a gamete. Here, an egg with an abnormal number of sex chromosomes joins a normal sperm in fertilization; the resulting zygote has an abnormal number of sex chromosomes. Imbalances of sex chromosomes upset normal development of reproductive structures.

contain any sex chromosome. A female is chromosomally XX, so each of the eggs she produces should contain a single X chromosome. When nondisjunction of sex chromosomes occurs, however, an egg may contain two X chromosomes or none at all. When a gamete with an abnormal number of sex chromosomes is joined with a normal gamete during fertilization, the resulting zygote has an abnormal number of sex chromosomes (Figure 19.16.

Turner syndrome occurs in individuals who have only a single X chromosome (XO). Approximately 1 in 5000 female infants is born with Turner syndrome, but this represents only a small percentage of the XO zygotes that are formed. Most of these XO zygotes are lost as miscarriages. A person with Turner syndrome has the external appearance of a female. The only hint of Turner syndrome may be a thick fold of skin on the neck. As she ages, however, she generally is noticeably shorter than her peers. Her chest is wide, and her breasts underdeveloped. In 90% of women with Turner syndrome, the ovaries are also poorly developed, leading to infertility. Pregnancy may be possible through in vitro fertilization (see Chapter 18), in which a fertilized egg from a donor is implanted in her uterus.

Klinefelter syndrome is observed in males who are XXY. Although the extra X chromosome can be inherited as a result

of nondisjunction during either egg or sperm formation, it is twice as likely to come from the egg. Increased maternal age may raise the risk slightly.

Klinefelter syndrome is fairly common. Approximately 1 in 500 to 1 in 1000 of all newborn males is XXY. However, not all XXY males display the symptoms of having an extra X chromosome. In fact, some of them live their lives without ever suspecting they are XXY. When there are signs that a male has Klinefelter syndrome, they do not usually show up until puberty. During the teenage years, the testes of an XY male gradually increase in size. In contrast, the testes of many XXY males remain small and do not produce an adequate amount of the male sex hormone, testosterone. As a result of testosterone insufficiency, these males may grow taller than average but remain less muscular. Secondary sex characteristics, such as facial and body hair, may fail to develop fully. The breasts may also develop slightly. The penis is usually of normal size, but the testes may not produce sperm; so, men with Klinefelter syndrome may be sterile.

Nondisjunction can also result in a female with three X chromosomes (XXX, triple-X syndrome) or a male with two Y chromosomes (XYY, Jacob syndrome, produced when the chromatids of a replicated Y chromosome fail to separate). Most women with triple-X syndrome (XXX) have normal

ETHICAL ISSUE

Trisomy 21

One in every 700 infants is born with three copies of chromosome 21 (trisomy 21), a condition known as *Down syndrome*. Symptoms of Down syndrome include moderate to severe mental impairment, short stature or shortened body parts due to poor skeletal growth, and characteristic facial features (Figure 19.A). Individuals with Down syndrome typically have a flattened nose, a forward-protruding tongue that forces the mouth open, upward-slanting eyes, and a fold of skin at the inner corner of each eye. Approximately 50% of all infants with Down syndrome have heart defects, and many of them die as a result of these defects. Blockage in the digestive system, especially in the esophagus or small intestine, is also common and may require surgery shortly after birth.

The risk of having a baby with Down syndrome increases with the mother's age. A 30-year-old woman is twice as likely to give birth to a child with Down syndrome as is a 20-year-old woman. After age 30, the risk rises dramatically. At age 45, a mother is 45 times as likely to give birth to a Down syndrome infant as is a 20-year-old woman.

Today, people with Down syndrome live longer and with a higher quality of life than they did in the past. These improvements are due to better health care, more effective teaching approaches, and a greater range of opportunities. Life expectancy is now approaching 60 years in many countries.

Prenatal screening for Down syndrome is common and usually recommended for pregnant women over 30 years of age. Approximately 95% of the "positive" screening tests are wrong. Nonetheless, *all* women who initially test positive for carrying a fetus with Down syndrome are encouraged to undergo more invasive tests, and 1% to 2% of the pregnancies tested by these procedures end in miscarriage. As a result, prenatal screening for Down syndrome poses a risk to 700,000 pregnancies each year.

Questions to Consider

Down Syndrome International is encouraging reviews of screening policies and public debate about the acceptance of genetic screening for mental and physical disabilities.

■ If you or a loved one were pregnant, would you advocate for prenatal screening for Down syndrome? Why or why not?

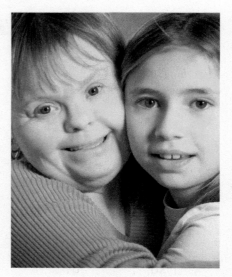

Figure 19.A A person with Down syndrome (shown on left) may be moderately to severely mentally impaired and has a characteristic appearance.

■ Who should pay for prenatal screening? The person? The health insurer? The government?

■ Do you agree that genetic screening for mental and physical disabilities should be recommended?

---

sexual development and are able to conceive children. Some triple-X females have learning disabilities and delayed language skills. Males with two Y chromosomes (XYY) are often taller than normal, and some have slightly lower than normal intelligence.

what would YOU do? If you had a son with Klinefelter syndrome, would you want him to have testosterone treatments after puberty? ■

LOOKING AHEAD

In this chapter, we considered cell division: mitosis, which gives rise to new body cells for growth and repair; and meiosis, which gives rise to the gametes (eggs and sperm). In Chapter 19a, we consider mitosis further and explore stem

cells, which are unspecialized cells that can divide continuously and develop into different tissue types.

CONSIDER THIS CASE

After trying to conceive for quite a while, Laura and her husband are pleased to find out that she is now pregnant. Because she is in her early 40s, she is undergoing prenatal testing to determine whether her fetus has Down syndrome (three copies of chromosome 21). The test results show that the fetus has two copies of chromosome 21, but that he is XYY. The doctor explains that during meiosis, sometimes chromosomes fail to separate, resulting in gametes with too many or too few chromosomes.

■ How would you explain to Laura that the extra chromosome resulted during sperm development?

■ Would you predict that the extra Y chromosome would cause the fetus to die?

Chapter Review

MasteringBiology®

Highlighting the Concepts

19.1 Two Types of Cell Division (pp. 394–395)

- The human life cycle requires two types of nuclear division—mitosis and meiosis. Mitosis, which occurs in growth and repair, creates cells that are exact copies of the original cell. Meiosis creates cells with only one copy of each homologous pair of chromosomes of the original cell. Gamete production requires meiosis.

19.2 Form of Chromosomes (p. 395)

- A chromosome contains DNA and proteins called histones. A gene is a segment of DNA that codes for a protein playing a structural or functional role in the cell. Genes are arranged along a chromosome in a specific order. Each of the 23 different kinds of chromosomes in human cells contains a specific sequence of genes.

- Somatic cells (all cells except eggs and sperm) are diploid; that is, they contain pairs of chromosomes, one member of each pair from each parent. Homologous chromosomes carry genes for the same traits. In humans, the diploid number of chromosomes is 46—or 23 homologous pairs. One pair of chromosomes, the sex chromosomes, determines gender. Males are XY, and females are XX. The other 22 pairs of chromosomes are called autosomes. Eggs and sperm are haploid; they contain only one set of chromosomes.

19.3 The Cell Cycle (pp. 395–396)

- The cell cycle consists of two major phases: interphase and cell division. Interphase is the period between cell divisions.

- During interphase, DNA and organelles become replicated in preparation for the cell to divide and produce two identical daughter cells. Somatic cell division consists of mitosis (division of the nucleus) and cytokinesis (division of the cytoplasm).

19.4 Mitosis: Creation of Genetically Identical Diploid Body Cells (pp. 396–398)

- In mitosis, the original cell, having replicated its genetic material, distributes it equally between its two daughter cells. There are four stages of mitosis: prophase, metaphase, anaphase, and telophase.

19.5 Cytokinesis (pp. 398–399)

- Cytokinesis, division of the cytoplasm, usually begins sometime during telophase. A band of microfilaments at the midline of the cell contracts and forms a furrow. The furrow deepens and eventually pinches the cell in two.

19.6 Karyotypes (p. 400)

- A karyotype is an arrangement of chromosomes based on their physical characteristics, such as length and position of the centromere.

19.7 Meiosis: Creation of Haploid Gametes (pp. 400–408)

- Meiosis, a special type of nuclear division that occurs in the ovaries or testes, begins with a diploid cell and produces up to four haploid cells that will become gametes (eggs or sperm).

- Meiosis is important because it reduces the number of chromosomes in gametes to one member of each pair, thereby keeping the chromosome number constant between generations. When a sperm fertilizes an egg, a diploid cell called a zygote is created. After many successful mitotic divisions, the zygote and its descendant cells may develop into a new individual.

- Before meiosis begins, the chromosomes are replicated, and the copies remain attached to one another by centromeres. The attached replicated copies are called sister chromatids.

- There are two cell divisions in meiosis. During the first meiotic division (meiosis I), members of homologous pairs are separated. Thus, the daughter cells contain only one member of each homologous pair (although each chromosome still consists of two replicated sister chromatids). During the second meiotic division (meiosis II), the sister chromatids are separated.

- Genetic recombination during meiosis results in variation among offspring from the same two parents. One cause of genetic recombination is crossing over, in which corresponding segments of DNA are exchanged between maternal and paternal homologues, creating new combinations of genes in the resulting chromatids.

- A second cause of genetic recombination is the independent assortment of maternal and paternal homologues into daughter cells during meiosis I. The orientation of the members of the pair relative to the poles of the cell determines whether a daughter cell will receive the maternal or the paternal chromosome from a given pair. Each pair aligns independently of the others.

- Nondisjunction is the failure of homologous chromosomes or sister chromatids to separate during cell division. It results in an abnormal number of chromosomes in the resulting gametes, and in zygotes created by fertilization involving these gametes, which generally results in death of the fetus. Nondisjunction of chromosome 21 can result in Down syndrome.

Recognizing Key Terms

chromosome *p. 395*
gene *p. 395*
somatic cells *p. 395*
homologous chromosome pair *p. 395*
diploid *p. 395*
sex chromosomes *p. 395*

autosomes *p. 395*
mitosis *p. 395*
cell cycle *p. 396*
interphase *p. 396*
centromere *p. 396*
chromatid *p. 396*
prophase *p. 396*

metaphase *p. 398*
anaphase *p. 398*
telophase *p. 398*
cytokinesis *p. 398*
karyotype *p. 400*
haploid *p. 400*
meiosis *p. 400*

synapsis *p. 401*
crossing over *p. 405*
independent assortment *p. 405*
nondisjunction *p. 406*
trisomy *p. 406*
monosomy *p. 406*

Reviewing the Concepts

1. The process of mitosis results in
   a. two haploid cells.
   b. two diploid cells.
   c. four haploid cells.
   d. four diploid cells.
2. DNA is synthesized (replicated) during
   a. interphase.
   b. prophase.
   c. metaphase.
   d. anaphase.
3. Crossing over occurs during which stage of meiosis?
   a. prophase I
   b. metaphase I
   c. prophase II
   d. metaphase II
4. Which of the following expresses an important difference between spermatogenesis and oogenesis?
   a. A sperm is haploid, and a mature ovum is diploid.
   b. During spermatogenesis, four functional sperm are produced; during oogenesis, one mature ovum and up to three polar bodies are formed.
   c. Spermatogenesis involves mitosis and meiosis, but oogenesis involves only meiosis.
   d. Crossing over occurs during spermatogenesis but not during oogenesis.
5. What kind of chromatid is attached at the centromere?
   a. sister
   b. mother

   c. daughter
   d. programmed
6. After mitosis, the number of chromosomes in a daughter cell is _____ those in the parent cell.
   a. one-half
   b. the same as
   c. twice
7. After meiosis, the number of chromosomes in a daughter cell is _____ those in the parent cell.
   a. one-half
   b. the same as
   c. twice
8. An abnormal number of chromosomes can result during meiosis because of
   a. crossing over.
   b. recombination.
   c. nondisjunction.
   d. synapsis.
9. During meiosis, the processes of _____ and _____ increase genetic diversity.
10. _____ chromosomes carry genes for the same traits.
11. _____ is the pairing of chromosomes during meiosis.
12. The stage of mitosis during which sister chromatids separate is _____.
13. The stage of meiosis during which sister chromatids separate is _____.

Applying the Concepts

1. A cell biologist is studying the cell cycle. She is growing the cells in culture, and they are actively dividing mitotically. One particular cell has half as much DNA as most of the other cells. Which stage of mitosis is this cell in? How do you know?
2. What would happen if the spindle fibers failed to form during mitosis?
3. What condition is indicated by the following karyotype?

Finding and Evaluating Information

We have seen that genes produce proteins that play a structural or functional role in the cell. Gametes are created by meiosis, and a random assortment of maternal and paternal chromosomes of each homologous pair are distributed to the gametes. When gametes fuse at fertilization, a zygote is created that contains homologous pairs of chromosomes, one member from the mother and the other from the father. The zygote undergoes many mitotic divisions in which genes are replicated and identical copies of chromosomes are distributed to daughter cells. Identical twins form from a single zygote, and the structure of their DNA is identical. Fraternal twins develop from different zygotes and, therefore, they share only 50% of their DNA.

You have undoubtedly noticed that mosquitoes are attracted to some people more than others. Skin scent is partly responsible for attracting mosquitoes. Researchers hypothesized that skin scents that attract mosquitoes are genetically based.[1] The following is an excerpt from Rob Stein on the National Public Radio report "Why Do Mosquitoes Like to Bite You Best? It's in Your Genes," April 22, 2015, 4:08 P.M. ET. You can read the entire article at http://www.npr.org/sections/health-shots/2015/04/22/401469931/why-do-mosquitoes-like-to-bite-you-best-its-in-your-genes.

". . . researchers brought 18 pairs of identical twins and 19 pairs of fraternal twins into the lab. Each person stuck a hand in one of the short arms of a Y-shaped plexiglass tube, as air was blown past the hand, toward 20 female *Aedes aegypti* mosquitoes clustered at the long end of the Y. Once released, the insects could choose between the twins—to fly upwind, along either side of the Y, presumably following the odor of the person they were most attracted to. (The scientists used a new batch of hungry mosquitoes in each trial, and also compared the results to trials that involved 'clean air' and nobody's hand.)

There was essentially no difference in the mosquitoes' response to genetically identical twins, the scientists found, but quite a bit of difference in their response to fraternal twins, who are as genetically different from each other as any other pair of siblings."

1. Based on this experimental design, is it valid to conclude that genetically determined skin odors determine one's attractiveness to mosquitoes?

2. Knowing that skin odor is important in attracting (or avoiding) mosquitoes, what question might you ask next?

3. How could this information be put to practical use?

4. Use at least three reliable sources to find additional factors that might cause a person to attract (or repel) mosquitoes. Cite your sources and explain why you chose them.

[1]G. M. Fernández-Grandon et al., "Heritability of attractiveness to mosquitoes," *PLoS One* 10 (4) [2015]: e0122716; doi:10.1371/journal.pone.0122716.

DID YOU KNOW?

- Some veterinarians are using a dog's own stem cells to treat arthritis.

- In the future, a procedure similar to liposuction may be used to extract abdominal fat as a source of stem cells to heal bone and joint injuries.

IN THE PREVIOUS CHAPTER, we considered cell division for growth and repair. In this chapter, we learn that, unlike most cells, stem cells are able to divide continuously and without becoming a specialized cell type. We will consider where they are found and the promises they may hold for the future.

19a.1 Stem Cells: Unspecialized Cells

Imagine growing new heart cells to repair damage from a heart attack. Think about curing Parkinson's disease by restoring the dopamine-producing neurons that are lacking in such patients. What about generating insulin-producing pancreatic islet cells to cure diabetes? Can we find a cure for multiple sclerosis, Alzheimer's disease, Lou Gehrig's disease, and spinal cord injuries? How? These goals may be possible to achieve by using stem cells—cells that continually divide and retain the ability to develop into many types of cells—to produce the needed type of cell. You might think of stem cells as a repair kit for the body.

The common thread among these disorders is that they are caused by too little cell division or by defective cell function. When there is too little cell division, the body cannot repair damaged tissue; for example, spinal cord injury cannot be repaired because neurons do not usually divide. Other disorders result from defective cell function; examples include Parkinson's disease, which is characterized by a lack of neurons that produce the neurotransmitter dopamine, and hemophilia, which is characterized by a lack of production of certain blood-clotting factors. If the damaged or defective cells could be replaced by healthy, functional cells, the disorders would be cured. Stem cells may be a source of functional cells to bring about those cures.

Most of the trillions of cells in your body have become specialized to perform a particular job. Muscle cells are specialized to contract, and neurons are specialized to conduct nerve impulses. The specialization of cells during embryonic development is directed by biological cues in each cell's immediate environment. The cues are usually provided by neighboring cells and include growth factors, surface proteins, salts, and contact with other cells. Because all cells within the same body have the same genetic makeup, the specialization of different cells to perform different functions means that particular genes in each type of cell have been turned on or off. Recall from Chapter 19 that specialized cells usually do not divide again.

Stem cells, in contrast, are relatively unspecialized cells that divide continually, creating a pool of undifferentiated cells for possible use. If stem cells are given the correct signals—exposure to a particular growth factor or hormone, for example—they can be coaxed into differentiating into a particular specialized cell type. The specialized cell types can then be used to treat diseases or regenerate injured tissues. As we will see, stem cells from different sources differ in the variety of specialized cell types they can develop into.

Stem cells are categorized by the degree of flexibility in their developmental path (Figure 19a.1). A fertilized egg can develop into all the types of cells in the body and is therefore considered to be *totipotent.* After about a week of development, the embryo is a source of embryonic stem cells, which can develop into nearly every type of cell. Because the developmental path of embryonic stem cells is so flexible, they are described as being *pluripotent.* In an adult, some stem cells remain able to differentiate into several types of cells and are called *multipotent.* Still other adult stem cells are *unipotent,* because they can differentiate into only one type of cell. Thus, embryonic stem cells are more versatile than are adult stem cells.

The source of stem cells used for therapeutic purposes influences the kinds of cells they can become as well as the likelihood of their rejection in the body of the person being treated. Each person's cells have self markers (MHC markers) identifying the cells as belonging in that body (see Chapter 13). These self markers are genetically determined, so the self markers of a relative's cells will be more similar than those of unrelated individuals. Cells that are not recognized as belonging in the body, because of the difference in the self markers, are usually attacked and killed by cells of the body's defense system. The self markers develop during prenatal development and early childhood. Thus, stem cells from an embryo or fetus have less developed self markers and are less likely to be rejected than are adult stem cells. Likewise, adult stem cells from the person being treated or a close relative are less likely to be rejected than are cells from an unrelated person.

19a.2 Sources of Human Stem Cells

Stem cells have several sources, including certain adult tissues, umbilical cord blood, and early embryos.

Adult Stem Cells: Unipotent and Multipotent

Adults have stem cells, but they are more difficult to locate than those in an embryo. Waiting in the bone marrow, brain, skin, liver, and other organs, adult stem cells remain ready to generate new cells for repair or replacement of old ones in many parts of the body. Diseased or dying cells provide biological cues that summon stem cells and prompt them to differentiate into the needed type of cell. When a stem cell divides in an adult, one

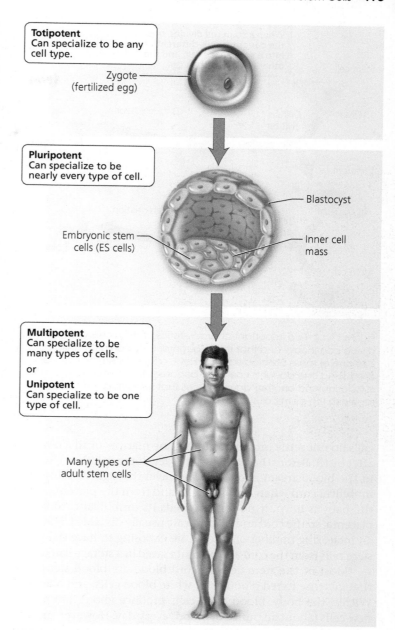

Totipotent
Can specialize to be any cell type.

Zygote (fertilized egg)

Pluripotent
Can specialize to be nearly every type of cell.

Blastocyst

Embryonic stem cells (ES cells)

Inner cell mass

Multipotent
Can specialize to be many types of cells.
or
Unipotent
Can specialize to be one type of cell.

Many types of adult stem cells

Figure 19a.1 Stem cells at different stages in human development. The degree of potency refers to the number of types of cells a stem cell can develop into.

daughter cell usually specializes to be a particular type of cell, and the other remains a stem cell (Figure 19a.2).

Adult stem cells do not seem to be as versatile as stem cells from an embryo. Whereas embryonic stem cells can transform into any cell type in the body, adult stem cells usually form one type of cell or form cells of a particular lineage only. For example, fat stem cells can form only fat, bone, and cartilage. However, we now know that adult stem cells are more versatile than was once believed.

Umbilical Cord and Placental Stem Cells: Multipotent

Blood from the umbilical cord and the embryonic part of the placenta (the chorion) are also good sources of stem cells. Stem

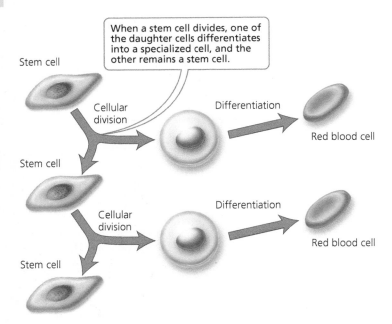

When a stem cell divides, one of the daughter cells differentiates into a specialized cell, and the other remains a stem cell.

Figure 19a.2 Two important characteristics of stem cells are that they divide continually and that their daughter cells can differentiate into one or more specialized cells. Here, a blood stem cell divides, producing one daughter cell that becomes specialized to perform a function and another daughter cell that remains a stem cell to replenish the stem cell supply.

cells do not settle into an infant's bone marrow until a few days after birth. Before that, during fetal development, they circulate in the bloodstream and therefore travel through vessels in the umbilical cord when circulating to and from the placenta. After the baby is born, it no longer needs its umbilical cord or the placenta, so the cord and placenta are usually discarded. However, an increasing number of parents are choosing to have the blood stem cells from the cord and placenta saved in a storage bank.

Most of the stem cells in cord blood are blood stem cells that give rise to red blood cells, white blood cells, and platelets. Within the body, blood stem cells produce about 260 billion new cells (about an ounce of blood) every day. However, umbilical cord blood also contains some stem cells that can turn into other kinds of cells—bone, cartilage, heart muscle, nerve tissue, and liver tissue.

Stem cells from umbilical cord blood and the placenta have some advantages over adult blood stem cells taken from bone marrow. Blood stem cells can be harvested from bone marrow, but the procedure is done in a hospital with the individual under general anesthesia. Stem cells are more easily extracted from umbilical cord blood because the cord is removed from the infant's body. Stem cells from cord blood are usually used to treat childhood diseases because the cord blood has a limited number of stem cells. However, the placenta has several times more stem cells and, when added to stem cells from cord blood, can be used to treat adult illnesses. Another advantage of using these stem cells is that they are less likely to be rejected by the recipient than are adult stem cells from bone marrow. The self markers on the cord blood stem cells or placental stem cells have not yet fully developed, so the match does not have to be as close as with adult stem cells from bone

marrow. Finally, stem cells from cord blood or the placenta are less likely to carry infections.

Because blood stem cells are able to produce an endless supply of blood cells, they hold promise for treating a host of blood conditions. For instance, some patients with the inherited disorders sickle-cell anemia and beta-thalassemia, in which abnormal forms of hemoglobin are produced, have already been treated successfully with stem cell therapy. Stem cells that produce normal hemoglobin can be transplanted into a person with the inherited anemia. Normal red blood cells then begin replacing the abnormal ones. Leukemia patients have also benefited from umbilical cord stem cells. Traditionally, leukemia has been treated with bone marrow transplants from family members or from donors from the National Marrow Donor Program who have close tissue types. However, most patients in need of a bone marrow transplant do not find donors with matching tissue types. Because the tissue markers on umbilical cord stem cells are immature, the cells are less likely to be rejected by the recipient.

Most of the medical benefits that may be achieved using umbilical cord or placental blood have yet to be realized. Nonetheless, there are already banks that store umbilical cord blood and placentas from newborn babies. Some parents pay a setup fee and an annual service fee to store their baby's cord blood and placenta just in case the child needs that blood or those stem cells some day. Government-owned banks collect and store thousands of samples of cord blood in hopes of having a tissue match for most individuals in the population. Researchers have developed ways to increase the number of umbilical cord blood stem cells by growing them in the laboratory.

The existence of umbilical cord blood banks raises certain social issues. Should blood stored in private blood banks be reserved only for the possible future need of the donor, or should it be made available for anyone in need whose tissue type matches? Should cord blood banks be privately owned or funded by the government? These are just a couple of the many questions remaining to be addressed.

Embryonic Stem Cells: Pluripotent

Embryonic stem cells can divide continually and specialize into nearly any cell type. They come from several sources.

Unused embryos from fertility clinics Most of the stem cells used for current research come from embryos that were created for reproductive purposes but were not used. Only a few days old, these embryos left in fertility clinics were destined for destruction. When the early embryo is about 6 to 7 days old, it is a rich source of stem cells because the cells it consists of are able to produce all the cells of the new individual. When stem cells are extracted from an early embryo, the embryo is about the size of the head of a pin and is called a *blastocyst* (see Chapter 18; see also Figure 19a.3). It is a sphere of cells containing a cluster of about 20 to 30 cells, known as the *inner cell mass,* adhering to one side of the sphere. The stem cells make up the inner cell mass. Embryonic stem cells are easy to harvest: the cells of the inner cell mass are extracted and cultured in the laboratory. They will continue to divide for years, creating a stem cell line.

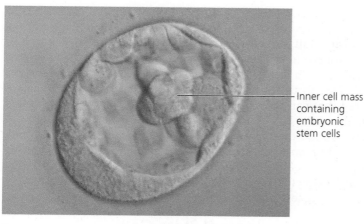

Figure 19a.3 Embryonic stem cells come from the inner cell mass, a cluster of 20 to 30 cells, from a 6- to 7-day-old embryo. At this age, the embryo is about the size of the head of a pin.

Inner cell mass containing embryonic stem cells

Somatic cell nuclear transfer

In *somatic cell nuclear transfer (SCNT)*, the nucleus from a somatic body cell is transferred to an egg from which the egg nucleus has been removed. The newly created cell is then stimulated to begin embryonic development. All the cells of the embryo are genetically identical. Thus, somatic cell nuclear transfer is a form of *cloning*—producing genetically identical copies of a cell or organism.

Dolly, born on July 5, 1996, was the first sheep—indeed, the first mammal—to be cloned from an adult cell (Figure 19a.4). She was created using somatic cell nuclear transfer, illustrated in Figure 19a.5. In Dolly's case, the nucleus of a mammary cell from an adult sheep's udder was placed into an egg from which the nucleus had been removed. (Dolly was named after Dolly Parton, a country singer known for her mammary "cells" as well as for her voice.) The goal of Dr. Ian Wilmut, the Scotsman whose work resulted in Dolly, was to develop techniques eventually leading to the production of animals that could be used as factories for manufacturing proteins, such as hormones, that would benefit humans. Cloning could make genetic engineering (discussed in Chapter 21) more efficient. If an adult could

Figure 19a.4 Dolly, the first animal cloned from an adult cell, was created using a technique called somatic cell nuclear transfer.

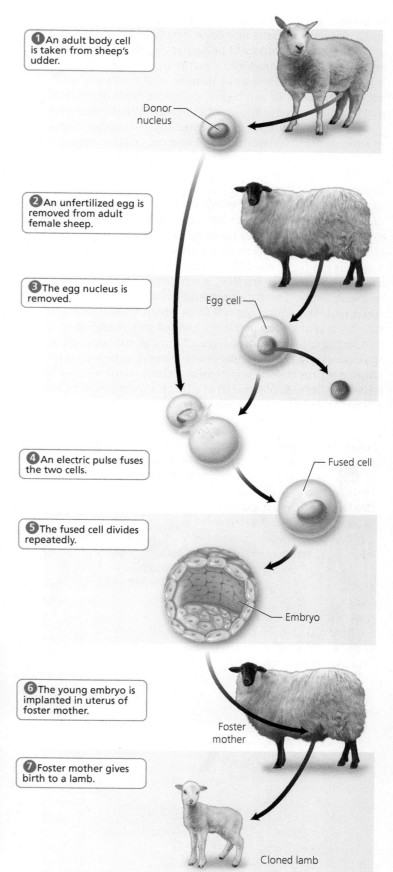

❶ An adult body cell is taken from sheep's udder.

Donor nucleus

❷ An unfertilized egg is removed from adult female sheep.

❸ The egg nucleus is removed.

Egg cell

❹ An electric pulse fuses the two cells.

Fused cell

❺ The fused cell divides repeatedly.

Embryo

❻ The young embryo is implanted in uterus of foster mother.

Foster mother

❼ Foster mother gives birth to a lamb.

Cloned lamb

Figure 19a.5 Somatic cell nuclear transfer used for reproductive cloning

be cloned, a scientist would need to engineer an animal with a particular desired trait only once. Then, when the animal was old enough for scientists to be sure it had the desired trait, the animal could be reproduced exactly, in multiple copies. Cloning from an adult instead of from an embryo is advantageous because the scientist can be certain before cloning that the animal has the desired traits. In other words, "What you see is what you get." Since Dolly's birth, scientists have cloned several kinds of animals using the technique of somatic cell nuclear transfer.

Discussions about cloning often become heated when the possibility of human cloning is raised. In these discussions, a distinction is often drawn between reproductive cloning and therapeutic cloning. *Therapeutic cloning* would produce a clone of "replacement cells" having the same genetic makeup as a given patient so that they could be used in the patient's medical therapy without concern of rejection by the immune system. The cells produced would be embryonic stem cells created using somatic cell nuclear transfer, a variant of the technique used to create Dolly. The patient would donate a somatic cell to be fused with the donor egg cell from which the original nucleus had been removed. The newly created cell would then begin developing into an embryo (Figure 19a.6). (If the patient's disease were genetic, a normal form of the relevant gene would be substituted for the defective gene before the nucleus was put in the enucleated egg. Replacement of a specific gene has been accomplished in mice but has not yet been done in humans.)

Researchers recently created human embryonic stem cells using a variation of SCNT to combine an enucleated human egg and an adult human skin cell. Once the fused cell develops into an embryo (6 to 7 days), stem cells can be removed and treated with growth factors that make them develop into several types of cells. In this way, patient-specific stem cells can be generated that can then be transplanted into the patient to replace faulty cells. For example, neurons might be transplanted to cure Parkinson's disease or to repair spinal cord damage. Indeed, using human somatic cell nuclear transplant (hSCNT), scientists formed an embryonic clone of a woman with type 1 diabetes. They extracted healthy insulin-producing stem cells that are now being tested in mice for safety.

Induced Pluripotent Stem Cells

Suppose one could turn back the clock and stimulate an adult cell to revert to a pluripotent stem cell. Researchers have done just that—they caused adult human skin cells to revert to pluripotent stem cells that could differentiate into any type of tissue. These cells, called induced pluripotent stem cells (iPSCs), bring stem cells created from human cells closer to clinical use, because they do not destroy an embryo.

what would YOU do? Some countries—Mexico, China, and India, for example—are offering stem cell treatments. If you had a disease that stem cell therapy might address, would you travel abroad for treatment even though the safety and effectiveness were not proven? What factors would influence your decision? ■

19a.3 Potential Uses for Stem Cells

The use of stem cells is just beginning to blossom. Let's consider some of their potential uses.

Replacement for Damaged Cells

In the United States, thousands of clinical trials are in progress or looking for recruits. For example, clinical trials are under way to determine the effectiveness of umbilical cord stem cells to repair and replace nerve cells in children with cerebral palsy, a condition in which neurons are damaged at birth.

To date, most studies on stem cells as a source of replacement cells or as factories to produce proteins or hormones that the body is not making have been done on nonhuman animals. Insulin-producing stem cells have eliminated symptoms of type 1 diabetes in mice. In rats, bone marrow stem cells move toward heart muscle with damage similar to that occurring in a heart attack. In the damaged heart muscle, stem cells promote heart muscle strength.

Growing New Organs

Regenerative medicine is still in its infancy, but it is growing rapidly. Its aim is to rebuild or repair damaged organs by coaxing stem cells to grow and fill in tissue scaffolds that were engineered in the laboratory. In 2004, a German man had his jaw removed because of cancer. Doctors created a

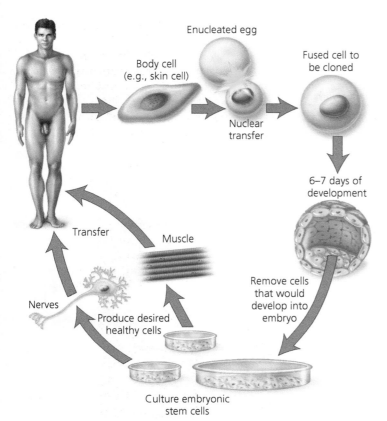

Enucleated egg

Body cell
(e.g., skin cell)

Fused cell to
be cloned

Nuclear
transfer

6–7 days of
development

Transfer

Muscle

Remove cells
that would
develop into
embryo

Nerves

Produce desired
healthy cells

Culture embryonic
stem cells

Figure 19a.6 Potential method for human therapeutic cloning using somatic cell nuclear transfer

Q: Why is the nucleus removed from the donor egg?

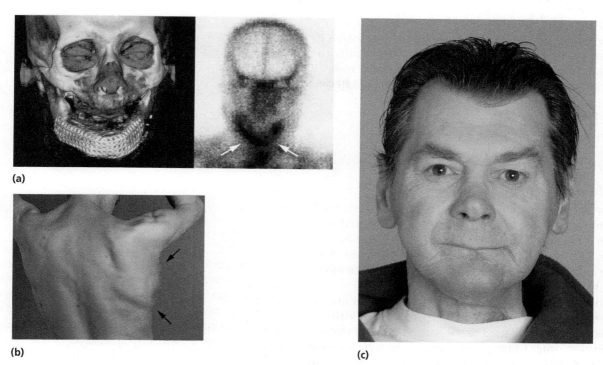

(a)

(b)

(c)

Figure 19a.7 Adult stem cells from bone marrow were used to grow a new jaw to replace one that had been removed because of cancer. (a) A mold in the shape of the missing jaw was created out of mesh and seeded with bone marrow cells and bone growth factor. (b) The mold was placed in the muscle of the man's back until bone filled the mold. (c) The new jaw was then implanted to replace the missing jaw.

mesh mold in the shape of the jawbone that had been removed, and they implanted the mold into the muscle below the man's shoulder blade, along with some cow-derived bone mineral, a growth factor to stimulate bone growth, and blood extracted from the man's bone marrow, which contained stem cells (Figure 19a.7). The mold was left in place on the man's shoulder until bone scans showed that new bone had formed around the mold. The new jaw then was removed, along with some muscle and blood vessels, and implanted in the correct location. Four weeks later, the man could chew solid food—a bratwurst sandwich!

Since then, other organs, including urinary bladders and tracheas, have been grown and transplanted. In each case, doctors fashioned a scaffold in the correct shape of the desired structure. The patient's own cells were grown in a Petri dish. As the cells formed layers of tissue, the tissue was shaped into a new structure, which was then implanted into the patient. The new structure grew from the patient's cells and was, therefore, not rejected.

Today, doctors are using three-dimensional (3D) printers to bioprint structures. First, a scaffold is prepared, using a 3D printer. Next, cells are removed from the desired organ, separated into cell type, and cultured (or stem cells from the patient's fat or blood can be used to generate the appropriate cell types). Then, modified inkjet printers are used to apply the cells layer-by-layer to precise locations on the scaffold. The cells grow into a replacement structure. So far, only simple structures—flat, tubular, or hollow—have been printed. However, the hope is that someday we will be able to produce even complicated structures, such as hearts and kidneys, for transplantation.

An exciting application of regenerative medicine is "regrowing" limbs of wounded soldiers returning from war (Figure 19a.8). Many soldiers are so badly mutilated by explosives that limbs must be amputated. Now there is hope that some limbs can be saved. The secret is an application of a powder created from pig bladders, nicknamed "magic pixie dust."

Figure 19a.8 Corporal Isais Hernandez's leg was severely injured by a mortar round. New tissue was grown in the wound using a powder created from pulverized pig bladders.

The pig bladders have an extracellular matrix that contains the protein collagen. Researchers think that the powder works by attracting stem cells in the body and giving these cells the chemical signals to make new tissues. The new limbs have all the appropriate tissue types, including skin, muscle, and nerve.

STOP and THINK

Why would chemical signals be necessary for the development of new tissues?

Testing New Drugs

Before a new drug can go to clinical trials, it must be shown to be safe for animals and for human cells cultured in Petri dishes. The problem is that not all tissues will survive in tissue culture. For example, heart cells, brain cells, and liver cells do not. Stem cells may be a way to test new drugs for safety and effectiveness before testing them on humans.

Researchers are also using iPSCs to create cells that display the characteristics of cells with a particular disease. Cell cultures of these cells could then be used to study the nature of the disease or to develop drugs to treat the disease. Skin samples from patients with Alzheimer's disease are being collected with an interest in converting them into pluripotent stem cells for such purposes.

LOOKING AHEAD

In Chapter 19, we considered how cells copy their genetic material and undergo mitosis, creating cells for growth and repair, or undergo meiosis, creating gametes for reproduction. In this chapter, we considered stem cells, which divide endlessly. In the next chapter, we will relate what we learned about cell division to genetic inheritance.

CONSIDER THIS CASE

Grandpa Jack has Parkinson's disease, a condition causing the death of those neurons in the brain that produce the neurotransmitter dopamine, thereby resulting in hand tremors and other movement problems. Parkinson's disease is not yet curable, but medication can help symptoms. Grandpa hears about a company that claims it will cure his Parkinson's disease by using his own fat stem cells to replace his dopamine-producing neurons.

■ Could adult fat stem cells form neurons?

20 Genetics and Human Inheritance

- When identical twins are conceived, they start out with the same fingerprints, but during weeks 6 through 13 of pregnancy, they each touch the amniotic sac and develop unique ridges and lines on their fingers that result in different fingerprints.

- You have fewer genes than corn has. Scientists believe that humans have about 25,000 genes and that corn has about 59,000 genes.

- Your traits are determined by only 2% of your genetic material.

IN CHAPTER 19, we considered how chromosomes and the genes they carry are distributed during cell division. We learned that mitosis is necessary for growth and repair of body tissues. We also learned that in humans, meiosis is necessary to prepare the gametes needed for reproduction. In Chapter 19a, we discussed stem cells, which divide endlessly and hold promise for curing conditions that are caused by too little cell division or defective cells. In this chapter, we will see that the genes we receive at the moment of conception influence all the biochemical reactions taking place inside our cells, our susceptibility to disease, our behavior patterns, and even our life span. Our environment is also an important influence, but our genes provide the basic blueprint for our possibilities and limitations. In this chapter, you will learn more about the genetic foundation that has been so important in shaping who you are. You will discover how heritable traits are passed to new generations and how to predict the distribution of traits from one generation to the next.

20.1 Principles of Inheritance

The understanding of meiosis we gained in Chapter 19 helps us answer important questions about inheritance: Why is your brother the only sibling with Mom's freckles and widow's peak (a hairline that comes to a point on the forehead)? How can you have blue eyes when both your parents are brown eyed? Will you be bald at 40, like Dad? Let's delve more deeply into how chromosomes, meiosis, and heredity are related.

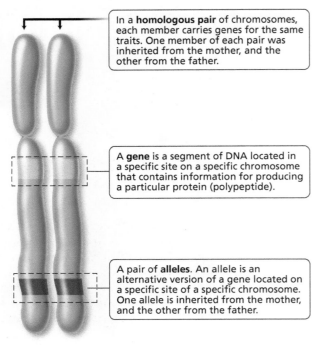

In a **homologous pair** of chromosomes, each member carries genes for the same traits. One member of each pair was inherited from the mother, and the other from the father.

A **gene** is a segment of DNA located in a specific site on a specific chromosome that contains information for producing a particular protein (polypeptide).

A pair of **alleles**. An allele is an alternative version of a gene located on a specific site of a specific chromosome. One allele is inherited from the mother, and the other from the father.

Figure 20.1 Important terms in genetics

Before beginning, you may want to review some of the terms that were introduced in Chapter 19 and that are summarized in Figure 20.1. Recall that somatic (body) cells have a pair of every chromosome. Thus, human cells have 23 pairs of chromosomes. One member of each pair was inherited from the female parent, and the other from the male parent. The chromosomes that carry genes for the same traits are a *homologous pair of chromosomes,* or homologues. Chromosomes are made of DNA and protein. Certain segments of the DNA of each chromosome function as genes. A **gene** directs the synthesis of a specific protein that can play either a structural or a functional role in the cell.[1] (In some cases, the gene directs the synthesis of a polypeptide that forms part of a protein.) In this way, the gene-determined protein can influence whether a certain **trait,** or characteristic, will develop. For instance, the formation of your brother's widow's peak was directed by a protein coded for by a gene that he inherited from Mom. Genes for the same trait are found at the same specific location on homologous chromosomes.

Different versions of a gene are called **alleles.** Alleles produce different versions of the trait they determine. For example, there is a gene that determines whether freckles will form. One allele of this gene causes freckles to form; the other does not. Somatic cells carry two alleles for each gene, one allele on each homologous chromosome. If a person has at least one allele for freckles, melanin will be deposited, and freckles will form. If neither homologue bears the freckle allele that leads to melanin deposition, for example, the person will not have freckles.

Individuals with two copies of the same allele of a gene are said to be **homozygous** (*homo,* same; *zygo,* joined together)

[1]This is a simplified definition of *gene*. As we will see in Chapter 21, some genes contain regulatory regions of DNA within their boundaries. Also, some genes code for RNA molecules that are needed for the production of a protein but are not part of it.

for that trait. Individuals with different alleles of a given gene are said to be **heterozygous** (*hetero,* different; *zygo,* joined together). When the effects of a certain allele can be detected regardless of whether an alternative allele is also present, the allele is described as a **dominant allele.** Dimples and freckles are human traits dictated by dominant alleles. An allele whose effects are masked in the heterozygous condition is described as a **recessive allele.** Because of this masking, only homozygous recessive alleles are expressed. Some disorders result from recessive alleles; examples include cystic fibrosis, in which excessive mucus production impairs lung and pancreatic function; and albinism, in which the pigment melanin is missing in the hair, skin, and eyes. It is customary to designate a dominant allele with a capital letter and a recessive allele with a lowercase letter—*A* and *a,* for example.

We observe the dominant form of the trait whether the individual is homozygous dominant (*AA*) or heterozygous (*Aa*) for that trait. As a consequence, we cannot always tell exactly which alleles are present. It is important to remember that an individual's genetic makeup is not always revealed by the individual's appearance. A **genotype** is the precise set of alleles a person possesses for a given trait or traits. It tells us whether the individual is homozygous or heterozygous for a given gene. A **phenotype,** in contrast, is the *observable* physical trait or traits of an individual. Figure 20.2 shows the genotype or genotypes for several phenotypes in humans (for example, the freckled phenotype has two genotypes: *FF* and *Ff*). Table 20.1 summarizes terms commonly used in genetics as they apply to the inheritance of freckles, which is determined by a dominant allele.

Gamete Formation

Recall from Chapter 19 that the members of each homologous pair of chromosomes segregate during meiosis I, with each homologue going to a different daughter cell. Thus, an egg or a sperm has only one member of each homologous pair. Consider what this fact means for inheritance. Because the alleles for each gene segregate during gamete formation, half the gametes bear one allele, and half bear the other. This principle, known as the *law of segregation,* explains how, for every gene in our chromosomes, one of the alleles comes from our mother and one comes from our father.

Furthermore, each pair of homologous chromosomes lines up at the midline of the cell during meiosis I independently of the other pairs. The orientation of the paternal and maternal homologues relative to the poles of the cell (that is, with regard to which homologue is closer to which pole) is entirely random. What this fact means for inheritance is that pairs of alleles for genes on different chromosomes segregate into gametes independently. This principle, known as the *law of independent assortment,* explains why the mixture of alleles that came from the mother and alleles that came from the father is different in every gamete.

Mendelian Genetics

During the nineteenth century, Gregor Mendel, a monk who grew up in a region of what was then Austria and is now part of the Czech Republic, worked out much of what we know today about the laws of heredity by performing specific crosses of pea

Freckles: *FF* or *Ff*   No freckles: *ff*

Widow's peak: *WW* or *Ww*   Straight hairline: *ww*

Unattached earlobes: *EE* or *Ee*   Attached earlobes: *ee*

Tongue rolling: *TT* or *Tt*

Figure 20.2 Genotypes for selected human phenotypes

Table 20.1	Review of Common Terms in Genetics	
Genotypes: The Alleles That Are Present	Description	Phenotype: The Observable Trait (Examples)
FF	Homozygous dominant: • Two dominant alleles present • Dominant phenotype expressed	Freckles
Ff	Heterozygous: • Different alleles present • Dominant phenotype expressed	Freckles
ff	Homozygous recessive: • Two recessive alleles present • Recessive phenotype expressed	No freckles

One-trait crosses We begin our discussion by using Mendel's ideas to consider the inheritance of a single trait, using the example of freckles, a characteristic determined by a dominant allele. Suppose a freckled female who is homozygous dominant (*FF*) had a child with a man who is homozygous recessive with no freckles (*ff*; Figure 20.3). The following sequence of steps allows us to predict the degree of likelihood that their child will have freckles.

1. **Identify the possible gametes that each parent can produce.** We know that alleles segregate during meiosis, but in this example, both parents are homozygous. Therefore, each can produce only one type of gamete (as far as freckles are concerned). The female produces gametes (eggs) with the dominant allele (*F*), and the male produces gametes (sperm) with the recessive allele (*f*).

2. **Use a Punnett square to determine the probable outcome of the genetic cross.** A *Punnett square* is a diagram used to predict the genetic makeup of the offspring of individuals of particular genotypes. In a Punnett square, columns are set up and labeled to represent each of the possible gametes of one parent—let's say the father (Figure 20.4). Remember, the alleles of each gene segregate during meiosis. In this case, then, the diagram would contain two columns to represent the gametes of the male without freckles, each labeled with a recessive allele, *f*. In a similar manner, rows are established across the columns and labeled to represent all the possible gametes formed by the other parent, in this case, the mother with freckles. This Punnett square would have two rows, each labeled *F*. Each square in the resulting table is then filled in by combining the labels of the corresponding rows and columns. The squares represent the possible offspring of these parents. In this first case, all the children would have freckles and would be heterozygous for the trait (*Ff*).

Now let's consider why it is possible for parents who are both heterozygous for the freckle trait (*Ff*) to have a child without freckles. The *F* and *f* alleles segregate during meiosis. So half the gametes bear the *F* allele, and half bear the *f* allele (Figure 20.5a). This time the two rows in the Punnett square are labeled with *F* and *f*, and so are the two columns (Figure 20.5b). After filling the boxes according to the labels on rows and columns, we see that the probable genotypes of the children would be homozygous dominant (*FF*), heterozygous (*Ff*), and homozygous

plants. Although Mendel knew nothing about chromosomes, his ideas about the inheritance of traits are consistent with what we now know about the movement of chromosomes during meiosis. Mendel's ideas are used today to predict the outcome of hereditary crosses.

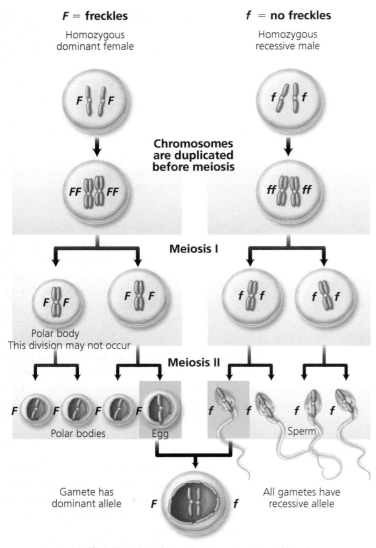

Fertilization produces heterozygous offspring

Figure 20.3 Gamete formation by a female who is homozygous dominant for freckles (*FF*), a male who is homozygous recessive for no freckles (*ff*), and the heterozygous (*Ff*) individual resulting from the union of these gametes.

recessive (*ff*), in a genotypic ratio of 1 *FF* : 2 *Ff* : 1 *ff*. The ratio of phenotypes of children with freckles (*FF* and *Ff*) compared with children without freckles (*ff*) would be 3 : 1. This ratio means that each child born to this couple will have a 75% (3/4) chance of having freckles. But there is a 1 in 4, or 25%, chance that each child will not have freckles. A cross in which both parents are heterozygous for one trait of interest is called a *monohybrid cross*.

STOP and THINK

At the beginning of the chapter, we raised a question about why only one sibling, your hypothetical brother, inherited your mother's freckles. Implicit in the way we phrased the question was that there is at least one other sibling (you), who, like your father, does not have freckles. Use a Punnett square to explain why the mother in this example must be heterozygous for the freckle trait.

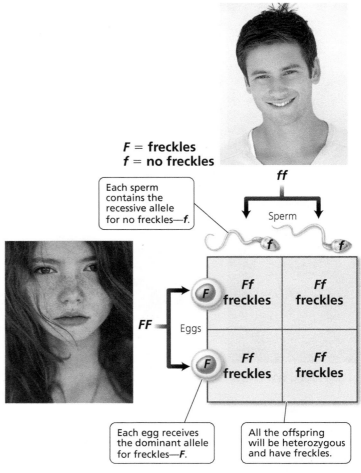

Figure 20.4 This Punnett square illustrates the probable offspring from a cross between a homozygous dominant female with freckles (*FF*) and a homozygous recessive male without freckles (*ff*). The columns are labeled with the possible gametes the male could produce (one gamete per column). The rows are labeled with the possible gametes the female could produce (one gamete per row). Combining the labels on the corresponding rows and columns yields the genotype of possible offspring.

Two-trait crosses We use the same steps to predict the probable outcome for inheritance of two traits of interest that we used for inheritance of a single trait—as long as the genes for the two traits are on different chromosomes.

1. **Identify the possible gametes that each parent can produce.** Like freckles, a widow's peak is controlled by a dominant allele. What would the children look like if the parents were a woman who is homozygous for both freckles and a widow's peak (*FFWW*) and a man with no freckles and a straight hairline (*ffww*)? To answer that question, we begin by determining the possible gametes each mate can produce. Because they are homozygous for both traits, the woman can produce only gametes bearing dominant alleles (*FW*), and the man can produce only gametes with the recessive alleles (*fw*).

2. **Use a Punnett square to determine the probable outcome of the genetic cross.** In this case, each parent can produce only one type of gamete, so all the children will have the same genotype and the same phenotype. All the children will be heterozygous for each trait (*FfWw*) and will have both freckles and a widow's peak.

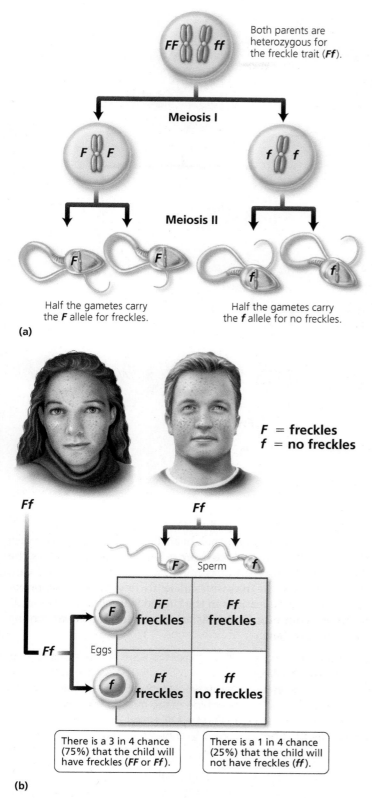

(a)

Half the gametes carry the **F** allele for freckles.

Half the gametes carry the **f** allele for no freckles.

F = freckles
f = no freckles

Ff

Ff

Sperm

FF
freckles

Ff
freckles

Ff
freckles

ff
no freckles

Eggs

There is a 3 in 4 chance (75%) that the child will have freckles (**FF** or **Ff**).

There is a 1 in 4 chance (25%) that the child will not have freckles (**ff**).

(b)

Figure 20.5 (a) Gamete formation by a person who is heterozygous for the freckle trait (*Ff*). (b) A Punnett square showing the probable outcome of a mating between two people who are heterozygous for the freckle trait (*Ff*).

Suppose one of these children mates with someone who is also heterozygous for freckles and a widow's peak. This would be a *dihybrid cross,* a mating of individuals who are both heterozygous for two traits of interest. Would it be possible for this couple to have a child who had neither freckles nor a widow's peak? It *would* be possible, but the chances are only 1 in 16. Let's see why.

First, determine the possible gametes that each parent could produce (Figure 20.6). Keep in mind that alleles for a gene segregate and that genes for different traits that are located on different chromosomes will segregate independently of one another. There are, therefore, four possible allele combinations in gametes produced by a person who is heterozygous for these two different genes. The gametes are *FW, Fw, fW,* and *fw.* In this instance, we need to construct a Punnett square with *four* columns, because this time there are four possible male gametes, and four rows labeled with the possible female gametes. Each type of gamete has an equal chance of joining with any other type at fertilization. The squares are filled by combining the labels of the corresponding columns and rows, giving us the possible genotypes of the offspring. Notice in Figure 20.7 that the relative numbers of phenotypes possible for the next generation are 9 freckled, widow's peak; 3 freckled, straight hairline; 3 no freckles, widow's peak; 1 no freckles, straight hairline. We see, then, that the expected phenotypic ratio resulting from a dihybrid cross is always 9 : 3 : 3 : 1.

Pedigrees

It is sometimes important to find out the genotype of a human with a dominant phenotype for a particular trait. Because there are two possible genotypes for a dominant trait (homozygous dominant and heterozygous dominant), we cannot know genotype based on phenotype alone. However, we can often deduce the unknown genotype by looking at the expression of the trait in the person's ancestors or descendants. A chart showing the genetic connections between individuals in a family is called a **pedigree.** Family or medical records are used to fill in the pattern of expression of the trait in question for as many family members as possible. Pedigrees are useful not just in determining an unknown genotype but also in predicting the chances that one's offspring will display the trait. Pedigrees for the inheritance of genetic disorders caused by a dominant allele on one of the non-sex chromosomes (called *autosomal dominant*) and of genetic disorders caused by recessive alleles on a pair of non-sex chromosomes (called *autosomal recessive*) are shown in Figure 20.8. We will discuss genes on sex chromosomes later in the chapter.

Marfan syndrome is an autosomal dominant disorder. This syndrome is a connective tissue disorder in which a dominant allele for the production of an elastic connective tissue protein, fibrillin, produces a nonfunctional protein. Because connective tissue is widespread in the body, so are the symptoms of Marfan syndrome. Connective tissue is an important component in blood vessel walls, heart valves, tendons, ligaments, and cartilage. A serious problem caused by Marfan syndrome is weakness in the walls of large blood vessels because they can tear or burst.

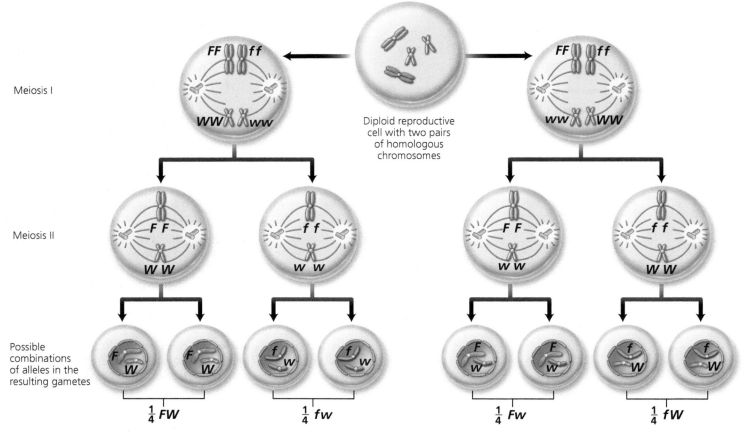

Meiosis I

Diploid reproductive cell with two pairs of homologous chromosomes

Meiosis II

Possible combinations of alleles in the resulting gametes

$\frac{1}{4}$ FW $\frac{1}{4}$ fw $\frac{1}{4}$ Fw $\frac{1}{4}$ fW

Figure 20.6 A person who is heterozygous for two genes that are located on different chromosomes can produce four different types of gametes.

Q: If a parent were homozygous recessive for freckles and heterozygous for widow's peak, how many types of gametes could form?

STOP and **THINK**

If the pedigree in Figure 20.8a were depicting the inheritance of Marfan syndrome, what would be the genotype of the males in the third generation who have Marfan syndrome? How do you know?

Genetic disorders are often caused by recessive alleles, so knowing whether the parents carry the allele will help predict both the possibility and the likelihood of that child being homozygous for the trait and therefore born with the condition (Figure 20.8b). For example, cystic fibrosis (CF), a disorder characterized by the production of abnormally thick mucus, is controlled by a recessive allele. Approximately 1 in every 2000 infants in the United States is born with CF. It is a leading cause of childhood death; for children with the disorder, average length of life is 24 years. The three primary signs of CF are abnormally salty sweat, digestive problems, and respiratory problems. Many children with CF suffer from malnutrition because mucus clogs the pancreatic ducts, preventing pancreatic digestive enzymes from reaching the small intestine, where they would otherwise function in digestion. Thick mucus also plugs the respiratory passageways, making breathing difficult and increasing susceptibility to lung infections such as pneumonia (Figure 20.9).

Because CF is inherited as a recessive allele, children with CF are usually born to normal, healthy parents who had no idea they carried the trait. A **carrier** is someone who displays the dominant phenotype but is heterozygous for a trait and can, therefore, pass the recessive allele to descendants. Approximately 1 in 22 Caucasians in the United States is a carrier for CF. (CF is less common among Asian Americans and is rare among African Americans.)

STOP and **THINK**

If the pedigree in Figure 20.8b were depicting the inheritance of CF, what would be the genotype of the male in the third generation who has CF? How do you know? Which individuals are carriers for the trait? How do you know?

The U.S. Surgeon General urges all Americans to create a pedigree of their family health history. The Surgeon General's Health Initiative website (www.hhs.gov/familyhistory) provides a computerized tool for creating a pedigree, but it can also be done without a computer. To create your own pedigree, collect information from your relatives about their own and their ancestors' health at your next family gathering. On the pedigree, indicate which individuals have experienced high blood pressure, a heart attack or stroke, cancer, diabetes, or any other disease common

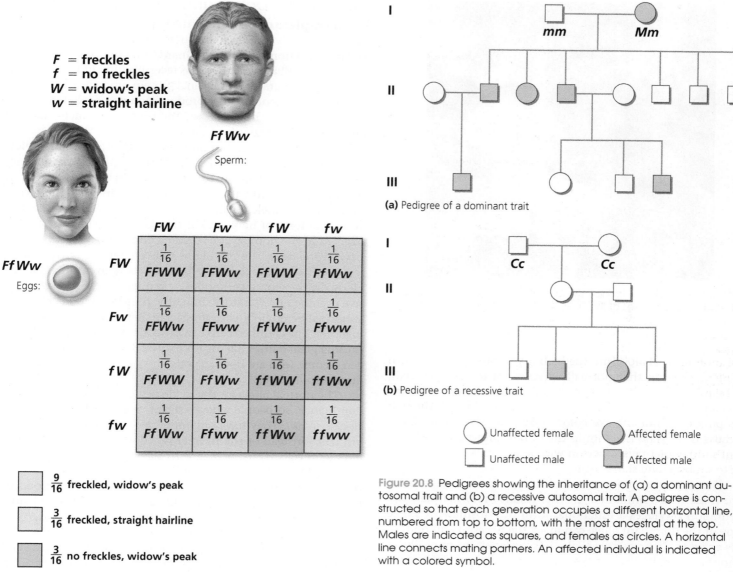

F = freckles
f = no freckles
W = widow's peak
w = straight hairline

FfWw

Sperm:

FfWw
Eggs:

	FW	Fw	fW	fw
FW	$\frac{1}{16}$ FFWW	$\frac{1}{16}$ FFWw	$\frac{1}{16}$ FfWW	$\frac{1}{16}$ FfWw
Fw	$\frac{1}{16}$ FFWw	$\frac{1}{16}$ FFww	$\frac{1}{16}$ FfWw	$\frac{1}{16}$ Ffww
fW	$\frac{1}{16}$ FfWW	$\frac{1}{16}$ FfWw	$\frac{1}{16}$ ffWW	$\frac{1}{16}$ ffWw
fw	$\frac{1}{16}$ FfWw	$\frac{1}{16}$ Ffww	$\frac{1}{16}$ ffWw	$\frac{1}{16}$ ffww

$\frac{9}{16}$ freckled, widow's peak

$\frac{3}{16}$ freckled, straight hairline

$\frac{3}{16}$ no freckles, widow's peak

$\frac{1}{16}$ no freckles, straight hairline

Figure 20.7 A dihybrid cross is a mating of individuals heterozygous for two traits, each governed by a gene on a different chromosome. Analyzed on a Punnett square, this cross illustrates the law of independent assortment—that is, each allele pair is inherited independently of others found on different chromosomes. The phenotypes of the offspring of a dihybrid cross would be expected to occur in a 9 : 3 : 3 : 1 ratio.

in your family. This health history may help predict your risk of developing certain diseases and encourage you to take preventive action before problems develop.

Dominant and Recessive Alleles

You may wonder what makes an allele dominant or recessive. In many cases, the dominant allele produces a normal, functional protein, but the recessive allele either produces the protein in an altered form that does not function properly, or it does not produce any protein. Consider the inheritance of the most

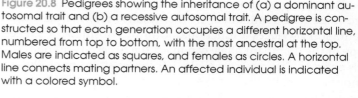

(a) Pedigree of a dominant trait

(b) Pedigree of a recessive trait

○ Unaffected female ● Affected female
□ Unaffected male ▨ Affected male

Figure 20.8 Pedigrees showing the inheritance of (a) a dominant autosomal trait and (b) a recessive autosomal trait. A pedigree is constructed so that each generation occupies a different horizontal line, numbered from top to bottom, with the most ancestral at the top. Males are indicated as squares, and females as circles. A horizontal line connects mating partners. An affected individual is indicated with a colored symbol.

Figure 20.9 Cystic fibrosis, controlled by a recessive gene, is a condition in which abnormally thick mucus is produced, causing serious digestive and respiratory problems. This child with cystic fibrosis is using a therapeutic toy to enhance airflow. When she exhales with enough force, the ribbons wave.

Figure 20.10 A person with albinism lacks the brown pigment melanin in the skin, hair, and irises of the eyes.

common form of albinism, the inability to produce the brown pigment melanin that normally gives color to the eyes, hair, and skin. Because of the lack of melanin, a person with albinism has pale skin and white hair (Figure 20.10). A child with the trait has pink eyes, but the eye color darkens to blue in an adult. Because there is no melanin in the skin to protect against sunlight's ultraviolet rays, a person with albinism is quite vulnerable to sunburn and skin cancer.

The ability to produce melanin depends on the enzyme tyrosinase. The dominant allele that results in normal skin pigmentation produces a functional form of tyrosinase. A single copy of the dominant allele can make the necessary amount of this enzyme. The recessive allele that causes albinism produces a nonfunctional form of tyrosinase. If two copies of the recessive allele are present, melanin cannot be formed and albinism results.

Codominant Alleles

The examples we have described so far represent **complete dominance,** a situation in which a heterozygous individual exhibits the trait associated with the dominant allele but not that of the recessive allele. In other words, the dominant allele produces a functional protein, and the protein's effects are apparent, but the recessive allele produces a less functional protein or none at all, and its effects are not apparent. However, complete dominance is not the only possibility for a heterozygous genotype. In some cases, both alleles produce functional proteins. In this situation, the effects of *both* alleles are apparent in the heterozygous phenotype.

The inheritance of type AB blood is an example of **codominance.** Two alleles, I^A and I^B, result in the production of two different polysaccharides on the surface of red blood cells. In persons with type AB blood, both alleles are expressed, and their red blood cells have both A and B polysaccharides on their surface. (We return to the example of blood groups shortly.)

Incomplete Dominance

In **incomplete dominance,** the expression of a trait in a heterozygous individual is somewhere between the expression of the trait in a homozygous dominant individual and the expression of the trait in a homozygous recessive individual. The dominant allele generates a functional protein product. The recessive allele does not generate that product. As a result, a heterozygous person has only one "dose" of the protein product—half the amount in a homozygous dominant person.

Sickle-cell hemoglobin provides an example of incomplete dominance (Figure 20.11). Recall from Chapter 11 that hemoglobin is the pigment in red blood cells that carries oxygen. A red blood cell filled with normal hemoglobin (Hb^A) is a biconcave disk. The allele for sickling hemoglobin (Hb^S) produces an abnormal form of hemoglobin that is less efficient in binding oxygen. In the homozygous sickling condition (Hb^SHb^S), called *sickle-cell anemia,* the red blood cells contain only the abnormal form of hemoglobin. When the oxygen content of the blood drops below a certain level, as might occur during excessive exercise or respiratory difficulty, these red blood cells with abnormal hemoglobin become sickle shaped and tend to clump together. The clumped cells can break open and clog capillaries, causing great pain. Vital organs may be damaged by lack of oxygen. People who are homozygous for sickle-cell anemia usually die at a young age.

The normal allele for the sickle-cell gene shows incomplete dominance, so people who are heterozygous Hb^AHb^S have the *sickle-cell trait.* They have only one "dose" of normal hemoglobin (Hb^A) instead of the normal two doses needed for healthy red blood cells. Thus, people with sickle-cell trait are generally healthy, but sickling and clumping of red cells may occur if there is a prolonged drop in the oxygen content of the blood, as might happen during travel at high elevations. (Sickle-cell anemia is discussed in more detail in Chapter 11.)

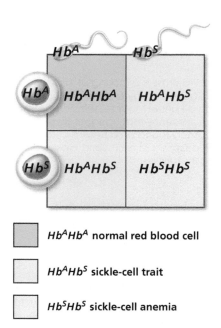

Figure 20.11 The inheritance of sickle-cell trait ($Hb^A Hb^S$) is an example of incomplete dominance.

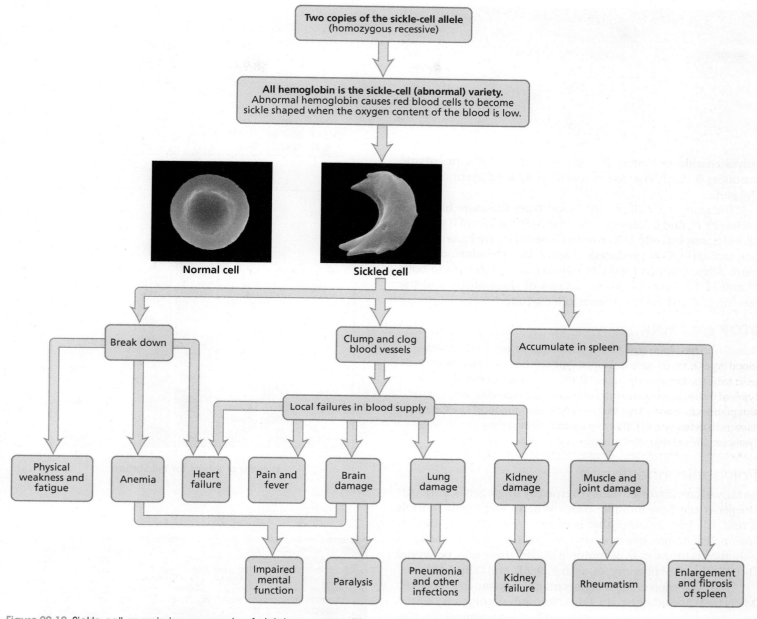

Figure 20.12 Sickle-cell anemia is an example of pleiotropy, a condition in which a single gene has many effects.

STOP and THINK

Straight hair shows incomplete dominance over curly hair. A homozygous dominant person has straight hair; a heterozygous person has wavy hair; and a homozygous recessive person has curly hair. What is the probability that a curly-haired person and a wavy-haired person would have a child with wavy hair?

Pleiotropy

Besides providing an example of incomplete dominance, sickle-cell anemia is an example of **pleiotropy:** one gene leading to many effects. As you can see in Figure 20.12, the sickling of red blood cells caused by the abnormal hemoglobin has effects throughout the body. The sickled cells can break down, clog blood vessels, and accumulate in the spleen. These effects can damage the heart, brain, lungs, kidneys, and muscles and joints.

Multiple Alleles

Many genes have more than two alleles. When three or more forms of a given gene exist, they are referred to as **multiple alleles.** Keep in mind, however, that one individual has only two alleles for a given gene (one on each homologue), even if multiple alleles exist in the population.

The ABO blood types (discussed in Chapter 11) provide an example of multiple alleles. Blood type is determined by the presence of certain polysaccharides (sugars) on the surface of red blood cells. Type A blood has the A polysaccharide; type B has the B polysaccharide; type AB has both A and B polysaccharides; and type O has neither. A specific enzyme directs the synthesis of each kind of

Table 20.2	The Relationship between Genotype and ABO Blood Types	
Genotype	**Blood Type**
$I^A I^A$, $I^A i$	A
$I^B I^B$, $I^B i$	B
$I^A I^B$	AB
ii	O

polysaccharide: one enzyme produces A, and a different enzyme produces B. Each enzyme is specified by a different allele of the gene.

The gene controlling ABO blood types therefore has three alleles: I^A, I^B, and i. Alleles I^A and I^B specify the A and B polysaccharides, respectively. When both these alleles are present, both polysaccharides are produced. I^A and I^B are, therefore, codominant. Allele i, which produces no enzyme, is recessive to both I^A and I^B. The possible combinations of these alleles and the resulting blood types are shown in Table 20.2.

STOP and THINK

A man who has blood type AB is named as the father of a child with blood type O. The mother has blood type B. Is it possible for the named man to be the father of this child? (*Hint*: What are the possible genotypes of the man, woman, and child? Given each possible genotype of this man and woman, what gametes could each produce? Use Punnett squares to determine whether any combination of these genotypes could produce a child with the same genotype as this child.)

Polygenic Inheritance

So far, we have discussed traits governed by single genes, although the genes may have multiple alleles. When a single gene controls a trait, the trait usually either is present or is not, even though incomplete dominance or environmental factors may modify its expression. In the case of multiple alleles, there may be several distinct classes of phenotypes, as in A, B, AB, and O blood types.

The expression of most traits is much more variable, however. Many traits, including height, skin color, and eye color, vary almost continuously from one extreme to another. Environment can play a role in creating such a smooth continuum. For instance, diet and disease influence adult height, and exposure to sunlight darkens skin color. But even when all environmental factors are equal, considerable variation still exists in the expression of certain traits. Such variation results from **polygenic inheritance**—that is, the involvement of two or more genes, often on different chromosomes, in producing a trait. The more genes involved, the smoother the gradations and the greater the extremes of trait expression.

Although human height is probably controlled by more than three genes, for our purposes we will imagine it is determined by only three, partly to simplify our discussion but also to show how much variation in expression is possible even with as few as three genes—*A, B,* and *C*—interacting to determine a trait. Let's assume that the dominant alleles (*A, B, C*) of each gene add height and the recessive alleles (*a, b, c*) do not. How tall would we expect the children to be if both parents were of medium height and heterozygous for all three genes? As you can see in Figure 20.13, there would be seven genetic height

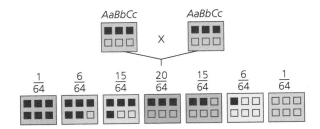

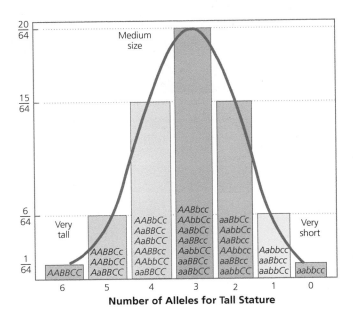

(a)

(b)

Figure 20.13 Human height varies along a continuum. (a) One reason is that height is determined by more than one gene (polygenic inheritance). This figure shows the distribution of alleles for tallness in children of two parents of medium height, assuming that three genes are involved in the determination of height. The top line of boxes shows the parental genotypes, and the second line of boxes indicates the possible genotypes of the offspring. Alleles for tallness are indicated with dark squares. (b) Students organized according to height.

classes, ranging from very short to very tall. The probability of the children having either extreme of stature is slim, 1/64. The most likely probability (a 20/64 chance) is that they will be of medium height, like their parents.

Skin color is also determined by several genes. The allele for the kind of albinism described previously prevents melanin production, so if a person is homozygous recessive for this allele, no melanin can be deposited in the skin. In addition, probably at least four other genes are involved in determining the amount of melanin deposited in the skin. Two alleles for each of four genes would create nine classes of skin color, ranging from pale to dark.

Genes on the Same Chromosome

Scientists estimate that about 20,000 to 25,000 human genes are distributed among the 23 pairs of chromosomes. Thus, each chromosome bears a great number of genes. Genes on the same chromosome tend to be inherited together because an entire chromosome moves into a gamete as a unit. Genes that tend to be inherited together are described as being *linked*. We see, then, that linked genes *usually* do not assort independently. *Usually* is emphasized here because there is a mechanism that can unlink genes on the same chromosome: crossing over (discussed in Chapter 19).

Sex-Linked Genes

Recall from Chapter 19 that one pair of chromosomes consists of the sex chromosomes. There are two kinds of sex chromosomes, X and Y. They are not truly homologous, because the Y chromosome is much smaller than the X chromosome, and they do not carry all of the same genes.[2] The Y chromosome carries very few genes, but it is important in determining gender. If a particular gene found only on the Y chromosome is present, an embryo will develop as a male. Without that gene (whether because there is no Y chromosome or because the gene is missing from the Y chromosome), an embryo will develop as a female. In contrast, most of the genes on an X chromosome have nothing to do with sex determination. For instance, genes for certain blood-clotting factors and for the pigments in cones (the photoreceptors responsible for color vision) are found on the X chromosome but not on the Y chromosome. Furthermore, the X chromosome has about as many genes as a typical autosome does, but the Y chromosome has relatively few. Thus, most genes on the X chromosome have no corresponding alleles on the Y chromosome and are known as **X-linked genes.**

Because most X-linked genes have no homologous allele on the Y chromosome, their pattern of inheritance is different from that of autosomes. A male is XY and therefore will express virtually all of the alleles on his single X chromosome, *even alleles that are recessive.* A female, in contrast, is XX, so she does not always express recessive X alleles. As a result, the recessive phenotype of X-linked genes is much more common in males than in females

[2]X and Y are considered to be a homologous pair because they each have a small region at one end that carries some of the same genes. During meiosis, the tiny homologous region on X and Y will pair in synapsis. As a result, they segregate into gametes in the same way that autosomes do.

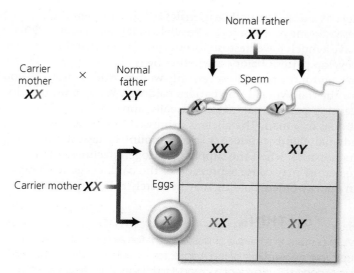

Figure 20.14 Genes that are X linked have a different pattern of inheritance from genes on autosomes, as seen in this cross between a carrier mother and a father who is normal for the trait. The recessive allele is indicated in red. Notice that each son has a 50% chance of displaying the recessive phenotype. All daughters will appear normal, but each daughter has a 50% chance of being a carrier.

(Figure 20.14). Furthermore, a son cannot inherit an X-linked recessive allele from his father. To be male, a child must have inherited his father's Y chromosome, not his father's X chromosome. Consequently, a son can inherit an X-linked recessive allele only from his mother. A daughter, however, can inherit an X-linked recessive allele from either parent. She must be homozygous for the recessive allele to show the recessive phenotype. If she is heterozygous for the trait, she will have a normal phenotype but be a carrier for that trait. Among the disorders caused by X-linked recessive alleles are red-green color blindness, two forms of hemophilia, and Duchenne muscular dystrophy. Red-green color blindness, the inability to distinguish red and green, is discussed in Chapter 9. Hemophilia (discussed in Chapter 11) is a bleeding disorder caused by a lack of a blood-clotting factor: hemophilia A is due to lack of blood-clotting factor VIII, and hemophilia B is due to lack of clotting factor IX. Duchenne muscular dystrophy is discussed in Chapter 6.

STOP and THINK

Why is Duchenne muscular dystrophy inherited from one's mother but usually expressed only in sons? (*Hint:* Consider its mode of inheritance.)

Sex-Influenced Genes

The expression of certain autosomal genes, those not located on the sex chromosomes, is powerfully influenced by the presence of sex hormones and so differs in males and females. Traits expressed by such genes are described as *sex-influenced* traits.

Male pattern baldness, premature hair loss on the top of the head but not on the sides, is an example of a sex-influenced trait. Male pattern baldness is much more common in men than in women because its expression depends on both the presence of the allele for baldness and the presence of testosterone, the male sex hormone. The allele for baldness, then, acts as a dominant allele in males because of their high level of testosterone and as a recessive allele in females because females have a much lower testosterone level. A male with the allele will develop pattern baldness whether he is homozygous or heterozygous for the trait. However, only women who are homozygous for the trait will develop pattern baldness. When a woman does develop pattern baldness, it usually appears later in life than it does in a man. The allele is expressed in women because the adrenal glands produce a small amount of testosterone. After menopause, when the supply of estrogen declines, adrenal testosterone may cause expression of the baldness gene. However, in many women, balding may be merely thinning of hair.

STOP and THINK

Male pattern baldness was passed from father to son through at least four generations of the Adams family. John Adams (1735–1826), the second U.S. president, passed it to his son, John Quincy Adams (1767–1848), the sixth U.S. president. He, in turn, passed the gene to his son, Charles Francis Adams (1807–1886), a diplomat, who passed it to his son, Henry Adams (1838–1918), a historian. Why does father-to-son transmission of the trait rule out X-linked inheritance?

20.2 Breaks in Chromosomes

Chromosomes can break, which may lead to other alterations in structure. Breakage can be caused by certain chemicals, radiation, or viruses. Breakage also occurs as an essential part of crossing over. Although it does not happen often, chromosomes can be misaligned when crossing over occurs. Then, when the pieces reattach, one chromatid will have lost a segment, and the other will have gained a segment.

The loss of a piece of chromosome is called a **deletion.** The most common type of deletion occurs when the tip of a chromosome breaks off and then, during cell division, does not move into the same daughter cell as the rest of the chromosome. Deletion of more than a few genes on an autosome is usually lethal, and the loss of even small regions causes disorders.

In humans, the most common deletion, the loss of a small region near the tip of chromosome 5, causes cri-du-chat syndrome (meaning "cry of the cat"). An infant with this syndrome has a high-pitched cry that sounds like a kitten meowing. The unusual sound of the cry is caused by an improperly developed larynx (voice box). Infants with this syndrome have a round face; wide-set, downward-sloping eyes with a fold of skin at the corner of each eye; and misshapen ears (Figure 20.15). Although the condition is not usually fatal, it does cause severe mental impairment.

The addition of a piece of chromosome is called a **duplication.** The effects of a duplication depend on its size and position. In general, however, a small duplication is less harmful than a deletion of comparable size. A small region of chromosome 9 is sometimes duplicated, producing cells containing three copies of this segment. The result is intellectual disability, accompanied by facial characteristics that may include a bulbous nose; wide-set, squinting eyes; and a lopsided grin.

Genetic disorders also occur when certain sequences of DNA are duplicated multiple times. Fragile X syndrome provides an example. The syndrome is so named because an abnormally long

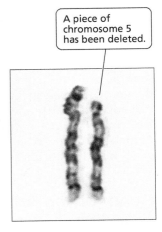

A piece of chromosome 5 has been deleted.

Figure 20.15 Occurring in 1 of every 50,000 live births, cri-du-chat syndrome is the most common genetic deletion found in humans. It is caused by the loss of a small region near the tip of chromosome 5.

sequence of repeats caused by duplication makes the X chromosome fragile and easily broken. Besides making the chromosome fragile, the repeated DNA can shut down the activity of the entire chromosome. Fragile X syndrome is the most common form of inherited mental impairment, affecting roughly 1 in 1250 males and 1 in 2500 females. It is not known, however, exactly how Fragile X syndrome causes the impairment. Other characteristics may include attention deficit, hyperactivity, autistic symptoms, large ears, long face, and flat feet (Figure 20.16).

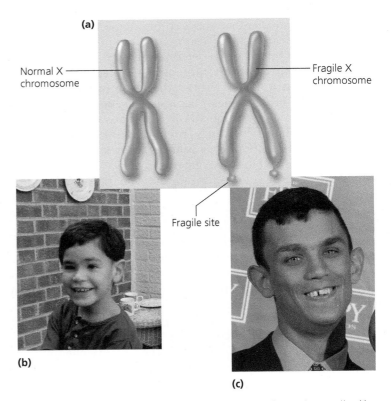

(a)

Normal X chromosome

Fragile X chromosome

Fragile site

(b)

(c)

Figure 20.16 Fragile X syndrome. (a) Duplication of a region on the X chromosome makes the chromosome fragile and easily broken. (b) A child with Fragile X syndrome appears normal. (c) Characteristics of an adult with Fragile X syndrome include a long face and large ears. In addition, Fragile X syndrome causes mental impairment.

20.3 Detecting Genetic Disorders

More than 4000 disorders are known to have their roots in our genes. Tests are now available to look for predispositions to many of these genetic disorders. Some tests can even confirm the presence of a suspected disease-related allele in a particular person. Knowledge about the presence or absence of a faulty gene can be very helpful to couples who are planning a family. Normal, healthy parents can carry recessive alleles for disorders such as CF and Tay-Sachs disease (a disorder of lipid metabolism that causes death, usually between the ages of 1 and 5; discussed in Chapter 3), which they may pass on to their children. Testing is available for both of these recessive alleles. You can read more about the pros and cons of genetic testing in the Ethical Issue essay, *Gene Testing*.

When specific tests are unavailable, pedigree analysis can help prospective parents determine whether they *might* be carriers of recessive alleles. It cannot answer the question with certainty, but it does allow people to weigh the risks of passing a lethal allele to their children versus the possibility of having a child who is not affected.

Prenatal Genetic Testing

Prenatal testing of a fetus is usually recommended when a defective gene runs in the family or when the mother is older than 35 (because age increases the risk of problems due to failure of the homologous chromosomes to separate; see Chapter 19). Two procedures are available for diagnosing genetic problems in the fetus: amniocentesis and chorionic villi sampling. Although it is possible to look for more than 100 disorders with these procedures, tests are run only for those disorders that are common as well as any that are of particular concern in that pregnancy. Reassuring results from either form of prenatal testing cannot guarantee a healthy baby, even though these tests are highly accurate in detecting genetic disorders.

In **amniocentesis,** a needle is inserted through the lower abdomen into the uterus, and a small amount of amniotic fluid is withdrawn. Floating in the amniotic fluid are living cells that were sloughed off the fetus. These cells are grown in the laboratory for a week or two and then examined for abnormalities in the number of chromosomes and for the presence of certain alleles that are likely to cause specific diseases. Biochemical tests are also done on the fluid to detect certain chemicals that indicate problems. For example, a high level of alpha-fetoprotein, a substance produced by the fetus, suggests a problem with the development of the central nervous system (a neural tube defect).

Amniocentesis is usually done between 15 and 20 weeks after the woman's last menstrual period, when there is enough amniotic fluid to minimize the risk of injuring the fetus. Amniocentesis is generally safe for both the mother and the fetus, but it does carry a small risk of triggering a miscarriage or of needle injury to the mother and subsequent infection or bleeding.

Chorionic villi sampling (CVS) removes and analyzes a small amount of tissue containing chorionic villi, the small, fingerlike projections of the part of the placenta called the *chorion* (see Chapter 18). Cells of the chorion have the same genetic material as those of the fetus. Gentle suction is then used to remove a small tissue sample, which can be analyzed for genetic abnormalities.

There are pros and cons to CVS. Advantages are that it can be performed several weeks earlier in the pregnancy than amniocentesis can, and the results are available within a few days. If there is a genetic problem in the fetus and the couple wishes to terminate the pregnancy, the procedure can thus be performed earlier in the pregnancy, when it is safer for the mother. When abortion is not chosen, early diagnosis allows more time to plan the safest time, location, and method of delivery. A disadvantage of CVS is that it has a slightly greater risk of triggering miscarriage than does amniocentesis.

If detected early enough, certain birth defects can be prevented. Congenital adrenal hyperplasia (an overgrowth of the adrenal glands), for instance, will cause a female fetus to develop abnormal genitalia, unless she is treated with hormones from week 10 to week 16 of gestation. Early diagnosis of this disorder through CVS can tell a physician whether hormone treatment is needed.

Noninvasive genetic prenatal testing looks for chromosomal abnormalities—primarily trisomy 21, trisomy 13, and trisomy 18—in fetal cell–free DNA found in a sample of the mother's blood. These noninvasive screening tests can be done much earlier in a pregnancy and don't risk a miscarriage. However, the rate of false positives (detecting abnormalities that don't exist) is higher than with invasive prenatal tests. So, if abnormalities are detected, this type of testing should be followed by amniocentesis or CVS.

Newborn Genetic Testing

A simple blood test is used routinely to screen newborns for phenylketonuria (PKU), an inherited metabolic disorder. People with PKU produce a defective enzyme that prevents them from converting phenylalanine (an amino acid in food) to tyrosine. As a result, they have too much phenylalanine in their bodies and too little tyrosine, an imbalance that somehow causes brain damage. Although nothing can be done to correct the enzyme, diagnosis of the genetic disorder allows doctors and parents to prevent brain damage by keeping the infant on a strict diet that excludes most phenylalanine. Nearly all proteins contain phenylalanine, so it is often necessary to substitute a specially prepared mixture of amino acids for most protein-containing foods, such as meat. It is also necessary to avoid foods containing the artificial sweetener NutraSweet, which contains aspartame, consisting of the amino acids phenylalanine and aspartic acid. When aspartame is digested, phenylalanine is separated from aspartic acid and can reach dangerous levels.

Adult Genetic Testing

Many predictive genetic tests for adults are now available or being developed. These tests identify people who are at risk of getting a disease but do not yet have symptoms. They are simple tests that can usually be done with a small blood sample. When steps can be taken to prevent the disease, predictive genetic tests can be lifesaving. For instance, colon cancer will develop in nearly everyone who has the alleles for familial adenomatous

ETHICAL ISSUE

Gene Testing

Genetic screening is the practice of testing people who have no symptoms to determine whether they carry genes that will influence their chances of developing certain genetic diseases. Genetic screening technologies are advancing rapidly, and their use is gaining popularity. However, genetic screening raises many ethical questions.

Among the advantages of genetic testing is that it enables people who discover they are at risk for a treatable or preventable condition to take steps to reduce their risk. By informing people that they carry a recessive allele they were unaware of or a dominant allele that is not expressed until late in life, genetic screening can also help reduce the incidence of serious genetic disorders in future generations. Consider Tay-Sachs disease, an autosomal recessive disorder that causes the death of children, usually by the age of 5. Tay-Sachs disease is especially prevalent in descendants of Jewish people from eastern Europe. As a result of voluntary screening programs, the number of children born with Tay-Sachs disease has decreased tenfold in many communities.

Genetic testing also has a dark side. The psychological consequences of test results can be devastating. Many genetic disorders cannot be prevented or treated. How does a person who may have one of these disorders prepare for the consequences of knowing now what will result in his or her death? Huntington's disease, for example, is caused by a dominant allele that provides no hints of its existence until relatively late in life, usually past child-bearing years. About 60% of people with Huntington's disease are diagnosed between the ages of 35 and 50. The gene causes degeneration of the brain, leading to muscle spasms, personality disorders, and death, usually within 10 to 15 years. Because Huntington's disease is caused by a dominant allele, a bearer has a 50% chance of passing it to his or her children. Thus, a person whose parent died of Huntington's disease might well be tested and receive the good news that the test did not detect the allele. But it is equally likely that the allele *will* show up in the test. Many persons at risk for Huntington's disease prefer to live without knowing their possible fate.

There is also concern that the results of genetic tests will not remain private information but instead be used by employers as well as life and health insurers. If you were an employer who had genetic information about prospective employees, would you choose to invest time and money in training a person who carried an allele that increased the risk of cancer, heart disease, Alzheimer's disease, or alcoholism? As an insurer, would you knowingly cover such a carrier?

The results of genetic testing can have both positive and negative consequences for individuals being tested and for their families. Who, then, should decide whether screening should be done, for which genes, on whom, and in which communities? At first blush, one might be tempted to say, "There oughta be a law!" Should we leave ethical issues to judges and legislators? Should moral matters be decided by society or clergy? Or should they be personal decisions? These are not easy questions to answer, or even to think about—yet if we do not take part in the debate, we will be allowing others to decide these crucial issues for us.

Questions to Consider

- If genetic testing *is* done, should the person being tested be told the results no matter what? If the affected person is an infant, should the parents always be told the results, even if the condition is poorly understood? How do we balance helping such children with the possibility of stigmatizing them?

- We live in a world of limited resources. In addition to deciding who should be tested, we must decide who should pay the bill. Both testing and treatment are expensive. Should testing be done only when treatment or preventive measures are available? How much say should the agent that pays for the procedure have in deciding who is tested and who receives medical treatment?

polyposis, a condition in which thousands of benign polyps grow in the intestine. If the disorder is diagnosed, a person can be routinely inspected for colon polyps. Any polyps found can be removed, and cancer can be prevented. Genetic counselors help people understand their risks of developing inherited disorders and the medical consequences of such disorders.

Other predictive genetic tests look for alleles that might predispose a person to a disorder. A protein that transports cholesterol in the blood, called ApoE, comes in three forms, each specified by a different allele. Having two alleles for ApoE-2, one form of the protein, causes catastrophically high blood cholesterol levels, which can lead to heart attack and stroke. Knowing that a person has this genetic makeup, a physician could prescribe medication to lower blood cholesterol.

what would YOU do? Having two copies of another *ApoE* allele, *ApoE-4*, increases a person's risk of heart disease by 30% to 50%. It also nearly guarantees that the person will develop Alzheimer's disease by 80 years of age. Alzheimer's disease is an untreatable condition in which brain tissue degenerates, gradually robbing the person of memories, of the ability to function normally in society, and eventually of life itself (see Chapter 7). Suppose a genetic test that is performed out of concern for a person's risk of heart disease reveals the presence of two copies of *ApoE-4*. In your opinion, is a physician with this knowledge morally obligated to tell the patient about the inevitability of Alzheimer's disease? If your genes were tested and found to have two copies of *ApoE-4*, would you want to be told? Why or why not? ■

LOOKING AHEAD

In this chapter, we learned about the chromosomal basis of human inheritance. In the next chapter, we will look more closely at DNA and the mechanisms by which genes affect cellular activity and development.

CONSIDER THIS CASE

Katie and Doug have a child, Lulu, who has cri-du-chat syndrome, which is caused by the loss of a small region of chromosome 5. Katie's sister, Sarah, knows that 50% of her genes are the same as Katie's because they have the same parents. Sarah also knows that Lulu has a genetic syndrome, so she is afraid that her children may be born with cri-du-chat syndrome. Her doctor said, "Don't worry. Although cri-du-chat is a genetic condition, it is not inherited from either parent." Sarah is confused by this comment.

■ How would you explain the doctor's remark to Sarah?

Chapter Review   MasteringBiology®

Students Go to MasteringBiology for assignments, the eText, and the Study Area with animations, practice tests, and activities.

Professors Go to MasteringBiology for automatically graded tutorials and questions that you can assign to your students, plus Instructor Resources.

Highlighting the Concepts

20.1 Principles of Inheritance pp. 419–430)

■ Different forms of a gene are called alleles. An individual who has two of the same alleles is said to be homozygous. An individual with two different alleles for a gene is said to be heterozygous. The allele that is expressed in the heterozygous condition is described as dominant. The allele that is masked in the heterozygous condition is described as recessive.

■ The genotype for one or more traits consists of the specific alleles present in an individual. The phenotype refers to the observable expression of the trait or traits.

■ The alleles for each gene separate during gamete formation so that half the gametes receive one allele and the other half receive the other allele.

■ Each pair of alleles located on one kind of chromosome separate into gametes independently of the alleles of a gene pair located on a different kind of chromosome.

■ If a homozygous dominant individual (AA) mates with a homozygous recessive one (aa), the genotypes of all the offspring would be heterozygous (Aa) and the dominant phenotype. If heterozygous individuals (Aa) mate, the probable genotypes of children will be 1 in 4 (25%) homozygous dominant (AA) : 2 in 4 (50%) heterozygous dominant (Aa) : 1 in 4 (25%) homozygous recessive (aa). Their phenotypes will be 3 dominant : 1 recessive.

■ Pedigrees, which are diagrams constructed to show the genetic relationships among individuals in an extended family, are often useful in determining the unknown genotypes of humans showing dominant phenotypes.

■ In many cases, the dominant allele produces a functional protein, and the recessive allele produces a nonfunctional protein or no protein at all.

■ In complete dominance, the dominant allele completely masks the recessive allele. When two alleles are codominant, both are apparent in the phenotype. In incomplete dominance, the expression of the trait in a heterozygous individual is somewhere in between the expression of the trait in a homozygous dominant individual and the expression of the trait in a homozygous recessive individual.

■ Three or more alleles for a particular gene in a population are called multiple alleles. ABO blood types are determined by three alleles: I^A, I^B, and i. Blood type refers to the presence of certain polysaccharides on the surface of red blood cells.

■ Many traits, including height, skin pigmentation, and eye color, are determined by more than one gene (polygenic inheritance). Such traits show a wide range of variation. Moreover, when many genes are involved in determining a trait, the variation in expression can be continuous.

■ An X-linked gene is one that is located on the X chromosome and that has no corresponding allele on the Y chromosome. A recessive X-linked allele will always be expressed in a male, but in a female it will be expressed only in the homozygous condition.

■ The expression of a sex-influenced trait depends on both the presence of the allele and the presence of sex hormones. Therefore, the expression of the allele depends on the person's sex.

20.2 Breaks in Chromosomes (p. 430)

■ The loss of a piece of chromosome is called a deletion. The gain of a piece of chromosome is called a duplication. Either chromosome abnormality can cause a genetic disorder.

20.3 Detecting Genetic Disorders (pp. 431–432)

■ Tests such as amniocentesis and chorionic villi sampling (CVS) are available to determine whether a fetus is likely to develop a genetic disease. In amniocentesis, a sample of amniotic fluid is taken. The fluid and the fetal cells in the fluid are analyzed for genetic problems. CVS samples cells from the chorion of the placenta and analyzes them for genetic disorders.

Recognizing Key Terms

gene *p. 420*
trait *p. 420*
allele *p. 420*
homozygous *p. 420*
heterozygous *p. 420*
dominant allele *p. 420*

recessive allele *p. 420*
genotype *p. 420*
phenotype *p. 420*
pedigree *p. 423*
carrier *p. 424*
complete dominance *p. 426*

codominance *p. 426*
incomplete dominance
  p. 426
pleiotropy *p. 427*
multiple alleles *p. 427*
polygenic inheritance *p. 428*

X-linked genes *p. 429*
deletion *p. 430*
duplication *p. 430*
amniocentesis *p. 431*
chorionic villi sampling (CVS)
  p. 431

Reviewing the Concepts

1. Which of the following crosses could produce offspring with the recessive phenotype?
   a. *AA* × *aa*
   b. *Aa* × *Aa*
   c. *AA* × *Aa*
   d. *AA* × *AA*

2. All of the following crosses have a 50% probability of producing heterozygous offspring *except*
   a. *AA* × *aa*.
   b. *Aa* × *Aa*.
   c. *AA* × *Aa*.
   d. *Aa* × *aa*.

3. Which of the following is an example of a phenotype?
   a. a man with hemophilia
   b. a female carrier for cystic fibrosis
   c. XY
   d. a heterozygote

4. Huntington's disease is caused by a dominant allele. If a mother has Huntington's disease but the father does not carry the dominant allele, what is the probability that the first child will be normal?
   a. 0%
   b. 25%
   c. 50%
   d. 100%

5. In the previous example, what is the probability that the second child will be normal?
   a. 0%
   b. 25%
   c. 50%
   d. 100%

6. How many different gametes could a person with the genotype *Aabbcc* form? (The genes are on different chromosomes.)
   a. 2
   b. 4
   c. 16
   d. 64

7. How many different gametes could a person with the genotype *AaBbCc* form? (The genes are on different chromosomes.)
   a. 2
   b. 4
   c. 16
   d. 64

8. Cystic fibrosis is caused by a recessive allele, *c*. What is the probability that two people who are carriers for cystic fibrosis will have a child who is also a carrier?
   a. 0%
   b. 25%
   c. 50%
   d. 100%

9. A trait controlled by many genes is described as being _____.

10. The _____ of an individual is the physical expression of one or more genes of interest, and the _____ is the set of alleles the person possesses for the gene or genes of interest.

11. The genotype of a person with two copies of the same allele is _____ and the genotype of a person with two different alleles for a trait is _____.

12. Genes for different traits that are located on the same chromosome are described as being _____.

Applying the Concepts

1. Klaus has red-green color blindness, which is a sex-linked recessive trait. His wife, Helen, is homozygous for normal color vision. (Normal color vision is dominant to red-green color blindness.) What is the probability of their having a color-blind daughter? What is the probability of their having a color-blind son?

2. George and Sue have an infant, Sammy, who is lethargic, is vomiting, and has liver disease. Sammy is diagnosed with galactosemia, an autosomal recessive disorder in which the affected individuals are unable to metabolize the milk sugar galactose. Sammy is placed on a diet free of lactose and galactose and slowly recovers. George and Sue would like to have a second child. What are the chances that the second child will have galactosemia? (*Hint:* What are the genotypes of George and

Sue? Use a Punnett square to determine the expected results of a cross with those genotypes.)

3. Explain why the offspring of first cousins are more likely to have harmful recessive traits than are offspring of unrelated individuals.

4. A woman with blood type AB names a man with blood type O as the father of her child. The child has blood type AB. Could the man be the father? Why or why not?

5. Straight hair shows incomplete dominance over curly hair. A homozygous dominant person has straight hair; a heterozygote has wavy hair; and a homozygous recessive person has curly hair. The first child of a curly-haired person and a wavy-haired person has wavy hair. What is the probability that a second child would have wavy hair?

Finding and Evaluating Information

In this chapter, we have considered chromosome deletions and environmental effects on genes. The following is an excerpt from Gunjan Sinha's report in *Science Daily News*, "Smoking erases Y chromomes." You can read the entire report at Gunjan Sinha, *Science Daily News*, 4 December 2014, 2:15 P.M., <http://news.sciencemag.org/biology/2014/12/smoking-erases-y-chromosomes#disqus_thread>

"To conduct the study, molecular oncologist Jan Dumanski and statistician Lars Forsberg of Uppsala University in Sweden took advantage of data collected from three ongoing Swedish trials. The long-term studies are looking for associations between behavioral, lifestyle, or other traits and disease. As part of the studies, data and blood are collected periodically. Dumanski and Forsberg compared the DNA in blood cells of smokers to nonsmokers in more than 6000 men. The only factors that correlated with high Y chromosome loss were age and smoking, the team reports online today in *Science*[i], with smokers 2.4 to 4.3 times more likely to be missing Y chromosomes in their blood cells than nonsmokers."

1. Do the results of this study show that smoking causes the loss of the Y chromosome, as implied by the title of the report?

2. Use reliable sources to find other possible environmental effects on the structure of chromosomes. Evaluate the research methods to determine whether the conclusions are valid.

[i] J. Dumanski et al., "Smoking is associated with mosaic loss of chromosome Y," *Science* 347 (6217) [2015]: 81–83.

DNA and Biotechnology

21

DID YOU KNOW?

- Each year hundreds of children are reunited with their families by DNA testing.

- The DNA in each of your cells consists of about 3 billion chemical "letters," called nucleotides.

- If you unwound all the DNA in all your cells and attached the strands end to end, it would reach to the sun and back more than 600 times.

IN CHAPTER 20, we learned about the chromosomal basis of inheritance. In this chapter, we become familiar with the structure and function of DNA and discover how this molecule is able to serve as the basis of our genetic inheritance as well as the source for the diversity of life on Earth. We learn that the importance of DNA on a personal level is that it directs the synthesis of specific polypeptides (proteins) that play structural or functional roles in our bodies. We then consider the technology that our understanding of DNA has already made available and what possibilities such technology may hold for the future.

21.1 Form of DNA

DNA is sometimes referred to as the thread of life—and a very slender thread it is. When DNA is unwound, it measures a mere 50-trillionths of an inch in diameter. If all the DNA strands in a single cell were fastened together end to end, the thread would stretch more than 5 feet in length. DNA might also be considered the thread that ties all life together, because the DNA of organisms ranging from bacteria to humans is built from the same kinds of subunits. The order of these subunits encodes the information needed to make the proteins that build and maintain life.

Deoxyribonucleic acid, or **DNA,** is a double-stranded molecule resembling a ladder that is gently twisted to form a spiral called a *double helix,* as shown in Figure 21.1. Each side of the ladder, including half of each rung, is made from a string of repeating subunits called *nucleotides.* You may recall from Chapter 2 that a nucleotide is composed of three subunits, including one sugar (deoxyribose, in DNA), one phosphate, and one nitrogenous base. DNA contains four types of nitrogenous bases: adenine (A), guanine (G), thymine (T), and cytosine (C). The sides of the ladder

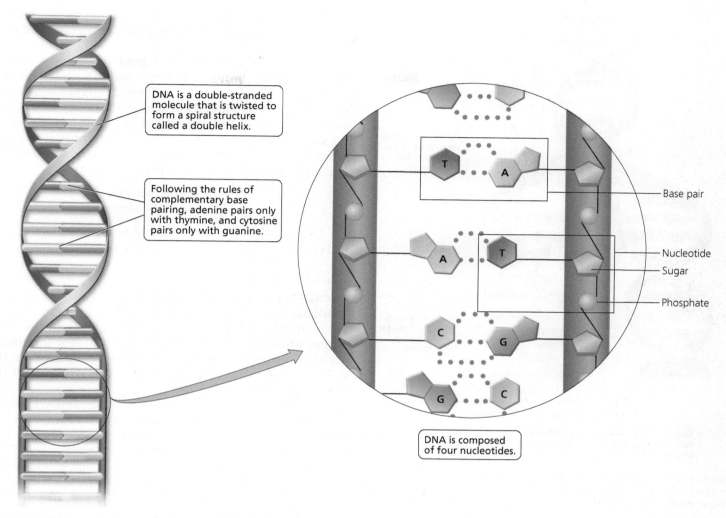

Figure 21.1 DNA is a double-stranded molecule that twists to form a spiral structure called a double helix.

are composed of alternating sugars and phosphates; the rungs consist of paired nitrogenous bases. The bases attach to each other according to the rules of **complementary base pairing:** adenine pairs *only* with thymine (creating an A–T pair), and cytosine pairs *only* with guanine (creating a C–G pair). Each base pair is held together by weak hydrogen bonds. The pairing of complementary bases is specific because of the shapes of the bases and the number of hydrogen bonds that can form between them. You may also recall from Chapter 2 that a molecule formed by the joining of nucleotides is known as a *nucleic acid.* Thus, DNA is a nucleic acid.

Because base pairing is so specific, the bases on one strand of DNA are *always* complementary to the bases on the other strand. Thus, the order of bases on one strand determines the sequence of bases on the other strand. For instance, if the sequence of bases on one strand were CATATGAG, what would the complementary sequence be? Remember, cytosine (C) always pairs with guanine (G), and adenine (A) always pairs with thymine (T). As a result, the complementary sequence on the opposite strand would be GTATACTC.

The DNA within each human cell has an astounding 3 billion base pairs. Although the pairing of adenine with thymine and cytosine with guanine is specific and does not vary, the sequence of bases throughout the length of different DNA molecules can vary in myriad ways. As we will see, genetic information is encoded in the exact sequence of bases.

21.2 Replication of DNA

For DNA to be the basis of inheritance, its genetic instructions must be passed from one generation to the next. Moreover, for DNA to direct the activities of each cell, its instructions must be present in every cell. These requirements dictate that DNA be copied before both mitotic and meiotic cell division (see Chapter 19). It is important that the copies be exact. The key to the precision of the copying process is that the bases are complementary.

❶ As you can see in Figure 21.2, the copying process, or **DNA replication,** begins when an enzyme breaks the weak hydrogen bonds that hold together the paired bases that make up nucleotide strands of the double helix, thereby "unzipping" and unwinding the strands. ❷ As a result, the nitrogenous bases on the separated regions of each strand are temporarily exposed, allowing each to serve as a template for a new strand. ❸ Free nucleotide bases, which are always present within the nucleus, can then attach to complementary bases on the open

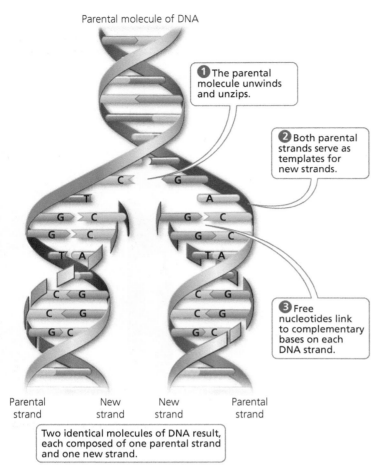

Parental molecule of DNA

1 The parental molecule unwinds and unzips.

2 Both parental strands serve as templates for new strands.

3 Free nucleotides link to complementary bases on each DNA strand.

| Parental strand | New strand | New strand | Parental strand |

Two identical molecules of DNA result, each composed of one parental strand and one new strand.

Figure 21.2 DNA replication is called semiconservative because each daughter molecule consists of one "parental" strand and one "new" strand.

DNA strands. Enzymes called *DNA polymerases* link the sugars and phosphates of the newly attached nucleotides to form a new strand. As each of the new double-stranded DNA molecules forms, it twists into a double helix.

Each strand of the original DNA molecule serves as a template for the formation of a new strand. This process is called **semiconservative replication** because in each of the new double-stranded DNA molecules, one original (parent) strand is saved (conserved) and the other (daughter) strand is new. The original (parental) strand of nucleotides in each new molecule of DNA. Look at Figure 21.2. Notice the original (parental) strand of nucleotides in each new molecule of DNA. Complementary base pairing creates two new DNA molecules that are identical to the parent molecule.

21.3 Gene Expression

The process of replication ensures that genetic information is passed accurately from a parent cell to daughter cells and from generation to generation. The next obvious question is, "How does DNA issue commands that direct cellular activities?" The answer is that DNA directs the synthesis of another nucleic acid—**ribonucleic acid, or RNA.** RNA, in turn, directs the synthesis of a polypeptide (a part of a protein) or a protein. The

protein may be a structural part of the cell or play a functional role, such as an enzyme that speeds up certain chemical reactions within the cell.

Recall from Chapter 20 that a **gene** is a segment of DNA that contains the instructions for producing a specific protein (or, in some cases, a specific polypeptide).[1] The sequence of bases in DNA determines the sequence of bases in RNA, which in turn determines the sequence of amino acids of a protein. We say that the gene is expressed when the protein it codes for is produced. The resulting protein is the molecular basis of the inherited trait; it determines the phenotype.

Gene expression:
DNA→RNA→Protein

To more fully appreciate how gene expression works, we will consider each step in slightly greater detail.

RNA Synthesis

Just as the CEO of a major company issues commands from headquarters instead of from the factory floor, DNA issues instructions from the cell nucleus and not from the cytoplasm, where the cell's work is done. RNA is the intermediary that carries the information encoded in DNA from the nucleus to the cytoplasm and directs the synthesis of the specified protein.

Like DNA, RNA is composed of nucleotides linked together, but there are some important differences between DNA and RNA, as shown in Table 21.1. First, the nucleotides of RNA contain the sugar ribose, instead of the deoxyribose found in DNA. Second, in RNA the nucleotide uracil (U) pairs with adenine, whereas in DNA thymine (T) pairs with adenine (A). Third, most RNA is single stranded. Recall that DNA is a double-stranded molecule.

The first step in converting the DNA message to a protein is to copy the message as RNA, by a process called **transcription.**

transcription
DNA → RNA → Protein

Table 21.1	Comparison of DNA and RNA	
	DNA	**RNA**
Similarities	Are nucleic acids	
	Are composed of linked nucleotides	
	Have a sugar-phosphate backbone	
	Have four types of bases	
Differences	Is a double-stranded molecule	Is a single-stranded molecule
	Has a sugar deoxyribose	Has a sugar ribose
	Contains the bases adenine, guanine, cytosine, and thymine	Contains the bases adenine, guanine, cytosine, and uracil (instead of thymine)
	Functions primarily in the nucleus	Functions primarily in the cytoplasm

[1]We will develop this concept as the chapter proceeds. Some genes code for a polypeptide that is only part of a functional protein. A gene can also code for RNA that forms part of a ribosome or that transports amino acids during protein synthesis.

Table 21.2   Review of the Functions of RNA

Molecule	Functions
Messenger RNA (mRNA)	Carries DNA's information in the sequence of its bases (codons) from the nucleus to the cytoplasm
Transfer RNA (tRNA)	Binds to a specific amino acid and transports it to be added, as appropriate, to a growing polypeptide chain
Ribosomal RNA (rRNA)	Combines with protein to form ribosomes (structures on which polypeptides are synthesized)

Three types of RNA are produced in cells. Each plays a different role in protein synthesis (Table 21.2). **Messenger RNA (mRNA)** carries DNA's instructions for synthesizing a particular protein from the nucleus to the cytoplasm. The order of bases in mRNA specifies the sequence of amino acids in the resulting protein, as we will see. Each **transfer RNA (tRNA)** molecule is specialized to bring a specific amino acid to where it can be added to a polypeptide that is under construction. **Ribosomal RNA (rRNA)** combines with proteins to form ribosomes, which are the structures on which protein synthesis occurs.

❶ Transcription begins with the unwinding and unzipping of the specific region of DNA to be copied; these actions are performed by an enzyme. The DNA message is determined by the order of bases in the unzipped region of the DNA molecule. ❷ One of the unwound strands of the DNA molecule serves as the template during transcription. RNA nucleotides present in the nucleus pair with their complementary bases on the template—cytosine with guanine and uracil with adenine (**Figure 21.3**). The signal to start transcription is given by a specific sequence of bases on DNA, called the **promoter.** The enzyme **RNA polymerase** binds with the promoter on DNA and then moves along the DNA strand, opening up the DNA helix in front of it and then aligning the appropriate RNA nucleotides and linking them together; the region of DNA that has been transcribed zips again after RNA polymerase passes by. Another sequence of bases on the DNA signals RNA polymerase to stop transcription. ❸ After transcription ceases, the newly formed strand of RNA, known as the *RNA transcript,* is released from the DNA.

Messenger RNA usually undergoes certain modifications before it leaves the nucleus (**Figure 21.4**). Most stretches of DNA between a promoter and the stop signal include regions that do not contain codes that will be translated into protein. These unexpressed regions of DNA are called *introns,* short for *intervening sequences.* The regions of mRNA corresponding to the introns are snipped out of the newly formed mRNA strand by enzymes before the strand leaves the nucleus. The remaining segments of DNA or mRNA, called *exons* for *expressed sequences,* splice together to form the sequence that directs the synthesis of a protein.

Protein Synthesis

The newly formed mRNA carries the genetic message (transcribed from DNA) from the nucleus to the cytoplasm, where it is translated into protein at the ribosomes. Just as we might

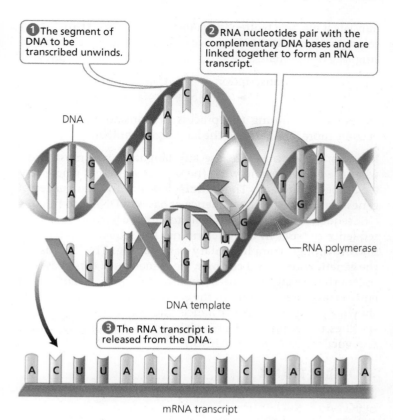

❶ The segment of DNA to be transcribed unwinds.

❷ RNA nucleotides pair with the complementary DNA bases and are linked together to form an RNA transcript.

DNA

RNA polymerase

DNA template

❸ The RNA transcript is released from the DNA.

mRNA transcript

Figure 21.3 Transcription is the process of producing RNA from a DNA template.

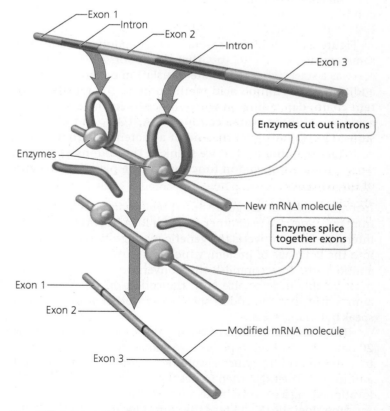

Exon 1
Intron
Exon 2
Intron
Exon 3

Enzymes

Enzymes cut out introns

New mRNA molecule

Enzymes splice together exons

Exon 1
Exon 2
Exon 3

Modified mRNA molecule

Figure 21.4 Newly formed messenger RNA is modified before it leaves the nucleus. Noncoding regions of DNA called introns are snipped out of the corresponding regions of mRNA molecule. Segments of mRNA that code for protein are then spliced together.

translate a message written in Spanish into English, **translation** converts the nucleotide language of mRNA into the amino acid language of a protein.

$$\text{DNA} \xrightarrow{\text{transcription}} \text{RNA} \xrightarrow{\text{translation}} \text{Protein}$$

Before examining the process of translation, we should become more familiar with the language of mRNA.

The genetic code To use any language, you must know what the words are and what they mean, as well as where sentences begin and end. The **genetic code** is the "language" of genes that translates the sequence of bases in DNA into the specific sequence of amino acids in a protein. We have seen that the sequence of bases in DNA determines the sequence of bases in mRNA through complementary base pairing. The "words" in the genetic code, called **codons,** are sequences of three bases on mRNA that specify 1 of the 20 amino acids or the beginning or end of the protein chain. All the codons of the genetic code are shown in Figure 21.5. For instance, the codon UUC on mRNA specifies the amino acid phenylalanine. (The complementary sequence on DNA would be AAG.)

STOP and THINK

Look at the mRNA transcript in Figure 21.3. Notice that the codon at the end of the mRNA strand is GUA. Which amino acid does this specify? (Use Figure 21.5.)

The four bases in RNA (A, U, C, and G) could form 64 combinations of three-base sequences. The number of possible codons, therefore, exceeds the number of amino acids. As Figure 21.5 indicates, several sets of codons code for the same amino acid. Note, too, that the codon AUG either can serve as a start signal to initiate translation or can specify the addition of the amino acid methionine to the growing protein chain, depending on where it occurs in the mRNA molecule. In addition, three codons (UAA, UAG, and UGA) are stop codons that signal the end of a protein and that do not code for an amino acid. If we think of the codons as genetic words, then a stop codon functions as the period at the end of the sentence.

Transfer RNA A language interpreter translates a message from one language to another. Transfer RNA (tRNA) serves as an interpreter that converts the genetic message carried by mRNA into the language of protein, which is a particular sequence of amino acids. To accomplish this conversion, a tRNA molecule must be able to recognize both the codon on mRNA and the amino acid that the codon specifies—in other words, it must speak both languages.

There are many kinds of tRNA—at least one for each of the 20 amino acids. Each type of tRNA molecule binds to a particular amino acid. Enzymes ensure tRNA binds with the correct amino acid. The tRNA then ferries the amino acid to the correct location along a strand of mRNA (Figure 21.6).

How does the tRNA know the correct location along mRNA? The location is determined by a sequence of three nucleotides on the tRNA called the **anticodon.** In a sense, the anticodon

First base	Second base				Third base
	U	**C**	**A**	**G**	
U	UUU Phenylalanine	UCU Serine	UAU Tyrosine	UGU Cysteine	U
	UUC Phenylalanine	UCC Serine	UAC Tyrosine	UGC Cysteine	C
	UUA Leucine	UCA Serine	UAA *stop*	UGA *stop*	A
	UUG Leucine	UCG Serine	UAG *stop*	UGG Tryptophan	G
C	CUU Leucine	CCU Proline	CAU Histidine	CGU Arginine	U
	CUC Leucine	CCC Proline	CAC Histidine	CGC Arginine	C
	CUA Leucine	CCA Proline	CAA Glutamine	CGA Arginine	A
	CUG Leucine	CCG Proline	CAG Glutamine	CGG Arginine	G
A	AUU Isoleucine	ACU Threonine	AAU Asparagine	AGU Serine	U
	AUC Isoleucine	ACC Threonine	AAC Asparagine	AGC Serine	C
	AUA Isoleucine	ACA Threonine	AAA Lysine	AGA Arginine	A
	AUG (start) Methionine	ACG Threonine	AAG Lysine	AGG Arginine	G
G	GUU Valine	GCU Alanine	GAU Asparagine	GGU Glycine	U
	GUC Valine	GCC Alanine	GAC Asparagine	GGC Glycine	C
	GUA Valine	GCA Alanine	GAA Glutamic acid	GGA Glycine	A
	GUG Valine	GCG Alanine	GAG Glutamic acid	GGG Glycine	G

Figure 21.5 The genetic code. Each sequence of three bases on the mRNA molecules, called a codon, specifies a specific amino acid, a start signal, or a stop signal.

Q: If the sequence of bases following a start signal were AACUCAGCC, which amino acids would be specified?

"reads" the language of mRNA by binding to a codon on the mRNA molecule according to the complementary base-pairing rules. When the tRNA's anticodon binds to the mRNA's codon, the specific amino acid attached to the tRNA is brought to the growing polypeptide chain. For example, a tRNA molecule with the anticodon AAG binds to the amino acid phenylalanine and ferries it to the mRNA molecule, where the codon UUC is presented for translation. Phenylalanine will then be added to the growing amino acid chain.

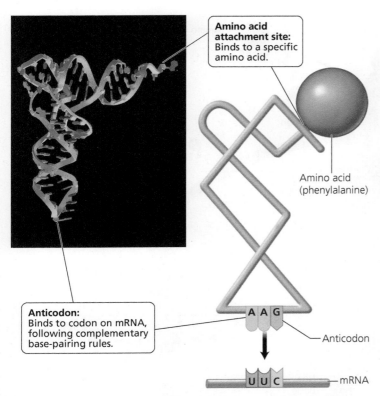

Amino acid attachment site: Binds to a specific amino acid.

Amino acid (phenylalanine)

Anticodon

Anticodon: Binds to codon on mRNA, following complementary base-pairing rules.

A A G

U U C — mRNA

Figure 21.6 A tRNA molecule is a short strand of RNA that twists and folds on itself. The job of tRNA is to ferry a specific amino acid to the ribosome and insert it in the appropriate position in the growing peptide chain.

Ribosomes Ribosomes function as the workbenches on which proteins are built from amino acids. A ribosome consists of two subunits (small and large), each composed of ribosomal RNA (rRNA) and protein. The subunits form in the nucleus and are shipped to the cytoplasm. They remain separate except during protein synthesis. The role of the ribosome in protein synthesis is to bring the tRNA bearing an amino acid close enough to the mRNA to interact. As you can see in Figure 21.7, when the two subunits fit together to form a functional ribosome, a groove for mRNA is formed. Two binding sites position tRNA molecules so that an enzyme in the ribosome can cause bonds to form between their amino acids.

Protein synthesis Translation—essentially, protein synthesis—can be divided into three stages: initiation, elongation, and termination.

1. **During initiation, the major players in protein synthesis (mRNA, tRNA, and ribosomes) come together** (Figure 21.8).

   ❶ The small ribosomal subunit attaches to the mRNA strand at the start codon, AUG.

   ❷ The tRNA with the complementary anticodon pairs with the start codon. The larger ribosomal subunit then joins the smaller one to form a functional, intact ribosome with mRNA positioned in a groove between the two subunits.

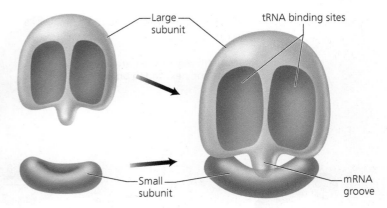

Large subunit

tRNA binding sites

Small subunit

mRNA groove

Figure 21.7 A ribosome consists of two subunits of different sizes. When the two subunits join together to form a functional ribosome, a groove for mRNA is formed. The ribosome has two binding sites for tRNA molecules. It also contains an enzyme that promotes the formation of a peptide bond between the amino acids that are attached to the tRNAs in the binding sites.

2. **Elongation of the protein occurs as additional amino acids are added to the chain** (Figure 21.9).

   ❶ *Codon recognition.* With the start codon positioned in one binding site, the next codon is aligned in the other binding site.

   ❷ *Peptide bond formation.* The tRNA bearing an anticodon that will pair with the exposed codon slips into place at the binding site, and the amino acid it carries forms a peptide bond with the previous amino acid with the assistance of enzymes.

   ❸ *Ribosome movement.* The tRNA in the first binding site leaves the ribosome. The ribosome moves along the mRNA molecule, carrying the growing peptide chain and the remaining tRNA with its amino acid to the first binding site. This movement positions the next codon

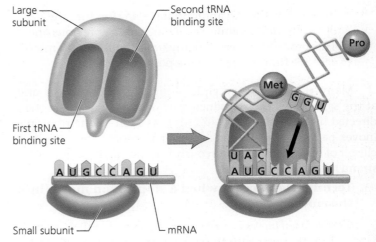

Large subunit

Second tRNA binding site

First tRNA binding site

Small subunit

mRNA

Pro

Met

G G U

U A C

A U G C C A G U

A U G C C A G U

❶ The small ribosomal subunit joins to mRNA at the start codon, AUG.

❷ A tRNA with complementary anticodon pairs with the start codon. Ribosomal subunits join to form a functional ribosome.

Figure 21.8 Initiation of translation

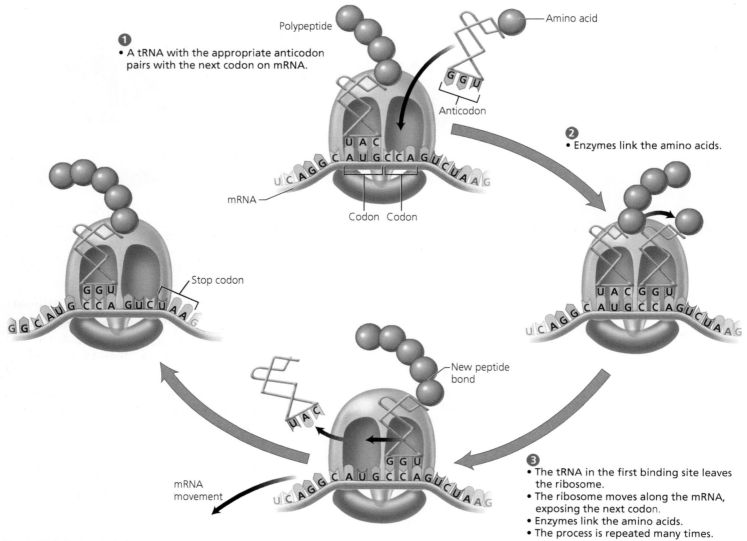

Polypeptide

❶
• A tRNA with the appropriate anticodon pairs with the next codon on mRNA.

Amino acid

Anticodon

UAC

CAUGCCAGUCUAAG

UCAGG

mRNA

Codon Codon

❷
• Enzymes link the amino acids.

UACGGU

CAUGCCAGUCUAAG

UCAGG

Stop codon

GGU

CCA GUCUAAG

GGCAUG

New peptide bond

mRNA movement

UAC

GGU

CAUGCCAGUCUAAG

UCAGG

❸
• The tRNA in the first binding site leaves the ribosome.
• The ribosome moves along the mRNA, exposing the next codon.
• Enzymes link the amino acids.
• The process is repeated many times.

Figure 21.9 Elongation of the polypeptide during translation

in the open site. An appropriate tRNA slips into the open site, and its amino acid binds to the previous one. This process is repeated many times, adding one amino acid at a time to the growing polypeptide chain.

Many ribosomes may glide along a given mRNA strand at the same time, each producing its own copy of the protein directed by that mRNA (Figure 21.10). As soon as one ribosome moves past the start codon, another ribosome can attach. A cluster of ribosomes simultaneously translating the same mRNA strand is called a **polysome.**

3. **Termination occurs when a stop codon moves into the ribosome** (Figure 21.11).

   ❶ *Stop codon moves into ribosome.* There are no tRNA anticodons that pair with the stop codons, so when a stop codon moves into the ribosome, protein synthesis is terminated.

   ❷ *Parts disassemble.* The newly synthesized polypeptide, the mRNA strand, and the ribosomal subunits then separate from one another.

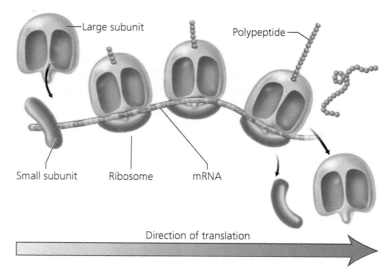

Large subunit

Polypeptide

Small subunit   Ribosome   mRNA

Direction of translation

Figure 21.10 A polysome is a group of ribosomes reading the same mRNA molecule.

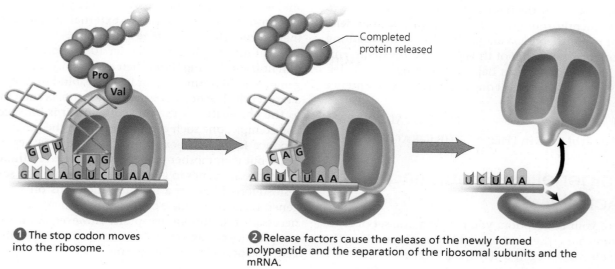

❶ The stop codon moves into the ribosome.

❷ Release factors cause the release of the newly formed polypeptide and the separation of the ribosomal subunits and the mRNA.

Figure 21.11 Termination of translation

STOP and THINK ....

Streptomycin is an antibiotic, a drug taken to slow the growth of invading bacteria and allow body defense mechanisms more time to destroy them. Streptomycin works by binding to the bacterial ribosomes and preventing an accurate reading of mRNA. Why would this process slow bacterial growth?

....

21.4 Mutations

DNA is remarkably stable, and the processes of replication, transcription, and translation generally occur with amazing precision. However, sometimes DNA is altered, and the alterations can change its message. Changes in DNA are called **mutations.** One type of mutation occurs when whole sections of chromosomes are duplicated or deleted, as discussed in Chapter 20. Now that we are familiar with the chemical structure of DNA and how it directs the synthesis of proteins, we can consider another type of mutation—a gene mutation. A gene mutation results from changes in the order of nucleotides in DNA. Although a gene mutation can occur in any cell, it can be passed on to offspring only if it is present in a cell that will become an egg or a sperm. A mutation that occurs in a body cell can affect the functioning of that cell and the subsequent cells produced by that cell, sometimes with disastrous effects, but it cannot be transmitted to a person's offspring.

One type of gene mutation is the replacement of one nucleotide pair by a different nucleotide pair in the DNA double helix. During DNA replication, bases may accidentally pair incorrectly. For example, adenine might mistakenly pair with cytosine instead of thymine. Repair enzymes normally replace the incorrect base with the correct one. However, sometimes the enzymes recognize that the bases are incorrectly paired but mistakenly replace the original base (the one on the old strand) rather than the new, incorrect one. The result is a complementary base pair consisting of the wrong nucleotides (Figure 21.12).

Other types of gene mutations are caused by the insertion or deletion of one or more nucleotides. Generally, a mutation of

this kind has more serious effects than does a mutation caused by substitution of one base pair for another. Recall that the mRNA is translated in units of three nucleotides (a unit called a codon). If one or two nucleotides are inserted or deleted, *all* the

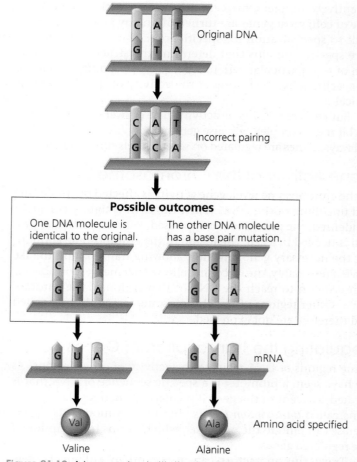

Figure 21.12 A base-pair substitution is a DNA mutation that results when a base is paired incorrectly. This may change the amino acid specified by the mRNA and alter the structure of the protein.

triplet codons that follow the insertion or deletion are likely to change. Consequently, mutations due to the insertion or deletion of one or two nucleotides can greatly change the resulting protein. A sentence consisting of three-letter words (representing codons) illustrates what can happen. Deleting a single letter from the sentence "The big fat dog ran" renders the sentence nonsensical:

| Original: | THE BIG FAT DOG RAN |
| After deletion of the E in THE: | THB IGF ATD OGR AN |

21.5 Epigenetics: Regulating Gene Activity

At the time of your conception, you received one set of chromosomes from your father and one set from your mother. The resulting zygote then began a remarkable series of cell divisions—some of which continue in many of your body cells to this day. With each division, the genetic information was faithfully replicated, and exact copies were parceled into the daughter cells. Thus, every nucleated cell you possess, except gametes, contains a complete set of identical genetic instructions for making every structure and performing every function in your body.

How, then, can liver, bone, blood, muscle, and nerve cells look and act so differently from one another? The answer is deceptively simple: Only certain genes are active in a certain type of cell; most genes are turned off in any given cell, which leads to specialization for specific jobs. The active genes produce specific proteins that determine the structure and function of that particular cell. Indeed, as cells become specialized for specific jobs, the timing of the activity of specific genes is critical.

But what controls gene activity? The answer to this question is a bit more complex, because gene activity is controlled in several ways. Genes are regulated on several levels simultaneously.

Gene Activity at the Chromosome Level

At the chromosome level, gene activity is affected by the coiling and uncoiling of the DNA. When the DNA is tightly coiled, or condensed, the genes are not expressed. When a particular protein is needed in a cell, the region of the chromosome containing the necessary gene unwinds, allowing transcription to take place. Presumably, the uncoiling allows enzymes responsible for transcription to reach the DNA in that region of the chromosome. Other regions of the chromosome remain tightly coiled and therefore are not expressed.

Regulating the Transcription of Genes

Some regions of DNA regulate the activity of other regions. As we have seen, a promoter is a specific sequence of DNA that is located adjacent to the gene it regulates. When regulatory proteins called *transcription factors* bind to a promoter, RNA polymerase can bind to the promoter, which begins transcription of the regulated genes.

Transcription factors can also bind to enhancers, segments of DNA that increase the *rate* of transcription of certain genes and, therefore, the amount of a specific protein that is produced. Enhancers also specify the timing of expression and a gene's response to external signals and developmental cues that affect gene expression.

You may recall from Chapter 10 that one of the ways certain hormones bring about their effects is by turning on specific genes. Steroid hormones, for instance, bind to receptors within a target cell. The hormone–receptor complex then finds its way to the chromatin in the nucleus and turns on specific genes. For example, one such complex turns on the genes in cells that produce facial hair—explaining why your father may have a beard but your mother probably does not, even though she has the necessary genes to grow one. In this case, the sex hormone testosterone binds to a receptor and turns on hair-producing genes. Facial hair follicle cells of both men and women have the necessary testosterone receptors. However, women usually do not produce enough testosterone to activate the hair-producing genes, so bearded women are rare.

STOP and THINK

Why do female athletes who inject themselves with testosterone to stimulate muscle development sometimes develop increased facial hair?

21.6 Genetic Engineering

The manipulation of genetic material for human purposes, a practice called **genetic engineering,** began almost as soon as scientists started to understand the language of DNA. Genetic engineering is part of the broader endeavor of **biotechnology,** a field in which scientists make controlled use of living cells to perform specific tasks. Genetic engineering has been used to produce pharmaceuticals and hormones, improve diagnosis and treatment of human diseases, increase food production from plants and animals, and gain insight into the growth processes of cells.

Recombinant DNA

The basic idea behind genetic engineering is to put a gene of interest—in other words, one that produces a useful protein or trait—into another piece of DNA to create **recombinant DNA,** which is DNA combined from two or more sources. The recombinant DNA, carrying the gene of interest, is then placed into a rapidly multiplying cell that quickly produces many copies of the gene. The final harvest may consist of large amounts of the gene product or many copies of the gene itself. Let's take a closer look at the procedure one step at a time (see Figure 21.13).

- **The gene of interest is sliced out of its original organism and spliced into vector DNA.** ❶ Both the DNA originally containing the gene of interest and the vector DNA, which receives the transferred gene and transports it to a new cell, are isolated and ❷ are cut at specific sequences that are recognized by a **restriction enzyme.** This is a type of enzyme that makes a staggered cut between specific base pairs in DNA, leaving several unpaired bases on each side of the cut. There are many kinds of restriction enzymes; each kind recognizes and cuts a different sequence

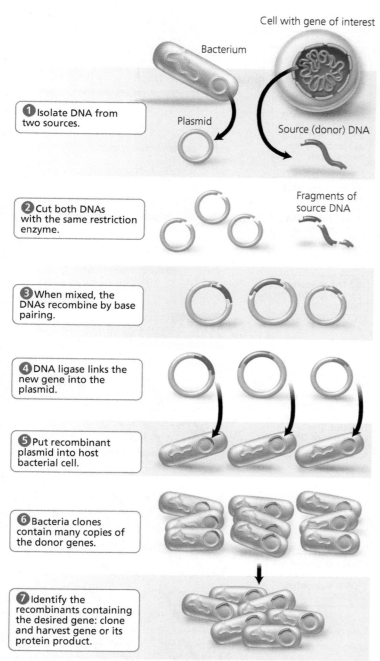

Figure 21.13 An overview of genetic engineering using plasmids

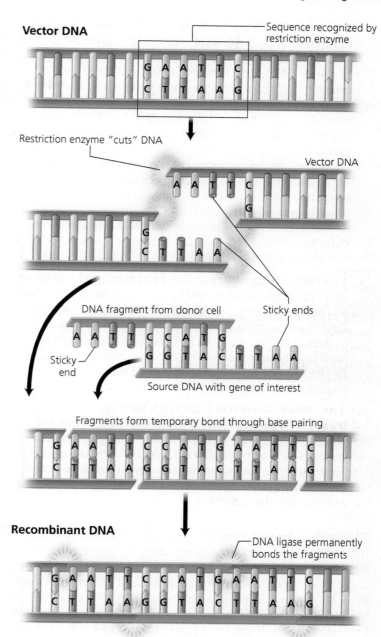

Figure 21.14 DNA from different sources can be spliced together using a restriction enzyme to make cuts in the DNA. A restriction enzyme makes a staggered cut at a specific sequence of DNA, leaving a region of unpaired bases on each cut end. The region of single-stranded DNA at the cut end is called a sticky end, because it tends to pair with the complementary sticky end of any other piece of DNA that has been cut with the same restriction enzyme, even if the pieces of DNA came from different sources.

of DNA. The stretch of unpaired bases produced on each side of the cut is called a *sticky end* because of its tendency to pair with the single-stranded stretches of complementary base sequences on the ends of other DNA molecules that were cut with the same restriction enzyme (Figure 21.14).

The sticky ends are the secret to splicing the gene of interest and the vector DNA. ❸ The sticky ends of DNA from different sources will be complementary and stick together as long as they have been cut with the same restriction enzyme. ❹ The initial attachment between sticky ends is temporary, but the ends can be "pasted" together permanently by another enzyme, DNA ligase. The resulting recombinant DNA contains DNA from two sources.

■ **The vector is used to transfer the gene of interest to a new host cell.** Biological carriers that ferry the recombinant DNA to a host cell are called **vectors.** A common vector is the bacterial **plasmid,** which is a small, circular piece of self-replicating DNA that exists separately from the bacterial chromosome.[2] As previously

[2]Plasmids seem to have evolved as a means to move genes between bacteria. A plasmid can replicate itself and pass, with its genes, into another bacterium.

described, the source DNA (that is, the source of the gene of interest) and the plasmid (vector) DNA are both treated with the same restriction enzyme. Afterward, fragments of source DNA, some of which will contain the gene of interest, will be incorporated into plasmids when their sticky ends join. ❺ The recombinant DNA is mixed with bacteria in a test tube. Under the right conditions, some of the bacterial cells will then take up the recombined plasmids.

Although the basic strategy is usually the same, there are many variations on this theme of transporting a gene into a new host. For instance, the gene of interest is sometimes combined with viral DNA. The viruses are then used as vectors to insert the recombinant DNA into a host cell. Cells other than bacteria, including yeast or animal cells, can also be used as vectors.

■ **The recombinant organism containing the gene of interest is identified and isolated from the mixture of recombinants**. ❻ When plasmids are used as vector DNA, each recombinant plasmid is introduced into a single bacterial cell, and each cell is then grown into a colony. Each colony contains a different recombinant plasmid. ❼ The bacteria containing the gene of interest must be identified and isolated.

■ **The gene is amplified through bacterial cloning or by use of a polymerase chain reaction.** After the colony containing the gene of interest has been identified, researchers usually amplify (that is, replicate) the gene, producing numerous copies. Gene amplification is accomplished using one of two techniques: bacterial cloning or a polymerase chain reaction.

Cloning   Bacteria containing the plasmid with the gene of interest can be grown in huge numbers by cloning. Each bacterium divides many times to form a colony. Thus, each colony constitutes a clone—a group of genetically identical organisms all descended from a single cell. In this case, all the members of the clone carry the same recombinant DNA. Later, the plasmids can be separated from the bacteria, a process that partially purifies the gene of interest. The plasmids then can be taken up by other bacteria that will thus become capable of performing a service deemed useful by humans. Alternatively, the plasmids can be transferred into plants or animal cells, creating transgenic organisms—organisms containing genes from another species.

Polymerase chain reaction (PCR) ❶   In the **polymerase chain reaction (PCR)** (Figure 21.15), the DNA of interest is unzipped, by gentle heating, to break the hydrogen bonds and form single strands. ❷ The single strands, which will serve as templates, are then mixed with *primers*—special short pieces of nucleic acid—one primer with bases complementary to each strand. The primers serve as start tags for DNA replication. Nucleotides and a special heat-resistant DNA polymerase, which promotes DNA replication, are also added to the mixture, ❸ which is then cooled to allow base pairing. ❹ Through base

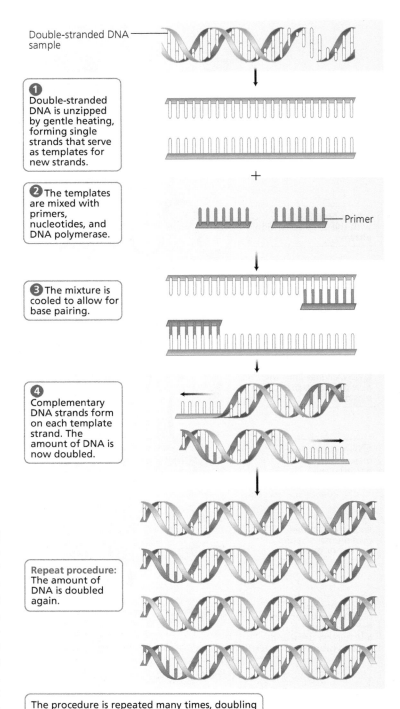

Double-stranded DNA sample

❶ Double-stranded DNA is unzipped by gentle heating, forming single strands that serve as templates for new strands.

❷ The templates are mixed with primers, nucleotides, and DNA polymerase.

Primer

❸ The mixture is cooled to allow for base pairing.

❹ Complementary DNA strands form on each template strand. The amount of DNA is now doubled.

Repeat procedure: The amount of DNA is doubled again.

The procedure is repeated many times, doubling the amount of DNA with each round.

Figure 21.15 The polymerase chain reaction (PCR) rapidly produces a multitude of copies of a single gene or of any desired segment of DNA. PCR amplifies DNA more quickly than does bacterial cloning. It has many uses besides genetic engineering, including DNA fingerprinting.

pairing, a complementary strand forms for each single strand. The procedure is then repeated many times, and each time the number of copies of the DNA of interest is doubled. In this way, billions of copies of the DNA of interest can be produced in a short time.

what would YOU do? Genetic engineering involves altering an organism's genes—adding new genes and traits to microbes, plants, or even animals. Do you think we have the right to "play God" and alter life-forms in this way? The U.S. Supreme Court has approved patenting of genetically engineered organisms, first of microbes and now of mammals, such as pigs, that are genetically modified for use in organ transplantation. If you were asked to decide whether it is ethical to patent a new life-form, how would you respond? ∎

Applications of Genetic Engineering

Genetic engineering has been used in two general ways.

■ **Genetic engineering provides a way to produce large quantities of a particular gene product.** The useful gene is transferred to another cell, usually a bacterium or a yeast cell, that can be grown easily in large quantities. The cells are cultured under conditions that cause them to express the gene, after which the gene product is harvested. For example, genetically engineered bacteria have been used to produce large quantities of human growth hormone (Figure 21.16). Treatment with growth hormone allows children with an underactive pituitary gland to grow to nearly normal height.

■ **Genetic engineering allows a gene for a trait considered useful by humans to be taken from one species and transferred to another species.** The transgenic organism then exhibits the desired trait. For example, scientists have endowed salmon with a gene from an eel-like fish. This gene causes the salmon to produce growth hormone year-round (something they do not normally do). As a result, the salmon grow faster than normal.

Environmental applications Genetic engineering also has environmental applications. For example, in sewage treatment plants, genetically engineered microbes lessen the amount of phosphate and nitrate discharged into waterways. Phosphate and nitrate can cause excessive growth of aquatic plants, which could choke waterways and dams, and of algae, which can produce chemicals that are poisonous to fish and livestock. Microorganisms are also being genetically engineered to modify or destroy chemical wastes or contaminants so that they are no longer harmful to the environment. For instance, oil-eating microbes that can withstand the high salt concentrations and low temperatures of the oceans have proven useful in cleaning up marine oil spills.

Livestock Genetic engineering has also been used on livestock. Genetically engineered vaccines have been created to protect piglets against a form of dysentery called scours, sheep against foot rot and measles, and chickens against bursal disease (a viral disease that is often fatal). Genetically engineered bacteria produce bovine somatotropin (BST), a hormone naturally produced by a cow's pituitary gland that enhances milk production. Injections of BST can boost milk production by nearly 25%.

Figure 21.16 Genetic engineering is used to produce large quantities of a desired protein or to create an organism with a desired trait. This boy has an underactive pituitary gland. Its undersecretion of growth hormone would have caused him to be very short, even as an adult. However, growth hormone from genetically engineered bacteria has helped him grow to an almost normal height.

Transgenic animals have been created by injecting the gene of interest into a fertilized egg in a Petri dish. The goals of creating transgenic animals include making animals with leaner meat, sheep with softer wool, cows that produce more milk, and animals that mature more quickly.

Pharmaceuticals Genes have been inserted into a variety of cells, ranging from microbes to mammals, to produce proteins for treating allergies, cancer, heart attacks, blood disorders, autoimmune disease, and infections.

Genetically engineered bacteria have also been used to create vaccines for humans. You may recall from Chapter 13 that a vaccine typically uses an inactivated bacterium or virus to stimulate the body's immune response to the active form of the organism. The idea is that the body will learn to recognize proteins on the surface of the infectious organism and mount defenses against any organism bearing those proteins. Because the organism used in the vaccine was rendered harmless, the vaccine cannot trigger an infection. Scientists produce genetically engineered vaccines by putting the gene that codes for the surface protein of the infectious organism into bacteria. The bacteria then produce large quantities of that protein, which can be purified and used as a vaccine. The vaccine cannot cause infection, because only the surface protein is used instead of the infectious organism itself.

Plants have also been used to generate therapeutic proteins. Engineered bananas that produce an altered form of the hepatitis B virus surface protein are being developed as an edible vaccine against the liver disease hepatitis B. Someday, you may eat a banana in order to be vaccinated, instead of receiving an injection against hepatitis B. In addition, plants are being engineered to produce "plantibodies," antibodies made by plants. For example, now under cultivation are soybeans containing human antibodies to the herpes simplex virus that causes genital herpes. As another example, a human gene for an antibody that binds to tumor cells has been transplanted into corn. The antibodies can then deliver radioisotopes to cancer cells, selectively killing them.

Pharming is a word that comes from combining the words *farming* and *pharmaceuticals*. In gene pharming, transgenic animals are created that produce a protein with medicinal value in their milk, eggs, or blood. ❶ The gene of interest is injected into an egg cell and ❷ implanted into a host mother. ❸ The transgenic offspring is identified. ❹ When the pharm animal is a mammal, the gene is expressed in mammary glands. ❺–❼ The desired protein is then extracted and purified from milk (Figure 21.17). For example, the gene for the protein alpha-1-antitrypsin (AAT) has been inserted into sheep that then secrete AAT in their milk. People with an inherited, potentially fatal form of emphysema (a lung disease) take AAT as a drug. It is also being tested as a drug to prevent lung damage in people with cystic fibrosis. The first drug made from the milk of a transgenic goat was an anticlotting drug called ATryn. It is given to people with a blood-clotting deficiency when they must undergo surgery. Researchers have also created a transgenic goat to produce milk containing lysozyme, an antibacterial agent. Lysozyme can be used to treat intestinal infections that kill millions of children in underdeveloped countries.

Agriculture Most of us experience some of the results of genetic engineering at our dinner tables (see the Health Issue essay, Genetically Modified Food). The most common traits that have been genetically engineered into crops are resistance to pests and resistance to herbicides. Scientists also have developed two virus-resistant strains of papaya and distributed them to papaya growers in Hawaii, saving the industry from ruin. In addition, different strains of rice have been genetically engineered to resist disease-causing bacteria and to withstand flooding of the paddy. Other plants have been genetically engineered to be more nutritious. For example, golden rice is a strain of rice that has been genetically engineered to produce high levels of beta-carotene, a precursor of vitamin A, which is in short supply in certain parts of the world. More than 100 million children worldwide suffer from vitamin A deficiency, and 500,000 of them go blind every year because of that deficiency. Although golden rice cannot supply a complete recommended daily dose of vitamin A, the amount it contains could be helpful to a person whose diet is very low in vitamin A. Other crops have also been created that grow faster, produce greater yields, and have longer shelf lives.

Gene Therapy

The problems associated with many genetic diseases arise because a mutant gene fails to produce a normal protein product. The goal of **gene therapy** is to cure genetic diseases by putting normal, functional genes into the body cells that were affected by the mutant gene. The functional gene would then produce the needed protein.

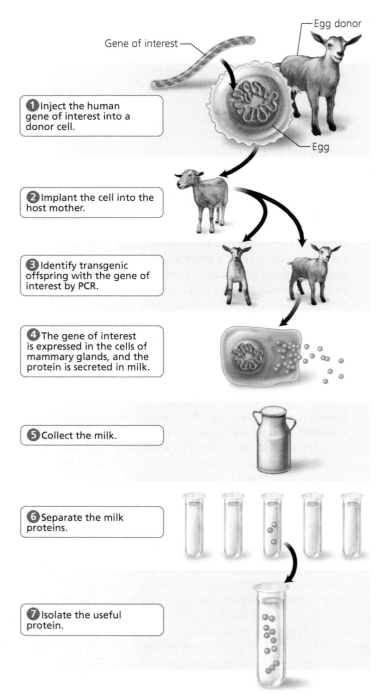

❶ Inject the human gene of interest into a donor cell.

❷ Implant the cell into the host mother.

❸ Identify transgenic offspring with the gene of interest by PCR.

❹ The gene of interest is expressed in the cells of mammary glands, and the protein is secreted in milk.

❺ Collect the milk.

❻ Separate the milk proteins.

❼ Isolate the useful protein.

Figure 21.17 The procedure for creating a transgenic animal that will produce a useful protein in its milk.

Methods of delivering a healthy gene ❶ One way a healthy gene can be transferred to a target cell is by means of viruses. Viruses generally attack only one type of cell. For instance, an adenovirus, which causes the common cold, typically attacks cells of the respiratory system. A virus consists largely of genetic material, commonly DNA, surrounded by a protein coat (see Chapter 13a). ❷ Isolate a healthy cell, such as a stem cell from the patient's bone marrow. ❸ Infect the patient's stem cell with modified virus carrying a healthy form of the gene. ❹ Return the genetically modified stem

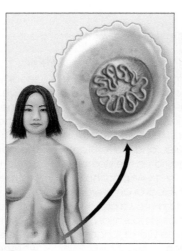

① Incorporate a healthy form of the gene into the virus.

② Remove bone marrow stem cells from the patient.

③ Infect the patient's stem cells with the virus that is carrying the healthy form of the gene.

④ Return the genetically engineered stem cells to the patient. The gene is expressed to produce the needed protein.

Figure 21.18 Gene therapy using a virus. In gene therapy, a healthy gene is introduced into a patient who has a genetic disease caused by a faulty gene.

cell to the patient. Once inside a cell, the viral DNA uses the cell's metabolic machinery to produce viral proteins. If a healthy gene is spliced into the DNA of a virus that has first been rendered harmless, the virus will deliver the healthy gene to the host cell and cause the desired gene product to be produced (Figure 21.18).

Another type of virus used in gene therapy is a retrovirus, a virus whose genetic information is stored as RNA rather than DNA. Once inside the target cell, a retrovirus rewrites its genetic information as double-stranded DNA and inserts the viral DNA into a chromosome of the target cell.

Gene therapy results

More than 4000 human diseases have been traced to defects in single genes. Although the U.S. Food and Drug Administration has not yet approved a gene therapy for any of these conditions, hundreds of clinical trials of gene therapies are currently under way, including trials of possible therapies for cystic fibrosis and cancer (discussed in Chapter 21a).

The first condition to be treated experimentally with gene therapy is a disorder referred to as *severe combined immunodeficiency disease (SCID)*. In children with SCID, the immune system is nonfunctional, leaving them vulnerable to infections. The cause of the problem is a mutant gene that prevents the production of an enzyme called adenosine deaminase (ADA). Without ADA, white blood cells never mature—they die while still developing in the bone marrow. The first gene therapy trial began in 1990, when white blood cells of a 4-year-old SCID patient, Ashanthi DeSilva, were genetically engineered to carry the ADA gene and then returned to her tiny body. Her own gene-altered white blood cells began producing ADA, and her body defense mechanisms were strengthened. Ashanthi's life began to change. She was not ill as often as she had been before. She could play with other children. However, the life span of white blood cells is measured in weeks, and when the number of gene-altered cells declined, new gene-altered cells had to be infused. Ashanthi is now about 30 years old and has a reasonably healthy immune system. However, she still needs repeated treatments.

Unfortunately, in 25 years of clinical trials, gene therapy has failed to meet its promises, but hope is still high. Reports of gene therapy successes with animal models or in early clinical trials are frequent. Interest in gene therapy is rising once again.

what would YOU do? Without treatment, children with X-SCID die at a young age. The gene therapy treatment for X-SCID that caused leukemia in four French boys does appear to have cured this deadly disorder in other patients. If you had a child with X-SCID, would you want him to have this gene therapy? Why or why not? What factors would you consider in making your decision? ■

21.7 Genomics

A **genome** is the entire set of genes carried by one member of a species—in our case, one person. **Genomics** is the study of entire genomes and the interactions of the genes with one another and the environment.

Human Genome Project

One goal of genomics is to determine the location and sequences of genes. Researchers have developed supercomputers that automatically sequence (determine the order of bases in) DNA. The supercomputers were put to use on a massive scale in the Human Genome Project, a worldwide research effort, completed in 2003, to sequence the human genome. As a result, we now have some idea of the locations of genes

HEALTH ISSUE

Genetically Modified Food

From dinner tables to diplomatic circles, people are discussing genetically modified (GM) food. This relatively recent interest is somewhat ironic, considering that people in the United States have been eating GM food since the mid-1990s. More than 70% of processed foods sold in the United States contain genetically modified ingredients. Yet many people vehemently object to GM food.

Why is something as common as GM food controversial? The concerns about it can generally be divided into three categories: health issues, social issues, and environmental issues. Let's explore these categories one at a time.

Health Concerns

A panel of the National Academy of Sciences (NAS) has issued a report saying that genetically engineered crops do not pose health risks that cannot also be caused by crops created by conventional breeding. However, because genetic engineering could produce unintended harmful changes in food, the NAS panel recommends scrutiny of GM foods before they can be marketed. Currently, the U.S. Department of Agriculture, the Food and Drug Administration (FDA), and the Environmental Protection Agency regulate genetically modified foods. The NAS panel concluded that the GM foods already on the market are safe.

A common safety concern is that GM foods may contain allergens (substances that cause allergies). After a protein is produced, the cell modifies it in various ways. The protein may be modified in the genetically modified plant differently from the way it would in an unmodified cell, and the modification could produce an allergen. Rigorous testing can reduce the likelihood that this may occur. Most known allergens share certain properties. They are proteins, relatively small molecules, and are resistant to heat, acid, and digestion in the stomach. If a protein produced by a GM plant has any of the properties typical of an allergen or is structurally similar to a known allergen, the FDA considers it to be a potential allergen and requires that the protein undergo additional allergy testing.

Bacterial resistance to antibiotics is a major threat to public health (see Chapter 13a). When bacteria are resistant to an antibiotic, the drug will not kill them and thus will no longer cure the human disease for which they are the cause. Some people worry about the scientific practice of putting genes for resistance to an antibiotic into GM crops as markers to identify the plants with the modified genes. Plant seedlings thought to be genetically modified are grown in the laboratory in the presence of an antibiotic. Only those seedlings with the gene for resistance will survive. Because of the way they were engineered, the surviving plants also contain the "useful" gene.

What concerns some people is that the genes for resistance to antibiotics could be transferred to bacteria, making the bacteria resistant to antibiotics. The receiving bacteria might be those that normally live in the human digestive system, or they might be bacteria ingested with food. It is not known whether genes can be transferred from a plant to a bacterium. However, it is known that bacteria can easily and quickly transfer genes for antibiotic resistance to one another. Thus, a harmless bacterium in the gut could transfer the gene for antibiotic resistance to a disease-causing bacterium.

The transfer of antibiotic-resistance genes from GM plants to bacteria could have serious consequences. For this reason, antibiotic-resistance marker genes are being phased out in favor of other marker genes, such as a green

The larger salmon in the back of the photo has been genetically modified to grow faster than the wild salmon in front.

along all 23 pairs of human chromosomes and the sequence of the estimated 3 billion base pairs that make up those chromosomes. Although the exact number of human genes is still not known for certain, scientists now estimate that the human genome consists of 20,000 to 25,000 genes, not 100,000 as originally thought. One reason for the smaller number of actual genes is that many gene families have related or redundant functions and therefore are able to share certain genes, so that fewer are needed to carry out all the body's functions. A second reason is that many genes are now known to code for parts of more than one protein.

In addition, researchers have identified and mapped to specific locations on specific chromosomes genes for more than 1400 genetic diseases. It is hoped that this information will give scientists a greater ability to diagnose, analyze, and eventually treat many of the 4000 diseases of humans that

fluorescent protein. Scientists also have developed a way to inactivate the antibiotic-resistance gene if it were to be transferred to bacteria.

Environmental Concerns

Proponents of GM foods argue that herbicide-resistant and pesticide-resistant crops reduce the need for spraying with herbicides and pesticides. So far, experience has shown that the validity of this argument depends on the crop. Pest-resistant cotton has substantially reduced the use of pesticides, but pest-resistant corn probably has not. Farmers who grow herbicide-resistant crops still spray with herbicides, but they change the type of herbicide they use to a type that is less harmful to animals.

Unfortunately, engineered crops containing insecticides could have undesirable effects. Genetically engineering insecticides into plants could hasten the development of insect resistance to that insecticide, making the insecticide ineffective—not just for the genetically modified crop, but for all crops.

Another concern is that genetically modified organisms could harm other organisms. For example, pollen from pest-resistant corn has been shown to harm monarch butterfly caterpillars. Fortunately, monarch caterpillars rarely encounter enough pollen to be harmed, and most of the pest-resistant corn grown in the United States today does not produce pollen that is harmful to monarch butterflies. However, farmers are increasing their use of certain herbicides to kill weeds, because their crops are genetically modified to resist the herbicides. The herbicides are killing milkweeds, which are essential for monarch butterfly survival. The loss of milkweed is reducing monarch butterfly populations.

A second example of a genetically modified organism that has the potential to harm other organisms is the salmon that produce more growth hormone and grow several times faster than their wild relatives do. These salmon are grown on fish farms. If the FDA grants approval, the gene-altered salmon could dramatically cut costs for fish farmers and consumers. However, when the genetically modified salmon are grown in tanks with ordinary salmon and food is scarce, the genetically modified salmon eat most of the food and some of their ordinary companions. What would happen if the genetically modified salmon escaped from their pens on the fish farm? They might mate with the wild salmon and create less healthy offspring or outcompete wild salmon for food, which could eventually cause the extinction of the wild salmon. Escape is possible. During the past few years, hundreds of thousands of fish have escaped from fish farms when floating pens were ripped apart by storms or sea lions. To minimize the risk that genetically modified salmon could destroy the population of wild salmon, scientists plan to breed the fish inland, sterilize the offspring, and ship only sterile fish to coastal pens. The sterilization procedure is effective in small batches of fish, but it is not known whether the procedure is completely effective in large batches of fish.

Critics of GM foods also point out that pollen from crops genetically engineered to resist herbicides can cause their wild relatives growing nearby to become "superweeds" that are resistant to many existing chemicals. In North Dakota, GM canola plants that are resistant to herbicides are growing along roadsides. Canola can hybridize with at least two wild weeds. The two original strains of GM canola were each resistant to a different herbicide. As a result of cross-pollination, some of the canola plants found in the wild are resistant to both herbicides, which suggests that the GM traits are stable in the wild and are evolving.

Social Concerns

Proponents of GM food claim that it can assist in the battle against world hunger. We have seen that genetic engineering can produce crops that resist pests and disease. It can also make possible crops with greater yields and crops that will grow in spite of drought, depleted soil, or excess salt, aluminum, or iron. Foods can also be genetically modified to contain higher amounts of specific nutrients.

Critics of using GM food to battle world hunger argue that the problem of hunger has nothing to do with an inability to produce enough food. The problem, they say, is a social one of distributing food so that it is available to the people who need it.

Some developing countries are resisting the use of GM seeds. Part of the resistance stems from lingering health concerns. However, many farmers in developing countries also object to GM seeds because the GM plants do not seed themselves. The need to buy seeds each year places a financial burden on poor farmers.

Questions to Consider

- Do you consider GM food to be a blessing or a danger to the world? What are your reasons?
- If a genetically modified organism that was created for food begins to cause environmental problems, who should be held accountable?
- Do you think that foods containing genetically modified components should be labeled as such?

have a known genetic basis. Researchers have already cloned the genes responsible for many genetic diseases, including Duchenne muscular dystrophy, retinoblastoma, cystic fibrosis, and neurofibromatosis. These isolated genes can now be used to test for the presence of the same disease-causing genes in specific individuals. As we saw in Chapter 20, some genetic tests can be used to identify people who are carriers for certain genetic diseases such as cystic fibrosis, allowing families to make choices based on known probabilities of bearing an affected child; similar tests can be used for prenatal diagnosis and for diagnosis before symptoms of the disease begin. After a disease-related gene has been identified, scientists can study it to learn more about the protein it codes for and perhaps discover ways to correct the problem.

We have also learned from the Human Genome Project that humans are identical in 99.9% of the sequences of their genes.

ENVIRONMENTAL ISSUE

Environment and Epigenetics

Your lifestyle may influence the health of your great grandchild. How is this possible? It can occur through epigenetics, which involves a stable alteration in gene expression *without* changes in DNA sequence. In other words, it regulates how genes are expressed without changing the proteins they encode. It does so when certain molecular tags bind to genes and turn them on or off In

We will consider two epigenetic processes: DNA methylation and histone acetylation. These processes alter gene expression by affecting how tightly packaged the DNA molecule is. DNA is packaged with proteins to form chromosomes. DNA methylation (adding a methyl group) turns off the activity of a gene by bringing in proteins that act to compact DNA into a tighter form. Histone acetylation, in contrast, makes the DNA less tightly coiled and gene expression easier.

We now know that epigenetic processes can be affected by the environment and that the pattern of DNA methylation is dynamic and changes over time. DNA methylation patterns can be affected by environmental factors, cause disease, be transmitted through generations, and, potentially, influence evolution. DNA is sensitive to the environment, so what we eat and the chemicals we are exposed to—including pesticides, tobacco smoke, hormones, and nutrients—may influence our health by affecting our gene expression patterns. For example, maternal nutrition during pregnancy can cause epigenetic changes in gene activity in the fetus that may increase susceptibility to obesity, type 2 diabetes, heart disease, and cancer. The quantity of food consumed during pregnancy alters the offspring's susceptibility to cardiovascular disease. Epigenetics is also thought to play a role in human behavioral disorders, such as autism spectrum disorders (discussed in Chapter 18a), Rett syndrome (a developmental disorder that affects the nervous system), and Fragile X syndrome (an inherited form of mental impairment). For example, there is some evidence that a gene needed to respond to oxytocin (a hormone important in social bonding) is turned off in some people with autism. As we will see in Chapter 21a cancer development is controlled by cancer-inhibiting and cancer-promoting genes. If cancer-inhibiting genes are turned off or cancer-promoting genes turned on, cancer can result. Changes in the pattern of gene expression are found in cancers of the cervix, prostate, breast, stomach, and colon.

Although DNA methylation patterns are considered to be stable, some studies suggest that methylation can be reversed in adulthood. Foods such as broccoli, onions, and garlic may reduce methylation, allowing genes to be expressed. Researchers are actively looking for drugs that will alter the pattern of methylation and cure cancer.

Questions to Consider
- Do you think that epigenetics increases or decreases a person's responsibility for his or her own behavior?
- Researchers may someday develop an "epigenetic diet" that favors positive changes in gene activity. Would you follow that diet? Do you think that pregnant women should be required to follow that diet?

As scientists gain greater understanding of the 0.1% of DNA that differs from person to person, they expect to learn more about why some people develop heart disease, cancer, or Alzheimer's disease and others do not.

The Epigenome

Consider this analogy: The genome—the sequence of nucleotides in DNA—is like the hardware of a computer that determines what the computer *can* do. The epigenome is like the software that tells the computer what it *will* do. The **epigenome** consists of chemicals that bind to specific genes and turn them on or off. Earlier in this chapter, we saw that cells become specialized to perform different functions because genes in certain cells are turned off when that region of DNA becomes tightly wrapped around histones and cannot be expressed; other regions of DNA in a cell remain uncoiled and can be expressed. In this way, chemicals of the epigenome determine the pattern of gene expression in each cell.

Although the genome is relatively stable, the epigenome is flexible. It varies throughout life in different cells, different tissues, and different people. The epigenome often plays a role in disease and cancer. Epigenetic tags respond to signals from the outside world, such as diet and stress. Indeed, the environment may affect which genes are turned on or off (see Environmental Issue essay, *Environment and Epigenetics*).

Microarray Analysis

A second goal of genomics is to understand the mechanisms that control gene expression. More than 95% of human DNA does not code for protein; however, some of these noncoding DNA sequences function as regulatory regions that determine when, where, and how much of certain proteins are produced. Because gene activity plays a role in many diseases, the study of how these regions turn genes on or off may lead to advances in diagnosis and treatment.

One of the tools researchers use in this effort is the *microarray,* which consists of thousands of DNA sequences stamped onto a single glass slide called a *DNA chip.* Researchers use microarrays to monitor large numbers of DNA segments to discover which genes are active and which are turned off under different conditions, such as in different tissue types, in different stages of development, or in health and disease. For example, they may use microarrays to identify genes that are active in cancerous cells but not in healthy cells (Figure 21.19). Presumably, the genes that are active in cancerous cells play a role in the development of cancer.

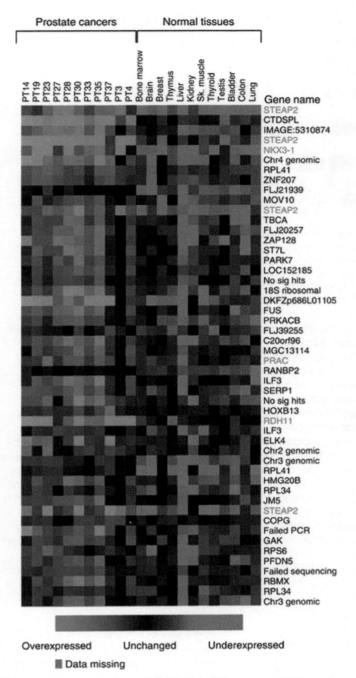

Figure 21.19 A comparison of microarrays showing the pattern of gene activity in prostate cancer and in normal tissue. The columns indicate the source of the tissue and the rows indicate the gene being analyzed. The genes that are active in tissue with prostate cancer (red or orange) but not in normal tissue probably play a role in the development of cancer.

Besides identifying gene activity in health and disease, microarray analysis is useful in identifying genetic variation in the members of a population. Some of these genetic differences are in the form of single-nucleotide polymorphisms (SNPs, or *snips*). These are DNA sequences that can vary by one nucleotide from person to person, and the differences in their protein products are thought to influence how we respond to stress and diseases, among other things. As researchers learn more about SNPs, they may be able to

develop treatments tailored to the genetic makeup of each individual. These are the kinds of discoveries that can open the door for gene therapy. Whereas individualized gene therapy may be useful in the future, we already use identification of individual differences in DNA on a regular basis in DNA fingerprinting (see the Ethical Issue essay, *Forensic Science, DNA, and Personal Privacy*).

what would **YOU** do?
Some people worry that once we know the location and function of every gene and have perfected the techniques of gene therapy, we will no longer limit gene manipulation to repairing faulty genes but will begin to modify genes to enhance human abilities. Should people be permitted to design their babies by choosing genes they consider superior? What do you think? Where should the line be drawn? Who should draw that line? Who should decide which genes are "good?" ∎

When SNPs are located near one another on a chromosome, they tend to be inherited together. A group of SNPs in a region of a chromosome is called a *haplotype*. The International HapMap Project is a scientific consortium whose purpose is to describe genetic variation between populations. Researchers collaborating on this project compare haplotype frequencies in groups of people who have a certain disease to those of a group without the disease, hoping to identify genes associated with the disease.

Comparison of Genomes of Different Species

The DNA of certain widely studied organisms, including the mouse, the fruit fly, a roundworm, yeast, slime mold, and the honeybee, has also been mapped. From these genomes, geneticists hope to gain some insight into basic biology, including fundamental principles of the organization of genes within the genome, gene regulation, and molecular evolution. Humans share many genes with other organisms. For example, we share 50% of our genes with the fruit fly and 90% of our genes with the mouse. These genetic similarities are evidence of our common evolutionary past. The genes and genetic mechanisms we share with other organisms are likely to be important in determining body form as well as influencing development and aging.

LOOKING AHEAD
In Chapter 19, we learned about the cell cycle. In Chapters 20 and 21, we learned about genes, their inheritance, and their regulation, and we also considered how mutations affect gene functions. In Chapter 21a, we use this information to understand cancer, a family of diseases in which mutations in genes that regulate the cell cycle cause a loss of control over cell division.

ETHICAL ISSUE

Forensic Science, DNA, and Personal Privacy

So-called DNA fingerprints, like the more conventional prints left by fingers, can help identify the individuals they belong to out of a large population. *DNA fingerprinting* refers to techniques of identifying individuals on the basis of unique features of their DNA. DNA fingerprints are possible because many regions of DNA are composed of small, specific sequences of DNA that are repeated many times. Most commonly used are repeated units of one to five bases, which are called *short tandem repeats (STRs)*. The number of times these sequences are repeated varies considerably from person to person, from a few to 100 repeats. Because of these differences, the segments can be used to match a sample of DNA to the person whose cells produced the sample.

The first step in preparing a DNA fingerprint is to extract DNA from a tissue sample. The type of tissue does not matter, and one type of tissue can be successfully compared to another type. Commonly used sources include blood, semen, skin, and hair follicles, because they are not too painful to remove, they are readily available, or they are left at a crime scene.

First, the amount of DNA is greatly increased using PCR, as described in Figure 21.15. The primers used are sequence specific for the regions on either side of the repeating region. This method produces many copies of the repeating region, which are then analyzed to determine the number of repeats present.

The FBI uses 13 STRs as a core set for forensic analysis. The resulting DNA fingerprint is unique to the person who produced the DNA. Moreover, any DNA sample taken from the same person

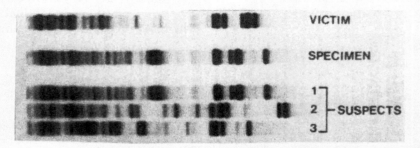

Figure 21.A The pattern of banding in a DNA fingerprint is determined by the sequence of bases in a person's DNA and is, therefore, unique to each person. A match between DNA fingerprints can identify the source of a tissue sample from a crime scene with a high degree of certainty. Which suspect's DNA fingerprint matches this specimen found at a crime scene?

would always be identical. But the fingerprint profiles resulting from the DNA of *different* people are always different (except perhaps for identical siblings), because the number and sizes of the fragments are determined by the unique sequence of bases in each person's DNA.

DNA fingerprinting has many applications, but the most familiar is probably its use in crime investigations. In these cases, the DNA fingerprint is usually created from a sample of tissue, such as blood or hair follicles, collected at the crime scene. A fingerprint can be produced from tissue left at the scene years before. This fingerprint is then compared with the DNA fingerprints of various suspects. A match reveals, with a high degree of certainty, the person who was the source of the sample from the crime scene (Figure 21.A).

Of course, the degree of certainty of a match between DNA fingerprints depends on how carefully the analysis was done. Because DNA fingerprints are being used as evidence in an increasing number of court cases each year, it is important that national standards be set to ensure the reliability of these molecular witnesses. It is generally easier to declare with certainty that two DNA fingerprints do *not* match than it is to be sure that they do. In the United States, more than

200 convicts have been found innocent through DNA testing during the past decade.

Has DNA testing gone too far? All states in the United States collect DNA samples from people convicted of sex crimes and murder. Several other states also collect DNA samples from people convicted of other felonies, such as robbery. About 30 states collect DNA samples from people accused of misdemeanors, including loitering, shoplifting, or vandalism. In many cases, the DNA is stored in a database, even if the person is found innocent of the crime. People who are simply cooperating with the investigation may also provide DNA samples. These, too, are added to a national database.

Questions to Consider

- Do you think everyone arrested for a crime should have the right to DNA fingerprinting to prove his or her innocence? If so, who should pay for the process?

- Is the creation of a national database of DNA fingerprints an invasion of privacy? Is it any more so than a database of actual fingerprints or mug shots?

- Under what conditions do you think DNA samples should be obtained?

CONSIDER THIS CASE

You are a crime scene investigator testifying at a murder trial. The DNA fingerprints shown on the right are those of a bloodstain at the murder scene (not the victim's blood) and those of seven suspects (numbered 1 through 7).

- Joe (number 2) claims he is innocent. Do these DNA fingerprints confirm his innocence?
- Which suspect's blood matches the bloodstain from the crime scene?

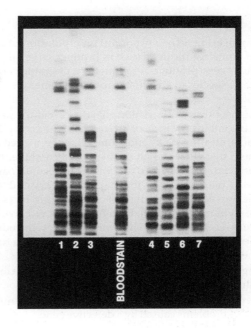

Chapter Review

MasteringBiology®

Highlighting the Concepts

21.1 Form of DNA (pp. 436–437)

- DNA consists of two strands of nucleotides linked by hydrogen bonds and twisted together to form a double helix. Each nucleotide consists of a phosphate, a sugar called deoxyribose, and one of four nitrogenous bases: adenine, thymine, cytosine, or guanine. The sugar and phosphate components of the nucleotides alternate along the two sides of the molecule. Pairs of bases meet and form hydrogen bonds in the interior of the double helix; these pairs resemble the rungs on a ladder.
- According to the rules of complementary base pairing, adenine binds only with thymine, and cytosine binds only with guanine.

21.2 Replication of DNA (pp. 437–438)

- DNA replication is semiconservative. Each new double-stranded DNA molecule consists of one old and one new strand. The enzyme DNA polymerase "unzips" the two strands of a molecule (the parent molecule), allowing each strand to serve as a template for the formation of a new strand. Complementary base pairing ensures the accuracy of replication.

21.3 Gene Expression (pp. 438–443)

- Genetic information is transcribed from DNA to RNA and then translated into a protein.
- Transcription is the synthesis of RNA by means of base pairing on a DNA template. RNA differs from DNA in that the sugar ribose replaces deoxyribose, and the base uracil replaces thymine. Most RNA is single stranded.
- Messenger RNA (mRNA) carries the DNA genetic message to the cytoplasm, where it is translated into protein. The genetic code is read in sequences of three RNA nucleotides; each triplet is called a codon. Each of the 64 codons specifies a particular amino acid or indicates the point where translation should start or stop.

- Transfer RNA (tRNA) interprets the genetic code. At one end of the tRNA molecule is a sequence of three nucleotides called the anticodon that pairs with a codon on mRNA in accordance with base-pairing rules. The tail of the tRNA binds to a specific amino acid.
- Each of the two subunits of a ribosome consists of ribosomal RNA (rRNA) and protein. A ribosome brings tRNA and mRNA together for protein synthesis.
- Translation of the genetic code into protein begins when the two ribosomal subunits and an mRNA assemble, with the mRNA sitting in a groove between the ribosome's two subunits. The mRNA attaches to the ribosome at the mRNA's start codon. Then the ribosome slides along the mRNA molecule, reading one codon at a time. Molecules of tRNA ferry amino acids to the mRNA and add them to a growing protein chain. Translation stops when a stop codon is encountered. The protein chain then separates from the ribosome.

21.4 Mutations (pp. 443–444)

- A point mutation is a change in one or a few nucleotides in the sequence of a DNA molecule. When one nucleotide is mistakenly substituted for another, the function of the resulting protein may or may not affect the function of the protein. The insertion or deletion of a nucleotide always changes the resulting protein.

21.5 Epigenetics: Regulating Gene Activity (p. 444)

- Gene activity is regulated at several levels. Usually, most of the DNA is folded and coiled. For a gene to be active, the region of DNA in which it is located must be uncoiled. Gene activity can be affected by other segments of DNA. Regions of DNA called enhancers can increase the amount of RNA produced. Chemical signals such as regulatory proteins or hormones can also affect gene activity.

21.6 Genetic Engineering (pp. 444–449)

■ Genetic engineering is the purposeful manipulation of genetic material by humans. It can be used to produce large quantities of a particular gene product or to transfer a desirable genetic trait from one species to another or to another member of the same species.

■ Genetic engineering uses restriction enzymes to cut the source DNA, which contains the gene of interest, and the vector DNA at specific places, creating sticky ends composed of unpaired complementary bases that allow the cut segments to recombine. The recombinant vector is then used to transfer the recombinant DNA to a host cell. Common vectors include bacterial plasmids and viruses. The host cell is often a type of cell that reproduces rapidly, such as a bacterium or yeast cell. Each time a host cell divides, both daughter cells receive a copy of the gene of interest. Introducing a gene from one species into a different species results in a transgenic plant or animal.

■ Genetic engineering has had many applications in plant and animal agriculture, environmental science, and medicine.

■ In gene therapy, a healthy form of a gene is introduced into body cells to correct problems caused by a defective gene.

21.7 Genomics (pp. 449–453)

■ A genome consists of all the genes in a single organism. Genomics is the study of genomes and the interaction between genes and the environment. It is now believed that the human genome consists of 20,000 to 25,000 genes.

■ The epigenome is a pattern of chemical tags that turn specific genes in a cell on or off.

■ Scientists use microarrays to analyze gene activity under different conditions. The microarray consists of DNA chips—glass slides with thousands of DNA segments stamped on them. The information may be helpful in treating genetic diseases. Microarray analysis also allows scientists to discover small differences in the gene sequences of people. Scientists hope to use this information to develop individualized treatments.

■ Large portions of our DNA are the same as the DNA in other organisms. The closer the evolutionary relationship, the greater the portion of DNA we have in common.

Recognizing Key Terms

deoxyribonucleic acid (DNA) *p. 436*
complementary base pairing *p. 437*
DNA replication *p. 437*
semiconservative replication *p. 438*
ribonucleic acid (RNA) *p. 438*
gene *p. 438*

transcription *p. 438*
messenger RNA (mRNA) *p. 439*
transfer RNA (tRNA) *p. 439*
ribosomal RNA (rRNA) *p. 439*
promoter *p. 439*
RNA polymerase *p. 439*
translation *p. 440*

genetic code *p. 440*
codon *p. 440*
anticodon *p. 440*
polysome *p. 442*
mutation *p. 443*
genetic engineering *p. 444*
biotechnology *p. 444*
recombinant DNA *p. 444*

restriction enzyme *p. 444*
vector *p. 445*
plasmid *p. 445*
polymerase chain reaction (PCR) *p. 446*
gene therapy *p. 448*
genome *p. 449*
genomics *p. 449*
epigenome *p. 452*

Reviewing the Concepts

1. What is the complementary base for thymine?
   a. adenine
   b. cytosine
   c. guanine
   d. uracil

2. Although the amount of any particular base in DNA will vary among individuals, the amount of guanine will always equal the amount of
   a. thymine.
   b. adenine.
   c. cytosine.
   d. uracil.

3. A codon is located on
   a. DNA.
   b. mRNA.
   c. tRNA.
   d. rRNA.

4. Translation produces
   a. a polypeptide chain.
   b. mRNA complementary to a template strand of DNA.
   c. tRNA complementary to mRNA.
   d. rRNA.

5. Choose the *incorrect* statement about restriction enzymes.
   a. They are used to create recombinant plasmids.
   b. They are necessary for translation.
   c. They are used to produce DNA fingerprints.
   d. They cut DNA at specific sequences.

6. Which codon on mRNA is the start signal for translation?
   a. CUG
   b. ATC
   c. AUG
   d. UAA

7. The polymerase chain reaction is a technique used to
   a. attach amino acids to a growing polypeptide chain.
   b. increase the number of copies of a small sample of DNA.
   c. splice DNA into a plasmid.
   d. regulate the transcription of genes.

8. What is a genome?
   a. a technique for creating recombinant DNA
   b. a technique for determining which genes are active under certain conditions
   c. the coding sequence of a gene
   d. the entire set of genes carried by one member of a species

9. What is microarray analysis?
   a. a technique for creating recombinant DNA
   b. a technique for determining which genes are active under certain conditions
   c. a technique used to identify the coding sequence of a gene
   d. the entire set of genes carried by one member of a species

10. The anticodon is located on a molecule of _____.
11. In RNA, the nucleotide _____ binds with adenine.
12. In genetic engineering, the staggered cuts in DNA that allow genes to be spliced together are made by _____.

Applying the Concepts

Use the genetic code in Figure 21.5 (page 442) to answer questions 1 and 2.

1. What would be the amino acid sequence in the polypeptide resulting from a strand of mRNA with the following base sequence?

   AUG ACA UAU GAG ACG ACU

2. The following are base sequences in four mRNA strands: one normal and three with mutations. (Keep in mind that translation begins with a start codon and ends with a stop codon.) Which of the mutated sequences is likely to have the most severe effects? Why? Which would have the least severe effects? Why?

Normal mRNA:	AUG ACA UAU GAG ACG ACU
Mutation 1:	AUG ACC UAC GAA ACG ACC
Mutation 2:	AUG ACU UAA GAG ACG ACA
Mutation 3:	AUG ACG UAU GAG ACG ACG

Finding and Evaluating Information

In this chapter we have seen two ways that gene activity can be altered. One way is through changes in the genome, the sequence of nucleotides in DNA. A more recently recognized way to modify gene activity is to alter the epigenome, the system of proteins and chemicals that can bind to DNA and turn genes on or off. In the next chapter, we will learn that both types of genetic alteration can lead to cancer.

The following is an excerpt from a report by Esha Dey on LiveScience.com[1] regarding a study published in *JAMA Oncology*[2] on epigenetic changes in cheek cells associated with smoking. You can read Dey's entire news report here: http://www.livescience.com/50857-cancer-signs-cells-epigenome-smoking.html

   "Smoking may bring on changes in cells that are linked with many cancers, including breast and gynecological cancers, a new study finds. These changes could provide an early warning sign of cancer, particularly in cheek cells, the research showed.

   "Researchers analyzed cheek swabs from 790 women, and found those who smoked were more likely to have certain changes associated with these cancers, which people may not realize are linked with smoking . . .

   "In the study, the researchers analyzed the epigenetic changes within cells, and found a "signature" of smoking. By looking for this signature, the researchers found they could differentiate between normal and cancerous tissue with near absolute certainty, including cancers in other parts of the body.

   "The signature could also be used to predict if a pre-cancerous lesion would progress to a full-blown invasive cancer, the researchers said.

   "The ability to quickly and easily identify such changes in cells could help doctors to predict and prevent cancers, the researchers said."

1. The epigenomic changes in cheek cells predicted risk of lung cancer development, as well as that of breast, cervical, and uterine cancer. The research samples were all from females. Do the results apply to men as well? How would you determine if they do?

2. Today we can do genome sequencing and epigenome mapping at a reasonable cost. Using reliable sources, find other genomic or epigenomic alterations with a specific disease of your choice. Do these disease-associated genetic changes have implications for prevention or treatment? Cite your sources.

[1]E. Dey, "Cancer may leave early warning signs in cheek cells," LiveScience.com, May 15, 2015.

[2]A. D. Teschendorff et al., "Correlation of smoking-associated DNA methylation changes in buccal cells with DNA methylation changes in epithelial cancer," *JAMA Oncology*. Published online May 14, 2015; doi:10.1001/jamaoncol.2015.1053 http://oncology.jamanetwork.com/article.aspx?articleid=2293216

Cancer

DID YOU KNOW?

- There are nearly 15 million cancer survivors in the United States, and that number is expected to reach 19 million by 2024.
- There are more than 200 types of cancer.

IN THE PREVIOUS FEW CHAPTERS, we learned about cell division, genes, and gene function. In this chapter, we consider how cancer cells escape the normal controls over cell division. We then learn about some causes of cancer and how we can reduce our risk of developing the disease. Finally, we identify some means of diagnosing and treating cancer.

Cancer, the "Big C," is perhaps the disease that people in the industrialized world dread the most—and with good reason. Cancer touches the lives of nearly everyone. One of every three people in the United States will develop cancer at some point in life, and the other two are likely to have a friend or relative with cancer.

21a.1 Uncontrolled Cell Division

All forms of cancer share one characteristic—uncontrolled cell division. Cancer cells may behave like aliens taking over our bodies, but they are actually traitorous cells from within our own bodies.

Benign or Malignant Tumors

An abnormal growth of cells can form a mass of tissue called a *tumor* or *neoplasm* (meaning "new growth"). However, not all tumors are cancerous: tumors can be either benign or malignant. A *benign tumor* is an abnormal mass of tissue that is surrounded by a capsule of connective tissue and that usually remains at the site where it forms. Its cells do not invade surrounding tissue or spread to distant locations, although the tumor can and does grow. In most cases, a benign tumor does not threaten life, because it can be removed completely by surgery.

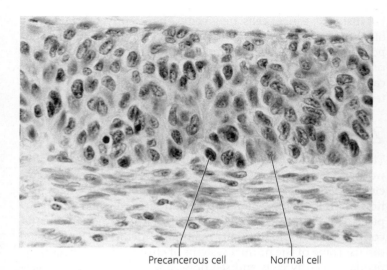

Precancerous cell   Normal cell

Figure 21a.1 Cancer cells have an abnormal appearance. In dysplasia, precancerous cells have large, irregularly shaped nuclei that contain increased amounts of DNA.

Q: Which chromosomes have extra copies in the karyotype of the cancer cell? Which have extra pieces in the karyotype of the cancer cell? Which are missing pieces in the karyotype of the cancer cell?

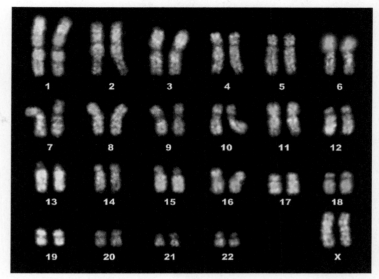

(a)

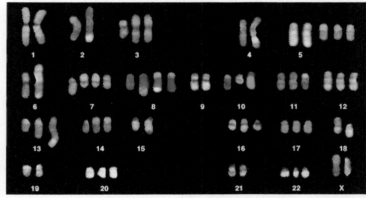

(b)

Figure 21a.2 A comparison of karyotypes from (a) a normal cell and (b) a cancerous cell shows that cancer cells contain extra chromosomes and chromosomes with extra pieces. (A karyotype is an arrangement of photographed chromosomes in their pairs, identified by physical features.)

Benign tumors can be harmful when they press on nearby tissues enough to interfere with the functioning of those tissues. If a "benign" tumor of that type is also inoperable, as may occur with a tumor in the brain, it can be life threatening. Even so, only *malignant tumors,* those that can invade surrounding tissue and spread to multiple locations throughout the body, are properly called cancerous. The spread of cancer cells from one part of the body to another is referred to as *metastasis.*

Stages of Cancer Development

Cells on their way to becoming cancerous are accumulating genetic damage. As a result, precancerous cells typically look different from normal cells. *Dysplasia* is the term used to describe the changes in shape, nuclei, and organization within tissues of precancerous cells (Figure 21a.1). The ragged edges of precancerous cells give them an abnormal shape. Their nuclei become unusually large and atypically shaped and may contain increased amounts of DNA. We can see the differences by comparing the chromosomes of a normal cell with those from a cancer cell. Notice in Figure 21a.2 that the cancer cell has extra copies of some chromosomes, is missing parts of some chromosomes, and has extra parts of other chromosomes. In a group, precancerous cells form a disorganized clump and, significantly, have an unusually high percentage of cells in the process of dividing.

Eventually, the tumor will reach a critical mass consisting of about a million cells. Although the tumor is still only a millimeter or two in diameter (smaller than a BB), the cells in the interior cannot receive a sufficient supply of nutrients, and their own waste is poisoning them. This tiny mass is now called *carcinoma in situ,* which literally means "cancer in place."

If a tumor this size is to continue growing, it must attract a blood supply. Some of the tumor cells will start to secrete chemicals that cause blood vessels to invade the tumor. This process marks an ominous point of transition, because the tumor cells

now have supply lines bringing in nutrients to support continued growth and carry away waste (Figure 21a.3). Of equal importance, the tumor cells have an escape route; they can enter the blood or nearby lymphatic vessels and travel throughout the body. Like cancerous seeds, the cancer cells that spread, or metastasize, can begin to form tumors in their new locations.

As long as a tumor stays in place, it can grow quite large, and a surgeon would still be able to remove it (depending on the location). However, once cancer cells leave the original tumor, they usually spread to so many locations that a surgeon's scalpel is no longer an effective weapon. At this point, chemotherapy or radiation is generally used to kill the cancer cells wherever they are hiding. (These treatments are discussed later in the chapter.) The original tumor is rarely a cause of death. Instead, the tumors that form in distant sites in the body are responsible for 90% of the deaths of people with cancer.

Once cancer cells have separated from the original tumor, they usually enter the cardiovascular or lymphatic system, which carries the renegade cells to distant sites. Thus, circulatory

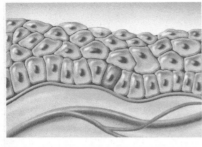

Initial tumor cell: One cell acquires mutations, causing loss of control of cell division.

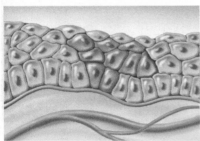

Cell divides more frequently than others.

Carcinoma in situ: Tumor remains at its site of origin.

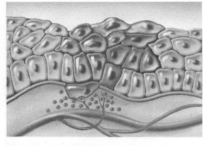

Cells of the tumor release growth factors to attract a blood supply.

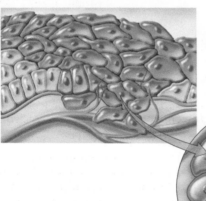

Cells of malignant tumor:
• Attract a blood supply
• Gain the ability to leave the other cells
• Spread to distant sites (metastasize)

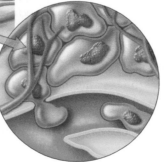

Figure 21a.3 The progression of cancer from the initial tumor cell to a malignant tumor

pathways in the body often explain the patterns of metastasis. For example, cancer cells escaping from tumors in most parts of the body, including the skin, encounter the next capillary bed in the lungs. Consequently, many cancers spread to the lungs. However, blood leaving the intestine travels directly to the liver, so colon cancer typically spreads to the liver.

The simplest explanation of how cancer causes death is that it interferes with the ability of body cells to function normally.

For instance, cancer cells are greedy. They deprive normal cells of nutrients and thereby weaken the cells, sometimes to the point of death. Cancer cells can also prevent otherwise healthy cells from performing their usual functions. In addition, tumors can block blood vessels or air passageways in the respiratory system or press on vital nerve pathways in the brain.

21a.2 Development of Cancer

The 30 trillion to 50 trillion cells in the human body generally work cooperatively, much like the members of any organized society. There are "rules," or controls, that tell a cell when and how often to divide, when to self-destruct, and when to stay in place. However, cancer cells are outlaws. They evade the many controls that would normally maintain order in the body. Let's discuss some of the normal systems of checks and balances that regulate healthy cells and see how cancer cells are able to get around these safeguards to divide indefinitely and spread out of control.

Recall from Chapter 19 that the cell cycle is the life cycle of the cell. During the cell cycle, there are checkpoints at which the cell determines whether conditions are favorable for moving on to the next stage. This is the cell's system of damage control. If a healthy cell detects damage, such as a mutated gene, it stops the cell cycle, assesses the damage, and begins repair. If the repair is successful, the cell cycle resumes. If the damage is recognized as too severe to repair, a program of cell death is initiated, as will be discussed shortly. Unfortunately, if the damage repair is unsuccessful or incomplete, genetic damage accumulates and can lead to cancer.

Tumor-suppressor genes are an important part of the cell's system of damage control. Some tumor-suppressor gene products detect damaged DNA.[1] When they do, other tumor-suppressor gene products serve as "managers of the cell's repair shop." These gene products assess the damage and coordinate the activities of other genes, whose products serve as "mechanics" and repair the damage. If the damage turns out to be too extensive, the manager activates still other genes whose products cause cell death. A particularly important tumor-suppressor gene is *p53*. We consider some of the activities of the p53 protein as we discuss the relationship between genes and cancer.

Lack of Restraint on Cell Division

When genes that regulate cell division are mutated, they usually do not function properly, and the cell loses control over cell division. Cancer is fundamentally a disease in which certain genes mutate and produce proteins that malfunction or produce proteins in abnormal amounts or in inappropriate locations. We now know that gene activity can be turned on or off by changes in how tightly the DNA is coiled without alterations in the DNA sequence. Thus, cancer can also result if tumor-suppressor genes are turned off or if oncogenes (cancer-promoting genes) are turned on.

Two types of genes usually regulate cell division: proto-oncogenes and the tumor-suppressor genes mentioned earlier.

[1]Recall that genes exert their effect through the proteins they code for. Thus, it is really the proteins that are acting.

Proto-oncogenes stimulate cell division in a variety of ways, for example, by producing growth factors or affecting their function or by producing proteins that affect the activity of certain genes. In contrast, tumor-suppressor genes inhibit or stop cell division. Thus, tumor-suppressor gene products act like brakes on cell division. The combined activities of these two types of genes allow the body to control cell division to divide and develop normally, repair defective cells, and replace dead cells.

When mutations affect the functioning of these gene products, the normal system of checks and balances that regulates cell division goes awry, and the disruption can result in the unrestrained cell division that characterizes cancer. A mutation in a tumor-suppressor gene can promote cancer by taking the brakes off cell division. The tumor-suppressor gene *p53* produces a protein that regulates another gene whose job it is to make a protein that keeps cells in a nondividing state. However, when *p53* mutates, cell division is no longer curbed. Mutant *p53* seems to be an important factor in more than half of all cancers. Two tumor-suppressor gene products that play a role in breast cancer—BRCA1 and BRCA2 proteins—initiate DNA repair. When these two genes mutate, damaged DNA is not repaired. Mutations then accumulate, which may set the cell on a course toward cancer.

A mutation in a proto-oncogene can also destroy the regulation of cell division. The mutated gene is called an *oncogene,* and it increases the stimulus for cell division or promotes cell division without a stimulus. An oncogene does to cell division what a stuck accelerator would do to the speed of a car. The proteins produced by many proto-oncogenes are growth factors or receptors for growth factors. When a proto-oncogene mutates and becomes an oncogene, the transformation often causes too much protein to be produced or makes the protein more active than usual. For example, the product of the *ras* gene normally signals the presence of a growth factor, which stimulates cell division. The *ras* oncogene protein is hyperactive and stimulates cell division even in the absence of growth factors. When normal cells are grown in tissue culture, they divide until they form a single layer of cells. If healthy cells contact a neighbor, they stop dividing. This phenomenon is called *contact inhibition.* But cancer cells do not exhibit contact inhibition. Instead, they continue to divide, pile up on one another, and form a tumor.

DNA Damage and Cell Destruction

When the genes that regulate cell division are faulty, backup systems normally swing into play to protect the body from the renegade cell. One such system is programmed cell death, also called *apoptosis,* in which cells activate a genetic suicide program in response to a biochemical or physiological signal. Activation of the so-called death genes prompts cells to manufacture proteins that then kill the cells. Often, the condemned cells go through a predictable series of physical changes that indicate the cell will die. During apoptosis, the outer membrane of the condemned cell produces bulges, called blebs, that are pinched off the cell (Figure 21a.4). The blebs indicate that the cell will break down into membrane-enclosed fragments that are engulfed and removed by other cells.

Cancer cells often fail to trigger apoptosis. Although it is not the only way that cancer cells evade this safeguard, a faulty

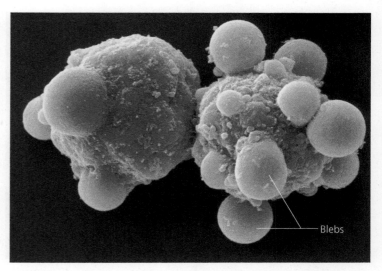

Blebs

Figure 21a.4 Programmed cell death is a backup system that protects the body from a cell in which the genes regulating cell division have been damaged. DNA damage that is too extensive to repair normally triggers a genetic suicide program that causes the cell to self-destruct, as these cells are doing. As the cell goes through programmed cell death, its plasma membrane forms bulges called blebs. Cancer cells are able to evade this protective mechanism.

p53 tumor-suppressor gene is often at least partly responsible. Besides producing a protein that inhibits cell division, the p53 protein normally prevents the replication of damaged DNA. If damage is detected, the p53 protein halts cell division until the DNA can be mended. If the damage is beyond repair, the p53 protein triggers the events that lead to programmed cell death.

In a cancer cell, however, a faulty p53 protein fails to initiate the events leading to cellular self-destruction, so the cells are free to divide in spite of genetic damage. Tumors containing cells with damaged *p53* genes grow aggressively and spread easily and quickly to new locations in the body. Cancer cells containing mutations in *p53* are difficult to kill with radiation or chemotherapy, because these techniques are intended to damage the DNA of the cancer cell and trigger programmed self-destruction. Because of mutations in *p53,* many cancer cells are simply unable to self-destruct in response to DNA damage.

Unlimited Cell Division

Healthy cells have yet another safeguard against unrestrained cell division: a mechanism that limits the number of times a cell can divide during its lifetime. When grown in the laboratory, most human cells divide only about 50 or 60 times before entering a nondividing state called *senescence.* Like sand running through an hourglass, cell division has a predetermined end.

How does a cell "count" the number of times it has divided? The answer might lie in telomeres—pieces of DNA at the tips of chromosomes that protect the ends of the chromosomes much like the plastic pieces on the ends of shoelaces protect the shoelace—or in telomerase, the enzyme that constructs

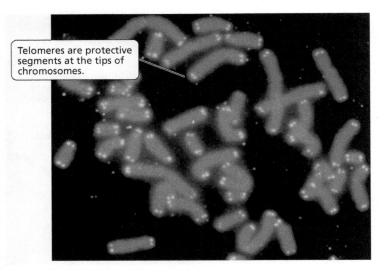

Telomeres are protective segments at the tips of chromosomes.

Figure 21a.5 Telomeres (shown here in yellow) may serve as molecular counting mechanisms that limit the number of times a cell can divide. Cancer cells retain the ability to construct new telomeres to replace the bits that are shaved off.

the telomeres (Figure 21a.5). Soon after an embryo is fully developed, most cells stop producing telomerase, putting an end to the maintenance of telomere length. Each time DNA is copied in preparation for cell division, a tiny piece of every telomere in the cell is shaved off, shortening the chromosomes slightly. When the telomeres are completely gone, the chromosome tips can fuse together, disrupting the genetic message and causing the cell to die. Telomeres, then, may be the cell's way of limiting the number of times division can occur. When the telomeres are gone, time is up for that cell. Thus, telomere length may serve both as a gauge of a cell's age and as an indicator of how long that line of cells will continue to divide.

The "fountain of youth" that bestows immortality on cancer cells and allows them to divide indefinitely is their unceasing production of telomerase. This enzyme reconstructs the telomeres after each cell division, stabilizing telomere length and protecting the important genes at chromosome tips. Although most types of mature human cells can no longer produce telomerase, the genes for telomerase apparently become turned on in most cancer cells. Telomerase is present in nearly 90% of biopsies of human cancerous tumors.

STOP and **THINK**

Why would telomerase activity serve as a tissue marker for cancerous cells?

Blood Supply to Cancer Cells

We have seen that cancer cells have escaped the normal cellular controls on cell division and are unable to issue the orders that would lead to their own death. Instead, they multiply and form a tumor.

As mentioned earlier, when a tumor reaches a critical size of about a million cells, its growth will stop unless it can attract a blood supply to deliver the nutrients it needs to support its growth and to remove waste. Cancer cells release special growth factors that cause capillaries to invade the tumor. These tiny

blood vessels become the tumor's lifeline, removing wastes and delivering fresh nutrients and additional growth factors that will spur tumor growth. They also serve as pathways by which the cancer cells are able to leave the tumor and spread to other sites in the body.

In a healthy person, blood vessel formation is uncommon and is usually limited to the repair of cuts or other wounds. Abnormal invasion of blood vessels into tissues can cause damage. To avoid such damage, cells produce a protein that prevents new blood vessels from forming in tissues. The gene that normally produces this protein is by now familiar—*p53*. Mutations in *p53* can block the production of the protein that prevents the attraction of blood vessels, allowing blood vessels to invade the tumor.

Adherence to Neighboring Cells

With access to blood vessels, the cancer cells can begin to spread. Their ability to travel through the body is yet another example of their freedom from normal cellular control mechanisms. Normal cells are "glued" in place by special molecules on their surfaces called *cellular adhesion molecules (CAMs)*. When most normal cells become "unglued" from other cells, they stop dividing, and their genetic program for self-destruction is activated.

Cancer cells must become "unglued" from other cells to travel through the body. One way cancer cells break loose is by secreting enzymes that break down the CAMs that hold them and their neighbors in place. In this way, their anchors are broken, and mechanical barriers that would prevent metastasis are breached. Unanchored cancer cells can continue dividing and evade self-destruction because their oncogenes send a false message to the nucleus saying that the cell is properly attached. Table 21a.1 presents a review of the control mechanisms that can fail, resulting in cancer.

Body Defense Cells

Despite all the safeguards that prevent cells from becoming cancerous, cancer cells develop in our bodies every day. Fortunately, certain body defense cells—natural killer cells and cytotoxic T cells (see Chapter 13)—usually kill those cancer cells. The processes that lead to the creation of cancer cells also produce new and slightly different proteins on cancer cell membranes. The defense cells recognize these proteins as nonself and destroy the cancer cells. But sometimes cancer cells evade destruction. Some types of cancer cells actively inhibit the defense cells, and some simply multiply so quickly that the defense cells cannot destroy them all. In either case, the tumor is able to grow and spread.

21a.3 Multiple Mutations

Healthy cells have interacting control systems that usually prevent cancer development. Normally, tumor-suppressor genes and proto-oncogenes regulate cell division so that it occurs only for growth and repair. If mutations occur, the cell will normally self-destruct before dividing and passing the genetic damage to its daughter cells. If those safeguards fail, the cell is usually prevented from dividing more than 50 to 60 times, because it lacks

Table 21a.1 Review of Control Mechanisms That Fail in Cancer	
Mechanisms That Protect Cells from Cancer	**Method of Evasion Used by Cancer Cells**
Genetic controls on cell division	
Proto-oncogenes stimulate cell division through effects on growth factors and certain other cell-signaling mechanisms	Oncogenes promote cell division
Tumor-suppressor genes inhibit cell division	Mutations in tumor-suppressor genes take the "brakes" off cell division
Programmed cell death	
A genetic program that initiates events leading to the death of the cell when damaged DNA is detected or another signal is received	Mutations in tumor-suppressor genes: mutant gene *p53* no longer triggers cell death when damaged DNA is detected
Limitations on the number of times a cell can divide	
Telomeres protect the ends of chromosomes, but a fraction of each is shaved off each time the DNA is copied; when the telomeres are gone, the chromosome tips can stick together, causing the cell to die	Genes to produce telomerase, the enzyme that reconstructs telomeres, are turned on in cancer cells so telomere length is stabilized
Controls that prevent the formation of new blood vessels	
These controls are normally in effect except in a few instances, such as wound healing	Cancer cells produce growth factors that attract new blood vessels and proteins that counter the normal proteins that inhibit blood vessel formation
Controls that keep normal cells in place	
Cellular adhesion molecules (CAMs) hold cells in place; unanchored cells stop dividing and self-destruct	Cancer cells' oncogenes send a false message to the nucleus that the cell is properly anchored

telomerase. If the telomerase gene is turned on, the cells will begin to starve due to lack of nutrients when the tumor consists of about a million cells. For a tumor to grow larger than this, the cells must attract a blood supply. To metastasize, cancer cells must break the molecules that anchor them in place.

With so many controls to prevent it, cancer development is a multistep process involving multiple mutations and changes in gene activity. The first mutation occurs and is passed on to all the descendant cells. Later—usually many years later—a second mutation occurs in one of the descendant cells containing the original mutation. Both mutations are passed to all the descendants of that cell. Many years later, a third mutation might occur in one of the daughter cells that already has two mutations. Each mutation brings the cell closer to becoming cancerous (Figure 21a.6).

Damage must occur in *at least* two genes (and most commonly more than six genes) before cancer occurs. For instance, colon cells must accumulate damage in at least one proto-oncogene and three tumor-suppressor genes before they become cancerous (Figure 21a.7). Furthermore, a tumor may contain different cell lines containing mutations in different sets of genes. In a recent study, researchers found 50,000 mutations in the lung tumor of a heavy smoker. The number of damaged genes needed to produce cancer explains why it is possible to inherit a predisposition to a certain form of cancer. A person who inherits only one mutant gene may be predisposed to cancer. But a second event, a mutation in at least one other gene, is required before uncontrolled cell division is unleashed.

21a.4 Cancer and Epigenomics

Gene mutations and epigenetics interact to cause cancer. We have focused on mutations, changes in the sequence of nucleotides in the genome that lead to cancer, but recall from Chapter 21

that the epigenome can also alter gene activity. The epigenome is a network of chemical tags that bind to DNA and turn specific genes on or off without altering the sequence of nucleotides. If tumor-suppressor genes are turned off, genetic mutations can

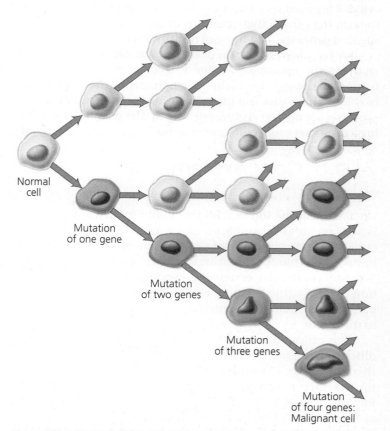

Figure 21a.6 Multiple mutations must occur and accumulate in a cell before the cell becomes cancerous.

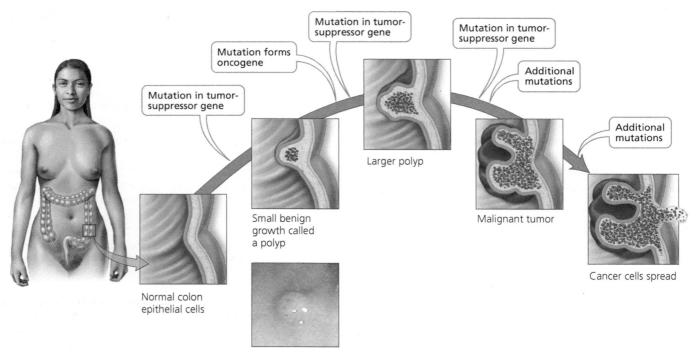

Figure 21a.7 Multiple mutations must occur in a single cell before it becomes cancerous. In colon cells, at least one proto-oncogene and three tumor-suppressor genes must mutate before the cells become cancerous.

accumulate, which could allow cancer development. On the other hand, if oncogenes are *not* turned off or are switched on, cell division can speed up in spite of inappropriate conditions. Indeed, the gene activity patterns of most cancers reveal fewer silenced genes than do those of healthy cells.

We have learned a great deal about cancer development by studying the epigenome. Some epigenetic modifications can be passed through generations, emphasizing the importance of the mother's diet and lifestyle during pregnancy. Epigenetic processes are also reversible, opening up the possibility of finding a drug that could cure cancer by turning key genes on or off.

21a.5 Cancer Stem Cell Hypothesis

Do *all* cells of the tumor have the ability to divide without restraint, metastasize, and form new tumors? Perhaps this is so, but an increasing number of scientists are suggesting that only some cells within the tumor are capable of continually dividing. According to the cancer stem cell hypothesis, only a subpopulation of cells within the tumor—cancer stem cells—have the capacity for unlimited self-renewal (replenishment) and give rise to the tumor.

The cancer stem cell hypothesis might explain why traditional methods of treating cancer—radiation and chemotherapy (discussed shortly)—may shrink tumors, although the tumors often return. Such treatments are aimed at killing rapidly dividing cells. The death of these cells would shrink the tumor. However, lingering cancer stem cells could replenish the population. Researchers are looking for ways to cure cancer by killing the cancer stem cells.

21a.6 Known Causes of Cancer

We have seen that many of the tactics a cancer cell uses to evade normal cellular safeguards are consequences of changes in genes. Those genetic changes are often brought about by viruses or by mutations caused by exposure to certain chemicals or to radiation.

Viruses

It is estimated that viruses cause about 5% of cancers in the United States (Table 21a.2). Some of the viruses that cause cancer have oncogenes among their genes. Once inside the host cell, the viral oncogene behaves as a host oncogene would, taking the cell one step closer to becoming cancerous. A viral oncogene is partly why the human papilloma virus that causes genital warts can cause cervical and penile cancer. If the viral genetic information is in the form of RNA, the enzyme reverse transcriptase uses viral RNA to synthesize viral DNA, which is then inserted into a

Table 21a.2 Some Viruses Linked to Human Cancer	
Virus	Types of Cancer
Human papilloma viruses (HPVs)	Cervical, penile, and other anogenital cancers in men and women
Hepatitis B and C viruses	Liver cancer
Epstein-Barr virus	B-cell lymphomas, especially Burkitt's lymphoma; nasopharyngeal carcinoma
Human T-cell leukemia virus (HTLV-1)	Adult T-cell leukemia
Cytomegalovirus (CMV)	Lymphomas and leukemias
Kaposi's sarcoma–associated herpesvirus	Kaposi's sarcoma

host cell chromosome. Proteins produced by the viral DNA may then drive the cellular proto-oncogene to be expressed in abnormal levels or in the wrong place or time. RNA viruses can also pick up a proto-oncogene from one host cell and introduce it into a new host cell, thus promoting cell division. In other cases, a virus causes cancer because viral DNA becomes inserted into the host DNA in a location that disrupts the functioning of a gene that influences cell division. The viral DNA could, for example, be inserted into a regulatory gene that controls a proto-oncogene, breaking the switch that turns off the gene. Some viruses interfere with the function of the immune system, lessening its ability to find and destroy cancer cells as they arise.

Chemicals

A *carcinogen* is an environmental agent that fosters the development of cancer. Some chemicals, especially certain organic chemicals, cause cancer by producing mutations. As we saw in Chapter 21, a mutation in as few as one nucleotide in a DNA sequence can alter a gene's message. Thus, even a small alteration in DNA can wreak havoc with a cell's regulatory mechanisms and lead to cancer.

Chemical carcinogens are around us most of the time—in air, food, water, and other substances in our environment. We can attempt to avoid contact with some of them. For instance, tobacco smoke contains a host of chemical carcinogens. Among them is one that specifically mutates the tumor-suppressor gene *p53* and another that specifically mutates one of the *ras* proto-oncogenes. Tobacco smoke is responsible for 30% of all cancer deaths in the United States and may contribute to as many as 60%. Excessive alcohol consumption is another cancer risk factor that can be avoided. Other chemical carcinogens are more difficult to steer clear of. These include benzene, formaldehyde, hydrocarbons, certain pesticides, and chemicals in some dyes and preservatives.

Some chemicals contribute to the development of cancer by stimulating cell division, which increases the chance of additional mutations arising. If a cancerous cell has already formed, this stimulation will cause the cancer to progress. Certain hormones can promote cancer in this way. For example, the female hormone estrogen stimulates cell division in the tissues of the breast and in the lining of the uterus (the endometrium). Sustained high levels of estrogen are linked with breast cancer,[2] and the incidence of endometrial cancer is elevated in postmenopausal women whose hormone replacement therapy consists entirely of estrogen. Estrogen does not seem to promote endometrial cancer when taken in combination with progesterone. However, since 2002, several studies have shown that postmenopausal women who take estrogen in combination with progesterone have a slightly greater risk of developing breast cancer. Furthermore, breast tumors in women taking combined hormone pills were larger and more likely to have spread than were tumors in women not taking hormone pills.

Radiation

Radiation, too, can lead to cancer by causing mutations in DNA. It is impossible to avoid exposure to radiation from natural sources, such as the ultraviolet light from the sun, cosmic rays,

[2]The link between estrogen and breast cancer is discussed in Chapter 17.

radon, and uranium. However, we can take reasonable precautions to minimize our risks. For example, sunlight's ultraviolet rays cause skin cancer. Although we probably would not choose to spend our lives entirely indoors to reduce the risk of skin cancer, it is wise to forgo sunbathing, as well as tanning lamps and tanning parlors. It is also a good idea to use a sunscreen whenever exposure to the sun is unavoidable.

STOP and THINK ....

A cancer cluster is a greater number of cancer cases in an area than would be expected in a similar area over a given length of time. It usually involves the same type of cancer and is caused by common exposure. If you were asked to investigate a cancer cluster, which of the cancer risks would you look for?

....

21a.7 Reducing the Risk of Cancer

Although we tend to think of cancer as one disease, it is in fact a family of more than 200 diseases, usually named for the organ in which the tumor arises. Cancers of the epithelial tissues are *carcinomas*. *Leukemias* are cancers of the bone marrow. *Sarcomas* are cancers of the muscle, bone, cartilage, or connective tissues. *Lymphomas* are cancers of the lymphatic tissues. *Adenocarcinomas* are cancers of the glandular epithelia. Figure 21a.8 shows the estimated number of cases of cancer and cancer deaths for various types of cancer, and Table 21a.3 indicates where in this textbook certain types of cancer are discussed.

Cancer is the second leading cause of death in industrialized countries, but the good news is that some lifestyle changes can greatly decrease your risk of developing cancer (Table 21a.4).

Table 21a.3	Some Discussions of Cancer in This Book
Cancer	Chapter
Skin	Chapter 4 (p. 78)
Leukemia	Chapter 11 (pp. 205–206)
Lung	Chapter 14 (pp. 282–283)
Colon, stomach, esophagus	Chapter 15 (pp. 291, 297)
Testis, prostate	Chapter 17 (pp. 337, 338–339)
Breast	Chapter 17 (pp. 348–349)
Cervical	Chapter 17a (p. 361)

Table 21a.4 Tips for Reducing Your Cancer Risk
1. Do not use tobacco. If you do, quit. Avoid exposure to secondhand smoke.
2. Reduce the amount of saturated fat in your diet, especially the fat from red meat.
3. Minimize your consumption of salt-cured, pickled, and smoked foods.
4. Eat at least five servings of fruit and vegetables every day.
5. Avoid excessive alcohol intake. If you consume alcohol, one or two drinks a day should be the maximum.
6. Watch your caloric intake, and maintain a healthy body weight.
7. Avoid excessive exposure to sunlight. Wear protective clothing. Use sunscreen.
8. Avoid unnecessary medical x-rays.
9. Have the appropriate screening exams on a regular basis. Women should have Pap tests and mammograms. Men should have prostate tests. All adults should have tests for colorectal cancer.

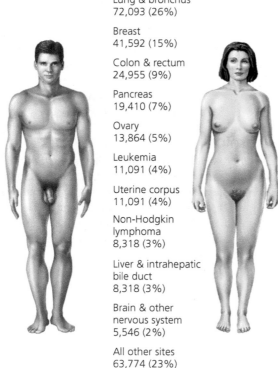

Estimated New Cases		**Estimated Deaths**	
Male	**Female**	**Male**	**Female**
Prostate 220,532 (26%)	Breast 234,949 (29%)	Lung & bronchus 87,402 (28%)	Lung & bronchus 72,093 (26%)
Lung & bronchus 118,748 (14%)	Lung & bronchus 103,322 (13%)	Prostate 28,094 (9%)	Breast 41,592 (15%)
Colon & rectum 67,856 (8%)	Colon & rectum 64,814 (8%)	Colon & rectum 24,972 (8%)	Colon & rectum 24,955 (9%)
Urinary bladder 59,374 (7%)	Uterine corpus 56,712 (7%)	Pancreas 21,851 (7%)	Pancreas 19,410 (7%)
Melanoma of the skin 42,410 (5%)	Thyroid 48,610 (6%)	Liver & intrahepatic bile duct 15,608 (5%)	Ovary 13,864 (5%)
Kidney & renal pelvis 42,410 (5%)	Melanoma of the skin 32,407 (4%)	Leukemia 15,608 (5%)	Leukemia 11,091 (4%)
Non-Hodgkin lymphoma 42,410 (5%)	Non-Hodgkin lymphoma 32,407 (4%)	Esophagus 12,486 (4%)	Uterine corpus 11,091 (4%)
Oral cavity & pharynx 33,928 (4%)	Kidney & renal pelvis 24,305 (3%)	Urinary bladder 12,486 (4%)	Non-Hodgkin lymphoma 8,318 (3%)
Leukemia 33,928 (4%)	Leukemia 24,305 (3%)	Non-Hodgkin lymphoma 12,486 (4%)	Liver & intrahepatic bile duct 8,318 (3%)
Liver & intrahepatic duct 25,446 (3%)	Pancreas 24,305 (3%)	Kidney & renal pelvis 9,365 (3%)	Brain & other nervous system 5,546 (2%)
All other sites 178,122 (21%)	All other sites 170,136 (21%)	All other sites 74,916 (24%)	All other sites 63,774 (23%)

Figure 21a.8 The American Cancer Society's 2015 estimates for the leading types of cancer in terms of new cases and deaths. The figures do not include basal and squamous cell skin cancer or in situ carcinomas other than those of the urinary bladder. The percentages may not total 100% because of rounding. (Source: American Cancer Society, Cancer Statistics 2015.)

Tobacco use and unhealthy diet are responsible for two-thirds of all cancer deaths in the United States. Tobacco smoke is the leading carcinogen, and it is obvious how to modify that risk.

A few simple dietary changes may reduce your risk of developing cancer. The best rules are to eat a well-balanced diet and to eat all foods in moderation. For instance, a high-fat diet is linked to colon and breast cancers. Most people in the United States consume far too much fat. Thus it is wise to reduce fat intake, especially saturated fat, which comes from animal sources such as red meat. Consuming large quantities of smoked, salt-cured, and nitrite-cured foods, such as ham, bologna, and salami, increases the risk of cancers of the esophagus and stomach.

A diet rich in fruits and vegetables can reduce your cancer risk because these foods are high in fiber, which can dilute the contents of the intestines, bind to carcinogens, and reduce the amount of time the carcinogens spend in the intestine by speeding passage of intestinal contents. The so-called colorful vegetables—those having colors other than green—are usually high in antioxidant vitamins, which may play a role in protecting against cancer. As their name implies, antioxidants interfere with oxidation, a process that can result in the formation of molecules called *free radicals* that can damage DNA and thereby

lead to cancer. The three major antioxidants are beta-carotene, vitamin E, and vitamin C. The first two are common in red, yellow, and orange fruits and vegetables, and the last abounds in citrus fruits, among other sources.

21a.8 Diagnosing Cancer

Early detection is critical to cancer survival because treatment is much more likely to be successful if the cancer has not yet spread. You know your own body better than anyone else does. The American Cancer Society suggests that you be alert for cancer's seven warning signs, the first letters of which spell the word CAUTION:

Change in bowel or bladder habit or function
A sore that does not heal
Unusual bleeding or bloody discharge
Thickening or lump in breast or elsewhere
Indigestion or difficulty swallowing
Obvious change in wart or mole
Nagging cough or hoarseness

But self-examination is not enough. There are additional ways to diagnose cancer—some more involved than others:

Table 21a.5 Recommended Cancer Screening Tests	
Guidelines suggested by the American Cancer Society for the early detection of cancer in people without symptoms, age 20 to 40	
Cancer-related checkup every 3 years	
Should include the procedures listed below plus health counseling (such as tips on quitting cigarette smoking) and examinations for cancers of the thyroid, testes, prostate, mouth, ovaries, skin, and lymph nodes. Some people are at higher than normal risk for certain cancers and may need to have tests more frequently.	
Breast cancer	• Exam by doctor every 3 years • Self-exam every month • One baseline breast x-ray ages 35 to 40
	Higher risk for breast cancer: personal or family history of breast cancer; never had children; had first child after 30
Uterine cancer	• Women should report any vaginal bleeding or discharge to their doctors
Cervical cancer	• Yearly Pap test beginning at age 21 or 3 years after sexual activity begins
	Higher risk for cervical cancer: early age at first intercourse; multiple sex partners
Guidelines suggested by the American Cancer Society for the early detection of cancer in people without symptoms, age 40 and over	
Cancer-related checkup every year	
Should include the procedures listed below plus health counseling (such as tips on quitting cigarette smoking) and examinations for cancers of the thyroid, testes, prostate, mouth, ovaries, skin, and lymph nodes. Some people are at higher than normal risk for certain cancers and may need to have tests more frequently.	
Colon and rectal cancer	• Fecal occult blood test every year after age 50 • Flexible sigmoidoscopy beginning at age 50 and every 5 years thereafter, or colonoscopy every 10 years
	Higher risk for colorectal cancer: personal or family history of colon or rectal cancer; personal or family history of polyps in the colon or rectum; ulcerative colitis
Breast cancer	• Exam by doctor every 3 years • Self-exam every month • Breast x-ray every year after 40
	Higher risk for breast cancer: personal or family history of breast cancer; never had children; had first child after 30
Uterine cancer	• Pelvic exam every year
Cervical cancer	• Yearly Pap test
	Higher risk for cervical cancer: early age at first intercourse; multiple sex partners
Endometrial cancer	• Endometrial tissue sample at menopause if at risk
	Higher risk of endometrial cancer: infertility, obesity, failure of ovulation, abnormal uterine bleeding, estrogen therapy
Prostate cancer	• Yearly prostate-specific antigen (PSA) blood test and digital rectal exam after age 50

- **Routine screening.** Many routine tests can detect cancer in people who do not have symptoms. You can perform some of the tests on yourself; others require a visit to a medical professional (Table 21a.5).

- **Imaging.** Many imaging techniques allow physicians to look inside the body and identify tumors. These include x-rays, computerized tomography (CT) scans, magnetic resonance imaging (MRI), and ultrasound (Figure 21a.9).

- **Biopsy.** Biopsy is the removal and analysis of a small piece of tissue suspected to be cancerous. A biopsy is often done using a needle instead of surgery. In either case, cells are then examined under a microscope to see whether they have the characteristic appearance of cancer cells.

- **Tumor marker tests.** When cancer is suspected, certain blood tests can be used to search for tumor markers, which are chemicals produced either by the cells of the tumor or by body cells in response to a tumor. Prostate cells, for example, produce prostate-specific antigen (PSA). Men normally have low levels of PSA in their blood; however, abnormal proliferation of prostate cells, as would occur if a tumor were developing, can raise those levels. Thus, elevated blood PSA levels suggest the presence of prostate cancer. Currently, PSA is the only tumor marker

that is useful in the original diagnosis of a cancer, but other tumor markers may reveal whether certain cancers have spread or returned. For example, blood levels of a marker called TA-90 can help determine whether melanoma (a

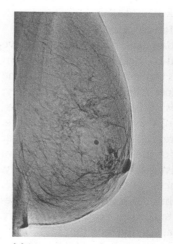 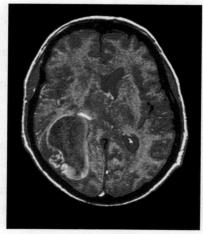

(a) Mammogram of a breast cancer tumor (light blue area)

(b) MRI of a cancerous brain tumor (bright purple area)

Figure 21a.9 Imaging techniques such as x-rays or MRIs can detect tumors.

type of skin cancer) has spread. The tumor marker CA 125 can identify ovarian cancer. CA 15-3 indicates a recurrence of breast cancer, and CEA indicates a recurrence of colon cancer.

- **Genetic tests.** DNA analysis of cells found in certain bodily fluids or excretions can identify gene mutations associated with certain cancers: sputum is examined for signs of lung cancer, urine for signs of bladder cancer, and feces for signs of colon cancer. Other signs of cancer can be detected by still other tests. For instance, as noted earlier, the enzyme telomerase is produced by cancer cells but rarely by normal ones. A test for telomerase appears to be helpful in diagnosing certain cancers, but this test is still in an experimental stage.

21a.9 Treating Cancer

The conventional cancer treatments—surgery, radiation therapy, and chemotherapy—are still the mainstays of cancer treatment. But many new treatments hold promise.

Surgery

When a cancerous tumor is accessible and can be removed without damaging vital surrounding tissue, surgery is usually performed to eradicate the cancer or remove as much as possible. If every cancer cell is removed, as can be done with early tumors (carcinoma in situ), a complete cure is possible. However, if cancer cells have begun to invade surrounding tissue or have spread to distant locations, surgery alone cannot "cure" the cancer. If the cancer has spread, surrounding tissue and perhaps even nearby lymph nodes may also be removed. Unfortunately, more than half of all tumors have already metastasized by the time of diagnosis, so further treatment is necessary.

Radiation

If cancer has spread from the initial site but is still localized, surgery is usually followed by radiation therapy. In some cases, such as cancer of the larynx (voice box), localized tumors that are difficult to remove surgically without damaging surrounding tissue may be treated with radiation alone.

As we have seen, radiation damages DNA, and extensive DNA damage triggers programmed cell death. The greatest harm caused by radiation is done to cells that are dividing rapidly. The intended targets of radiation, cancer cells, are dividing actively; but so are the cells of several types of tissues, called renewal tissues, whose cells normally continue dividing throughout life. These tissues include cells of the reproductive system, cells that replace layers of skin or the lining of the stomach, cells that give rise to blood cells, or cells that give rise to hair. Unfortunately, radiation cannot distinguish cancer cells from renewal tissue, so good cells are sacrificed in killing the harmful ones. The destruction of renewal tissues leads to the side effects of radiation, such as temporary sterility, nausea, anemia, and hair loss.

Advances in radiation treatment are reducing damage to healthy tissue near the tumor. Intensity-modulated radiation therapy, often used to treat cancers of the prostate, head, and neck, uses computers to deliver precise doses of radiation to the three-dimensional shape of the tumor by controlling the intensity of multiple radiation beams. In radiation treatment for prostate cancer, initial studies show that damage to the rectum is reduced if a filler material that is also used in cosmetic surgery is injected into the tissue between the radiation source and the rectum to protect the healthy tissue.

Chemotherapy

When cancer is thought to have spread by the time of diagnosis, chemotherapy is often used. In general, the drugs used in chemotherapy reach all parts of the body and kill all rapidly dividing cells, just as radiation does. Some of the drugs block DNA synthesis, others damage DNA, and a few others prevent cell division by interfering with other cellular processes. The side effects are similar to those that accompany radiation therapy.

New chemotherapy techniques target the malignant tissue more precisely, thus sparing healthy cells. One technique uses magnetic fields to pull extremely small metallic beads coated with chemotherapy drugs into the tumor to kill the cancer cells. In another method of targeting only cancer cells, the doctor injects the patient with a light-activated chemotherapy drug. This drug is absorbed by all cells of the body but stays in cancer cells longer than in normal cells. After a few days, when the photosensitive drug remains only in cancer cells, light of a particular wavelength is directed precisely at the cancer cells. When the drug absorbs the light, it produces an active form of oxygen that kills the cells, damages blood vessels that deliver nutrients to the tumor, and causes the immune system to attack the cancer cells.

As we have seen, the idea underlying radiation and chemotherapy is that the damage they do to DNA in rapidly dividing cells will cause the cells to self-destruct. However, *p53*, the gene that detects DNA damage and initiates programmed cell death, is mutant in more than half of all cancers. As a result, even though the treatment succeeds in damaging the DNA in cancer cells, the cells do not always self-destruct, and treatment fails.

Targeted Cancer Treatment

In recent years, there has been a major change in the way doctors and scientists think about cancer. Gone are the days when the only aim was to kill the cancer cells. As researchers have learned more about the molecular biology of cancer, new ways of slowing its progression or dealing with it as a genetic disease have been developed.

As we have learned more about the genetics underlying cancer, a new treatment strategy has begun—develop drugs to target the molecular and cellular causes of cancer. Researchers can sequence the genome and map the epigenome to find the faulty genes. One success story is the treatment of a particularly aggressive type of leukemia. Researchers identified the faulty gene and the abnormal protein it produced. This protein signals the cell to divide, resulting in too many immature white blood cells. Gleevec is a drug that prevents the action of the faulty protein, allowing the white blood cell numbers to decrease.

Immunotherapy

Cytotoxic T cells of the immune system continually search the body for abnormal cells, such as cancer cells, and kill any they find (see Chapter 13). The goal of immunotherapy, then, is to boost the patient's immune system so that it becomes more effective in destroying cancer cells. One form of immunotherapy involves administering factors normally secreted by lymphocytes, including interleukin-2 (which stimulates lymphocytes that attack cancer cells), interferons (which stimulate the immune system and also directly affect tumor cells), and tumor necrosis factor (which directly affects cancer cells, causing them to self-destruct).

Two types of vaccines can be used in the battle against cancer. One type is a vaccine against a virus that causes cancer.

For example, a vaccine against four of the human papilloma viruses that cause cervical cancer is available. Two of these viruses, HPV16 and HPV18, cause 70% of the cases of cervical cancer. Federal health officials now recommend that all girls 9 to 12 years of age and boys 11 to 12 years of age receive this vaccination.

The other type of vaccine is being tested in clinical trials, with promising results. It is designed to work by stimulating T cells to attack and kill cancer cells. Unlike most vaccines, these vaccines cannot *prevent* disease (cancer); they can only treat it. Cancer vaccines contain dead cancer cells, parts of cells, or proteins from cancer cells. Recall that vaccines cause the immune system to fight cells having the same characteristics as the cells in the vaccine. A vaccine strategy is now available to treat prostate cancer. Vaccines are being tested to treat melanoma (a deadly form of skin cancer) and leukemia, as well as cancers of the kidney, prostate, colon, and lung.

Inhibition of Blood Vessel Formation

The formation of blood vessels is a critical step in the life of a tumor, because blood vessels bring nourishment and provide a pathway for cell migration. Researchers are working on ways to cut off these lifelines and starve the tumor. Many drugs have been developed for this purpose, and some have been approved by the U.S. Food and Drug Administration (FDA). When a certain drug that blocks blood vessel formation is combined with chemotherapy, the survival rate of patients with colorectal cancer improves.

Gene Therapy

More than 400 clinical trials are currently using gene therapy to treat cancer, but the FDA has not yet approved any means of gene therapy for cancer treatment. Nearly all these studies are in very early stages. One of the treatment strategies being tested is to insert normal tumor-suppressor genes into the cancerous cells. For instance, you may recall that gene *p53* normally triggers programmed cell death when DNA damage is detected but that this gene is often faulty in cancer cells. Researchers hope that inserting a healthy form of *p53* into cancer cells will lead to their death, causing the tumor to shrink.

One of the most promising approaches using gene therapy is to insert a gene into tumor cells that sensitizes the cells to a drug that will kill them. This method is now being evaluated as treatment for brain, ovarian, and prostate cancers. A viral gene for the enzyme thymidine kinase is inserted into the tumor cells, and when the gene is expressed, the resulting enzyme sensitizes the cells to a drug called ganciclovir. The drug is inactive except inside those cells that produce the enzyme coded for by the inserted gene. Thus, only the tumor cells are killed.

what would YOU do? If a child has cancer, it is the parents' responsibility to decide whether to continue treatment. What factors would you consider to be ethical reasons for stopping treatment? ■

LOOKING AHEAD

In this and the previous few chapters, we considered genes and inheritance. We have seen that meiosis and mutations increase variability in a population. In the next chapter, we will see that this genetic variability in a population is important for evolution by natural selection.

CONSIDER THIS CASE

Emma is turning 12 and needs a physical exam before attending summer camp. Excited about camp, Emma and her mother head to the doctor's office. Following the exam, Doc Smith says, "Emma is in great shape. However, I suggest that she get the HPV vaccine to prevent cervical cancer."

■ How would you respond to Emma's mom if she asked why a vaccine should be given now, before Emma is sexually active?
■ How would you explain that a virus can cause cancer?

Evolution and Our Heritage

22

IN CHAPTER 21A, we learned how mutations in certain genes lead to loss of control over cell division and the development of cancer. In this chapter, we consider mutations in a different light. We focus on evolution and how mutations, along with processes such as genetic drift, gene flow, and natural selection, cause changes in allele frequencies within populations. We also address such questions as these: How did life arise and evolve on Earth? How has evolution shaped species, including our own? What were our ancestors like?

22.1 Evolution of Life on Earth

Evolution can broadly be defined as descent with modification from a common ancestor. It is the process by which Earth's life-forms have changed from their earliest beginnings to today. But how did life first arise on Earth?

Earth is estimated to be 4.5 billion years old. Evidence from physical and chemical changes in Earth's crust and atmosphere indicates that life has existed on Earth for about 3.8 billion years. The environment of the early Earth was very different from that of today and would have been an extremely hostile place for most organisms (Figure 22.1). Earth's crust was hot and volcanic. Intense lightning and ultraviolet radiation struck Earth's surface, and the atmosphere contained almost no gaseous oxygen (O_2). Scientists agree on the scarcity of oxygen but debate the other components of the early atmosphere. Most models suggest that carbon dioxide (CO_2), nitrogen (N_2), and water (H_2O) were present. Other gases that may have been present include carbon monoxide (CO), hydrogen (H_2), methane (CH_4), sulfur dioxide (SO_2), and hydrogen sulfide (H_2S). Once the crust cooled, water vapor condensed as rain, and runoff collected in depressions to form early seas.

Figure 22.1 Representation of the early Earth

How did life evolve under these conditions? In the following sections, we present a sequence of events for the origin of life on Earth. The sequence, known as **chemical evolution,** indicates that life evolved from chemicals, slowly increasing in complexity over a period of perhaps 300 million years.

Small Organic Molecules

Current scientific evidence indicates that conditions of the early Earth favored the synthesis of small organic molecules from inorganic molecules. Specifically, the low-oxygen atmosphere of the primitive Earth encouraged the joining of simple molecules to form complex molecules. The low-oxygen atmosphere was important because oxygen attacks chemical bonds. Additionally, the energy required for the joining of simple molecules could have come from the lightning and intense ultraviolet (UV) radiation striking the primitive Earth. (UV radiation was likely more intense during those times than it is now, because young suns emit more UV radiation than do mature suns and because the early Earth lacked an ozone layer to shield it from UV radiation.)

In 1953, Stanley Miller and Harold Urey of the University of Chicago tested the hypothesis that organic molecules could be synthesized from inorganic ones. These scientists re-created in their laboratory conditions presumed similar to those of the early Earth (Figure 22.2). Miller and Urey discharged electric sparks (meant to simulate lightning) through an atmosphere that contained some of the gases thought to be present in the early atmosphere. They generated a variety of small organic molecules, supporting the hypothesis that organic molecules could be synthesized from inorganic ones.

The atmospheric composition used in the Miller–Urey experiment differed somewhat from the composition currently favored by scientists who study characteristics of the early Earth. Even so, many simulations conducted by other scientists using different gas mixtures (and energy sources) have produced organic compounds in varying amounts. Taken as a whole, these experiments demonstrate that organic molecules can be synthesized from inorganic molecules.

Another possibility is that impacts from comets or meteorites produced the early organic molecules that were critical to the origin of life. Comets, for example, carry small molecules such as water (H_2O), carbon dioxide (CO_2), and ammonia (NH_3). The impact of comets with Earth could have provided the energy necessary for chemical reactions that yielded the organic compounds required for the origin of life. Recent laboratory re-creations of comet impacts have produced amino acids.

Macromolecules

The early organic molecules accumulated in the oceans and over a long period formed a complex mixture. The small molecules then joined to form macromolecules, such as proteins and nucleic acids. Evidence indicates that this joining could have occurred when the small molecules were washed onto clay or

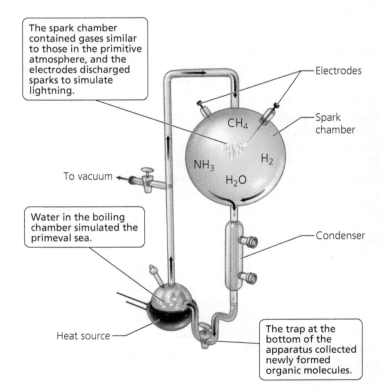

The spark chamber contained gases similar to those in the primitive atmosphere, and the electrodes discharged sparks to simulate lightning.

Electrodes

Spark chamber

CH_4

NH_3 H_2

To vacuum

H_2O

Water in the boiling chamber simulated the primeval sea.

Condenser

Heat source

The trap at the bottom of the apparatus collected newly formed organic molecules.

Figure 22.2 Apparatus used by Miller and Urey to test the hypothesis that organic molecules could be synthesized from inorganic ones

hot sand or lava. Other evidence points to deep-sea vents as important locations for the synthesis of small organic molecules and their joining to form larger molecules.

Which macromolecule led to the formation of the first cells? Some evidence indicates that RNA was the critical macromolecule, because it can act as an enzyme and because its self-replicating abilities would have allowed information to be transferred from one generation to the next. Cells today store their genetic information as DNA. Thus, if RNA was the first genetic material, then DNA evolved later from an RNA template. Other evidence indicates that proteins were the macromolecules that led to the first cells. Amino acids, peptides, and proteins are more chemically stable than nucleotides and nucleic acids when exposed to salt (such as would occur in primordial seas) and intense UV radiation (such as that presumed to have struck the early Earth).

Early Cells

The newly formed organic macromolecules aggregated into droplet-like structures that were the precursors of cells. The early droplets displayed some of the same properties as living cells, such as the ability to maintain an internal environment different from surrounding conditions.

Fossil evidence indicates that the earliest cells were prokaryotes. Recall from Chapter 3 that prokaryotic cells lack membrane-enclosed organelles, such as the nucleus, and are typically smaller than eukaryotic cells. These early prokaryotic cells relied on anaerobic metabolism (metabolism in the absence of oxygen). Eventually, some of these cells captured energy from sunlight and made their own complex organic molecules from CO_2 and H_2O in their environment. This process, known as *photosynthesis,* produced oxygen as a by-product. Oxygen began to accumulate in the environment. Next came cells that could use the now abundant oxygen to harness energy from stored organic molecules; these cells used cellular respiration (aerobic metabolism; see Chapter 3).

So the question arises: How did more complex cells arise from these early prokaryotic cells? It's possible that some of the organelles within eukaryotic cells appeared when other, smaller organisms became incorporated into the early, primitive cells. Mitochondria, for example, may be descendants of once free-living bacteria. These bacteria either invaded or were engulfed by the ancient cells and formed a mutually beneficial relationship with them. This idea is called the **endosymbiont theory,** and it provides an explanation for the origin of some features of eukaryotic cells, including mitochondria. It is unclear whether endosymbiosis was a factor in the origin of other eukaryotic features, such as the membrane-bound nucleus. An additional possibility is that infolding of the plasma membrane of an ancient prokaryote produced some of the organelles (for example, the endoplasmic reticulum or Golgi complex) found in eukaryotic cells of today.

Fossils of prokaryotic cells have been dated at 3.5 billion years old, and scientists estimate that the first prokaryotic cells arose around 3.8 billion years ago. As we discuss later in the chapter, fossils are rarely formed and found, so the origin for a group of organisms is estimated to occur earlier than the oldest fossil evidence for that group. Eukaryotic cells evolved about 1.8 billion years ago. Multicellularity evolved in eukaryotes around 1.6 billion years ago and eventually led to organisms such as

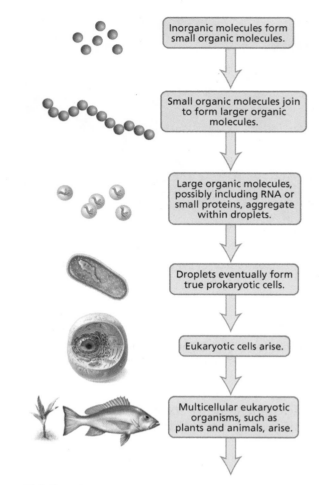

Figure 22.3 Steps in the origin of life on Earth

plants, fungi, and animals. Figure 22.3 summarizes steps in the origin of life on Earth.

22.2 Scale of Evolutionary Change

Evolution occurs on two levels. One level, microevolution, is small; and the other, macroevolution, is large. **Microevolution** occurs through changes in allele frequencies within a population over a few generations. **Macroevolution,** conversely, consists of larger-scale evolutionary change over longer periods of time, such as the origin of groups of species (for example, mammals) and mass extinctions (the catastrophic disappearance of many species). We begin with microevolution, examining genetic variation within populations and describing the causes of microevolution. We then turn to the larger-scale phenomena of macroevolution.

Microevolution

Look around, and you will see variation in almost any group of individuals belonging to the same species. Consider your classmates. They do not all look alike, and, unless you are an identical twin, you probably do not precisely resemble your brothers or sisters. Before looking at what makes individuals in such a group different, let's define some basic terminology. A **population** is a group of individuals of the same species living in a particular area. A population of bluegill sunfish inhabits a pond, and a population of deer mice inhabits a small tract of forest. A **gene pool** consists of all the alleles of all the genes of all individuals in a population. (Recall from Chapter 20 that a *gene* is a segment of DNA on a chromosome that directs the synthesis of a specific protein, whereas *alleles* are different forms of a gene.) Now let's take a closer look at what makes individuals in a population different and examine some of the ways that variation can appear in populations.

Sexual reproduction and mutation produce variation in populations. Sexual reproduction shuffles alleles already present in the population. As discussed in Chapters 19 and 20, the gametes (eggs or sperm) of any one individual show substantial genetic variation that results from crossing over and independent assortment during meiosis. Also, the combination of gametes that unite at fertilization is a chance event. Of the millions of sperm produced by a male, only one fertilizes the egg. This union produces a new individual with a new combination of alleles.

New genes and *new* alleles originate by **mutation,** a change in the nucleotide sequence of DNA. Mutations occur at a low rate in any set of genes, so their contribution to genetic diversity in large populations is quite small. Mutations can appear spontaneously from mistakes in DNA replication, or they can be caused by outside sources such as radiation or chemical agents. Only mutations in cell lines that produce eggs or sperm can be passed to offspring.

Recall that microevolution involves changes in the frequency of certain alleles relative to others within the gene pool of a population. Some of the processes that produce those changes are genetic drift, gene flow, mutation, and natural selection.

Genetic drift   **Genetic drift** occurs when allele frequencies within a population change randomly because of chance alone. This process is usually negligible in large populations. However, in small populations, chance events can cause allele frequencies to drift randomly from one generation to the next (Figure 22.4). Two mechanisms that facilitate genetic drift in natural populations are the bottleneck effect and the founder effect. In both effects, a small, random, nonrepresentative sample from the original population produces the next generation.

Sometimes, dramatic reductions in population size occur because of natural disasters that kill many individuals at random. Consider a population that experiences a flood in which most members die. With fewer remaining individuals contributing to the gene pool, the genetic makeup of the survivors may not be representative of the original population. This change in the gene pool is the **bottleneck effect,** so named because the population experiences a dramatic decrease in size—much as the size of a bottle decreases at the neck. Certain alleles may be more or less common in the flood survivors than in the original population simply by chance. In fact, some alleles may be completely lost, thereby reducing overall genetic variability among survivors.

Genetic drift also occurs when a few individuals leave their population and establish themselves in a new, somewhat isolated place. By chance alone, the genetic makeup of the colonizing individuals is probably not representative of the full gene pool of the population they left. Genetic drift in new, small colonies is called the **founder effect.**

Gene flow   Another cause of microevolution is **gene flow,** which occurs when individuals move into and out of populations. As individuals come and go, they carry with them their unique sets of genes. Gene flow occurs if these individuals successfully interbreed (mate and produce offspring) with the resident population, adding to the gene pool.

The cessation of gene flow can be important to the formation of new species. A **species** is a population or group of populations whose members are capable of successful interbreeding. Such interbreeding must occur under natural conditions and produce fertile offspring. But consider what happens when a population becomes geographically isolated from other populations of the same species. For example, over the course of geologic time, sea level fluctuates. During periods when sea level decreases, a previously offshore island may reconnect with a continent. When sea level increases, the island will redevelop offshore. Suppose that during the period of low sea level, a continuous population of frogs extends across the landscape. As sea level rises, however, and the island redevelops, the island population of frogs will be isolated from the mainland population. Frogs cannot cross saltwater, so the island population is effectively genetically isolated from the mainland population. The island population may take a separate evolutionary route as distinctly different sets of allele frequencies and mutations accumulate. Eventually, the isolated island population may become so different that it cannot successfully interbreed with the mainland population. At this point, there are two species of frogs instead of one. This process is called **speciation.**

Mutation   Mutations, you will recall, are rare changes in the DNA of genes; they are the third way that the frequencies of certain alleles can change relative to others within gene pools. Mutations produce new alleles that, when transmitted in gametes, cause an immediate change in the gene pool. Essentially the new (mutant) allele is substituted for another allele. Like gene flow, mutation can introduce new alleles to a population that are then acted upon by natural selection. If the frequency of the mutant allele increases in a population, it is not because mutations are suddenly occurring more frequently. Instead, possession of the mutant allele might confer some advantage that enables individuals with the mutant allele to produce more offspring than can individuals who lack the allele. In other words, the increased frequency in a population of the mutant allele relative to others results from natural selection, our next focus.

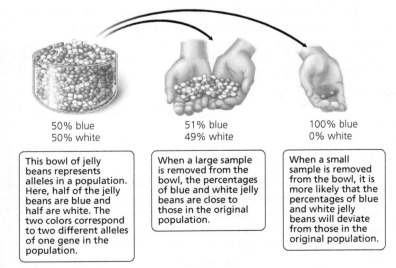

50% blue
50% white

51% blue
49% white

100% blue
0% white

This bowl of jelly beans represents alleles in a population. Here, half of the jelly beans are blue and half are white. The two colors correspond to two different alleles of one gene in the population.

When a large sample is removed from the bowl, the percentages of blue and white jelly beans are close to those in the original population.

When a small sample is removed from the bowl, it is more likely that the percentages of blue and white jelly beans will deviate from those in the original population.

Figure 22.4 Genetic drift has greater effects in small populations.

Natural selection In his book *On the Origin of Species* (1859), Charles Darwin argued that species were not specially created, unchanging forms. He maintained instead that modern species are descendants of ancestral species. Put another way, present-day species evolved from past species. Darwin also proposed that evolution occurred by the process of natural selection. His ideas can be summarized briefly as follows:

1. Individual variation exists within a species. Some of this variation is inherited.

2. Some individuals have more surviving offspring than do others because their particular inherited characteristics make them better suited to their local environment; this is the process of **natural selection.**

3. Evolutionary change occurs as the traits of individuals that survive and reproduce become more common in the population. Traits of less successful individuals become less common.

According to Darwin's ideas, an individual's evolutionary success can be measured by fitness (sometimes called *Darwinian fitness* or *evolutionary fitness*). **Fitness** compares the number of reproductively viable offspring among individuals. Individuals with greater fitness—that is, producing more successful offspring—have more of their genes represented in future generations. To succeed in terms of evolution, one must reproduce (Figure 22.5). Indeed, you could live more than 100 years, but your individual fitness would be zero if you did not reproduce. Some of the diseases or conditions discussed in earlier chapters are associated with zero fitness because they cause sterility (such as Turner syndrome) or death before reproductive maturity (such as Tay-Sachs disease).

One result of natural selection is that populations become better suited to their particular environment. This transformation of the population toward better fitness in their environment is called **adaptation.** If the environment changes, however, the individuals who have become most finely attuned to the initial environment could lose their advantage, and other individuals with different alleles might be selected by nature to leave more offspring. If the environment once again stabilizes, the population reestablishes itself around a new set of allele frequencies that better meet the new environmental conditions.

Figure 22.5 Fitness is the number of offspring left by an individual. These grandparents clearly have high fitness.

The evolution of life-long lactose tolerance provides an example of natural selection in humans. Lactose is the sugar found in milk (Chapter 2). Lactase is the enzyme that breaks down lactose into two smaller sugars, making milk easier to digest. In babies, the gene that codes for lactase is turned on. Some time after weaning, the lactase gene is turned off, so most adults in the world are lactose intolerant and milk consumption causes digestive upset. In Asian countries, for example, more than 90% of adults are lactose intolerant. In other regions, however, some populations have developed life-long lactose tolerance (also called lactase persistence). Mutations that keep the lactase gene permanently switched on are common among Europeans today, and in some Northern European countries, lactose intolerance can be as low as 5% of adults. New research has revealed that lactose tolerance did not always characterize Europeans: DNA sequences collected from 7000-year-old fossils of ancient Europeans do not carry the mutations for life-long lactose tolerance. Current evidence indicates that the emergence of lactose tolerance is linked to dependence on dairy cows. Cattle were domesticated in the Middle East and North Africa between 7500 and 9000 years ago, and later brought to Europe. Once Europeans depended on dairy cattle, being able to digest milk into adulthood would be beneficial: milk would provide extra nutrition and, in times of drought, serve as an excellent source of water. The mutations for life-long lactose tolerance arose randomly (which is true for all mutations), and they became beneficial in the presence of dairy cows. Natural selection favored individuals carrying the lactose tolerance mutations, and the mutations spread throughout dairy-dependent European populations. Parallel situations occurred in certain populations of the Middle East and Africa, where random mutations that caused the lactase gene to be permanently switched on arose and spread through nomadic populations dependent on dairy cattle.

Natural selection does not lead to perfect organisms. It can act on available variation only, and the available variation may not include the traits that would be ideal. Also, natural selection can only modify existing structures; it cannot produce completely new and different structures from scratch. Finally, organisms have to do many different things to survive and reproduce—such as escaping from predators and finding food, shelter, and mates—and it simply is not possible to be perfect at everything. Indeed, adaptations often are compromises between the many competing demands the organism faces.

STOP and THINK

Low genetic variation is associated with populations that have experienced dramatic reductions in size. Once such populations return to their previous size, it can take a very long time for genetic variation to increase. What two ways can new alleles restore genetic variation, and why does it take so long?

Macroevolution

Large-scale evolutionary change is macroevolution. Whereas microevolution involves changes in the frequencies of alleles within populations, macroevolution produces changes in groups of species, such as might occur with major shifts in climate. Our discussion of macroevolution begins with a description of how species are named. We then consider how their evolutionary histories can be analyzed and diagrammed.

Scientific names   Systematic biology deals with the naming, classification, and evolutionary relationships of organisms. A universal system for naming and classifying organisms is essential for communicating information about them. Scientists use the naming system that Swedish naturalist Carl Linnaeus developed more than 200 years ago. Each organism is given a Latin binomial, or two-part name, consisting of the genus name followed by the specific epithet (the term *specific,* here, means "relating to species"). For example, humans are in the genus *Homo,* and our specific epithet is *sapiens,* so our binomial is *Homo sapiens.* By convention, the genus name and specific epithet are italicized, the first letter of the genus name is always capitalized, and the specific epithet is all lowercase. Sometimes, the genus name is abbreviated: *H. sapiens.*

Linnaeus also developed a system for classifying organisms using a series of increasingly broad categories: species, genus, family, order, class, phylum, and kingdom. Similar species were placed in the same genus; similar genera (the plural of genus) were placed in the same family; similar families in the same order, and so on. Above the kingdom level, scientists have added the category domain to Linnaeus's scheme (the three domains are Archaea, Bacteria, and Eukarya; see Chapter 1). Sometimes the Linnaean categories have subdivisions, for example, subphyla within phyla. Figure 22.6 presents the categories to which humans belong.

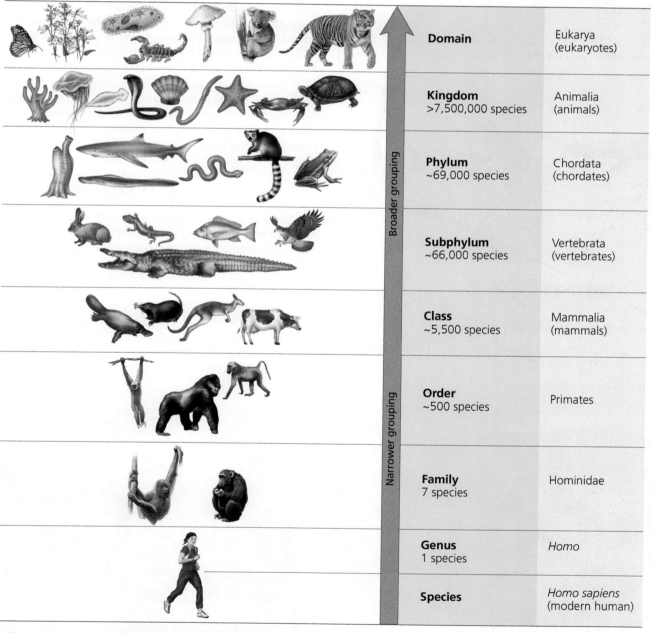

Domain	Eukarya (eukaryotes)
Kingdom >7,500,000 species	Animalia (animals)
Phylum ~69,000 species	Chordata (chordates)
Subphylum ~66,000 species	Vertebrata (vertebrates)
Class ~5,500 species	Mammalia (mammals)
Order ~500 species	Primates
Family 7 species	Hominidae
Genus 1 species	*Homo*
Species	*Homo sapiens* (modern human)

(Broader grouping → Narrower grouping)

Figure 22.6 Categories in the classification of living organisms. Any organism, including a human being, can be classified using a hierarchy of increasingly general categories. Modern humans are called *Homo sapiens.* We are placed in the family Hominidae, along with gorillas (two species), chimpanzees (two species, common chimpanzee and bonobo), and orangutans (two species). We are the only living species in our genus (*Homo*).

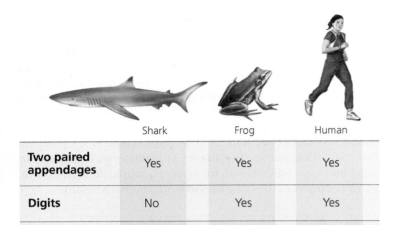

	Shark	Frog	Human
Two paired appendages	Yes	Yes	Yes
Digits	No	Yes	Yes
Hair	No	No	Yes

(a) A character matrix is used to construct a phylogenetic tree.

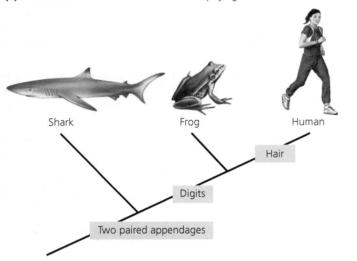

(b) A sample tree developed from the above character matrix

Figure 22.7 A phylogenetic tree depicts hypotheses about evolutionary relationships among organisms.

Phylogenetic trees   **Phylogenetic trees** are branching diagrams used by scientists to depict hypotheses about evolutionary relationships among species or groups of species. Such trees can illustrate in simple graphic form concepts that are difficult to express in words.

Scientists developing hypotheses about these relationships may begin by creating a character matrix, such as the example in Figure 22.7a. The character matrix can then be used to construct a phylogenetic tree. Typical matrices consist of vertical columns representing species or other groups, and horizontal rows representing "characters" that are either present or absent in those species or groups. Figure 22.7a shows a simple matrix comparing a shark (fish), frog (amphibian), and human (mammal) in regard to the presence or absence of three characters: two paired appendages (fins or limbs), individual digits, and hair. A phylogenetic tree based on the results from the matrix is shown in Figure 22.7b. This tree indicates that humans and frogs have more in common with one another (two paired appendages and individual digits) than either has with sharks (two paired appendages), and thus humans and frogs are likely to share a more recent common ancestor. The tree also shows that humans differ from frogs in having hair.

22.3 Evidence of Evolution

We know that evolution has occurred throughout Earth's history because the physical evidence of evolution surrounds us. Such evidence comes from many sources, including the fossil record, biogeography, molecular biology, and the comparison of anatomical and embryological structures.

Fossil Record

Earth is littered with silent relics of organisms that lived long ago (Figure 22.8). We find, for example, tiny spiders preserved in resin that dripped as sticky sap from some ancient tree. We find

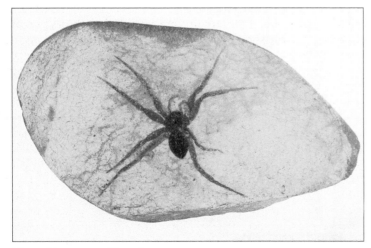

(a) A spider preserved in amber

Figure 22.8 A sampling of past life in fossils

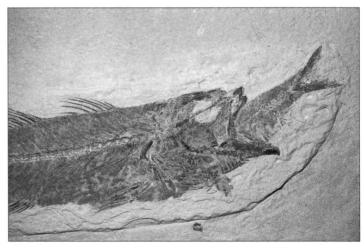

(b) An ancient act of predation preserved in sedimentary rocks mineralized bones and teeth, hardened remains that tell us much about the ancestry of today's vertebrates (animals with a backbone). We also find impressions, such as footprints, of organisms that lived in the past. These preserved remnants and impressions of past organisms are **fossils.** Most fossils occur in sedimentary rocks, such as limestone, sandstone, shale, and chalk. These rocks form when sand and other particles settle to the bottoms of rivers, lakes, and oceans; accumulate in layers; and harden. Fossils also occur in volcanic ash, tar pits, and a few other specialized conditions.

Fossilization is any process by which fossils form (Figure 22.9). In a typical case, ❶ an organism dies and settles to the bottom of a body of water. If not destroyed by scavengers, ❷ the organism is buried under accumulating layers of sediment. Soft parts usually decay. ❸ Hard parts, such as bones, teeth, and shells, may be preserved if they become impregnated with minerals from surrounding water and sediments. As new layers of sediment are added, the older (lower) layers solidify under the pressure generated by overlying sediments. ❹ Eventually, if geologic processes lift up the sediments and the water disappears, weather may erode the surface of the rock formation and expose the fossil.

Fossils provide strong evidence of evolution. Fossils of extinct organisms show both similarities to and differences from living species. Similarities to other fossil and modern species are used to assess degrees of evolutionary relationships. Often, fossils reveal combinations of features not seen in any living forms. Such combinations help us understand how major new adaptations arose. Sometimes we are lucky enough to find transitional forms that closely link ancient organisms to modern species. For example, several fossil whales have been discovered in the past 30 or so years; these fossils document a progression from terrestrial forms with forelimbs and hind limbs, to more aquatic forms with reduced hind limbs, to modern whales, which are fully aquatic and have no hind limbs (Figure 22.10a). Additionally, some fossil whale remains have been discovered that have an anklebone with a diagnostic shape; the bone is the astragalus, and the shape is that of a double pulley (Figure 22.10b). The double-pulley astragalus is characteristic of artiodactyls (an order of hoofed mammals that includes hippos, deer, cows, and pronghorn). Discovery of this anklebone with a double-pulley shape in fossil whales provides strong support for a close phylogenetic relationship between whales and artiodactyls.

Radiometric dating can be used to obtain estimates of the *absolute ages* of rocks and fossils. This technique relies on measuring the proportions of a radioactive isotope and its decay product. For example, radioactive potassium decays at a constant rate to form argon, so the ratio of radioactive potassium to argon in a fossil can be used to estimate the absolute age of the fossil. The *relative ages* of fossils can be determined because fossils found in deeper layers of rock are typically older than those found in layers closer to the surface. These kinds of observations enable scientists to piece together the chronological emergence of different kinds of organisms. For example, fishes are the first fossil vertebrates to appear in deep (old) layers of rock. Above those layers, fossils of amphibians appear, then reptiles, then mammals, and finally birds. This chronological sequence for the appearance of the major groups of vertebrates has been supported by other lines of evidence, some of which we consider later in this section.

Although the fossil record tells us much about past life, it has limitations. First, fossils are relatively rare. When most animals or plants die, their remains are eaten by predators or scavengers or are broken down by microorganisms, chemicals, or mechanical processes. Even if a fossil should form, the chances are small that it will be exposed by erosion or other forces and not be destroyed by those same forces before it is discovered. Second, the fossil record represents a biased sampling of past life. Aquatic plants and animals have a much higher probability of being buried in deep sediment than do terrestrial organisms. Thus, aquatic organisms are more likely to be preserved. Large animals with a hard skeleton are far more likely to be preserved than are small animals with soft parts. Organisms from large, enduring populations are more likely to be represented in the fossil record than are those from small, quickly disappearing populations. Despite these limitations, fossils document that life on Earth has not always been the same as it is today. The simple fact of these changes is potent evidence of evolution.

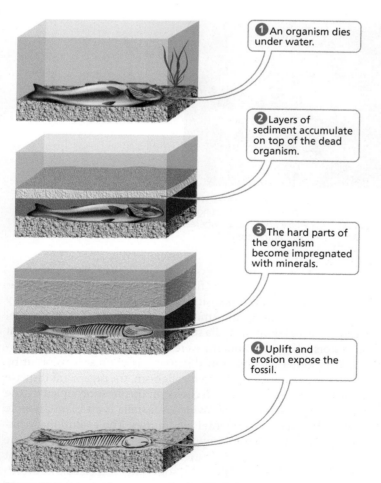

❶ An organism dies under water.

❷ Layers of sediment accumulate on top of the dead organism.

❸ The hard parts of the organism become impregnated with minerals.

❹ Uplift and erosion expose the fossil.

Figure 22.9 A typical sequence for fossilization

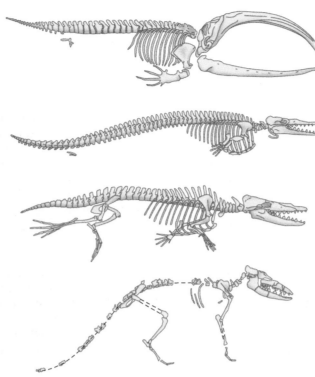

Bowhead whale, *Balaena mysticetus*
• Extant
• 15 to 18 m long
• Fully marine
• Vestigial pelvis and hind limbs

Dorudon
• 40 million years ago
• 6 m long
• Fully marine
• Reduced hind limbs
• No connection of pelvis to vertebral column

Rodhocetus
• 46 million years ago
• 3 m long
• Spent time on land and in water
• Hind limbs
• Pelvis connected to vertebral column

Pakicetus
• 52 million years ago
• 1.8 m long
• Spent time on land and in water
• Hind limbs
• Pelvis connected to vertebral column

(a) Several fossils reveal that whales evolved from terrestrial mammals that returned to the water.

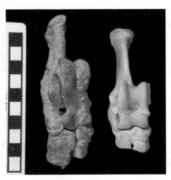

(b) Discovery in fossil whales of an ankle bone (astragalus) with a double-pulley shape links whales and artiodactyls (an order of hoofed mammals that includes hippos, cows, deer, and pronghorn). In the left photograph, the astragalus on the left is from the fossil whale *Rodhocetus,* whereas that on the right is from a modern-day pronghorn (shown in the right photograph).

Figure 22.10 The evolution of whales as revealed by transitional fossils

STOP and THINK

A visit to any natural history museum will reveal that most fossils of animals are bones. On very rare occasions, the soft tissues of animals are preserved. Describe a special set of circumstances that could lead to the mineralization of soft tissues, such as muscle.

Geographic Distributions

Biogeography is the study of the geographic distribution of organisms. Geographic distributions often reflect evolutionary history and relationships because related species are more likely than unrelated species to be found in the same geographic area. A careful comparison of the animals in a given place with those occurring elsewhere can yield clues about the relationship of the groups. If groups of animals have been separated, biogeography can tell us how long ago the separation occurred.

For example, today we find many species of marsupials—mammals such as opossums and kangaroos—in Australia but only a few in North and South America. The presence of so many species of marsupials in Australia suggests that they arose from distant ancestors whose descendants were not replaced by animals arriving from other regions. New distributions of organisms occur by two basic mechanisms. In one mechanism, the organisms disperse to new areas. In the other mechanism, the areas occupied by the organisms move or are subdivided. Australia is an island, remote from other major continental landmasses. The evolutionary history of the Australian marsupials involves both dispersal and the movement of continents. Current fossil evidence indicates that marsupials evolved in China, and some later dispersed into North America. From North America, some marsupials dispersed southward into South America, then to Antarctica, and later to Australia, to which Antarctica was attached at the time (Figure 22.11). As

ETHICAL ISSUE

Conducting Research on Nonhuman Primates

Chimpanzees look and behave somewhat differently from the way we do. Still, it is hard to look into their eyes and not see something of ourselves. Chimpanzees are our closest living relatives, sharing a remarkably high percentage of our DNA sequence. Nevertheless, we use them and other nonhuman primates in invasive scientific research that might benefit us. Is this ethical?

Using nonhuman primates in research is costly and controversial. Even so, they often are preferred as subjects because they are so similar to humans. For example, human and nonhuman primates possess brains with similar organization, develop comparable plaques in their arteries, and experience many of the same changes in anatomy, physiology, and behavior with age. In some cases, Nobel Prize–winning research has resulted from the contributions of research with nonhuman primates, including development of vaccines for yellow fever (1951) and polio (1954) and insight into how visual information is processed in the brain (1981). Research with nonhuman primates has also led to significant advances in our understanding of Alzheimer's disease, AIDS, and severe acute respiratory syndrome (SARS).

The care and use of nonhuman primates (and other vertebrate animals) in research is regulated by federal agencies such as the Public Health Service and the U.S. Department of Agriculture. Animal research also is regulated at the local level. Each college, university, or research center has an Institutional Animal Care and Use Committee whose members include veterinarians, researchers, and members of the public. In addition to federal and local oversight, scientists and animal care personnel are striving to improve housing for captive nonhuman primates and to consider their psychological well-being. Even with such efforts, controversy and questions remain.

Questions to Consider

- Should we ban the use of nonhuman primates in medical research? If we do, will such a ban slow the progress in fighting diseases such as AIDS and Alzheimer's? If you or a loved one had one of these illnesses, would you feel differently about research using nonhuman primates?

- Nonhuman primates represent a fraction of the animals used in research. More than 90% of research animals are rodents, such as rats, mice, and guinea pigs. Where would you draw the line when deciding which (if any) animals are acceptable for use in research that might benefit us?

Marsupials originated in the Northern Hemisphere (probably in what is now China) at least 125 million years ago. Some moved to North America and later dispersed southward.

Marsupials arrived in South America, Antarctica, and Australia, continents that were close together at the time.

The subsequent drifting apart of the southern continents set Australia off on its own, allowing its marsupials to evolve in isolation.

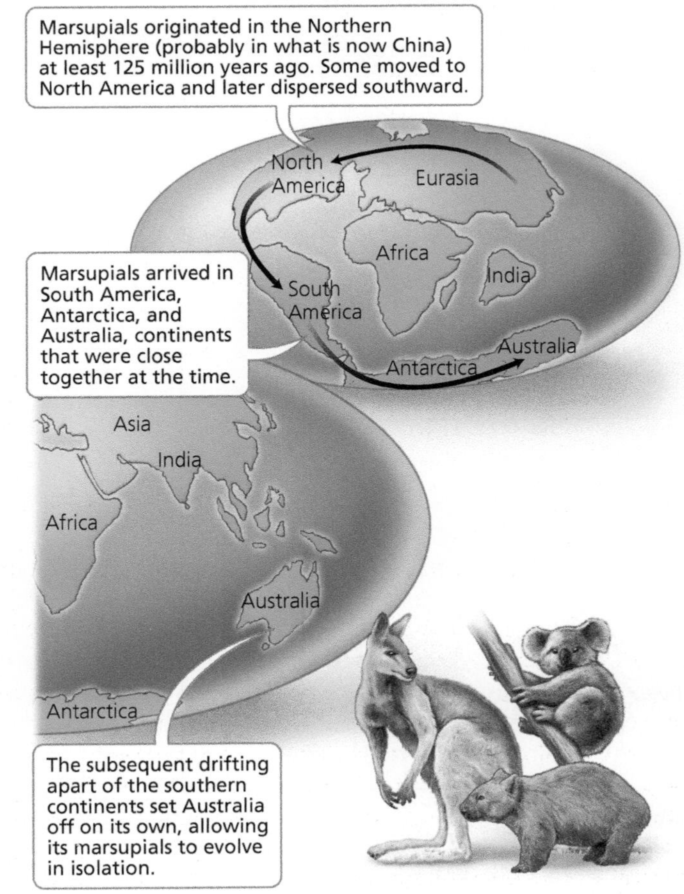

Figure 22.11 The story of marsupials and Australia involves both dispersal and movement of continents.

Australia and other landmasses slowly shifted to form the modern continental arrangement, the ancestors of today's marsupials were carried away to evolve in isolation in Australia.

Comparative Molecular Biology

Evidence of evolution can come from molecules that are the basic building blocks of life. For example, scientists can compare the sequences of amino acids in proteins or the nucleotide sequences in DNA. As described in Chapter 21, the Human Genome Project has provided information on the location of genes along our chromosomes and the order of the base pairs that make up our chromosomes. In 2005, the chimpanzee's genome was described and compared with that of humans. Such comparison revealed that the two genomes are strikingly similar; for example, the DNA sequence that can be directly compared between chimp and human genomes is about 99% identical. The genomes of the remaining great apes were published in 2011 (orangutan) and 2012 (gorilla).

Because of background radiation and errors in copying DNA, single-nucleotide changes in DNA, called *point mutations,* occur constantly over evolutionary time with clocklike regularity. The rates of these changes vary from gene to gene. Once calibrated against the fossil record, these **molecular clocks** allow scientists to compare DNA sequences in two species as a way to estimate the amount of time that has passed since the two species diverged from a single common ancestor. The more different the sequences, the more time that has elapsed since their common ancestor. For example, comparison of DNA sequences tells us that humans and chimpanzees diverged from a common ancestor about 6 million years ago, making chimpanzees our closest living relatives. (See the Ethical Issue essay, *Conducting Research on Nonhuman Primates.*)

Comparative Anatomy and Embryology

Comparative anatomy, as its name suggests, is the comparison of the anatomies (physical structures) of different species. Common, or shared, traits among different species have long been considered a measure of relatedness. Put simply, two species with more shared traits are considered more closely related than are two species without shared traits (this principle underlies the use of character matrices to construct phylogenetic trees). For example, many very different vertebrates share similarities in the bones of their forelimbs, showing that they have an ancestor in common (Figure 22.12). Structures that are similar and that arose from a common ancestry are called **homologous structures.** The forelimbs that support bird wings and bat wings are homologous structures. Sometimes, however, similarities are not inherited from a common ancestor. For example, bird wings and insect wings both permit flight, but they are made from entirely different structures. Whereas bird wings consist of forelimbs, insect wings are not true appendages; they are extensions of the insect's cuticle (exoskeleton). Thus, the wings of birds and insects do not reflect common ancestry.

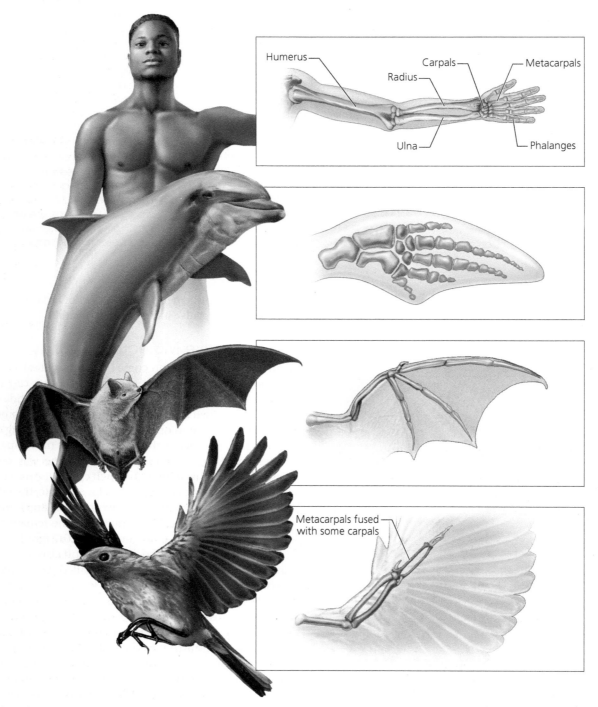

Figure 22.12 Homologous structures. The similarity of the forelimb bones of humans, dolphins, bats, and birds indicates that these organisms share a common ancestry.

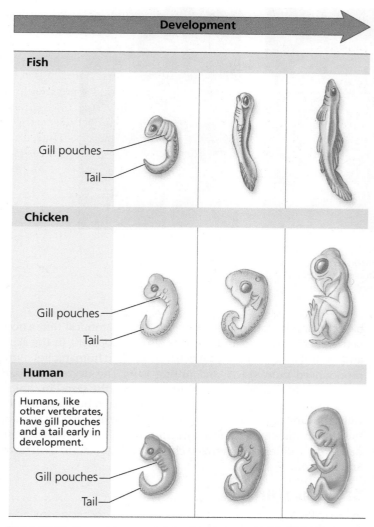

Development

Fish

Gill pouches

Tail

Chicken

Gill pouches

Tail

Human

Humans, like other vertebrates, have gill pouches and a tail early in development.

Gill pouches

Tail

Figure 22.13 Resemblance early in development indicates common descent. Embryos in the different representative vertebrates are not to scale; they have been drawn to the same approximate size to permit comparison.

Instead, birds and insects independently evolved wings because of similar ecological roles and selection pressures, in a process known as **convergent evolution.** Structures that are similar because of convergent evolution are called **analogous structures.**

Homologous structures arise from the same kind of embryonic tissue. Hence, comparative embryology, the comparative study of early development, also can be a useful tool for studying evolution. Common embryological origins can be considered evidence of common descent. For example, 4-week-old human embryos closely resemble embryos of other vertebrates, including fish. Indeed, human embryos at 4 weeks' gestation come complete with a tail and gill pouches, as shown in Figure 22.13. As development proceeds, the gill pouches of fish develop into gills. The gill pouches of humans develop into other structures, such as the auditory tubes connecting the middle ear and throat. Nevertheless, the fact that human, fish, and all other vertebrate embryos look very similar at early stages of development indicates common descent from an ancient ancestor.

We have learned about microevolution, macroevolution, and the evidence for evolution. Now let's look at our own past and see how humans evolved.

22.4 Human Evolution

We begin our discussion of human evolution with the primates, an order of mammals that includes humans, apes, monkeys, and related forms (such as lemurs). Fossil evidence indicates that primates evolved about 65 million years ago. The oldest primate fossils are about 55 million years old, and, as mentioned previously, organisms are assumed to evolve earlier than when they first appear in the fossil record. Comparison of DNA sequences indicates that primates evolved about 90 million years ago. Despite debate over when primates evolved, current evidence indicates that the first primates were small (20 to 30 grams), arboreal (tree-living) mammals that ate insects.

Primate Characteristics

Primates have several distinguishing characteristics. Many of these characteristics reflect an arboreal lifestyle specialized for the visual hunting and manual capture of insects. For example, primates have flexible, rotating shoulder joints and exceptionally mobile digits with sensitive pads on their ends. Flattened nails replace claws. In many primate species, the big toe is separated from the other toes, and thumbs are opposable to other fingers. Thus, primates have grasping feet *and* hands, features that help in the pursuit and capture of insects along branches. In addition, a complex visual system (forward-facing eyes with stereoscopic vision) and a large brain relative to body size provide the well-developed depth perception, hand–eye coordination, and neuromuscular control needed by arboreal insectivores. The relatively large brain is also associated with complex social behavior (for example, members of social groups may form long-term alliances) and reliance on learned behavior (for instance, tool use may be passed from one individual to the next through observation and imitation). Also, most primates give birth to only one infant at a time and provide extensive parental care—these characteristics may reflect the difficulty of carrying and rearing multiple infants in trees.

Modern primates are divided into two main groups (suborders). One suborder contains lemurs, lorises, and pottos, grouped together because they retain ancestral primate features such as small body size (Figure 22.14). The other suborder contains monkeys, apes, and humans (Figure 22.15).

In the past, the term *hominid* was used to describe members of the human lineage, such as species in the genera *Australopithecus* and *Homo* (discussed later in this chapter). At that time, human and prehuman species were the only members of the family Hominidae. Primate classification has changed, however, and apes now are included in the family Hominidae (refer again to Figure 22.6). Thus, the term *hominid* now includes apes and humans (members of the family Hominidae). The term **hominin** now is used for the human lineage and its immediate ancestors (members of the subfamily Homininae). As described earlier, molecular evidence suggests that the lines leading to modern humans and chimpanzees diverged about 6 million years ago. Molecular data further indicate that, after chimpanzees,

(a) Ring-tailed lemur   **(b)** Slender loris   **(c)** Potto

Figure 22.14 Examples of modern primates from the suborder whose members retain ancestral features. The female loris with young in part (b) illustrates many of the features characteristic of all primates, including grasping hands and feet, forward-facing eyes, and small litter size.

gorillas are our next closest living relatives, followed by orang-utans and then gibbons. Figure 22.16 shows these hypothesized relationships among living primates.

Comparison of human and chimp skeletal anatomy

Humans are the most terrestrial of primates. Many aspects of our skeletal anatomy reflect this terrestrial lifestyle and our upright stance while walking. Walking on two feet is called **bipedalism.** Our S-shaped spine and relatively large patella (kneecap) reflect a bipedal gait. Although chimpanzees can walk on two feet, they typically use quadrupedal knuckle-walking when moving on the ground. Their hand bones are more robust than ours because they bear weight during terrestrial locomotion. Chimps also spend time in trees, where they use their arms in locomotion. Thus, the arms of chimps are long and exceptionally strong; the strength is reflected in the extensive areas on the scapula (shoulder blade) for the attachment of large arm muscles. Unlike humans, chimps have opposable

big toes, another adaptation for climbing. Anatomical differences between chimpanzees and humans also are apparent in the skull and teeth. Chimps have a smaller braincase than humans, but more pronounced brow ridges and jutting jaws. The degree of *sexual dimorphism* (difference in appearance between the sexes) in canine teeth also is more pronounced in chimps than in humans; specifically, the canines are larger in males than in females in both species, but the sex difference is greater in chimps. Figure 22.17 shows some of the major differences between chimps and humans in their teeth and skeleton.

STOP and THINK

In the following discussion of our ancestry, we describe the species that led to us. At some point the line *became* us. Before you start reading about our ancestry, what qualities would you now say are necessary for a species to qualify as human?

(a) Black-headed spider monkey   **(b)** Chacma baboons   **(c)** Bornean orangutans   **(d)** Western gorilla

Figure 22.15 Monkeys (such as spider monkeys and baboons) and apes (such as orangutans and gorillas) are placed with humans in another suborder.

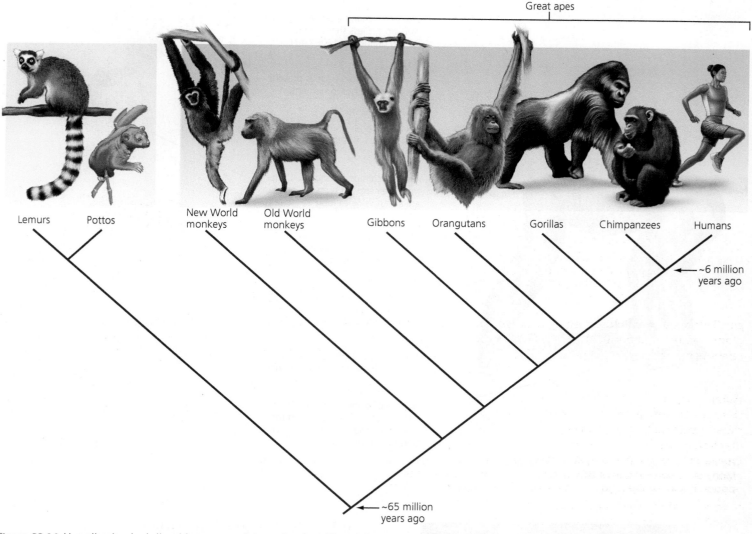

Figure 22.16 Hypothesized relationships among living primates. (Figures are not drawn to scale.)

Misconceptions

Several popular misconceptions about human evolution exist among nonscientists. One misconception is the idea that we descended from chimpanzees or any of the other modern apes. Humans and chimpanzees represent separate phylogenetic branches that diverged about 6 million years ago. Thus the common ancestor of humans and chimpanzees was different from any modern species of ape.

Another misconception is that modern humans evolved in an orderly, stepwise fashion. We often see such a stepwise progression depicted in drawings, sometimes humorously, and its appeal lies in its simplicity. However, as is so often the case, the real story is far more complex. The path to modern humans has been fraught with unsuccessful phenotypes leading to dead end after dead end. In fact, the path looks more like a family "bush" than an orderly progression from primitive to modern.

A final misconception is that, over the course of human evolution, the various bones and organ systems evolved simultaneously and at the same rate. They did not. There is no reason to believe that the human brain evolved at the same rate as, say, the appendix or the foot. Instead, different traits evolved at different times and rates, by a phenomenon known as **mosaic evolution.**

Trends in Hominin Evolution

Several evolutionary trends are apparent in the history of hominins. Bipedalism evolved early and set the stage for the evolution of other characteristics, such as increases in brain size. Cultural developments, such as tool use and language, are linked to increases in brain size. Once the hands were freed from the requirements of locomotion, they could be used for tasks such as making tools. Evidence that bipedalism preceded increases in brain size and cultural developments comes from fossilized hominin footprints found in Tanzania, Africa. These footprints, estimated to be about 3.6 million years old, were apparently made by two adults and a child (Figure 22.18). The footprints clearly predate the oldest stone tools from 2.6 million years ago. Other changes associated with upright posture include the S-shaped curvature of the vertebral column (the lumbar curve); modifications to the bones and muscles of the pelvis, legs, and feet; and positioning

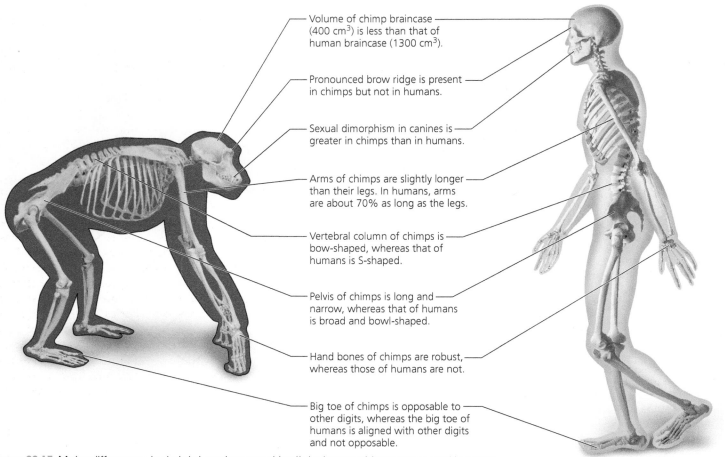

Volume of chimp braincase (400 cm³) is less than that of human braincase (1300 cm³).

Pronounced brow ridge is present in chimps but not in humans.

Sexual dimorphism in canines is greater in chimps than in humans.

Arms of chimps are slightly longer than their legs. In humans, arms are about 70% as long as the legs.

Vertebral column of chimps is bow-shaped, whereas that of humans is S-shaped.

Pelvis of chimps is long and narrow, whereas that of humans is broad and bowl-shaped.

Hand bones of chimps are robust, whereas those of humans are not.

Big toe of chimps is opposable to other digits, whereas the big toe of humans is aligned with other digits and not opposable.

Figure 22.17 Major differences in skeletal anatomy and teeth between chimpanzees and humans. Many of these traits reflect differences in locomotion and stance. Whereas chimpanzees are quadrupedal knuckle-walkers, humans are bipedal with an upright stance.

of the skull on top of the vertebral column (refer again to the human skeleton in Figure 22.17).

The faces of hominins also changed. For example, the forehead changed from sloping to vertical, and sites of muscle attachment, such as the brow ridges and crests on the skull, became smaller. The jaws became shorter, and the nose and chin more prominent. The overall size difference between males and females decreased. Males of our early ancestors appear to have been 1.5 times as heavy as females. Modern human males weigh about 1.2 times as much as females.

In the following discussion of our ancestors, we focus on the hominins that we know the most about—those in the genus *Australopithecus* and the genus *Homo*. We also mention some recent finds of older hominins. Keep in mind that as new hominin fossils are found and genetic studies conducted, the dates for the origin of some species may be pushed back.

Figure 22.18 These hominin footprints from Laetoli, Tanzania, predate the oldest known tools and thus provide evidence that bipedalism preceded increases in brain size and cultural trends such as toolmaking. The larger prints were made by two individuals, one following in the other's footsteps. The smaller prints may have been made by a child walking with the two individuals.

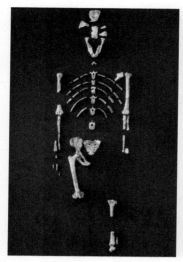

(a) The remarkably complete skeleton of Lucy

(b) Reconstruction of Lucy on display at the St. Louis Zoo

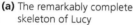

Figure 22.19 Fossilized remains and reconstruction of Lucy, a young female of the hominin species *Australopithecus afarensis.* She was named Lucy because the Beatles' song "Lucy in the Sky with Diamonds" was playing the night Donald Johanson and his coworkers celebrated her discovery.

Australopithecines The first hominin remains discovered were given the genus name *Australopithecus,* meaning "southern ape." Species within *Australopithecus* are sometimes collectively termed australopithecines. *Australopithecus anamensis,* considered the earliest species of the australopithecine line, is known from a small number of fossils found in Kenya and Ethiopia and dated between 4.2 and 3.9 million years old. The most spectacular australopithecine fossil found to date is that of a young adult female of the species *Australopithecus afarensis* (because she was found in the Afar region of Ethiopia). The scientists who discovered her in 1974 named her Lucy. More than 60 pieces of Lucy's bones were found; when the bones were arranged, scientists estimated that, at death, she was about 1 m (3 ft) tall and weighed about 30 kg (66 lb; Figure 22.19). Her bones were determined to be 3.2 million years old. As more remains were found, it became apparent that the males of Lucy's species were somewhat taller (about 1.5 m, or about 5 ft) and heavier (about 45 kg, or 99 lb). The brain of *A. afarensis* was similar in size to that of modern chimpanzees or gorillas—about 430 cm³ (26 in.³). Although many aspects of the anatomy of *A. afarensis* suggest adaptations for living in trees, the remains also indicate bipedalism. In *A. afarensis,* we see an example of mosaic evolution—bipedalism evolving before substantial increases in brain size.

In 1994, researchers found hominin remains in Ethiopia that were older than those of *A. anamensis.* Dated at 4.4 million years old, the fossils were assigned to the species *Ardipithecus ramidus.* The remains, which included parts from more than 30 individuals, took 15 years to fully excavate and analyze. The most striking find was a partial skeleton (125 pieces) of a female now called Ardi. Eleven papers published in 2009 detailed the anatomy of *A. ramidus* and its implications for human evolution. Because the shape of Ardi's pelvis indicated that it was good for both climbing and upright walking, the research team suggested that *A. ramidus* displayed facultative bipedalism. In

other words, when moving along tree branches Ardi may have walked upright atop the branches as well as climbed with all four limbs. They further proposed that she walked upright on the ground, but not as well as later hominins. It is possible that *Ardipithecus* gave rise to the genus *Australopithecus,* which most scientists think led to our own genus, the genus *Homo.* It also is possible that *Ardipithecus* was a side branch, not along the path that led to us. A recent study of the base of the skull of *Ardipithecus ramidus* links *Ardipithecus* to *Australopithecus* and humans. The base of the skull is a key region because of its association with the brain and posture.

About 3 million years ago, when *A. afarensis* had been in existence for nearly 1 million years, several new hominin species appeared in the fossil record. Evidence indicates that *Australopithecus africanus,* one of these new species, was a hunting-and-gathering omnivore. *A. africanus,* like *A. afarensis,* was a gracile (or slender) hominin. Three more "robust" hominins (previously within *Australopithecus,* but now placed in a separate genus, *Paranthropus*) also appeared and are thought to have been savanna-dwelling vegetarians. The robust hominins had massive skulls, heavy facial bones, pronounced brows, and huge teeth. Whatever they ate, it required a lot of chewing. It is unclear whether Lucy's species, *A. afarensis,* gave rise to these other species or simply lived at the same time as they did. Whereas the robust hominins appear to have been evolutionary dead ends, descendants of *A. afarensis* may have led to genus *Homo.*

Homo habilis *Homo habilis* ("handy man"), the first member of the modern genus of humans, appeared in the fossil record about 2.5 million years ago. The remains classified as *H. habilis* are highly variable, causing some researchers to question their classification. Some researchers maintain the remains are varied enough to represent more than one species. *H. habilis* differed from *A. afarensis* primarily in brain size. The cranial capacity of *H. habilis* has been estimated at between 500 and 800 cm³ (30 and 49 in.³). *H. habilis* may have been the first hominin to use stone tools. Simple stone tools, dating from 2.5 million to 2.7 million years ago, have been found in Africa. Whether these tools were used by *H. habilis* or one of the species of robust hominins is unclear. Some evidence suggests that *H. habilis* was capable of rudimentary speech. Casts of one brain made from reassembled skull fragments indicate a bulge in the area of the brain important in speech (see Chapter 8).

Homo ergaster and *Homo erectus* A new hominin, *Homo ergaster* ("working man"), appeared in the fossil record about 1.9 million years ago. The name reflects the many tools found with the remains. Traditionally, scientists had classified these remains as *Homo erectus* ("upright man"), but they now differentiate them from *H. erectus.* *H. ergaster* appears to have originated in East Africa and coexisted there for several thousand years with some of the robust hominins.

H. erectus is thought to have diverged from *H. ergaster* around 1.6 million years ago. *H. erectus* was a wanderer, believed by many to be the first hominin to migrate out of Africa, spreading to Asia. *H. erectus* was larger than earlier hominins (up to 1.85 m, or 6 ft tall, and weighing at least 65 kg, or 143 lb) and less sexually dimorphic. *H. erectus* had a brain volume of

(a) The Neanderthals had an appearance adapted for life in a cold climate. Some anthropologists consider Neanderthals to be a subspecies of our own species; others consider them a separate species.

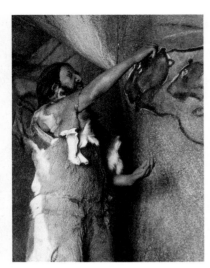

(b) The Cro-Magnons were quite similar to us in appearance, and some anthropologists believe they were responsible for the disappearance of the Neanderthals.

Figure 22.20 Relatively recent representatives of the genus *Homo*. These photographs were taken at a museum display.

about 1000 cm^3 (61 in.^{3}). Evidence indicates that *H. erectus* used sophisticated tools and weapons and may have used fire. *H. erectus* disappeared from most locations about 400,000 years ago, but some remains from Java have been dated at only 50,000 years. The Java remains indicate that at least one population of *H. erectus* existed at the same time as modern humans (*Homo sapiens*).

Homo heidelbergensis, Homo sapiens, **and** *Homo neanderthalensis* The origins of anatomically modern humans over the past 500,000 years are difficult to trace with certainty, and different interpretations exist. Traditionally, fossils that did not quite resemble modern humans were classified as Archaic *Homo sapiens.* Scientists now place these fossils in the species *Homo heidelbergensis;* the name refers to Heidelberg, Germany, where a fossil lower jaw intermediate between those of earlier forms and *H. sapiens* was found. *H. heidelbergensis* may have evolved from *H. ergaster* and not *H. erectus. H. heidelbergensis* ranges from about 800,000 years ago to about 130,000 years ago, which is when the first anatomically modern human remains show up in the fossil record. Thus, scientists postulate that *H. sapiens* and *H. neanderthalensis* evolved from *H. heidelbergensis.*

The oldest fossil evidence for modern humans (*H. sapiens,* or "thinking man") comes from Africa and is about 130,000 years old. *H. sapiens* differs from earlier humans in having a larger brain (1300 cm^3, or 79 in.^{3}), flat forehead, absent or very small brow ridges, prominent chin, and a very slender body form.

Neanderthals (*H. neanderthalensis*), close evolutionary relatives of ours, are known to have been in Europe and Asia from about 200,000 years ago to 30,000 years ago. Neanderthals had distinct features apparently adapted for life in a cold climate. Some Neanderthals lived in caves (Figure 22.20a). Neanderthal burial sites have been discovered, making them the first hominins known to have buried their dead. Also, the discovery of

50,000-year-old remains of sick, injured, and elderly individuals suggests that Neanderthals cared for the less fortunate among them. Interestingly, Neanderthals had a larger braincase than do *H. sapiens* and a slightly larger brain volume (about 1450 cm^3, or 88 in.^{3}). However, these features may not correlate with intelligence but rather with the Neanderthals' more massive body. They had larger bones, suggesting heavier musculature, and rather short legs. They also had a thick brow ridge, large nose, broad face, and well-developed incisors and canines.

Neanderthals vanished from the fossil record some 30,000 years ago for still mysterious reasons. Some scientists suggest they were outcompeted or simply killed outright by a form of *H. sapiens* called Cro-Magnons (Figure 22.20b). Other scientists suggest that interbreeding between anatomically modern humans and Neanderthals might have resulted in the loss of the Neanderthal phenotype. Scientists now have a first version of the Neanderthal genome, developed from DNA recovered from the bones of three female Neanderthals whose remains were estimated at 38,000 years old. A comparison of the Neanderthal genome with those of present-day humans from different parts of the world suggests that following their migration from Africa 50,000 to 80,000 years ago, modern humans bred with Neanderthals in the Middle East before extending their range into Eurasia. The scientists estimate that 1% to 4% of the genes of present-day non-Africans came from Neanderthals.

In 2010, scientists announced the discovery of a finger bone in the Denisova cave in Siberia. The bone, estimated to be 41,000 years old, contained DNA, which allowed near-complete sequencing of the genome within the bone cells. This analysis of ancient DNA revealed that the bone was from an entirely new lineage of hominin. This new species of *Homo* was given the name Denisovans. A few other fossils—two teeth and a toe bone—have been recovered from different individuals of the same population. Comparison of the genomes of Denisovans, Neanderthals, and modern humans indicates that the three species shared a common ancestor about 1 million years ago. Then, around 800,000 years ago, the ancestors of modern humans branched off, and the Denisovans and Neanderthals split about 640,000 years ago. The genome comparisons also indicated interbreeding among the three lineages.

In 2003, hominin remains were discovered in a cave on the island of Flores in Indonesia, and in 2004, a description of the remains was published. The remains display a peculiar mix of primitive features (for example, small brain size) and derived features (for example, small canines). Some researchers suggest the remains represent a new hominin species, *Homo floresiensis,* estimated to have lived between 95,000 and 17,000 years ago (note that this species would have overlapped in time with *H. sapiens*). The remains indicate that adults were about 3 feet (1 meter) in height and weighed between 66 and 77 pounds (30 and 35 kilograms). The small build earned the species the nickname of "the Hobbit," after the tiny fictional humanoids in J. R. R. Tolkien's book. Others suggest the remains are from individuals of *H. sapiens* who suffered from a pathological condition such as microcephaly (a neurodevelopmental disorder charac-

terized by a small head), Laron syndrome (a form of dwarfism caused by insensitivity to growth hormone), or hypothyroidism (reduced growth and development due to undersecretion of thyroid hormone). Most recently, some of the scientists who raised the possibility of microcephaly published two papers claiming the recovered skull and leg bones are consistent with an individual of our own species with Down syndrome. Debate continues, as does the study of stone artifacts from the cave and nearby sites.

The above description reveals that around 50,000 years ago, we shared the Earth with *Homo erectus, Homo neanderthalensis,* the Denisovans (providing recent analyses of the fossils and DNA are not refuted), and possibly *Homo floresiensis.* The major hominin species are shown in Figure 22.21.

About 12,000 years ago, *H. sapiens* changed from a nomadic lifestyle to a more sedentary one. Associated with this change were two major milestones in human history: the domestication of animals and the cultivation of crops. For example, mammals were domesticated for protection (dogs), food (cattle, pigs, and goats), transport (horses, camels, and donkeys), wool (llamas and alpacas), and rodent control (cats and ferrets). Agriculture began with the cultivation of cereal grains about 9000 years ago.

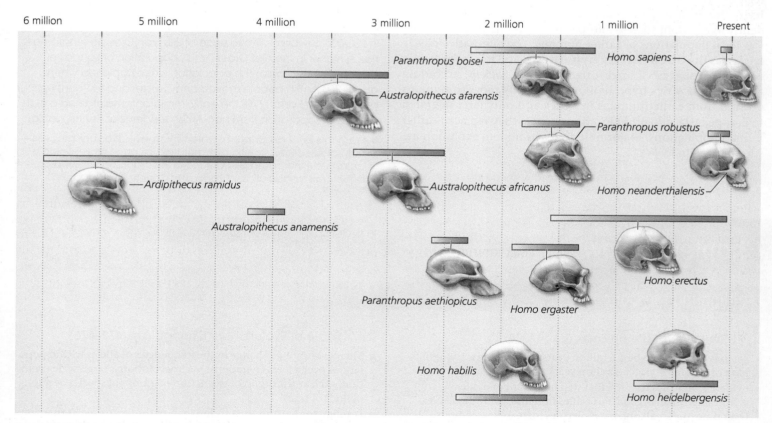

Figure 22.21 The major hominin species. Horizontal purple lines indicate the length of time each species existed. The Denisovans and *Homo floresiensis* also may have coexisted with modern humans, Neanderthals, and *H. erectus.*

Q: Does this figure support or contradict the notion that humans evolved in an orderly, stepwise manner from primitive to modern? Explain your answer.

Table 22.1	Review of Some Milestones in Human Evolution	
Hominin	Years Ago	Milestone
Ardipithecus ramidus	6–4 million	Bipedalism (facultative)
Homo habilis	2.4–1.6 million	Tool use, speech
Homo erectus	1.6 million–50,000	Fire, migration
Homo neanderthalensis	200,000–30,000	Buried their dead
Homo sapiens	130,000–present	Domestication of animals, agriculture

what would **YOU** do?

Human remains can tell scientists much about the diets, diseases, lifestyles, and genetic relationships of our ancestors. Such information can help piece together our evolutionary past. Sometimes, however, keeping human remains for scientific study conflicts with the wishes of modern-day descendants who want their ancestors' remains returned to them for reburial. In the United States, many museums and universities are developing policies for the treatment and disposition of Native American and Native Hawaiian remains. How should human remains be treated, and who should get them? If you were a museum director developing a policy for the treatment of human remains, what would you do? ■

Did modern humans evolve several times in different regions? The idea that they did is known as the **multiregional hypothesis.** It suggests that modern humans evolved independently in locations such as Europe, Asia, and Africa from distinctive local populations of earlier humans. The alternative idea is known as the **Out of Africa hypothesis,** and it is more widely accepted. It suggests a single origin for all *H. sapiens.* According to the Out of Africa hypothesis, anatomically modern humans evolved from earlier humans in Africa and only later migrated to Europe, Asia, and other locations, where they replaced earlier human populations. Major milestones in human evolution are summarized in Table 22.1.

LOOKING AHEAD

In Chapter 22, we learned about evolution. In Chapter 23, we focus on ecology, the study of the interactions between organisms and between organisms and their environments.

CONSIDER THIS CASE

Ellis–van Creveld syndrome is an inherited condition in which bone growth is disrupted. The disorder, which is caused by a recessive allele, is associated with dwarfism, extra fingers and toes, and dental abnormalities. Many people with the syndrome also have heart defects, which can be life threatening. Ellis–van Creveld syndrome is very rare in the general population, where estimates of its prevalence range from 1 in 60,000 newborns to 1 in 200,000 newborns. Prevalence of Ellis–van Creveld syndrome is much higher in the Old Order Amish population of Lancaster County, Pennsylvania. This population was established when about 200 Amish people moved from Switzerland to Pennsylvania between 1720 and 1770; the early immigrants maintained a high degree of separation from non-Amish residents of Pennsylvania.

■ From this brief description, which microevolutionary process—natural selection, genetic drift, mutation, or gene flow—would best explain the increased prevalence of Ellis–van Creveld syndrome in the Amish population of Lancaster County, Pennsylvania?

Chapter Review   MasteringBiology®

Highlighting the Concepts

22.1 Evolution of Life on Earth (pp. 470–472)

■ Earth is estimated to be 4.5 billion years old, and life is thought to have originated about 3.8 billion years ago.
■ Evidence indicates that the first step in the origin of life was the synthesis of small organic molecules from inorganic molecules. Over time, the small organic molecules increased in complexity and formed macromolecules. Macromolecules aggregated into droplets that became the precursors to cells.
■ First prokaryotic cells evolved, then eukaryotic cells, and eventually multicellularity, which led to the appearance on Earth of organisms such as plants and animals.

22.2 Scale of Evolutionary Change (pp. 472–476)

■ Microevolution is change in the frequencies of alleles within populations over a few generations. Macroevolution is large-scale evolution, such as the origin or extinction of groups of species over long periods of time.
■ Populations are groups of individuals of the same species that live in a particular area. Sexual reproduction and mutation produce variation in populations.
■ A gene pool is a collection of all the alleles of all the genes of all the individuals in a population.
■ Causes of microevolution include genetic drift, gene flow, mutation, and natural selection.

■ Systematic biology encompasses the naming, classification, and evolutionary relationships of organisms.

22.3 Evidence of Evolution (pp. 476–481)

■ Fossils are the preserved remnants and impressions of past organisms. The fossil record provides evidence of evolution by documenting that life on Earth has not always been the same as it is today.

■ Molecules that are the basic building blocks of life can be compared for evidence of evolution. For example, scientists compare the nucleotide sequences in DNA of different species to gauge relatedness and to estimate the time of divergence from a most recent common ancestor.

■ Comparative anatomy and embryology also provide evidence of evolution. Species with more shared traits are considered more likely to be related. Structures that have arisen from common ancestry are called homologous structures and usually arise from the same embryonic tissue.

22.4 Human Evolution (pp. 481–488)

■ Humans are primates, an order of mammals that also includes lemurs, monkeys, and apes. Primates have forward-facing eyes with stereoscopic vision, flexible shoulder joints, and grasping hands and feet. Flattened nails—rather than claws—cover their sensitive digits.

■ The term *hominin* refers to the human lineage and its immediate ancestors, such as species within the genera *Australopithecus* and *Homo*.

■ Bipedalism evolved early on in hominins and set the stage for increased brain size, which in turn was associated with cultural trends such as tool use and language.

■ The oldest hominin remains found to date are those of *Ardipithecus ramidus,* estimated to be at least 4.4 million years old. The remains suggest facultative bipedalism. Other early human genera include *Australopithecus* and *Paranthropus*.

■ *Homo habilis* exhibited speech and tool use. *H. erectus* used fire and was the first hominin to migrate out of Africa. *H. neanderthalensis* buried their dead. *H. sapiens* domesticated animals and cultivated crops.

■ The multiregional hypothesis suggests that *H. sapiens* evolved independently in different regions from distinctive populations of early humans. The Out of Africa hypothesis suggests that modern humans evolved from early humans in Africa and then dispersed to other regions, where they replaced existing hominin species.

Recognizing Key Terms

evolution *p. 470*
chemical evolution *p. 471*
endosymbiont theory *p. 472*
microevolution *p. 472*
macroevolution *p. 472*
population *p. 472*
gene pool *p. 473*
mutation *p. 473*

genetic drift *p. 473*
bottleneck effect *p. 473*
founder effect *p. 473*
gene flow *p. 473*
species *p. 473*
speciation *p. 473*
natural selection *p. 474*
fitness *p. 474*

adaptation *p. 474*
phylogenetic trees *p. 476*
fossil *p. 477*
biogeography *p. 478*
molecular clock *p. 479*
homologous structure *p. 480*
convergent evolution *p. 481*

analogous structure *p. 481*
hominin *p. 481*
bipedalism *p. 482*
mosaic evolution *p. 483*
multiregional hypothesis *p. 488*
Out of Africa hypothesis *p. 488*

Reviewing the Concepts

1. Which of the following was in very short supply in the environment of early Earth?
   a. lightning
   b. volcanoes
   c. gaseous oxygen (O_2)
   d. UV radiation

2. The earliest cells were
   a. prokaryotic.
   b. eukaryotic.
   c. present more than 10 billion years ago.
   d. part of multicellular organisms.

3. Which of the following does *not* produce variation in populations?
   a. bottleneck effect
   b. mutation
   c. crossing over
   d. independent assortment

4. Which of the following occurs when fertile individuals move into and out of populations?
   a. genetic drift
   b. speciation
   c. mutation
   d. gene flow

5. Which of the following features of an organism would promote fossilization?
   a. terrestrial existence
   b. member of a small population

   c. soft body parts
   d. aquatic existence

6. Which of the following is *not* characteristic of primates?
   a. high parental investment in a small number of young
   b. forward-facing eyes
   c. claws
   d. grasping feet and hands

7. Choose the *incorrect* statement.
   a. Humans descended from chimpanzees.
   b. Whereas chimps are primarily quadrupedal knuckle-walkers, humans have a bipedal gait.
   c. Chimps are more arboreal than humans, and this is reflected in their longer and stronger arms.
   d. Chimps, but not humans, have opposable big toes.

8. Which of the following primates is our closest living relative?
   a. gorilla
   b. orangutan
   c. chimpanzee
   d. gibbon

9. The Out of Africa hypothesis suggests
   a. multiple origins for modern humans.
   b. that Cro-Magnons outcompeted Neanderthals and forced them out of Africa.
   c. that modern humans evolved in an orderly, stepwise fashion.
   d. a single origin for all *H. sapiens*.

10. Which of the following is *not* a trend in human evolution?
    a. increases in brain volume
    b. decreased sexual dimorphism in body size
    c. more prominent brow ridges and crests on skull
    d. change from arboreal to terrestrial existence

11. Which hominin was probably the first to migrate out of Africa?
    a. *Australopithecus afarensis*
    b. *Homo sapiens*
    c. *Homo erectus*
    d. *Australopithecus africanus*

12. Where did the major events of human evolution occur?
    a. Africa
    b. South America
    c. Europe
    d. North America

13. Which of the following hominin characteristics evolved the earliest?
    a. bipedalism
    b. large brain
    c. language
    d. use of fire

Applying the Concepts

1. A friend of yours believes that all organisms were specially created. You believe in evolution and want to present your case to your friend. What would you say?
2. Can life arise on Earth from inorganic material today? Why or why not?
3. You are a biologist exploring the dense tropical rain forests of Brazil. You notice an unfamiliar, medium-sized mammal moving above you in the trees. What characteristics should this animal display to be classified as a primate?
4. Tay-Sachs disease has zero fitness because it causes death before the individual reaches reproductive age. How does a trait with zero fitness persist in a population?

Finding and Evaluating Information

In two articles published in August 2014 in *Proceedings of the National Academy of Sciences (PNAS)*,[1,2] Maciej Henneberg, Robert B. Eckhardt, Kenneth Hsü, and colleagues provide evidence that the skull and thighbones of LB1, a specimen designated as belonging to a new species of hominin, *Homo floresiensis*, instead represent an individual of *H. sapiens* with Down syndrome. David Pacchioli reported on these findings for ScienceDaily. The following is an excerpt from his report. You can read the entire article at: www.sciencedaily.com/releases/2014/08/140804151510.htm:

> "In October 2004, excavation of fragmentary skeletal remains from the island of Flores in Indonesia yielded what was called 'the most important find in human evolution for 100 years.' Its discoverers dubbed the find *Homo floresiensis*, a name suggesting a previously unknown species of human. Now detailed reanalysis by an international team of researchers including Robert B. Eckhardt, professor of developmental genetics and evolution at Penn State, Maciej Henneberg, professor of anatomy and pathology at the University of Adelaide, and Kenneth Hsu", a Chinese geologist and paleoclimatologist, suggests that the single specimen on which the new designation depends, known as LB1, does not represent a new species. Instead, it is the skeleton of a developmentally abnormal human and, according to the researchers, contains important features most consistent with a diagnosis of Down syndrome.

"The skeletal sample from Liang Bua cave contains fragmentary remains of several individuals,' Eckhardt said. 'LB1 has the only skull and thighbones in the entire sample.'

"No substantial new bone discoveries have been made in the cave since the finding of LB1."

1. *PNAS* is a prestigious journal with an impact factor of 9.809. The impact factor reflects the average number of citations that articles in recent issues of the journal receive. Thus, the impact factor can serve as an indicator of a journal's importance (i.e., the more citations each article receives, the higher the impact factor and the more important the journal). Does the fact that the two papers refuting the existence of *H. floresiensis* were published in *PNAS* influence your evaluation of the authors' evidence and arguments? If so, in what way?

2. Given that fossils are rarely formed and found, does the fact that a new species was named on the basis of one skull and one thighbone seem reasonable?

3. Considering variation within populations, how many different individuals would you like to see in a sample, before proposing a new species?

4. Where would you look for additional information on *Homo floresiensis*, and how would you evaluate the reliability of the sources you find?

[1]M. Henneberg et al., "Evolved developmental homeostasis disturbed in LB1 from Flores, Indonesia, denotes Down syndrome and not diagnostic traits of the invalid species *Homo floresiensis*," *PNAS* [2014]; doi: 10.1073/pnas.1407382111.

[2]R. B. Eckhardt et al., "Rare events in earth history include the LB1 human skeleton from Flores, Indonesia, as a developmental singularity, not a unique taxon," *PNAS* [2014]; doi: 10.1073/pnas.1407385111.

Appendices

Appendix 1

Answers to Reviewing the Concepts Questions

Chapter 1
1. d
2. c
3. a
4. b
5. c
6. c
7. a
8. c

Chapter 2
1. b
2. a
3. d
4. a
5. d
6. b
7. b
8. a
9. d
10. b
11. c
12. denaturation
13. Phospholipids

Chapter 3
1. b
2. d
3. d
4. c
5. a
6. d
7. c
8. b
9. a
10. a
11. c
12. Cytoplasm
13. Oxygen
14. fermentation

Chapter 4
1. b
2. a
3. a
4. b
5. a
6. d
7. a
8. c
9. d
10. c
11. c
12. a
13. a
14. a

Chapter 5
1. c
2. d
3. d
4. c
5. a
6. c
7. d
8. b
9. c
10. b
11. c
12. c
13. calcium, phosphorus
14. sprain

Chapter 6
1. c
2. c
3. c
4. a
5. a
6. a
7. b
8. b
9. d
10. d
11. d
12. actin, myosin
13. sarcomere

Chapter 7
1. a
2. c
3. b
4. b
5. b
6. c
7. a
8. c
9. c
10. b
11. a
12. a
13. myelin sheath
14. sodium-potassium pump

Chapter 8
1. a
2. d
3. d
4. c
5. d
6. b
7. b
8. d
9. a
10. a
11. c
12. d
13. a
14. a
15. d

Chapter 9
1. a
2. b
3. d
4. a
5. b
6. a
7. a
8. c
9. c
10. b
11. a

Chapter 10
1. a
2. c
3. d
4. c
5. d
6. a
7. d
8. c
9. c
10. a
11. gigantism; acromegaly
12. adrenal cortex

Chapter 11
1. b
2. c
3. b
4. a
5. a
6. a
7. d
8. c

Chapter 12
1. a
2. b
3. b
4. b
5. b
6. d
7. c
8. b
9. a
10. d
11. c

Chapter 13
1. a
2. d
3. b
4. a
5. c
6. d
7. b
8. a
9. d
10. c
11. b
12. natural killer cells
13. histamine
14. plasma cells
15. macrophages (dendritic cells, B cells)

Chapter 14
1. a
2. b
3. b
4. d
5. b
6. b
7. b
8. a
9. d
10. a
11. a
12. epiglottis
13. carbonic anhydrase

Chapter 15
1. b
2. d
3. d
4. a
5. d
6. c
7. a
8. b
9. c
10. b
11. c
12. c
13. b
14. chime
15. liver
16. starch
17. cholecystokinin

Chapter 16
1. c
2. b
3. a
4. c
5. a
6. c
7. a
8. c
9. d
10. Hemodialysis
11. internal; smooth; external; skeletal

Chapter 17
1. a
2. b
3. a
4. a
5. c
6. a
7. b
8. c
9. c
10. epididymis
11. oviduct

Chapter 18
1. d
2. c
3. a
4. a
5. b
6. d
7. c
8. c
9. b
10. b
11. d
12. d

Chapter 19
1. b
2. a
3. a
4. b
5. a
6. b
7. a
8. c
9. a
10. a
11. b
12. a
13. b
14. a
15. c
16. crossing over, independent assortment
17. homologous
18. synapsis

Chapter 20
1. b
2. a
3. a
4. c
5. c
6. a
7. c
8. polygenic
9. phenotype
10. homozygous
11. linked

Chapter 21
1. a
2. c
3. b
4. a
5. d
6. c
7. b
8. c
9. b
10. tRNA
11. uracil
12. restriction enzyme

Chapter 22
1. c
2. a
3. a
4. d
5. d
6. c
7. a
8. c
9. d
10. c
11. c
12. a
13. a

Chapter 23
1. a
2. b
3. b
4. d
5. c
6. d
7. c
8. c
9. niche
10. secondary consumer, carnivore

Chapter 24
1. a
2. d
3. d
4. b
5. c
6. a
7. c
8. a

Appendix 2

Hints for Applying the Concepts Questions

Chapter 1

1. Each part of the question asks about a different group of Swedish children. Choose the correct group from the key, and look at the line on the graph of the appropriate color.

Chapter 2

1. What functions do triglycerides perform in your body?
2. Cellulose is an important form of dietary fiber.
3. Consider the following qualities of water: polarity, heat of vaporization, and high heat capacity.
4. Consider the harmful effects of radiation on the body.

Chapter 3

1. Anesthetics need to cross the plasma membranes of nerve cells.
2. Mitochondria process energy for cells, and thus they occur in large numbers in cells with a high demand for energy.
3. Which element of the cytoskeleton forms structures involved in cleaning the respiratory tract?

Chapter 4

1. Does cartilage have a blood supply?
2. What physiological mechanisms raise body temperature? What physiological mechanisms lower body temperature?
3. Where is connective tissue found?

Chapter 5

1. What happens to bone density if no stress is placed on the bone?
2. What kind of activity builds bone density?
3. What structure would indicate that the bone was still capable of growth?

Chapter 6

1. What role does acetylcholine play in muscle contraction?
2. What causes tendinitis? How is it treated?
3. What role do calcium ions play in muscle contraction?
4. Which fibers are darker in color: fast-twitch or slow-twitch fibers? How do the properties of fast-twitch fibers differ from those of slow-twitch fibers?

Chapter 7

1. What effect does an inhibitory neurotransmitter have on the postsynaptic neuron?
2. What would happen if a neurotransmitter were not removed from the synapse?
3. What factors cause ions to cross the membrane during an action potential? What role do potassium ions play in the action potential?
4. What role does the myelin sheath play in the conduction of an action potential?

Chapter 8

1. What are the functions of the spinal cord? Would the location of the injury affect which functions are lost?
2. What is the function of the sympathetic nervous system?
3. What could happen if the sensory nerves from the tongue were anesthetized?
4. What structure of the brain is important in transferring short-term memory to long-term memory?

Chapter 9

1. In what type of vision are distant objects seen more clearly than nearby objects?
2. What part of the ear is responsible for equilibrium?
3. What changes when you shift your focus from an object in the distance to a nearby object?

Chapter 10

1. Cortisone is a glucocorticoid.
2. Which internal system of communication is relatively slow? Which is relatively fast?
3. Theresa's symptoms and the timing of their onset suggest melatonin may be involved.
4. What hormones are produced by the adrenal cortex?

Chapter 11

1. Are the white blood cells that are produced in leukemia functional?
2. What regulates the circulating number of red blood cells?
3. What is the function of red blood cells? How is iron related to the ability of red blood cells to carry out their function?
4. Which antibodies against antigens on red blood cells does Raul have?
5. What could happen if either of Elizabeth's babies had Rh-positive blood?
6. What are the functions of platelets?

Chapter 12

1. What happens if the valves do not close properly?
2. The pressure that propels blood through the arteries is equal to the pressure against the arterial walls. What force generates this pressure? What is the relationship between high blood pressure and atherosclerosis?
3. What happens in the lymph nodes when you get sick?

Chapter 13

1. Is a vaccine effective immediately?
2. How specific is the immune response?
3. What role do helper T cells play in the immune response?
4. How long does it take antibodies to form after the first exposure to an antigen?

Chapter 14

1. What factors regulate breathing rate and tidal volume?
2. What is the function of the cilia in the respiratory tubules?
3. Does inhalation or expiration involve muscle contraction? Which is a passive process?

Chapter 15

1. What role does the pancreas play in digestion?
2. What is the relationship between diarrhea and water reabsorption?
3. What would cause skin to develop a yellow tone? What might the cause of the yellow skin tone have to do with a tattoo?
4. What substance is released into the small intestine when fatty food enters the small intestine?

Chapter 16

1. Beer is a diuretic.
2. Consider the functions of the kidneys and the ways to replace these functions.
3. Which region of the nephron is involved in filtration?

Chapter 17

1. When making your recommendation for a means of contraception, consider its effectiveness in preventing pregnancy, this couple's need for protection against STDs, and the health effects of the means of contraception.
2. What happens to the endometrium during menstruation?
3. What does warm temperature have to do with sperm count?

Chapter 18

1. How does fetal circulation differ from circulation after birth?
2. Consider the concept of critical periods in development.
3. Consider the hormones involved in milk production and ejection.
4. Consider the potential role of free radicals in aging.

Chapter 19

1. What is nondisjunction?
2. What is the function of the spindle fibers?
3. Look at Figure 19.16.

Chapter 20

1. Color blindness is a sex-linked trait.
2. What are the genotypes of George and Sue? Use a Punnett square to determine the expected results from a cross with those genotypes.
3. A recessive trait is expressed only in the homozygous condition.
4. Recessive alleles are not expressed.
5. Use a Punnett square to determine the outcome of the cross.

Chapter 21

1. What is the start codon? What is the stop codon? What amino acids do the other codons code for?
2. Translate each of the mRNA strands. Remember that more than one codon can code for the same amino acid.

3. Which DNA fingerprint matches the one from the bloodstain at the scene?

Chapter 22

1. Describe the evidence in support of evolution.
2. Consider chemical evolution and the conditions of the early Earth.
3. What characteristics distinguish primates from other mammals?
4. Tay-Sachs disease is caused by a recessive allele.

Chapter 23

1. On average, what percentage of the energy available at one trophic level is available to the next level?
2. What happens to mercury as it moves up the food chain?
3. Average rainfall and temperature largely determine the organisms found in a given location.

Chapter 24

1. What will happen to the size of each population as the prereproductive individuals reach reproductive age?
2. a. What factors regulate population size?
   b. How might Asian carp affect factors regulating the population size of other species of fish?
3. How would spending differ between a young, growing population and an aging population?
4. The size of the population influences how quickly individuals are added to the population.

Appendix 3

Answers to Figure Questions

Chapter 1

Figure 1.4: Add another arrow from Form a Question to indicate Hypothesis 2. All the steps that are currently shown leading from "Hypothesis" would be repeated for Hypothesis 2.

Chapter 2

Figure 2.17: The triglyceride would be a liquid at room temperature because the kink in the unsaturated fatty acid in part (b) would prevent close packing of adjacent molecules.

Chapter 3

Figure 3.4: The scanning electron microscope should be used because it allows visualization of the surface structure of a specimen and provides a detailed three-dimensional view.

Chapter 4

Figure 4.12: An elevation in blood calcium level would be sensed by receptors. In response, a control center in the brain would stimulate the thyroid gland to increase production of calcitonin, which lowers blood calcium level. If the calcium level dropped too low, receptors would signal the control center in the brain. In response, the control center would stimulate the parathyroid glands to increase production of parathyroid hormone, which would raise blood calcium levels.

Chapter 5

Figure 5.2: Calcium is needed for replacing the cartilage with bone in the skeleton of the fetus.

Chapter 6

Figure 6.9: ATP stored in muscles

Figure 6.10: Slow-twitch muscle cells for cross-country skiing; fast-twitch muscle cells for weight lifting

Chapter 7

Figure 7.3: Saltatory conduction, which increases the speed of conduction, is possible only on myelinated axons. The increased speed is important when nerve impulses must travel long distances.

Chapter 8

Figure 8.3: The corpus callosum connects the hemispheres, allowing them to communicate.

Figure 8.5: Areas with greater sensitivity and motor control have a proportionally larger area of representation on the cortex than do areas with less sensitivity and motor control, such as the forearm.

Chapter 8a

Figure 8a.3: Probably over .05%; probably under .05%

Chapter 9

Figure 9.4: The lower body trunk and inner thigh

Chapter 10

Figure 10.4: Water-soluble hormones exert their effects without ever entering the target cell; they activate second messengers in the cell. Also, water-soluble hormones activate existing proteins (enzymes) rather than stimulating the synthesis of new proteins.

Chapter 11

Figure 11.7: AB+

Chapter 12

Figure 12.7: The semilunar valves open, and the atrioventricular (AV) valves close.

Chapter 13

Figure 13.8: Helper T cells activate both naive cytotoxic T cells and naive B cells. Thus, helper T cells turn on both the cell-mediated and the antibody-mediated adaptive immune responses.

Chapter 13a

Figure 13.a2: The glycoprotein on its surface. It is the fit between the glycoprotein and the host cell receptor that determines whether the virus can infect the cell.

Chapter 14

Figure 14.2: Nasal cavity, pharynx, trachea, bronchi, bronchioles, alveoli

Chapter 15

Figure 15.8: Circular folds, villi, and microvilli

Figure 15.11: The capillary beds are in the small intestine and the liver. The liver monitors and adjusts blood content.

Chapter 16

Figure 16.7: The walls of glomerular capillaries have pores that allow many substances (but not red blood cells) to move out of the capillaries.

Chapter 17

Figure 17.9: LH, because the surge in LH levels triggers ovulation

Chapter 17a

Figure 17a.7: If HIV DNA is not inserted into the host cell chromosome, it cannot produce HIV RNA or HIV-specified proteins.

Chapter 18

Figure 18.13: In the fetus, the foramen ovale (between the right and left atria) and the ductus arteriosus (on the pulmonary trunk) divert blood away from the lungs, which are not yet functional.

Chapter 18a

Figure 18a.3: At present, there is no approved medical test (e.g., blood test or scan of the brain) for ASD; instead, doctors rely on several tools to assess behavioral symptoms. Typically, delays detected during routine developmental screening are further evaluated through parent interviews; psychological testing; and assessments of speech, language, and hearing.

Chapter 19

Figure 19.3: At the start of interphase, a chromosome is a single strand of DNA. At the end of interphase, a chromosome consists of two sister chromatids that are replicate copies of the original strand of DNA held together by a centromere,

Chapter 19a

Figure 19a.6: The egg nucleus is removed so that the only genetic information directing development will come from the adult cell nucleus. The donor nucleus has genes for the desired trait.

Chapter 20

Figure 20.6: Two types: fW and fw

Chapter 21

Figure 21.5: Asparagine, serine, alanine

Chapter 21a

Figure 21a.1: Chromosomes 3, 5, 7, 8, 10, 11, 12, 13, 14, 16, 17, 20, and 22 have extra copies. Chromosomes 2, 4, 6, and 13 have extra pieces. Chromosomes 3, 4, 5, 6, 7, 8, 10, 13, 14, and 18 are missing pieces.

Chapter 22

Figure 22.21: This figure contradicts the notion of an orderly progression from primitive to modern because it shows that more than one species of hominin existed simultaneously at some points in the past.

Chapter 23

Figure 23.7: It would be a tertiary consumer.

Chapter 24

Figure 24.6: More-industrialized and affluent nations consume more of Earth's resources than poorer, less industrialized nations do.

Glossary

A

Accommodation A change in the shape of the lens of the eye brought about by contraction of the smooth muscle of the ciliary body that changes the degree to which light rays are bent so that an image can be focused on the retina.

Acetylcholine A neurotransmitter found in both the central nervous system and the peripheral nervous system. It is the neurotransmitter released at neuromuscular junctions that causes muscle contraction.

Acetylcholinesterase An enzyme that breaks the neurotransmitter acetylcholine into its inactive components, acetate and choline. Acetylcholinesterase stops the action of acetylcholine at a synapse.

Acid Any substance that increases the concentration of hydrogen ions in solution.

Acinar cells Exocrine cells of the pancreas that secrete digestive enzymes into ducts that empty into the small intestine.

Acquired immune deficiency syndrome See *AIDS*.

Acromegaly A condition characterized by enlarged soft tissues and thickened bones of the extremities. It is caused by overproduction of growth hormone in adulthood.

Acrosome A membranous sac on the head of a sperm cell that contains enzymes that facilitate sperm penetration into the egg during fertilization.

ACTH See *adrenocorticotropic hormone*.

Actin The contractile protein that makes up the major portion of the thin filaments in muscle cells. An actin (thin) filament is composed of actin, troponin, and tropomyosin. In muscle cells, contraction occurs when actin interacts with another protein called myosin.

Actin filaments The thin filaments in muscle cells composed primarily of the protein actin and essential to muscle contraction. In addition to actin, thin filaments contain two other proteins important in the regulation of muscle contraction: tropomyosin and troponin.

Action potential A nerve impulse. An electrochemical signal conducted along an axon. A wave of depolarization caused by the inward flow of sodium ions followed by repolarization caused by the outward flow of potassium ions.

Active immunity Immune resistance in which the body actively participates by producing memory B cells and memory T cells after exposure to an antigen, either naturally or through vaccination.

Active site A specific location on an enzyme where the substrate binds.

Active transport The movement of molecules across the plasma membrane, usually against a concentration gradient (from a region of lower concentration to one of higher concentration) with the aid of a carrier protein and energy (usually in the form of adenosine triphosphate, or ATP) supplied by the cell.

Acute renal failure An abrupt, complete or nearly complete, cessation of kidney function.

Adaptation The process by which populations become better attuned to their particular environments as a result of natural selection.

Adaptive immune responses Body defense responses that are acquired by exposure to cells or substances that do not belong in the body. Antibody-mediated responses and cell-mediated responses are involved. Adaptive responses have memory for the pathogen that triggered them.

Adaptive trait A characteristic (structure, function, or behavior) of an organism that makes an individual better able to survive and reproduce in its natural environment. Adaptive traits arise through natural selection.

Addison's disease An autoimmune disorder characterized by fatigue, loss of appetite, low blood pressure, and increased skin pigmentation resulting from undersecretion of glucocorticoids and aldosterone.

Adenosine triphosphate (ATP) A nucleotide that consists of the sugar ribose, the base adenine, and three phosphate groups. ATP is the energy currency of all living cells.

ADH See *antidiuretic hormone*.

Adhesion junction A specialized junction between cells in which protein filaments hold together the plasma membranes of adjacent cells; a desmosome.

Adipose tissue A type of loose connective tissue that contains cells specialized for storing fat.

Adolescence The stage in postnatal development that begins with puberty. It is a period of rapid physical and sexual maturation during which the ability to reproduce is achieved. Adolescence ends with the cessation of growth in the late teens or early twenties.

Adrenal cortex The outer region of the adrenal gland that secretes glucocorticoids, mineralocorticoids, and gonadocorticoids.

Adrenal glands The body's two adrenal glands are located on top of the kidneys. The outer region of each adrenal gland secretes glucocorticoids, mineralocorticoids, and gonadocorticoids, and the inner region secretes epinephrine and norepinephrine.

Adrenal medulla The inner region of the adrenal gland that secretes epinephrine and norepinephrine.

Adrenaline See *epinephrine*.

Adrenocorticotropic hormone (ACTH) The anterior pituitary hormone that controls the synthesis and secretion of glucocorticoid hormones from the cortex of the adrenal glands.

Adulthood The stage in postnatal development that is generally reached somewhere between 18 and 21 years of age and during which bodily changes continue as part of the growth and aging process.

Advance directive A legal document that allows you to convey in advance your wishes for end-of-life care.

Afferent (sensory) neuron A nerve cell specialized to conduct nerve impulses from the sensory receptors *toward* the central nervous system.

Age structure The number of males and females of each age in a population. The ages are often grouped into prereproductive, reproductive, and postreproductive categories. Generally, only individuals of reproductive age add to the size of the population.

Agglutinate To clump together.

Aging The normal and progressive alteration in the structure and function of the body. Aging is possibly caused by declines in critical body systems, disruption of cell processes by free radicals, slowing or cessation of cell division, and decline in the ability to repair damaged DNA.

Agranulocytes The white blood cells without granules or with very small granules in their cytoplasm, including monocytes and lymphocytes.

AIDS Acquired immune deficiency syndrome. A diagnosis of AIDS is made when an HIV-positive person develops one of the following conditions: (1) a helper T cell count below 200 cells per mm³ of blood; (2) 1 of 26 opportunistic infections, the most common of which are *Pneumocystis jiroveci* pneumonia and Kaposi's sarcoma, a cancer of connective tissue that affects primarily the skin; (3) a loss of more than 10% of body weight (wasting syndrome); or (4) dementia (mental incapacity, such as forgetfulness or inability to concentrate).

Albinism A genetic inability to produce the brown pigment melanin that normally gives color to the eyes, hair, and skin.

Aldosterone A hormone (the primary mineralocorticoid) released by the adrenal cortex that stimulates the reabsorption of sodium within kidney nephrons.

Allantois The extraembryonic membrane whose blood vessels become part of the umbilical cord, the ropelike connection between the embryo (and later the fetus) and the placenta.

Allele An alternative version of a gene. One of two or more slightly different versions of a gene that code for different forms of the same trait.

Allergen An antigen that stimulates an allergic response.

Allergy A strong immune response to an antigen (an allergen) that is not usually harmful to the body.

Allometric growth The change in the relative rates of growth of various parts of the body. Such growth helps shape developing humans and other organisms.

Alveolus (plural, alveoli) A thin-walled rounded chamber. In the lungs, the alveoli are the surfaces for gas exchange. They form clusters at the end of each bronchiole that are surrounded by a vast network of capillaries. The alveoli greatly increase the surface area for gas exchange.

Amino acid The building blocks of proteins consisting of a central carbon atom bound to a hydrogen atom, an amino group (NH₂), a carboxyl group (COOH), and a side chain designated by the letter R. There are 20 amino acids important to human life; our bodies can synthesize some amino acids (nonessential amino acids), whereas others cannot be synthesized and must be obtained from the foods we eat (essential amino acids).

Amniocentesis A method of prenatal testing for genetic problems in a fetus in which amniotic fluid is withdrawn through a needle so that the fluid can be tested biochemically and the cells can be cultured and examined for genetic abnormalities.

Amnion The extraembryonic membrane that encloses the embryo (and later the fetus) in a fluid-filled space called the amniotic cavity. Amniotic fluid forms a protective cushion that can be examined as part of prenatal testing in a procedure known as *amniocentesis*.

Ampulla A wider region in a canal or duct. In the inner ear, an ampulla is found at the base of each semicircular canal.

Anabolic steroids Synthetic hormones that mimic testosterone and stimulate the body to build muscle and increase strength. Steroid abuse can have many dangerous side effects.

Anabolism The building (synthetic) chemical reactions within living cells, as when cells build complicated molecules from simple ones. Compare with *catabolism*.

Anal canal The canal between the rectum and the anus. Feces pass through the anal canal.

Analgesic A substance, such as Demerol, that relieves pain.

Analogous structure A structure of one organism that is similar to that of another organism because of convergent evolution and not because the organisms share a common ancestry. Compare with *homologous structures*.

Anaphase In mitosis, the phase when the chromatids of each chromosome begin to separate, splitting at the centromere. Now separate entities, the chromatids are considered chromosomes, and they move toward opposite poles of the cell.

Anaphylactic shock An extreme allergic reaction that occurs within minutes after exposure to a substance to which a person is allergic. It can cause pooling of blood in capillaries, which causes dizziness, nausea, and sometimes unconsciousness and extreme difficulty in breathing. Anaphylactic shock can lead to death.

Androgen A steroid sex hormone secreted by the testes in males and produced in small quantities by the adrenal cortex in both sexes.

Anemia A condition in which the blood's ability to carry oxygen is reduced. It can result from too little hemoglobin, too few red blood cells, or both.

Anencephaly A neural tube defect that involves incomplete formation of the brain and results in stillbirth or death shortly after birth.

Anesthesia The drug-induced loss of the sensation of pain. It may be general, regional, or local.

Aneurysm A blood-filled sac in the wall of an artery caused by a weak area in the artery wall.

Angina pectoris Choking or strangling chest pain, usually experienced in the center of the chest or slightly to the left, that is caused by a temporary insufficiency of blood flow to the heart. It begins during physical exertion or emotional stress, when the demands on the heart are increased and the blood flow to the heart muscle can no longer meet the needs.

Angioplasty A procedure that widens the channel of an artery obstructed because of atherosclerosis. It involves inflating a tough, plastic balloon inside the artery.

Angiotensin I Renin converts angiotensinogen into this protein.

Angiotensin II A protein that stimulates the adrenal gland to release aldosterone.

ANH **See** *atrial natriuretic hormone.*

Anorexia nervosa An eating disorder characterized by deliberate self-starvation, a distorted body image, and low body weight.

Antagonistic pairs Muscles arranged in pairs so that the actions of the members of the pair are opposite to one another. This arrangement is characteristic of most skeletal muscles.

Antibody A Y-shaped protein produced by plasma cells during an adaptive immune response that recognizes and binds to a specific antigen because of the shape of the molecule. Antibodies defend against invaders in a variety of ways, including neutralization, agglutination and precipitation, or activation of the complement system.

Antibody-mediated immune responses Immune system responses conducted by B cells that produce antibodies and that defend primarily against enemies that are free in body fluids, including toxins or extracellular pathogens, such as bacteria or free viruses.

Anticodon A three-base sequence on transfer RNA (tRNA) that binds to the complementary base pairs of a codon on the mRNA.

Antidiuretic hormone (ADH) A hormone manufactured by the hypothalamus but stored in and released from the posterior pituitary. It regulates the amount of water reabsorbed by the distal convoluted tubules and collecting ducts of nephrons. ADH causes water retention at the kidneys and elevates blood pressure. It is also called *vasopressin*.

Antigen A substance that is recognized as foreign by the immune system. Antigens trigger an immune response.

Antigen-presenting cell (APC) A cell that presents an antigen to a helper T cell, initiating an immune response toward that antigen. An important type of antigen-presenting cell is a macrophage.

Aorta The body's main artery that conducts blood from the left ventricle toward the cells of the body. The aorta arches over the top of the heart and gives rise to the smaller arteries that feed the capillary beds of the body tissues.

Apoptosis A series of predictable physical changes in a cell that is undergoing programmed cell death. Apoptosis is sometimes used as a synonym for *programmed cell death*.

Appendicular skeleton The part of the skeleton that includes the pectoral girdle (shoulders), the pelvic girdle (pelvis), and the limbs (arms and legs).

Appendix A slender closed pouch that extends from the large intestine near the juncture with the small intestine.

Aqueous humor The fluid within the anterior chamber of the eye. It supplies nutrients and oxygen to the cornea and lens and carries away their metabolic wastes.

Arachnoid The middle layer of the meninges (the connective tissue layers that protect the central nervous system).

Areolar connective tissue A type of loose connective tissue composed of cells in a gelatinous matrix. It serves as a universal packing material between organs and anchors skin to underlying tissues and organs.

Arrector pili The tiny, smooth muscles attached to the hair follicles in the dermis.

Arteriole A small blood vessel located between an artery and a capillary. Arterioles serve to regulate blood flow through capillary beds to various regions of the body. They also regulate blood pressure. Arterioles are barely visible to the unaided eye.

Artery A large-diameter muscular tube (blood vessel) that transports blood away from the heart toward the cells of body tissues. Arteries conduct blood low in oxygen to the lungs and blood high in oxygen to the body tissues. Arteries typically have thick muscular and elastic walls that dampen the blood pressure pulsations caused by heart contractions.

Arthritis An inflammation of a joint.

Artificial insemination A treatment for infertility in which sperm are deposited in the woman's cervix or vagina at about the time of ovulation.

ASD **See** *autism spectrum disorder.*

Asperger's disorder **See** *autism spectrum disorder.*

Association neuron An interneuron. These neurons are located within the central nervous system between sensory and motor neurons and serve to integrate information.

Asthma A condition marked by spasms of the muscles of bronchioles, making airflow difficult. It is often triggered by allergy.

Astigmatism Irregularities in the curvature of the cornea or lens that cause distortions of a visual image because the irregularities cause light rays to converge unevenly.

Atherosclerosis A narrowing of the arteries caused by thickening of the arterial walls and a buildup of lipid (primarily cholesterol) deposits. Atherosclerosis reduces blood flow through the vessel, choking off the vital supply of oxygen and nutrients to the tissues served by that vessel.

Atom A unit of matter that cannot be further broken down by chemical means; it is composed of subatomic particles, which include protons (positively charged particles), neutrons (with no charge), and electrons (with negative charges).

Atomic number The number of protons in the nucleus of an atom.

ATP **See** *adenosine triphosphate.*

Atrial fibrillation Rapid, ineffective contractions of the atria of the heart.

Atrial natriuretic hormone (ANH) The hormone released by cells in the right atrium of the heart in response to stretching of the heart caused by increased blood volume and pressure. ANH decreases water and sodium reabsorption by the kidneys, resulting in the production of large amounts of urine.

Atrioventricular (AV) bundle A tract of specialized cardiac muscle cells that runs along the wall between the ventricles of the heart and conducts an electrical impulse that originated in the sinoatrial (SA) node and was conducted to the AV node to the ventricles. The bundle forks into right and left branches and then divides into many other specialized cardiac muscle cells, called Purkinje fibers, that penetrate the walls of the ventricles.

Atrioventricular (AV) node A region of specialized cardiac muscle cells located in the partition between the two atria. It receives an electrical signal that spreads through the atrial walls from the sinoatrial node and relays the stimulus to the ventricles by means of a bundle of specialized muscle fibers, called the atrioventricular bundle, that runs along the wall between the ventricles.

Atrioventricular (AV) valves Heart valves located between the atria and the ventricles that keep blood flowing in only one direction, from the atria to the ventricles. The right AV valve consists of three flaps of tissue and is also called the *tricuspid valve*. The left AV valve consists of two flaps of tissue and is also called the *bicuspid valve* or the *mitral valve*.

Atrium (plural, atria) An upper chamber of the heart that receives blood from veins and pumps it to a ventricle.

Auditory tubes Small tubes that join the upper region of the pharynx (throat) with the middle ear. They help to equalize the air pressure between the middle ear and the atmosphere. Also called *Eustachian tubes*.

Autism **See** *autism spectrum disorder.*

Autism spectrum disorder (ASD) A neurodevelopmental disorder characterized by deficits in social communication and interaction and by the performance of repetitive and restricted patterns of behavior. Hyper- or hyporeactivity to sensory input is also characteristic of the disorder. Four previously distinct neurodevelopmental disorders—autistic disorder (also called *autism*), Asperger's disorder (sometimes called *Asperger's syndrome*), pervasive developmental disorder not otherwise specified (PDD-NOS), and childhood disintegrative disorder—now are subsumed under the single category ASD.

Autoimmune disorder An immune response misdirected against the body's own tissues.

Autonomic nervous system The part of the peripheral nervous system that governs the involuntary, unconscious activities that maintain a relatively stable internal environment. The autonomic nervous system has two branches: the sympathetic and the parasympathetic.

Autosomes The 22 pairs of chromosomes (excluding the pair of sex chromosomes) that determine the expression of most inherited characteristics of a person.

Autotroph An organism that makes its own food (organic compounds) from inorganic substances. The autotrophs include photoautotrophs, which use the energy of light, and chemoautotrophs, which use the energy in chemicals.

Axial skeleton The part of the skeleton that includes the skull, the vertebral column, the breastbone (sternum), and the rib cage.

Axon A long extension from the cell body of a neuron that carries an electrochemical message away from the cell body toward another neuron or effector (muscle or gland). The tips of the axon release a chemical called a neurotransmitter that can affect the activity of the receiving cell. Typically, there is one long axon on a neuron.

Axon terminal The tip of a branch of an axon that releases a chemical (neurotransmitter) that alters the activity of the target cell. A synaptic knob.

B

Bacterium A prokaryotic organism.

B cell **See** *B lymphocyte*.

B lymphocyte B cell. A type of white blood cell important in antibody-mediated immune responses that can transform into a plasma cell and produce antibodies.

Balanced polymorphism A phenomenon in which natural selection maintains two or more alleles for a trait in a population from one generation to the next. It occurs when the environment changes frequently or when the heterozygous condition is favored over either homozygous condition.

Ball-and-socket joint A joint, such as the shoulder and hip joints, that allows motion in all directions.

Barr body A structure formed by a condensed, inactivated X chromosome in the body cells of female mammals.

Basal body The structure that anchors the microtubules of a cilium or flagellum to a cell. It contains nine triplets of microtubules arranged in a ring.

Basal cell carcinoma The most common type of skin cancer, occurring in the rapidly dividing cells of the basal layer of the epidermis.

Basal metabolic rate (BMR) A measure of the minimum energy required to keep an awake, resting body alive. It generally represents between 60% and 75% of the body's energy needs.

Base Any substance that reduces the concentration of hydrogen ions in solution.

Basement membrane A noncellular layer beneath epithelial tissue that binds the epithelial cells to underlying connective tissue. It helps epithelial tissue resist stretching and forms a boundary.

Basilar membrane The floor of the central canal in the cochlea of the inner ear that supports the spiral organ (of Corti), which is the true site of hearing; when the basilar membrane vibrates in response to sound, hair cells on the spiral organ are bent, generating electrochemical messages that are interpreted as sound.

Basophil A white blood cell that releases histamine, a chemical that both attracts other white blood cells to the site and causes blood vessels to widen during an inflammatory response.

Benign tumor An abnormal mass of tissue that usually remains at the site where it forms.

Bicuspid valve A heart valve located between the left atrium and ventricle. It is also called the *mitral valve* or the left *atrioventricular (AV) valve*.

Bile A mixture of water, ions, cholesterol, bile pigments, and bile salts that emulsifies fat (keeps fat as small globules), facilitating digestion by lipase. Bile is produced by the liver, is stored in the gallbladder, and acts in the small intestine.

Bilirubin A yellow pigment produced from the breakdown of the heme portion of hemoglobin by liver cells. It is excreted by the liver in bile.

Binary fission A type of asexual reproduction in which the genetic information is replicated and then a cell—a bacterium, for example—or organism divides into two equal parts.

Biodiversity The number and variety of all living things in a given area. It includes genetic diversity, species diversity, and ecological diversity.

Biogeochemical cycle The recurring process by which materials (for example, carbon, water, nitrogen, and phosphorus) cycle between living and nonliving systems and back again.

Biogeography The study of the geographic distribution of organisms. New distributions of organisms occur when organisms move to new areas (dispersal) and when areas occupied by the organisms move or are subdivided.

Biological magnification The tendency of a nondegradable chemical to become more concentrated in organisms as it passes along a food chain.

Biomass In ecosystems, the dry weight of the body mass of a group of organisms in a particular habitat.

Biopsy The removal and examination, usually microscopic, of a piece of tissue to diagnose a disease, usually cancer.

Biosphere The part of Earth in which life is found. It encompasses all of Earth's living organisms.

Biotechnology The industrial or commercial use or alteration of living organisms, cells, or molecules to achieve specific useful goals.

Bioterrorism The use of biological agents, such as viruses, parasites, or bacteria, to intimidate or attack societies or governments. There is concern that biological agents could be intentionally introduced into food or water supplies, for example.

Bipedalism Walking on two feet. This trait evolved early in hominin evolution and set the stage for the evolution of other characteristics, such as increases in brain size.

Bipolar neuron A neuron that has only two processes. The axon and the dendrite extend from opposite sides of the cell body. Bipolar neurons are receptor cells found only in some of the special sensory organs, such as in the retina of the eye and in the olfactory membrane of the nose.

Birth defects Developmental defects present at birth. Such defects involve structure, function, behavior, or metabolism and may or may not be hereditary.

Birth rate The number of births per a specified number of individuals in the population during a specific length of time.

Bladder A muscular saclike organ that receives urine from the two ureters and temporarily stores it until release into the urethra.

Blastocyst The stage of development consisting of a hollow ball of cells. It contains the inner cell mass, a group of cells that will become the embryo, and the trophoblast, a thin layer of cells that will give rise to part of the placenta.

Blind spot The region of the retina where the optic nerve leaves the eye and on which there are no photoreceptors. Objects focused on the blind spot cannot be seen.

Blood Connective tissue that consists of cells and platelets suspended in plasma, a liquid matrix.

Blood–brain barrier A mechanism that protects the central nervous system by selecting the substances permitted to enter the cerebrospinal fluid from the blood. The barrier results from the relative impermeability of the capillaries in the brain and spinal cord.

Blood pressure The force exerted by the blood against the walls of the blood vessels. It is caused by the contraction of the ventricles and is influenced by vasoconstriction.

Blood type A characteristic of a person's red blood cells determined on the basis of large molecules on the surface of the plasma membrane.

Blue baby Newborn whose foramen ovale, the fetal opening between the right and left atria of the heart, fails to close. As a result, much of the infant's blood still bypasses the lungs and is low in oxygen. The condition can be corrected with surgery.

BMR See *basal metabolic rate.*

Bolus A small, soft ball of food mixed with saliva.

Bone Strong connective tissue with specialized cells in a hard matrix composed of collagen fibers and mineral salts.

Bone marrow The soft material filling the cavities in bones. Yellow bone marrow serves as a fat-storage site. Red bone marrow is the site where blood cells are produced.

Bone remodeling The ongoing process of bone deposition and absorption in response to hormonal and mechanical factors.

Bottleneck effect The genetic drift associated with dramatic, unselective reductions in population size such that the genetic makeup of survivors is not representative of the original population.

Brain The organ composed of neurons and glial cells that receives sensory input and integrates, stores, and retrieves information and directs motor output.

Brain waves The patterns recorded in an EEG (electroencephalogram) that reflect the electrical activity of the brain and are correlated with the person's state of alertness.

Breast The front of the chest, especially either of the two protuberant glandular organs (mammary glands) that in human females and other female mammals produce milk to nourish newborns.

Breathing center A region in the medulla of the brain that controls the basic breathing rhythm.

Breech birth Delivery in which the baby is born buttocks first rather than head first. It is associated with difficult labors and umbilical cord accidents.

Bronchi (singular, bronchus) The respiratory passageways between the trachea and the bronchioles that conduct air into the lungs.

Bronchial tree The term given to the air tubules in the respiratory system because their repeated branching resembles the branches of a tree.

Bronchioles A series of small tubules branching from the smallest bronchi inside each lung.

Bronchitis Inflammation of the mucous membranes of the bronchi, causing excess mucus and a deep cough.

Brush border A fuzzy border of microvilli on the surface of absorptive epithelial cells of the small intestine.

Buffer A substance that prevents dramatic changes in pH by removing excess hydrogen ions from solution when concentrations increase and adding hydrogen ions when concentrations decrease.

Bulbourethral glands Male accessory reproductive glands that release a clear, slippery liquid immediately before ejaculation. Also called *Cowper's glands.*

Bulimia nervosa An eating disorder characterized by binge eating followed by purging by means of enemas, laxatives, diuretics, or self-induced vomiting.

Bursa (plural, bursae) A flattened sac containing a thin film of synovial fluid that surrounds and cushions certain synovial joints. Bursae are common in locations where ligaments, muscles, skin, or tendons rub against bone.

Bursitis Inflammation of a bursa (a sac in a synovial joint that acts as a cushion). Bursitis causes fluid to build up within the bursa, resulting in intense pain that becomes worse when the joint is moved and cannot be relieved by resting in any position.

C

C-section See *cesarean section.*

Calcitonin (CT) A hormone secreted by the thyroid gland when blood calcium levels are high. It stimulates the removal of calcium from the blood and inhibits the breakdown of bone.

Callus A mass of repair tissue formed by collagen fibers secreted from fibroblasts or woven bone that forms around and links the ends of a broken bone.

Capillary A microscopic blood vessel between arterioles and venules with walls only one cell layer thick. It is the site where the exchange of materials between the blood and the tissues occurs.

Capillary bed A network of true capillaries servicing a particular area. Precapillary sphincters regulate blood flow through the capillary bed. When the sphincters relax, blood fills the capillary bed, and materials can be exchanged between the blood and the tissues. When the sphincters contract, blood flows directly from an arteriole to a venule, bypassing the capillaries.

Carbaminohemoglobin The compound formed when carbon dioxide binds to hemoglobin.

Carbohydrate An organic molecule that provides fuel for the human body. Carbohydrates, which we know as sugars and starches, can be classified by size into the monosaccharides, disaccharides, and polysaccharides.

Carbon footprint A measure of the amount of carbon dioxide that enters the atmosphere due to the activities of a person or population; it includes personal activities and the activities needed for production and waste removal of the products consumed.

Carbonic anhydrase An enzyme in the red blood cells that catalyzes the conversion of unbound carbon dioxide to carbonic acid.

Carcinogen A substance that causes cancer.

Carcinoma in situ A tumor that has not spread; "cancer in place."

Cardiac cycle The events associated with the flow of blood through the heart during a single heartbeat. It consists of systole (contraction) and diastole (relaxation) of the atria and then of the ventricles of the heart.

Cardiac muscle A contractile tissue that makes up the bulk of the walls of the heart. Cardiac muscle cells are cylindrical and have branching interconnections between them. Cardiac muscle cells are striped (striated) and have a single nucleus. Contraction of cardiac muscle is involuntary.

Cardiovascular Pertaining to the heart and blood vessels.

Cardiovascular system The organ system composed of the heart and blood vessels. The cardiovascular system distributes blood, delivers nutrients, and removes wastes.

Carnivore An animal that obtains energy by eating other animals. A secondary consumer.

Carpal tunnel syndrome A condition of the wrist and hand whose symptoms may include numbness or tingling in the affected hand, along with pain in the wrist, hand, and fingers that results from repeated motion in the hand or wrist, causing the tendons to become inflamed and press against the nerve.

Carrier An individual who displays the dominant phenotype but is heterozygous for a trait and can therefore pass the recessive allele to descendants.

Carrying capacity The number of individuals of a given species that a particular environment can support for a prolonged time period. The carrying capacity of the environment is determined by such factors as availability of resources, including food, water, and space; ability to clean away wastes; and predation pressure.

Cartilage A type of specialized connective tissue with a firm gelatinous matrix containing protein fibers for strength. The cartilage cells (chondrocytes) lie in small spaces (lacunae) within the matrix.

Catabolism Chemical reactions within living cells that break down complex molecules into simpler ones, releasing energy from chemical bonds. Compare with *anabolism*.

Cataract A cloudy or opaque lens in the eye. Cataracts reduce visual acuity and may be caused by glucose accumulation associated with type 1 and type 2 diabetes mellitus, excessive exposure to sunlight, and exposure to cigarette smoke.

CD4 cell See *helper T cell*.

Cecum A pouch that hangs below the junction of the small and large intestines; the appendix extends from the cecum.

Cell The smallest structure that shows all the characteristics of life.

Cell adhesion molecule (CAM) A molecule that pokes through the plasma membranes of most cells and helps hold cells together to form tissues and organs.

Cell body The part of a neuron that contains the organelles and nucleus needed to maintain the cells.

Cell cycle The entire sequence of events that a cell goes through from its origin in the division of a parent cell through its own division into two daughter cells. The cell cycle consists of two major phases: interphase and cell division.

Cell differentiation The process by which cells become specialized with respect to structure and function.

Cell-mediated immune responses Immune system responses conducted by T cells that protect against cellular threats, including body cells that have become infected with viruses or other pathogens and cancer cells.

Cell theory This fundamental organizing principle of biology states that (1) a cell is the smallest unit of life; (2) cells make up all living things, from unicellular to multicellular organisms; and (3) new cells arise from preexisting cells.

Cellular respiration The oxygen-requiring pathway by which glucose is broken down by cells to yield carbon dioxide, water, and energy.

Cellulose A structural polysaccharide found in the cell walls of plants. Humans lack the enzymes necessary to digest cellulose, so it passes unchanged through our digestive tract. Although cellulose has no value as a nutrient, it is an important form of dietary fiber known to facilitate the passage of feces through the large intestines.

Cementum A calcified but sensitive part of a tooth that covers the root.

Central nervous system (CNS) The brain and the spinal cord.

Centriole A structure, found in pairs, within a centrosome. Each centriole is composed of nine sets of triplet microtubules arranged in a ring.

Centromere The region of a replicated chromosome at which sister chromatids are held together until they separate during cell division.

Centrosome The region near the nucleus that contains centrioles. It forms the mitotic spindle during prophase.

Cerebellum A region of the brain important in sensory–motor coordination. It is largely responsible for posture and smooth body movements.

Cerebral cortex The extensive area of gray matter covering the surfaces of the cerebrum. It is often referred to as the conscious part of the brain. The cerebral cortex has sensory, motor, and association areas.

Cerebral white matter A region of the cerebrum beneath the cortex consisting primarily of myelinated axons grouped into tracts that allow various regions of the brain to communicate with one another.

Cerebrospinal fluid The fluid bathing the internal and external surfaces of the central nervous system. It serves as a shock absorber, supports the brain, nourishes the brain, delivers chemical messengers, and removes waste products.

Cerebrovascular accident See *stroke*.

Cerebrum The largest and most prominent part of the brain, composed of the cerebral hemispheres. It is responsible for thinking, sensory perception, originating most conscious motor activity, personality, and memory.

Cervical cap A barrier means of contraception consisting of a small rubber dome that fits snugly over the cervix and is held in place partly by suction. It prevents sperm from reaching the egg.

Cervix The narrow neck of the uterus that projects into the vagina, whose opening provides a passageway for materials moving between the vagina and the body of the uterus.

Cesarean section A procedure by which the baby and placenta are removed from the uterus through an incision in the abdominal wall and uterus. The term is often shortened to *C-section*.

Chancre A painless bump that forms during the first stage of syphilis at the site of contact, usually within 2 to 8 weeks of the initial contact.

Chemical digestion A part of the digestive process that involves breaking chemical bonds so that complex molecules are broken into their component subunits. Chemical digestion produces molecules that can be absorbed into the bloodstream and used by the cells.

Chemical evolution The sequence of events by which life evolved from chemicals, slowly increasing in complexity over perhaps 300 million years.

Chemistry The branch of science concerned with the composition and properties of material substances, including their abilities to change into other substances.

Chemoreceptor A sensory receptor specialized to respond to chemicals. We describe the input from the chemoreceptors of the mouth as taste (gustation) and from those of the nose as smell (olfaction). Other chemoreceptors monitor levels of chemicals, such as carbon dioxide, oxygen, and glucose, in body fluids.

Childhood The stage in postnatal development that runs from about 13 months to 12 or 13 years of age. It is a time of continued growth during which gross and fine motor skills improve and coping skills develop. With the exception of the reproductive system, organ systems become fully functional.

Chitin A structural polysaccharide found in the exoskeletons (hard outer coverings) of animals such as insects, spiders, and crustaceans.

Chlamydia A genus of bacteria. In this text, it is an infection (usually sexually transmitted) caused by *Chlamydia trachomatis*, commonly causing urethritis and pelvic inflammatory disease.

Cholecystokinin A hormone secreted by the small intestine that stimulates the pancreas to release its digestive enzymes and the gallbladder to contract and release bile.

Chordae tendineae Strings of connective tissue that anchor the atrioventricular valves to the wall of the heart, preventing the backflow of blood.

Chorion The extraembryonic membrane that becomes the embryo's major contribution to the placenta.

Chorionic villi Fingerlike projections of the chorion of the embryo that grow into the uterine lining of the mother during formation of the placenta and become part of the placenta.

Chorionic villi sampling (CVS) A procedure for screening for genetic defects of a fetus by removing a piece of chorionic villi and examining the cells for genetic abnormalities.

Choroid The pigmented middle layer of the eyeball that contains blood vessels.

Chromatid One of the two identical replicates of a duplicated chromosome. The two chromatids that make up a chromosome are held together by a centromere and are referred to as sister chromatids. During cell division, the two strands separate and each becomes a chromosome in one of the two daughter cells.

Chromatin DNA and associated proteins in a dispersed, rather than condensed, state.

Chromosomal mutation A change in DNA in which a section of a chromosome becomes rearranged, duplicated, or deleted.

Chromosome DNA (which contains the genetic information of a cell) and specialized proteins, primarily histones.

Chronic renal failure A progressive and often irreversible decline in the rate of glomerular filtration.

Chylomicron A particle formed when proteins coat the surface of the products of lipid digestion, making lipids soluble in water and allowing them to be transported throughout the body.

Chyme The semifluid mass created during digestion once the food has been churned and mixed with the gastric juices of the stomach.

Cilia Extensions of the plasma membrane found on some cells, such as those lining the respiratory tract, that move in a back-and-forth motion. They are usually shorter and much more numerous than flagella but have the same 9 + 2 arrangement of microtubules at their core.

Ciliary body A portion of the middle coat of the eyeball near the lens that consists of smooth muscle and ligaments. Contractions of the smooth muscle of the ciliary body change the shape of the lens, which then focuses images on the retina.

Circulatory system An organ system composed of the cardiovascular system (heart and blood vessels) and the lymphatic system (lymphatic vessels and lymphoid tissues and organs).

Circumcision The surgical removal of the foreskin of the penis, usually performed when the male is an infant.

Cirrhosis A chronic disease of the liver in which the liver becomes fatty and the liver cells are gradually replaced with scar tissue.

Citric acid cycle The cyclic series of chemical reactions that follows the transition reaction and yields two molecules of adenosine triphosphate (one from each acetyl CoA that enters the cycle) and several molecules of nicotine adenine dinucleotide (NADH) and flavin adenine dinucleotide ($FADH_2$), carriers of high-energy electrons that enter the electron transport chain. This phase of cellular respiration occurs inside the mitochondrion and is sometimes called the *Krebs cycle.*

Cleavage A rapid series of mitotic cell divisions in which the zygote first divides into two cells, and then four cells, and then eight cells, and so on. Cleavage usually begins about 1 day after fertilization as the zygote moves along the oviduct toward the uterus.

Climax community The relatively stable community that eventually forms at the end of ecological succession and remains if no disturbances occur.

Clitoris A small, erectile body in the female that plays a role in sexual stimulation. It develops from the same embryological structure from which the glans penis develops in the male.

Clonal selection The hypothesis that, by binding to a receptor on a lymphocyte surface, an antigen selectively activates only those lymphocytes able to recognize that antigen and programs that lymphocyte to divide, forming an army of cells specialized to attack the stimulating antigen.

Clone A population of identical cells descended from a single ancestor.

CNS See *central nervous system.*

Cocaine A psychoactive drug extracted from the leaves of the coca plant that stimulates the central nervous system.

Cochlea The snail-shaped portion of the inner ear that contains the actual organ of hearing, the spiral organ (of Corti).

Codominance The condition in which the effects of both alleles are separately expressed in a heterozygote.

Codon A three-base sequence on messenger RNA (mRNA) that specifies 1 of the 20 common amino acids or the beginning or end of the protein chain.

Coenzyme An organic molecule such as a vitamin that functions as a cofactor and helps enzymes convert substrate to product.

Cofactor A nonprotein substance such as zinc, iron, and vitamins that helps enzymes convert substrate to product. It may permanently reside at the active site of the enzyme or may bind to the active site at the same time as the substrate.

Collagen fibers Strong insoluble protein fibers common in many connective tissues.

Collecting ducts Within the kidneys, the tubes that receive filtrate from the distal convoluted tubules of many nephrons and that eventually drain into the renal pelvis. Some tubular secretion occurs along collecting ducts.

Colon The division of the large intestine composed of the ascending colon, the transverse colon, and the descending colon.

Colostrum A cloudy yellowish fluid produced by the breasts in the interval after birth when milk is not yet available. Its composition is different from that of milk.

Columnar epithelium A type of epithelial tissue composed of tall, rectangular cells that are specialized for secretion and absorption.

Coma An unconscious state caused by trauma to neurons in regions of the brain responsible for stimulating the cerebrum, particularly those in the reticular activating system or thalamus. Coma can result from mechanical shock, such as might be caused by a blow to the head; tumors; infections; drug overdose (from barbiturates, alcohol, opiates, or aspirin); or failure of the liver or kidneys.

Combination birth control pill A means of hormonal contraception that consists of a series of pills with synthetic forms of estrogen and progesterone. The hormones in the pills mimic the effects of natural hormones ordinarily produced by the ovaries and inhibit FSH and LH secretion by the anterior pituitary gland and, therefore, prevent the development of an egg and ovulation.

Common cold An upper respiratory infection caused by one of the adenoviruses.

Community An assortment of organisms of various species interacting in a defined habitat.

Compact bone Very dense, hard bone, containing internal spaces of microscopic size and narrow channels that contain blood vessels and nerves. It makes up the shafts of long bones and the outer surfaces of all bones.

Complement system A group of about 20 proteins that enhances the body's defense mechanisms. The complement system destroys cellular pathogens by creating holes in the plasma membrane, making the cell leaky, enhancing phagocytosis, and stimulating inflammation.

Complementary base pairing The process by which specific bases are matched: adenine with thymine (in DNA) or with uracil (in RNA) and cytosine with guanine. Each base pair is held together by weak hydrogen bonds.

Complementary proteins A selection of foods, each containing incomplete proteins, that provide ample amounts of all essential amino acids when combined.

Complete dominance In genetic inheritance, the dominant allele in a heterozygote completely masks the effect of the recessive allele. Complete dominance often occurs because the dominant allele produces a functional protein and the recessive allele produces a less functional protein or none at all.

Complete protein A protein that contains ample amounts of all the essential amino acids. Animal sources of protein are generally complete proteins.

Compound A molecule that contains two or more different elements.

Computed tomography (CT scanning) A method of visualizing body structures, including the brain, using an x-ray source that moves in an arc around the body part to be imaged, thereby providing different views of the structure.

Concentration gradient A difference in the number of molecules or ions between two adjacent regions. Molecules or ions tend to move away from an area where they are more concentrated to an area where they are less concentrated. Each type of molecule or ion moves in response to its own concentration gradient.

Conclusion An interpretation of the data collected in an experiment.

Condom, female A barrier means of contraception used by a female that consists of a loose sac of polyurethane held in place by flexible rings (one at each end). It is used to prevent sperm from entering the female reproductive tract, and it also reduces the risk of spreading sexually transmitted infections.

Condom, male A barrier means of contraception consisting of a thin sheath of latex or animal intestines that is rolled onto an erect penis, where it prevents sperm from entering the vagina. A latex condom also helps prevent the spread of sexually transmitted diseases.

Cones Photoreceptors in the eye responsible for color vision. There are three types of cone cells: blue, green, and red.

Confounding variable In a controlled experiment, it is a second factor that differs between the control group and the experimental group.

Conjoined twins Individuals that develop from a single fertilized ovum that fails to completely split in two at an early stage of cleavage. Such twins have nearly identical genetic material and thus are always the same gender. They may be surgically separated after birth.

Connective tissue Tissue that binds together and supports other tissues of the body. All connective tissues contain cells in an extracellular matrix, which consists of protein fibers and a noncellular ground substance.

Constipation Infrequent, difficult bowel movements of hard feces. Constipation occurs when feces move through the large intestine too slowly and too much water is reabsorbed.

Consumer In ecosystems, an organism that obtains energy and raw materials by eating the tissues of other organisms.

Contact inhibition The phenomenon whereby cells placed in a dish in the presence of growth factors stop dividing once they have formed a monolayer. This may result from competition among the cells for growth factors and nutrients. Cancer cells do not display density-dependent contact inhibition and continue to divide, piling up on one another until nutrients run out.

Continuous ambulatory peritoneal dialysis (CAPD) A method of hemodialysis whereby the peritoneum, one of the body's own selectively permeable membranes, is used as the dialyzing membrane. It is an alternative to the artificial kidney machine during kidney failure.

Contraceptive sponge A barrier means of contraception consisting of a sponge containing spermicide.

Control group In a controlled scientific experiment, the control group is the one in which the variable is unaltered for comparison to the experimental group.

Controlled experiment An experiment in which the subjects are divided into two groups, usually called the *control group* and the *experimental group*. Ideally, the groups differ in only the factor(s) of interest.

Convergence In vision, the process by which the eyes are directed toward the midline of the body as an object moves closer. Convergence is necessary to keep the image focused on the fovea of the retina.

Convergent evolution The process by which two species become more alike because they have similar ecological roles and selection pressures. For example, birds and insects independently evolved wings.

Core temperature The temperature in body structures below the skin and subcutaneous layers.

Cornea A clear, transparent dome located in the front and center of the eye that both provides the window through which light enters the eye and helps bend light rays so that they focus on the retina.

Coronary arteries The arteries that deliver blood to cardiac muscle.

Coronary artery bypass A technique for bypassing a blocked coronary blood vessel to restore blood flow to the heart muscle. Typically, a segment of a leg vein is removed and grafted so that it provides a shunt between the aorta and a coronary artery past the point of obstruction.

Coronary artery disease (CAD) A condition in which fatty deposits associated with atherosclerosis form on the inside of coronary arteries, obstructing the flow of blood. It is the underlying cause of most heart attacks.

Coronary circulation The system of blood vessels that services the tissues of the heart itself.

Coronary sinus A vessel that returns deoxygenated blood collected from the heart muscle to the right atrium of the heart. The coronary sinus is formed from the merging of cardiac veins.

Corpus callosum A band of myelinated axons (white matter) that connects the two cerebral hemispheres so they can communicate with one another.

Corpus luteum A structure in the ovary that forms from the follicle cells remaining in the ovary after ovulation. The corpus luteum functions as an endocrine structure that secretes estrogen and progesterone.

Covalent bond A chemical bond formed when outer shell electrons are shared between atoms.

Cowper's glands See *bulbourethral glands*.

Cranial nerves Twelve pairs of nerves that arise from the brain and service the structures of the head and certain body parts such as the heart and diaphragm. Cranial nerves can be sensory, motor, or mixed.

Cranium The portion of the skull that forms the cranial (brain) case. It is formed from eight (sometimes more) flattened bones, including the frontal bone, two parietal bones, the occipital bone, two temporal bones, the sphenoid bone, and the ethmoid bone.

Creatine phosphate A compound stored in muscle tissue that serves as an alternative energy source for muscle contraction.

Cretinism A condition characterized by dwarfism, mental retardation, and slowed sexual development. It is caused by undersecretion of thyroid hormone during fetal development or infancy.

Cristae Infoldings of the inner membrane of a mitochondrion.

Cross-bridges Myosin heads. Club-shaped ends of a myosin molecule that bind to actin filaments and can swivel, causing the actin filaments to slide past the myosin filaments, which results in muscle contraction.

Cross-tolerance The development of tolerance for a drug that is not used, caused by the development of tolerance to another, usually similar, drug.

Crossing over The breaking and rejoining of nonsister chromatids of homologous pairs of chromosomes during meiosis (specifically at prophase I when homologous chromosomes pair up side by side). Crossing over results in the exchange of corresponding segments of chromatids and increases genetic variability in populations.

Crown The part of a tooth that is visible above the gum line. It is covered with enamel, a nonliving material that is hardened with calcium salts.

CT scanning See *computed tomography*.

Cuboidal epithelium A type of epithelial tissue composed of cube-shaped cells that are specialized for secretion and absorption.

Culture Social influences that produce an integrated pattern of knowledge, belief, and behavior.

Cupula A pliable gelatinous mass covering the hair cells within the ampulla of the semicircular canals of the inner ear and whose movement bends hair cells, triggering the generation of nerve impulses that are interpreted by the brain as movement of the head.

Cushing's syndrome A condition characterized by accumulation of fluid in the face and redistribution of body fat caused by prolonged exposure to cortisol.

Cutaneous membrane The skin. It is thick, relatively waterproof, and dry.

Cystitis Inflammation of the urinary bladder caused by bacteria.

Cytokinesis The division of the cytoplasm and organelles into two daughter cells during cell division. Cytokinesis usually occurs during telophase.

Cytoplasm The part of a cell that includes the aqueous fluid within the cell and all the organelles with the exception of the nucleus.

Cytoskeleton A complex network of protein filaments within the cytoplasm that gives the cell its shape, anchors organelles in place, and functions in the movement of entire cells or certain organelles or vesicles within cells. The cytoskeleton includes microtubules, microfilaments, and intermediate filaments.

Cytotoxic T cell A type of T lymphocyte that directly attacks infected body cells and tumor cells by releasing chemicals called perforins that cause the target cells to burst.

D

Darwinian fitness See *fitness*.

Decomposer An organism that obtains energy by consuming the remains or wastes of other organisms. Decomposers release inorganic materials that can then be used by producers. Bacteria and fungi are important decomposers.

Deductive reasoning A logical progression of thought proceeding from the general to the specific. It involves making specific deductions based on a larger generalization or premise. The statement is usually in the form of an "if-then" premise.

Deforestation Removing trees from an area without replacing them.

Dehydration synthesis The process by which polymers are formed. Monomers are linked together through the removal of a water molecule.

Deletion Pertaining to chromosomes, the loss of a nucleotide or segment of a chromosome.

Denaturation The process by which changes in the environment of a protein, such as increased heat or changes in pH, cause it to unravel and lose its three-dimensional shape. Change in the shape of a protein results in loss of function.

Dendrite A process of a neuron specialized to pick up messages and transmit them toward the cell body. There are typically many short branching dendrites on a neuron.

Dense connective tissue Connective tissue that contains many tightly woven fibers and is found in ligaments, tendons, and the dermis.

Density-dependent regulating factor One of many factors that have a greater impact on the population size as conditions become more crowded. Such factors include disease and starvation.

Density-independent regulating factor One of many factors that regulate population size by causing deaths that are not related to the density of individuals in a population. Such factors include natural disasters.

Dentin A hard, bonelike substance that forms the main substance of teeth. It is covered by enamel on the crown and by cementum on the root.

Deoxyribonucleic acid (DNA) The molecular basis of genetic inheritance in all cells and some viruses. A category of nucleic acids that usually consists of a double helix of two nucleotide strands. The sequence of nucleotides carries the instructions for assembling proteins.

Depolarization A change in the difference in electrical charge across a membrane that moves it from a negative value toward 0 mV. During a nerve impulse (action potential), depolarization is caused by the inward flow of positively charged sodium ions.

Dermis The layer of the skin that lies just below the epidermis and is composed of connective tissue. The dermis contains blood vessels, oil glands, sensory structures, and nerve endings. The dermis does not wear away.

Desertification The process by which overfarming and overgrazing transform marginal farmlands and rangelands to deserts.

Desmosome A type of junction between cells that anchors adjacent cells together.

Detrital food web Energy flow begins with detritus (organic material from the remains of dead organisms) that is eaten by a primary consumer.

Detritivore An organism that obtains energy by consuming the remains or wastes of other organisms. Detritivores release inorganic materials that can then be used by producers.

Detrusor muscle A layer of smooth muscle within the walls of the urinary bladder. It plays a role in urination.

Diabetes insipidus A condition characterized by excessive urine production caused by inadequate antidiuretic hormone (ADH) production.

Diabetes mellitus A group of diseases characterized by excessive urine production, an abnormally high blood glucose level, and the presence of glucose in the urine. Caused by deficient production of insulin (type 1) or increased resistance to insulin (type 2 and gestational diabetes).

Diaphragm A broad sheet of muscle that separates the abdominal and thoracic cavities. When the diaphragm contracts, inhalation occurs.

Diaphragm, contraceptive A barrier means of contraception that consists of a dome-shaped soft rubber cup on a flexible ring. A diaphragm is used in conjunction with a spermicide to prevent sperm from reaching the egg.

Diarrhea Abnormally frequent, loose bowel movements. Diarrhea occurs when feces pass through the large intestine too quickly and too little water is reabsorbed. Diarrhea sometimes leads to dehydration.

Diastole Relaxation of the heart. Atrial diastole is the relaxation of the atria. Ventricular diastole is the relaxation of the ventricles.

Diastolic pressure The lowest blood pressure in an artery during the relaxation of the heart. In a typical, healthy adult, the diastolic pressure is about 80 mm Hg.

Dietary fiber The nondigestible carbohydrate part of plant foods that forms support structures of stems, seeds, and leaves. Dietary fiber is important for heart and colon health.

Digestive system The organ system that breaks down and absorbs food. The digestive system includes the mouth, esophagus, stomach, small intestine, and large intestine. Associated structures include the teeth, tongue, salivary glands, liver, gallbladder, and pancreas.

Dilation stage The first stage of true labor. It begins with the onset of contractions and ends when the cervix has fully dilated to 10 cm (4 in.).

Diploid The condition of having two sets of chromosomes in each cell. Somatic (body) cells are diploid.

Disaccharide A molecule formed when two monosaccharides covalently bond to each other through dehydration synthesis. It is known as a double sugar.

Distal convoluted tubule The section of the renal tubule where reabsorption and secretion occur.

Diuretic A substance that promotes urine production. Alcohol is a diuretic.

DNA (deoxyribonucleic acid) The molecular basis of genetic inheritance in all cells and some viruses. A category of nucleic acids that usually consists of a double helix of two nucleotide strands. The sequence of nucleotides carries the instructions for assembling proteins.

DNA fingerprint The pattern of DNA fragments that have been cut by a restriction enzyme and sorted by size. Each person has a characteristic, individual DNA fingerprint.

DNA library A large collection of cloned recombinant DNA fragments containing the entire genome of an organism.

DNA ligase An enzyme that catalyzes the formation of bonds between the sugar and the phosphate molecules that form the sides of the DNA ladder during replication, repair, or the creation of recombinant DNA.

DNA polymerase Any one of the enzymes that catalyze the synthesis of DNA from free nucleotides using one strand of DNA as a template.

Dominant allele The allele that is fully expressed in the phenotype of an individual who is heterozygous for that gene. The dominant allele usually produces a functional protein, whereas the recessive allele does not.

Dopamine A neurotransmitter in the central nervous system thought to be involved in regulating emotions and in the brain pathways that control complex movements.

Dorsal nerve root The portion of a spinal nerve that arises from the back (posterior) side of the spinal cord and contains axons of sensory neurons. It joins with the ventral nerve root to form a single spinal nerve, which passes through the opening between the vertebrae.

Doubling time The number of years required for a population to double in size at a given, constant growth rate.

Down syndrome A collection of characteristics that tend to occur when an individual has three copies of chromosome 21. It is also known as trisomy 21.

Drug cocktail A combination of drugs used to treat people who are HIV positive. The combination usually includes a drug that blocks reverse transcription and a protease inhibitor.

Ductus arteriosus A small vessel in the fetus that connects the pulmonary artery to the aorta. It diverts blood away from the lungs.

Ductus venosus A small vessel in the fetus through which most blood from the placenta flows, bypassing the liver.

Duodenum The first region of the small intestine. The duodenum receives chyme from the stomach and digestive juices from the pancreas and liver.

Duplication Pertaining to chromosomes, the duplication of a region of a chromosome that often results from fusion of a fragment from a homologous chromosome.

Dura mater The tough, leathery outer layer of the meninges that protects the central nervous system. Around the brain, the dura mater has two layers that are separated by a fluid-filled space containing blood vessels.

Dysplasia The changes in shape, nuclei, and organization of adult cells. It is typical of precancerous cells.

E

Eardrum **See** *tympanic membrane.*

ECG **See** *electrocardiogram.*

Ecological footprint A measure of the amount of productive land and water used by a person or population to produce products consumed and to remove the waste of products consumed.

Ecological pyramid A diagram in which blocks represent each tropic (feeding) level.

Ecological succession The sequence of changes in the species making up a community over time.

Ecology The study of the interactions among organisms and between organisms and their environment.

Ecosystem All the organisms living in a certain area that can potentially interact, together with their physical environment.

Ectoderm The primary germ layer that forms the nervous system, epidermis, and epidermal derivatives such as hair, nails, and mammary glands.

Ectopic pregnancy A pregnancy in which the embryo (blastocyst) implants and begins development in a location other than the uterus, most commonly in an oviduct (a tubal pregnancy).

Edema Swelling caused by the accumulation of interstitial fluid.

EEG **See** *electroencephalogram.*

Effector A muscle or a gland that brings about a response to a stimulus.

Effector cells Lymphocytes that are responsible for the attack on cells or substances not recognized as belonging in the body.

Efferent (motor) neuron A neuron specialized to carry information *away from* the central nervous system to an effector, either a muscle or a gland.

Egg A mature female gamete. An ovum. The egg contains nutrients and the mother's genetic contribution to the next generation.

EKG **See** *electrocardiogram.*

Elastic cartilage The most flexible type of cartilage because of an abundance of wavy elastic fibers in its matrix.

Elastic fibers Coiled proteins found in connective tissues that allow the connective tissue to be stretched and recoil. Elastic fibers are common in tissues that require elasticity.

Electrocardiogram (ECG or EKG) A graphical record of the electrical activities of the heart.

Electroencephalogram (EEG) A graphical record of the electrical activity of the brain.

Electron transport chain A series of carrier proteins embedded in the inner membrane of the mitochondrion that receives electrons from the molecules of nicotine adenine dinucleotide (NADH) and flavin adenine dinucleotide ($FADH_2$) produced by glycolysis and the citric acid cycle. During the transfer of electrons from one molecule to the next, energy is released, and this energy is then used to make adenosine triphosphate (ATP). Oxygen is the final electron acceptor in the chain.

Element Any substance that cannot be broken down into simpler substances by ordinary chemical means.

Embolus A blood clot that drifts through the circulatory system and can lodge in a small blood vessel and block blood flow.

Embryo The developing human from week 3 through week 8 of gestation (the embryonic period).

Embryonic disk The flattened platelike structure that will become the embryo proper. It develops from the inner cell mass.

Embryonic period The period of prenatal development that extends from week 3 through week 8 of gestation. It is the period when tissues and organs form.

Emigration The departure of individuals from a population for some other area.

Emphysema A condition in which the alveolar walls break down, thicken, and form larger air spaces, making gas exchange difficult. This change results in less surface area for gas exchange and an increase in the volume of residual air in the lungs.

Enamel A nonliving material that is hardened with calcium salts and covers the crown of a tooth.

Encephalitis An inflammation of the meninges around the brain.

Endocardium A thin layer that lines the cavities of the heart.

Endocrine gland A gland that lacks ducts and releases its products (hormones) into the fluid just outside the cells.

Endocrine system The organ system that, along with the nervous system, functions in internal communication. It consists of endocrine glands, such as the pituitary gland and thyroid gland, and of organs, such as the kidneys and pancreas, that contain some endocrine tissue but have functions in addition to hormone secretion.

Endocytosis The process by which large molecules and single-celled organisms such as bacteria enter cells. It occurs when a region of the plasma membrane surrounds the substance to be ingested, then pinches off from the rest of the membrane, enclosing the substance in a saclike structure called a vesicle that is released into the cell. Two types of endocytosis are phagocytosis ("cell eating") and pinocytosis ("cell drinking").

Endoderm The primary germ layer that forms some organs and glands (for example, the pancreas, liver, thyroid gland, and parathyroid glands) and the epithelial lining of the urinary, respiratory, and gastrointestinal tracts.

Endometriosis A painful condition in which tissue from the lining of the uterus (the endometrium) is found outside the uterine cavity.

Endometrium The inner layer of the uterus consisting of connective tissue, glands, and blood vessels. The endometrium thickens and develops with each menstrual (uterine) cycle and is then lost as menstrual flow. It is the site of embryo implantation during pregnancy.

Endoplasmic reticulum The network of internal membranes within eukaryotic cells. Whereas rough endoplasmic reticulum (RER) has ribosomes attached to its surface, smooth endoplasmic reticulum (SER) lacks ribosomes and functions in the production of phospholipids for incorporation into cell membranes.

Endorphin A chemical released by nerve cells that binds to the so-called opiate receptors on the pain-transmitting neurons and quells the pain. The term is short for *endo*genous m*orphine*-like substance.

Endosymbiont hypothesis The hypothesis that organelles such as mitochondria were once free-living prokaryotic organisms that either invaded or were engulfed by primitive eukaryotic cells with which they established a symbiotic (mutually beneficial) relationship.

Endothelium The lining of the heart, blood vessels, and lymphatic vessels. It is composed of flattened, tight-fitting cells. The endothelium forms a smooth surface that minimizes friction and allows the blood or lymph to flow over it easily.

Enkephalin A chemical released by nerve cells that binds to the so-called opiate receptors on the pain-transmitting neurons and quells the pain.

Enzyme A substance (usually a protein, but sometimes an RNA molecule) that speeds up chemical reactions without being consumed in the process.

Enzyme-substrate complex Complex formed when a substrate binds to an enzyme at the active site.

Eosinophil The type of white blood cell important in the body's defense against parasitic worms. It releases chemicals that help counteract certain inflammatory chemicals released during an allergic response.

Epidermis The outermost layer of the skin, composed of epithelial cells.

Epidemiology The study of patterns of disease, including rate of occurrence, distribution, and control.

Epididymis A long tube coiled on the surface of each testis that serves as the site of sperm cell maturation and storage.

Epigenetics The study of changes in gene activity that are not caused by changes in DNA coding sequence. Instead, the chemicals in the environment bind to regions of DNA or histone to turn a gene on or off. Epigenetic changes can be passed through generations.

Epiglottis A part of the larynx that forms a movable lid of cartilage covering the opening into the trachea (the glottis).

Epinephrine Adrenaline. A hormone secreted by the adrenal medulla, along with norepinephrine, in response to stress. They initiate the physiological "fight-or-flight" reaction.

Epiphyseal plate A plate of cartilage that separates the head of the bone from the shaft, permitting the bone to grow. In late adolescence, the epiphyseal plate is replaced by bone, and growth stops. The epiphyseal plate is commonly called the *growth plate*.

Episiotomy An incision made to enlarge the vaginal opening, just before passage of the baby's head at the end of the second stage of labor.

Epithelial tissue One of the four primary tissue types. The tissue that covers body surfaces, lines body cavities and organs, and forms glands.

Equatorial plate A plane at the midline of a cell where chromosomes line up during mitosis or meiosis.

Erythrocyte A red blood cell. A nucleus-free biconcave cell in the blood that is specialized for transporting oxygen to cells and assists in transporting carbon dioxide away from cells.

Erythropoietin A hormone released by the kidneys when the oxygen content of the blood declines; it stimulates red blood cell production.

Esophagus A muscular tube that conducts food from the pharynx to the stomach using peristalsis.

Essential amino acid Any of the eight amino acids that the body cannot synthesize and, therefore, must be supplied in the diet.

Estrogen A steroid sex hormone produced by the follicle cells and the corpus luteum in the ovary. Estrogen helps oocytes mature, stimulates cell division in the endometrium and the breast with each uterine cycle, and maintains secondary sex characteristics. The adrenal cortex also secretes estrogen.

Ethanol The alcohol in an alcoholic drink.

Eukaryotic cell A cell with a nucleus and extensive internal membranes that divide it into many compartments and enclose organelles. Eukaryotes include cells in plants, animals, and all other organisms except bacteria and archaea.

Eustachian tubes Auditory tubes. Small tubes that join the upper region of the pharynx (throat) with the middle ear. They help to equalize the air pressure between the middle ear and the atmosphere.

Eutrophication The enrichment of water in a lake or pond by nutrients. Eutrophication is often caused by nitrogen or phosphate that washes into bodies of water.

Evolution Descent with modification from a common ancestor. It is the process by which life-forms on Earth have changed over time.

Excitatory synapse A synapse in which the response of the receptors for that neurotransmitter on the postsynaptic membrane increases the likelihood that an action potential will be generated in the postsynaptic neuron. The postsynaptic cell is excited because it becomes less negative than usual (slightly depolarized), usually as a result of the inflow of sodium ions.

Excretion The elimination of wastes and excess substances from the body.

Exhalation Breathing out (expiration) involves the movement of air out of the respiratory system into the atmosphere.

Exocrine glands Glands that secrete their product through ducts onto body surfaces, into the spaces within organs, or into a body cavity. Examples include the salivary glands of the mouth and the oil and sweat glands of the skin.

Exocytosis The process by which large molecules leave cells. It occurs when products packaged by cells in membrane-bound vesicles move toward the plasma membrane. Upon reaching the plasma membrane, the membrane of the vesicle fuses with it, spilling its contents outside the cell.

Exon The nucleotide sequences of a newly synthesized messenger RNA (mRNA) that are spliced together to form the mature mRNA that is ultimately translated into protein.

Exophthalmos A condition characterized by protruding eyes that is caused by the accumulation of interstitial fluid due to oversecretion of thyroid hormone.

Experimental group In a controlled scientific experiment, the experimental group is the one in which the variable is altered.

Expiration The process by which air is moved out of the respiratory system into the atmosphere. It is also called *exhalation*.

Expiratory reserve volume The additional volume of air that can be forcefully expelled from the lungs after normal exhalation.

Expulsion stage The second stage of true labor. It begins with full dilation of the cervix and ends with delivery of the baby.

External auditory canal The canal leading from the pinna of the ear to the eardrum (tympanic membrane).

External respiration The exchange of oxygen and carbon dioxide between the lungs and the blood.

External urethral sphincter A sphincter made of skeletal muscle that surrounds the urethra. This voluntary sphincter helps stop the flow of urine down the urethra when we wish to postpone urination.

Exteroceptor A sensory receptor that is located near the surface of the body and that responds to changes in the environment.

Extracellular fluid The watery solution outside cells. It is also called interstitial fluid.

Extraembryonic membranes Membranes that lie outside the embryo, where they protect and nourish the embryo and later the fetus. They include the amnion, yolk sac, chorion, and allantois.

F

Facial bones The bones that form the face. They include 14 bones that support several sensory structures and serve as attachments for most muscles of the face.

Facilitated diffusion The movement of a substance from a region of higher concentration to a region of lower concentration with the aid of a membrane protein that either transports the substance from one side of the membrane to the other or forms a channel through which it can move.

Farsightedness A condition in which distant objects are seen more clearly than near ones. Farsightedness occurs because either the eyeball is too short or the lens is too thin, causing the image to be focused behind the retina.

Fascicle A bundle of skeletal muscle fibers (cells) that forms a part of a muscle. Each fascicle is wrapped in its own connective tissue sheath.

Fast-twitch muscle cells Muscle fibers that contract rapidly and powerfully, with little endurance. They have few mitochondria and large glycogen reserves. They depend on anaerobic pathways to generate adenosine triphosphate (ATP) during muscle contraction.

Fat A triglyceride, which consists of glycerol and three fatty acids. Saturated fats come from animal sources and are solid at room temperature. Unsaturated fats come from plant sources and are liquid at room temperature.

Fatigue A state in which a muscle is physiologically unable to contract despite continued stimulation. Muscle fatigue results from a relative deficit of adenosine triphosphate (ATP).

Fat-soluble vitamin A vitamin that does not dissolve in water and is stored in fat. Examples are vitamins A, D, E, and K.

Fatty acid Chains of carbon atoms bonded to hydrogen atoms with an acidic group (COOH) at one end. Three fatty acids bond to a molecule of glycerol to form a triglyceride (fat).

Feces Waste material discharged from the large intestine during defecation. Feces consist primarily of undigested food, sloughed-off epithelial cells, water, and millions of bacteria.

Fermentation A pathway by which cells can harvest energy in the absence of oxygen. It nets only 2 molecules of ATP as compared with the approximately 36 molecules produced by cellular respiration.

Fertilization The union between an egg (technically a secondary oocyte) and a sperm. It takes about 24 hours from start to finish and usually occurs in a widened portion of the oviduct, not far from the ovary.

Fetal alcohol syndrome A group of characteristics in children born to mothers who consumed alcohol during pregnancy. It can include mental retardation, slow growth, and certain facial features such as an eye fold near the bridge of the nose.

Fetal period The period of prenatal development that extends from week 9 of gestation until birth. It is when rapid growth occurs.

Fetus The developing human from week 9 of gestation until birth (the fetal period).

Fever An abnormally elevated body temperature. Fever helps the body fight disease-causing invaders in a number of ways.

Fibrillation Rapid, ineffective contractions of the heart.

Fibrin A protein formed from fibrinogen by thrombin. It creates a web that traps blood cells, forming a blood clot.

Fibrinogen A plasma protein produced by the liver that is important in blood clotting. It is converted to fibrin by thrombin.

Fibroblasts Cells in connective tissue that secrete the protein fibers found in the matrix of the connective tissue. Fibroblasts also secrete collagen fibers for the repair of body tissues.

Fibrocartilage Cartilage with a matrix containing many collagen fibers. Fibrocartilage is found around the edges of joints and the intervertebral disks.

Fibrous joints Joints that are held together by connective tissue and lack a joint cavity. Most fibrous joints do not permit movement.

Fight-or-flight response The body's reaction to stress or threatening situations by the stimulation of the sympathetic division of the autonomic nervous system. Epinephrine and norepinephrine, hormones produced by the adrenal medulla, augment and prolong the response.

First messenger A water-soluble hormone that binds to a receptor on the plasma membrane of a target cell. This binding activates a molecule within the cell, called the second messenger, which influences enzyme activity there.

Fitness The average number of reproductively viable offspring left by an individual. It is sometimes called *Darwinian fitness*.

Flagellum A whiplike appendage of a cell that moves in an undulating manner. It is composed of an extension of the plasma membrane containing microtubules in a 9 + 2 array. In humans, it is found on sperm cells.

Floating ribs The last two ribs that do not attach directly to the sternum (breastbone).

Fluid mosaic A term used to describe the structure of the plasma membrane. Proteins interspersed throughout the lipid molecules give the membrane its mosaic quality. The ability of some proteins to move sideways gives the membrane its fluid quality.

Follicle A spherical structure in the ovary that contains an oocyte surrounded by one or more layers of follicle cells.

Follicle-stimulating hormone (FSH) A hormone secreted by the anterior pituitary gland that in females stimulates the development of the follicles in the ovaries, resulting in the development of ova (eggs) and the production of estrogen, and in males stimulates sperm production.

Fontanels The "soft spots" in the skull of a newborn. The membranous areas in the skull of a newborn that hold the skull bones together before and shortly after birth. The fontanels are gradually replaced by bone.

Food chain The successive series of organisms through which energy (in the form of food) flows in an ecosystem. Each organism in the series eats or decomposes the preceding one. It begins with the photosynthesizers and flows to herbivores and then to carnivores.

Food defense Precautions designed to prevent the *intentional* contamination of food.

Food safety Precautions designed to prevent the *unintentional* contamination of food.

Food web The interconnection of all the feeding relationships (food chains) in an ecosystem.

Foodborne illness An illness that results from ingesting contaminated food or water. Those caused by pathogens (bacteria, viruses, parasites) are considered infections, while those caused by chemicals or toxins are considered poisonings. Symptoms first appear in the gastrointestinal tract and include diarrhea and vomiting. Treatment usually involves giving fluids to prevent dehydration; antibiotics may be prescribed if the illness is caused by bacteria. Many foodborne illnesses go unreported.

Foramen magnum The opening at the base of the skull (in the occipital bone) through which the spinal cord passes.

Foramen ovale In the fetus, a small hole in the wall between the right atrium and left atrium of the heart that allows most blood to bypass the lungs.

Formed elements Cells or cell fragments found in the blood. They include platelets, white blood cells, and red blood cells.

Fossilization The process by which fossils form. Typically an organism dies in water and is buried under accumulating layers of sediments. Hard parts become impregnated with minerals from surrounding water and sediments. Eventually the fossil may be exposed when sediments are uplifted and wind erodes the rock formation.

Fossils The preserved remnants or impressions of past organisms. Most fossils occur in sedimentary rocks.

Founder effect Genetic drift associated with the colonization of a new place by a few individuals so that by chance alone the genetic makeup of the colonizing individuals is not representative of the population they left.

Fovea A small region on the retina that contains a high density of cones but no rods. Objects are focused on the fovea for sharp vision.

Frameshift mutation A mutation that occurs when the number of nucleotides inserted or deleted is not a multiple of three, causing a change in the codon sequence on the mRNA molecule as well as a change in the resulting protein.

Fraternal twins Individuals that develop when two oocytes are released from the ovaries and fertilized by different sperm. Such twins may or may not be the same gender and are as similar genetically as any siblings. They are also called dizygotic twins.

Free radicals Molecular fragments that contain an unpaired electron.

FSH See *follicle-stimulating hormone.*

Full-term infant Baby born at least 38 weeks after fertilization.

G

Gallbladder A muscular pear-shaped sac that stores, modifies, and then concentrates bile. Bile is released from the gallbladder into the small intestine.

Gamete A reproductive cell (sperm or egg) that contains only one copy of each chromosome. A sperm and egg fuse at fertilization, producing a zygote.

Gamete intrafallopian transfer (GIFT) A procedure in which eggs and sperm are collected from a couple and then inserted into the woman's oviduct, where fertilization may occur. If fertilization occurs, resulting embryos drift naturally into the uterus.

Ganglion (plural, ganglia) A collection of nerve cell bodies outside the central nervous system.

Gap junction A type of junction between cells that links the cytoplasm of adjacent cells through small holes, allowing physical and electrical continuity between cells.

Gastric gland Any one of several glands in the stomach mucosa that contribute to the gastric juice (hydrochloric acid and pepsin).

Gastric juice The mixture of hydrochloric acid (HCl) and pepsin released into the stomach.

Gastrin A hormone released from the stomach lining in response to the presence of partially digested proteins. Gastrin triggers the production of gastric juice by the stomach.

Gastrointestinal (GI) tract A long tubular system specialized for the processing and absorption of food that begins at the mouth and continues to the esophagus, stomach, intestines, and anus. Several accessory glands empty their secretions into the GI tract to assist digestion.

Gastrula The embryo during gastrulation, when cells move to establish primary germ layers.

Gastrulation Cell movements that establish the primary germ layers of the embryo. The embryo during this period is called a gastrula.

Gated ion channel An ion channel that is opened to allow ions to pass through or closed to prevent passage by changes in the shape of a protein that functions as a gate.

Gene A segment of DNA on a chromosome that directs the synthesis of a specific polypeptide that will play a structural or functional role in the cell. Some genes have regulatory regions of DNA within their boundaries. Also, some genes code for RNA molecules that are needed for the production of the polypeptide but are not part of it.

Gene flow Movement of alleles between populations as a result of the movement of individuals. It is a cause of microevolution.

Gene pool All of the alleles of all of the genes of all individuals in a population.

Gene therapy Treating a genetic disease by inserting healthy functional genes into the body cells that are affected by the faulty gene.

General senses The sensations that arise from receptors in the skin, muscles, joints, bones, and internal organs and include touch, pressure, vibration, temperature, a sense of body and limb position, and pain.

Genetic code The base triplets in DNA that specify the amino acids that go into proteins or that function as start or stop signals in protein synthesis. It is used to convert the linear sequence of bases in DNA to the sequence of amino acids in proteins.

Genetic drift The random change in allele frequencies within a population due to chance alone. It is a cause of microevolution that is usually negligible in large populations.

Genetic engineering The manipulation of genetic material for human practical purposes.

Genital herpes A sexually transmitted disease caused by the herpes simplex virus (HSV) that is usually characterized by painful blisters on the genitals. It is usually caused by HSV-2 but can be caused by HSV-1.

Genital warts Warts that form in the genital area caused by the human papilloma viruses (HPV). These viruses also cause cervical cancer, penile cancer, and oral cancer.

Genome The complete set of DNA of an organism, including all its genes.

Genotype The genetic makeup of an individual. It refers to precise alleles that are present.

Gestational diabetes Diabetes mellitus that develops during pregnancy. It is characterized by insulin resistance and normally resolves after delivery of the baby and placenta.

Gigantism A condition characterized by rapid growth and unusual height caused by abnormally high levels of growth hormone in childhood; also called giantism.

GIFT See *gamete intrafallopian transfer*.

Gingivitis An inflammation of the gums.

Gland Epithelial tissue that secretes a product.

Glaucoma A condition in which the pressure within the anterior chamber of the eye increases as a result of the buildup of aqueous humor. It can cause blindness.

Glial cells Nonexcitable cells in the nervous system that are specialized to support, protect, and insulate neurons. Also called *neuroglial cells* or *neuroglia*.

Global warming A long-term increase in atmospheric temperatures caused by a buildup of carbon dioxide (CO_2) and other greenhouse gases in the atmosphere. Greenhouse gases trap heat in the atmosphere.

Glomerular (Bowman's) capsule A cuplike structure surrounding the glomerulus of a nephron.

Glomerular filtration The process by which water and dissolved substances move from the blood in the glomerulus to the inside of Bowman's capsule.

Glomerulus A tuft of capillaries within the renal corpuscle of a nephron.

Glottis The opening to the airways of the respiratory system from the pharynx into the larynx.

Glucagon The hormone secreted by the pancreas that elevates glucose levels in the blood.

Glucocorticoids Hormones secreted by the adrenal cortex that affect glucose homeostasis, thereby influencing metabolism and resistance to stress.

Gluconeogenesis The conversion of noncarbohydrate molecules to glucose.

Glycemic response A measure that describes how quickly a serving of food is converted to blood sugar and how much the level of blood sugar is affected.

Glycogen The storage polysaccharide of animals. This complex carbohydrate is stored in the liver and muscles, where it serves as a short-term energy source that can be broken down to release energy-packed glucose molecules.

Glycolysis The splitting of glucose, a six-carbon sugar, into two three-carbon molecules called pyruvate. Glycolysis takes place in the cytoplasm of a cell and is the starting point for cellular respiration and fermentation.

GnRH See *gonadotropin-releasing hormone*.

Goiter, simple An enlarged thyroid gland caused by iodine deficiency.

Golgi complex An organelle consisting of flattened membranous disks that functions in protein processing and packaging.

Golgi tendon organs The highly branched nerve fibers located in the tendons that sense the degree of muscle tension.

Gonad An ovary in a female or a testis in a male. The gonads produce gametes (eggs or sperm) and sex hormones.

Gonadocorticoids The male and female sex hormones, androgens and estrogens, secreted by the adrenal cortex.

Gonadotropin-releasing hormone (GnRH) A hormone produced by the hypothalamus that causes the secretion of luteinizing hormone and follicle-stimulating hormone from the anterior pituitary gland.

Gonorrhea A sexually transmitted disease caused by the bacterium *Neisseria gonorrhoeae* that commonly causes urethritis and pelvic inflammatory disease. It may not cause symptoms, especially in women.

Graafian follicle A mature follicle in the ovary.

Graded potential A temporary local change in the membrane potential that varies directly with the strength of the stimulus.

Granulocytes White blood cells with granules in their cytoplasm. Examples are neutrophils, eosinophils, and basophils.

Graves' disease An autoimmune disorder caused by oversecretion of thyroid hormone. It is characterized by increased heart and metabolic rates, sweating, nervousness, and exophthalmos.

Gray matter Regions of the central nervous system that contain neuron cell bodies and unmyelinated axons. These regions are gray because they lack myelin. Gray matter is important in neural integration.

Greenhouse effect A process in which greenhouse gases trap heat in the atmosphere. Examples of greenhouse gases include carbon dioxide and methane. The greenhouse effect could lead to a rise in temperatures throughout the world.

Ground substance In connective tissue the ground substance forms the extracellular matrix that the cells are embedded in. It is composed of protein fibers and noncellular material.

Growth factor A type of signaling molecule that stimulates growth by stimulating cell division in target cells.

Growth hormone (GH) An anterior pituitary hormone with the primary function of stimulating growth through increases in protein synthesis, cell size, and rates of cell division. GH stimulates growth in general, especially bone growth.

Growth plate A plate of cartilage that separates each end of a long bone from its shaft, thereby permitting bone to grow. Also called an *epiphyseal plate*.

Gumma A large sore that forms during the third stage of syphilis.

H

Habitat The natural environment or place where an organism, population, or species lives.

Hair cells A type of mechanoreceptor that generates nerve impulses when bent or tilted. Hair cells in the inner ear are responsible for hearing and equilibrium.

Hair root plexus The nerve endings that surround the hair follicle and are sensitive to touch.

Hallucinogen A psychoactive drug that distorts sensory perception.

Haploid The condition of having one set of chromosomes, as in eggs and sperm.

HCG See *human chorionic gonadotropin.*

Health care agent A person selected in advance to make health care decisions for you should you be unable to make them for yourself. The selection is formalized by completing a health care proxy form.

Heart A muscular pump that keeps blood flowing through an animal's body. The human heart has four chambers: two atria and two ventricles.

Heart attack The death of heart muscle cells caused by an insufficient blood supply; a myocardial infarction.

Heart murmur Heart sounds other than "lub dup" that are created by turbulent blood flow. Heart murmurs can indicate a heart problem, such as a malfunctioning valve.

Heartburn A burning sensation behind the breastbone that occurs when acidic gastric juice backs up into the esophagus.

Heimlich maneuver A procedure intended to force a large burst of air out of the lungs to dislodge material lodged in the trachea.

Helper T cell The kind of T lymphocyte that serves as the main switch for the entire immune response by presenting the antigen to B cells and by secreting chemicals that stimulate other cells of the immune system. It is also known as a *T4 cell* or a *CD4 cell*, after the receptors on its surface.

Hematocrit The percentage of red blood cells in blood by volume. It is a measure of the oxygen-carrying ability of the blood.

Hemodialysis The use of artificial devices, such as the artificial kidney machine, to cleanse the blood during kidney failure.

Hemoglobin The oxygen-binding pigment in red blood cells. It consists of four subunits, each made up of an iron-containing heme group and a protein chain.

Hemolytic disease of the newborn A condition in which the red blood cells of an Rh-positive fetus or newborn are destroyed by anti-Rh antibodies previously produced in the bloodstream of an Rh-negative mother.

Hemophilia An inherited blood disorder in which there is insufficient production of blood-clotting factors. Hemophilia results in excessive bleeding in joints, deep tissues, and elsewhere. Hemophilia usually occurs in males.

Hepatitis An inflammation of the liver. Hepatitis is usually caused by one of six viruses.

Herbivore An animal that eats primary producers (green plants or algae). A primary consumer.

Herpes simplex virus See *HSV-1* and *HSV-2.*

Heterotroph An organism that cannot make its own food from inorganic substances and instead consumes other organisms or decaying material.

Heterozygote advantage The phenomenon in which the heterozygous condition is favored over either homozygous condition. It maintains genetic variation within a population in the face of natural selection.

Heterozygous The condition of having two different alleles for a particular gene.

High-density lipoprotein (HDL) A lipoprotein made in the liver and released into the blood that transports cholesterol away from the cells to the liver. HDLs are often called the "good" form of cholesterol.

Hinge joint A joint that permits motion in only one plane, such as the knee joint or the elbow.

Hippocampus The part of the limbic system of the brain that plays a role in converting short-term memory into long-term memory.

Histamine A substance released by basophils and mast cells during an inflammatory response that causes blood vessels to widen (dilate) and become more permeable.

Homeostasis The ability of living things to maintain a relatively constant internal environment in all levels of body organization.

Hominid A member of the family Hominidae, which now includes apes and humans. In the past, only humans and their immediate ancestors, such as species within the genus *Australopithecus*, were placed in Hominidae.

Hominin A member of the subfamily Homininae, which includes the human lineage and its immediate ancestors.

Homologous chromosomes A pair of chromosomes that bear genes for the same traits. One member of each pair came from each parent. Homologous chromosomes are the same size and shape and line up with one another during meiosis I.

Homologous structures Structures that have arisen from a common ancestry. Compare with *analogous structure.*

Homozygous The condition of having two identical alleles for a particular gene.

Hormonal implants A means of hormonal contraception consisting of silicon rods containing progesterone that are implanted under the skin in the upper arm and prevent pregnancy for up to 5 years.

Hormone A chemical messenger released by cells of the endocrine system that travels through the circulatory system to affect receptive target cells.

Host (vector) DNA The DNA that is recombined with pieces of DNA from another source (that might contain a desirable gene) in the formation of recombinant DNA.

HPV See *human papilloma virus.*

HSV-1 Herpes simplex virus 1. HSV-1 usually infects the upper half of the body and causes cold sores (fever blisters), but it can cause genital herpes if contact is made with the genital area.

HSV-2 Herpes simplex virus 2. HSV-2 causes genital herpes, but it can cause cold sores if contact is made with the mouth.

Human chorionic gonadotropin (HCG) A hormone produced by the cells of the early embryo (blastocyst) and the placenta that maintains the corpus luteum for approximately the first 3 months of pregnancy. HCG enters the bloodstream of the mother and is excreted in her urine. HCG forms the basis for many pregnancy tests.

Human papilloma virus (HPV) One of the group of viruses that commonly cause genital warts.

Hyaline cartilage A type of cartilage with a gel-like matrix that provides flexibility and support. It is found at the end of long bones as well as parts of the nose, ribs, larynx, and trachea.

Hydrocephalus A condition resulting from the excessive production or inadequate drainage of cerebrospinal fluid.

Hydrogen bond A weak chemical bond formed between a partially positively charged hydrogen atom in a molecule and a partially negatively charged atom in another molecule or in another region of the same molecule.

Hydrolysis The process by which polymers are broken apart by the addition of water.

Hydrophilic Water-loving. The heads of phospholipids (components of the plasma membrane) are hydrophilic.

Hydrophobic Water-fearing. The tails of phospholipids (components of the plasma membrane) are hydrophobic.

Hyperglycemia An elevated blood glucose level.

Hypertension High blood pressure. A high upper (systolic) value usually suggests that the person's arteries have become hardened and are no longer able to dampen the high pressure of each heartbeat. The lower (diastolic) value is generally considered more important because it indicates the pressure when the heart is relaxing.

Hyperthermia Abnormally elevated body temperature.

Hypertonic solution A solution with a higher concentration of solutes than plasma, for example.

Hypodermis The layer of loose connective tissue below the epidermis and dermis that anchors the skin to underlying tissues and organs.

Hypoglycemia Depressed levels of blood glucose often resulting from excess insulin.

Hypophysis See *pituitary gland*.

Hypothalamus A small brain region located below the thalamus that is essential to maintaining a stable environment within the body. The hypothalamus influences blood pressure, heart rate, digestive activity, breathing rate, and many other vital physiological processes. It acts as the body's "thermostat"; regulates food intake, hunger, and thirst; coordinates the activities of the nervous system and the endocrine system; and is part of the circuitry for emotions.

Hypothermia Abnormally low body temperature.

Hypothesis A testable explanation for a specific set of observations that serves as the basis for experimentation.

Hypotonic solution A solution with a lower concentration of solutes than plasma, for example.

I

ICSI See *intracytoplasmic sperm injection*.

Identical twins Individuals that develop from a single fertilized ovum that splits in two at an early stage of cleavage. Such twins have nearly identical genetic material and are always the same gender. They are also called monozygotic twins.

Immigration Movement of new individuals from other populations into an area.

Immune response The body's response to specific targets not recognized as belonging in the body.

Immune system The system of the body directly involved with body defenses against specific targets—pathogens, cells, or chemicals not recognized as belonging in the body.

Immunoglobulin (Ig) Any of the five classes of proteins that constitute the antibodies.

Implantation The process by which a blastocyst (pre-embryo) becomes embedded in the lining of the uterus. It normally occurs high up on the back wall of the uterus.

Impotence The inability to achieve or maintain an erection long enough for sexual intercourse.

In vitro fertilization (IVF) A procedure in which eggs and sperm are placed together in a dish in the laboratory. If fertilization occurs, early-stage embryos are then transferred to the woman's uterus, where it is hoped they will implant and complete development. It is a common treatment for infertility resulting from blocked oviducts.

Incomplete dominance In genetic inheritance, expression of the trait in a heterozygous individual is somewhere between expression of the trait in a homozygous dominant individual and a homozygous recessive individual.

Incomplete proteins Proteins that are deficient in one or more of the essential amino acids. Plant sources of protein are generally incomplete proteins.

Incontinence A condition characterized by the escape of small amounts of urine when sudden increases in abdominal pressure, perhaps caused by laughing, sneezing, or coughing, force urine past the external sphincter. This condition is common in women, particularly after childbirth, an event that may stretch or damage the external sphincter, making it less effective in controlling the flow of urine.

Incus The middle of three small bones in the middle ear that transmit information about sound from the eardrum to the inner ear. The incus is also known as the anvil.

Independent assortment Of chromosomes, the process by which homologous chromosomes and the alleles they carry segregate randomly during meiosis, creating mixes of maternal and paternal chromosomes in gametes. This is an important source of genetic variation in populations.

Independent assortment, law of In genetic inheritance, a principle stating that the alleles of unlinked genes (those located on different chromosomes) are randomly distributed to gametes.

Inductive reasoning A logical progression of thought proceeding from the specific to the general. It involves the accumulation of facts through observation until the sheer weight of the evidence forces some general statement about the phenomenon. A conclusion is reached on the basis of a number of observations.

Infancy The stage in postnatal development that roughly corresponds to the first year of life. It is a time of rapid growth when total body length usually increases by one-half and weight may triple.

Infertility The inability to conceive (become pregnant) or to cause conception (in the case of males).

Inflammatory response A nonspecific body response to injury or invasion by foreign organisms. It is characterized by redness, swelling, heat, and pain.

Influenza The flu. Influenza is a viral infection caused by any of the variants of influenza A or influenza B viruses.

Informed consent A document that a person must sign before participating in an experiment; it lists all possible harmful consequences that might result from participation.

Inguinal canal A passage through the abdominal wall through which the testes pass in their descent to the scrotum.

Inhalation Breathing in. Inhalation (inspiration) is the movement of air into the respiratory system.

Inhibin A hormone produced in the testes that increases with sperm count and inhibits follicle-stimulating hormone secretion and, therefore, inhibits sperm production.

Inhibiting hormone A hormone produced by the hypothalamus that inhibits hormone secretion by the anterior pituitary gland.

Inhibitory synapse A synapse in which the response of the receptors for that neurotransmitter on the postsynaptic membrane decreases the likelihood that an action potential will be generated in the postsynaptic neuron. The postsynaptic cell is inhibited because its resting potential becomes more negative than usual.

Innate defense responses Body defense responses that we are born with—barriers and chemical—to prevent entry of pathogens, and cells and chemicals that attack a pathogen if it breaks through outer barriers. These defense responses are nonspecific.

Inner cell mass A group of cells within the blastocyst that will become the embryo proper and some extraembryonic membranes.

Inner ear A series of passageways in the temporal bone that houses the organs for hearing (cochlea) and the sense of equilibrium (vestibular apparatus).

Inpatient A patient who is admitted to a hospital or clinic for treatment that requires a stay of at least one night.

Insertion The end of the muscle that is attached to the bone that moves when the muscle contracts.

Insoluble fiber A fiber that does not easily dissolve in water. These fibers include cellulose, hemicellulose, and lignin.

Inspiration Inhalation. The movement of air into the respiratory system.

Inspiratory reserve volume The volume of air that can be forcefully brought into the lungs after normal inhalation.

Insulin The hormone secreted by the pancreas that reduces glucose levels in the blood.

Insulin resistance The condition in which the body's cells fail to adequately respond to insulin. It characterizes type 2 diabetes mellitus and gestational diabetes.

Insulin shock A condition that results from severely depressed glucose levels in which brain cells fail to function properly, causing convulsions and unconsciousness. Often results when a diabetic injects too much insulin.

Integral proteins Proteins embedded in the plasma membrane, either completely or incompletely spanning the bilayer.

Integumentary system The skin.

Intercalated disks Thickenings of the plasma membranes of cardiac muscle cells that strengthen cardiac tissue and promote rapid conduction of impulses throughout the heart.

Intercostal muscles The layers of muscles between the ribs that raise and lower the rib cage during breathing.

Interferon A type of defensive protein produced by T lymphocytes that slows the spread of viruses already in the body by interfering with viral replication. Interferons also attract macrophages and natural killer cells, which kill the virus-infected cell.

Interleukin 1 A chemical secreted by a macrophage that activates helper T cells in an immune response.

Interleukin 2 A chemical released by a helper T cell that activates both B cells and T cells.

Intermediate filament A component of the cytoskeleton made from fibrous proteins. It maintains cell shape and anchors organelles such as the nucleus.

Internal respiration Movement of oxygen from the blood to the tissues, and movement of carbon dioxide from the tissues to the blood.

Internal urethral sphincter A thickening of smooth muscle at the junction of the bladder and the urethra. The action of this sphincter is involuntary and keeps urine from flowing into the urethra while the bladder is filling.

Interneuron An association neuron. Neurons located within the central nervous system between sensory and motor neurons that serve to integrate information.

Interoceptor A sensory receptor located inside the body, where it monitors conditions. Interoceptors play a vital role in maintaining homeostasis. They are an important part of the feedback loops that regulate blood pressure, blood chemistry, and breathing rate. Interoceptors may also cause us to feel pain, hunger, or thirst, thereby prompting us to take appropriate action.

Interphase The period between cell divisions when the DNA, cytoplasm, and organelles are duplicated and the cell grows in size. Interphase is also the time in the cell's life cycle when the cell carries out its functions in the body.

Interstitial cells Cells located between the seminiferous tubules in the testes that produce the steroid sex hormones, collectively called androgens.

Interstitial fluid The watery solution outside cells of the body. It also is called extracellular fluid.

Intervertebral disks Pads of cartilage that help cushion the bones of the vertebral column.

Intracytoplasmic sperm injection (ICSI) A procedure in which a tiny needle is used to inject a single sperm cell into an egg. It is an option for treating infertility when the man has few sperm or sperm that lack the strength or enzymes necessary to penetrate the egg.

Intrauterine device (IUD) A means of contraception consisting of a small plastic device that either is wrapped with copper wire or contains progesterone. It is inserted into the uterus to prevent pregnancy.

Intrinsic factor A protein secreted by the stomach necessary for the absorption of vitamin B_{12} from the small intestine.

Intron A portion of a newly formed mRNA that is cut out of the mature mRNA molecule and is not expressed (used to form a protein). An intervening sequence.

Ion An atom or group of atoms that carries an electric charge resulting from the loss or gain of electrons.

Ion channel A protein-lined pore or channel through a plasma membrane through which one type or a few types of ions can pass. Nerve cell ion channels are important in the generation and propagation of nerve impulses.

Ionic bond A chemical bond that results from the mutual attraction of oppositely charged ions.

Iris The colored portion of the eye. The iris regulates the amount of light that enters the eye.

Iron-deficiency anemia A reduction in the ability of the blood to carry oxygen due to an insufficient amount of iron in the diet, an inability to absorb iron from the digestive system, or blood loss.

Ischemia A temporary reduction in blood supply caused by obstructed blood flow. It causes reversible damage to heart muscle.

Islets of Langerhans See *pancreatic islets*.

Isotonic solution A solution with the same concentration of solutes as plasma, for example.

Isotopes Atoms that have the same number of protons but different numbers of neutrons.

IUD See *intrauterine device*.

IVF See *in vitro fertilization*.

J

Jaundice A condition in which the skin develops a yellow tone caused by the buildup of bilirubin in the blood and its deposition in certain tissues such as the skin. It is an indication that the liver is not handling bilirubin adequately.

Joint A point of contact between two bones; an articulation.

Junctional complexes Membrane specializations that attach adjacent cells to each other to form a contiguous sheet. There are three kinds of junctions between cells: tight junctions, desmosomes, and gap junctions.

Juxtaglomerular apparatus The region of the kidney nephron where the distal convoluted tubule contacts the afferent arteriole bringing blood into the glomerulus. Cells in this area secrete renin, an enzyme that triggers events eventually leading to increased reabsorption of sodium and water by the distal convoluted tubules and collecting ducts of nephrons.

K

Kaposi's sarcoma A cancer that forms tumors in connective tissue and manifests as pink or purple marks on the skin. It is common in people with a suppressed immune system, such as people living with HIV/AIDS, and is thought to be associated with a new virus in the herpes family, HHV-8.

Karyotype The arrangement of chromosomes based on physical characteristics such as length and location of the centromere. Karyotypes can be checked for defects in number or structure of chromosomes.

Keratinocytes Cells of the epidermis that undergo keratinization, the process in which keratin gradually replaces the contents of maturing cells.

Ketoacidosis A lowering of blood pH resulting from the accumulation of breakdown by-products of fats. This biochemical imbalance is characteristic of type 1 diabetes mellitus, in which it is called diabetic ketoacidosis (DKA).

Kidney stones Small, hard crystals formed in the urinary tract when substances such as calcium (the most common constituent), uric acid, or magnesium ammonium phosphate precipitate from urine as a result of higher-than-normal concentrations. They are also called renal calculi.

Kidneys Reddish, kidney bean–shaped organs that filter wastes and excess materials from the blood, assist the respiratory system in regulating blood pH, and maintain fluid balance by regulating the volume and composition of blood and urine.

Klinefelter syndrome A genetic condition resulting from nondisjunction of the sex chromosomes in which a person inherits an extra X chromosome that results in an XXY genotype. The person has a male appearance.

Krebs cycle See *citric acid cycle*.

L

Labia majora Two elongated skin folds lateral to the labia minora. They are part of the female external genitalia.

Labia minora Two small skin folds on either side of the vagina and interior to the labia majora. They are part of the external genitalia of a female.

Labor The process by which the fetus is expelled from the uterus and moved through the vagina and into the outside world. During labor, uterine contractions occur at regular intervals, are often painful, and intensify with walking. Labor is usually divided into the dilation stage, expulsion stage, and placental stage.

Lactation The production and ejection of milk from the mammary glands. The hormone prolactin from the anterior pituitary gland promotes milk production, and the hormone oxytocin released from the posterior pituitary gland makes milk available to the suckling infant by stimulating milk ejection, or let-down.

Lacteal A lymphatic vessel in an intestinal villus that aids in the absorption of lipids.

Lactic acid fermentation The process by which glucose is broken down by muscle cells when oxygen is low during strenuous exercise.

Lactose intolerance The inability to fully digest lactose, usually due to lactase deficiency. Bloating and diarrhea may occur following consumption of dairy products.

Lacuna (plural, lacunae) A tiny cavity. It contains osteocytes (bone cells) in the matrix of bone and cartilage cells in the matrix of cartilage.

Lanugo Soft, fine hair that covers the fetus beginning about the third or fourth month after conception.

Large intestine The final segment of the gastrointestinal tract, consisting of the cecum, colon, rectum, and anal canal. The large intestine helps absorb water, forms feces, and plays a role in defecation.

Laryngitis An inflammation of the larynx in which the vocal cords become swollen and can no longer vibrate and produce sound.

Larynx The voice box or Adam's apple. A boxlike cartilaginous structure between the pharynx and the trachea held together by muscles and elastic tissue.

Latent period Pertaining to muscle contraction, the interval between the reception of the stimulus and the beginning of muscle contraction.

Latin binomial The two-part scientific name that consists of the genus name followed by the specific epithet.

Lens A transparent, semispherical body of tissue behind the iris and pupil that focuses light on the retina.

Leukemia A cancer of the blood-forming organs that causes white blood cell numbers to increase. The white blood cells are abnormal and do not effectively defend the body against infectious agents.

Leukocytes White blood cells. They are cells of the blood including neutrophils, eosinophils, basophils, monocytes, B lymphocytes, and T lymphocytes. Leukocytes are involved in body defense mechanisms and the removal of wastes, toxins, or damaged, abnormal cells.

LH See *luteinizing hormone*.

Life expectancy The average number of years a newborn is expected to live.

Ligament A strong band of connective tissue that holds the bones together, supports the joint, and directs the movement of the bones.

Limbic system A collective term for several structures in the brain involved in emotions and memory.

Linkage The tendency for a group of genes located on the same chromosome to be inherited together.

Lipid A compound, such as a triglyceride, phospholipid, or steroid, that does not dissolve in water. Dietary lipids include fats, oils, and cholesterol. They provide 9 calories per gram.

Lipid-soluble hormone A hormone that moves easily through the plasma membrane of cells and combines with receptors inside target cells to activate certain genes and stimulate protein synthesis. Steroid hormones are lipid-soluble hormones. Steroids are derived from cholesterol and secreted by the ovaries, testes, and adrenal glands.

Liver A large organ that functions mainly in the production of plasma proteins, the excretion of bile, the storage of energy reserves, the detoxification of poisons, and the interconversion of nutrients.

Local signaling molecules Chemical messengers, such as neurotransmitters, prostaglandins, growth factors, and nitric oxide, that act locally rather than traveling to distant sites within the body.

Locus The point on a chromosome where a particular gene is found.

Longitudinal fissure A deep groove that separates the cerebrum into two hemispheres.

Long-term memory Memory that stores a large amount of information for hours, days, or years.

Loop of the nephron (loop of Henle) A section of the renal tubule that resembles a hairpin turn. Reabsorption occurs here.

Loose connective tissue Connective tissue, such as areolar and adipose tissue, that contains many cells in which the fibers of the matrix are fewer in number and more loosely woven than those found in dense connective tissue.

Low-density lipoprotein (LDL) A protein carrier in the blood that transports cholesterol to the cells. LDLs are often called the "bad" form of cholesterol.

Lower esophageal sphincter A ring of muscle at the juncture of the esophagus and the stomach that controls the flow of materials between the esophagus and the stomach. It relaxes to allow food into the stomach and contracts to prevent too much food from moving back into the esophagus.

Lumen The hollow cavity or channel of a tubule through which transported material flows.

Luteinizing hormone (LH) A hormone secreted by the anterior pituitary gland that in females stimulates ovulation and the formation of the corpus luteum (which produces estrogen and progesterone) and prepares the mammary glands for milk production. In males, it stimulates testosterone production by the interstitial cells within the testes.

Lymph The fluid within the vessels of the lymphatic system. It is derived from the fluid that bathes the cells of the body (interstitial fluid).

Lymph nodes Small nodular organs found along lymph vessels that filter lymph. The lymph nodes contain macrophages and lymphocytes, cells that play an essential role in the body's defense system.

Lymphatic system A body system consisting of lymph, lymphatic vessels, and lymphatic tissue and organs. The lymphatic system helps return interstitial fluid to the blood, transports the products of fat digestion from the digestive system to the blood, and assists in body defenses.

Lymphatic vessels The vessels through which lymph flows. A network of vessels that drains interstitial fluid and returns it to the blood supply and transports the products of fat digestion from the digestive system to the blood supply.

Lymphocyte A type of white blood cell important in nonspecific and specific (immune) body defenses. The lymphocytes include B lymphocytes (B cells) that transform into plasma cells and produce antibodies and T lymphocytes (T cells) that are important in defense against foreign or infected cells.

Lymphoid organs Various organs that belong to the lymphatic system, including the tonsils, spleen, thymus, and Peyer's patches.

Lymphoid tissue The type of tissue that predominates in the lymphoid organs except the thymus. The organs in which lymphoid tissue is found are the lymph nodes, tonsils, and spleen. Lymphoid tissue is an important component of the immune system.

Lymphoma Cancer of the lymphoid tissues. In people with AIDS, it commonly affects the B cells.

Lysosomal storage diseases Disorders such as Tay-Sachs disease that are caused by the absence of lysosomal enzymes. In these disorders, molecules that would normally be degraded by the missing enzymes accumulate in the lysosomes and interfere with cell functioning.

Lysosome An organelle that serves as the principal site of digestion within the cell.

Lysozyme An enzyme present in tears, saliva, and certain other body fluids that kills bacteria by disrupting their cell walls.

M

Macroevolution Large-scale evolutionary changes such as those that might result from long-term changes in the climate or position of the continents. Examples include mass extinctions and the evolution of mammals.

Macromolecule A giant molecule of life such as a nucleic acid, protein, or polysaccharide. A macromolecule is formed by the joining together of smaller molecules.

Macrophage A large phagocytic cell derived from a monocyte that lives in loose connective tissue and engulfs anything detected as foreign.

Magnetic resonance imaging (MRI) A means of visualizing a region of the body, including the brain, in which the picture results from differences in the way the hydrogen nuclei in the water molecules within the tissues vibrate in response to a magnetic field created around the area to be pictured.

Malignant tumor A cancerous tumor. An abnormal mass of tissue with cells that can invade surrounding tissue and spread to multiple locations throughout the body.

Malleus The first of three small bones in the middle ear that transmit information about sound from the eardrum to the inner ear. The malleus is also known as the hammer.

Malnourishment A form of hunger that occurs when the diet is not balanced and the right foods are not eaten.

Mammary glands The milk-producing glands in the breasts.

Marijuana A psychoactive drug consisting of the leaves, stems, and flowers of the Indian hemp plant, *Cannabis sativa*.

Mass The measure of how much matter is in an object.

Mast cells Small, mobile connective tissue cells often found near blood vessels. In response to injury, mast cells release histamine, which dilates blood vessels and increases blood flow to an area, and heparin, which prevents blood clotting.

Matrix In connective tissue, the matrix is the material in which the cells are embedded. The matrix consists of ground substance, which is made up of protein fibers and noncellular material.

Matter Anything that takes up space and has mass. Matter is made up of atoms.

Mechanical digestion A part of the digestive process that involves physically breaking food into smaller pieces.

Mechanoreceptor A sensory receptor that is specialized to respond to distortions in the receptor itself or in nearby cells. Mechanoreceptors are responsible for the sensations we describe as touch, pressure, hearing, and equilibrium.

Medulla oblongata The part of the brain stem containing reflex centers for some of life's most vital physiological functions: the pace of the basic breathing rhythm, the force and rate of heart contraction, and blood pressure. The medulla oblongata connects the spinal cord to the rest of the brain.

Medullary cavity The cavity in the shaft of long bones that is filled with yellow marrow.

Medullary rhythmicity center The region of the brain stem controlling the basic rhythm of breathing.

Meiosis A type of cell division that occurs in the gonads and gives rise to gametes. As a result of two divisions (meiosis I and meiosis II), haploid gametes are produced from diploid germ cells.

Meissner's corpuscles Encapsulated nerve cell endings that are common on the hairless, sensitive areas of the skin, such as the lips, nipples, and fingertips, and tell us exactly where we have been touched.

Melanin A pigment produced by the melanocytes of the skin. There are two forms of melanin: black-to-brown and yellow-to-red.

Melanocytes Spider-shaped cells located at the base of the epidermis that manufacture and store melanin, a pigment involved in skin color and absorption of ultraviolet radiation.

Melanoma The least common and most dangerous form of skin cancer. It arises in the melanocytes, the pigment-producing cells of the skin.

Melatonin A hormone secreted by the pineal gland that reduces jet lag and promotes sleep.

Membranous epithelium A type of epithelial tissue that forms linings and coverings. Depending on its location, it may be specialized to protect, secrete, or absorb.

Memory cell A lymphocyte (B cell or T cell) of the immune system that forms in response to an antigen and that circulates for a long period of time; such cells are able to mount a quick immune response to a subsequent exposure to the same antigen.

Meninges Three protective connective tissue membranes that surround the central nervous system: the dura mater, the pia mater, and the arachnoid.

Meningitis An inflammation of the meninges (protective coverings of the brain and spinal cord).

Menopause The end of a female's reproductive potential when ovulation and menstruation cease.

Menstrual (uterine) cycle The sequence of events that occurs on an approximately 28-day cycle in the uterine lining (endometrium) and involves the thickening of and increased blood supply to the endometrium and the loss of the endometrium as menstrual flow.

Merkel cells Cells of the epidermis found in association with sensory neurons where the epidermis meets the dermis.

Merkel disk The Merkel cell–neuron combination that functions as a sensory receptor for light touch, providing information about objects contacting the skin. It is found on both the hairy and the hairless parts of the skin.

Mesoderm The primary germ layer that gives rise to muscle, bone, connective tissue, and organs such as the heart, kidneys, ovaries, and testes.

Messenger RNA (mRNA) A type of RNA synthesized from and complementary to a region of DNA that attaches to ribosomes in the cytoplasm and specifies the amino acid order in the protein. It carries the DNA instructions for synthesizing a particular protein.

Metabolism The sum of all chemical reactions within living cells.

Metaphase In mitosis, the phase when the chromosomes, guided by the fibers of the mitotic spindle, form a line at the center of the cell. As a result of this alignment, when the chromosomes split at the centromere, each daughter cell receives one chromatid from each chromosome and thus a complete set of the parent cell's chromosomes.

Metastasize To spread from one part of the body to another part not directly connected to the first part. Cancerous tumors metastasize and form new tumors in distant parts of the body.

MHC markers Molecules on the surface of body cells that label the cell as "self."

Microevolution Changes in populations at the genetic level. The causes include genetic drift, gene flow, natural selection, and mutation.

Microfilament A component of the cytoskeleton made from the globular protein actin. Microfilaments form contractile units in muscle cells and aid in pinching dividing cells in two.

Microtubule A component of the cytoskeleton made from the globular protein tubulin. Microtubules are responsible for the movement of cilia and flagella and serve as tracks for the movement of organelles and vesicles.

Microvilli Microscopic cytoplasm-filled extensions of the cell membrane that serve to increase the absorptive surface area of the cell.

Midbrain A region of the brain stem that coordinates reflex responses to auditory and visual stimuli.

Middle ear An air-filled space in the temporal bone that includes the tympanic membrane (eardrum) and three small bones (the malleus, incus, and stapes; sometimes called the hammer, anvil, and stirrup). It serves as an amplifier of sound pressure waves.

Minerals Inorganic substances that are not broken down during digestion and are important in regulating cellular processes.

Mineralocorticoids Hormones secreted by the adrenal cortex that affect mineral homeostasis and water balance.

Minipill A birth control pill that contains only progesterone.

Mitochondrion (plural, mitochondria) An organelle within which most of cellular respiration occurs in a eukaryotic cell. Cellular respiration is the process by which oxygen and an organic fuel such as glucose are consumed and energy is released and used to form ATP.

Mitosis A type of nuclear division occurring in somatic cells in which two identical cells, called daughter cells, are generated from a single cell. The original cell first replicates its genetic material and then distributes a complete set of genetic information to each of its daughter cells. Mitosis is usually divided into prophase, metaphase, anaphase, and telophase. Mitosis is essential to cell division.

Mitral valve A heart valve located between the left atrium and left ventricle that prevents the backflow of blood from the ventricle to the atrium. It is also called the *bicuspid valve* or the *left atrioventricular (AV) valve.*

Molecular clock The idea that there is a constant rate of divergence of macromolecules (such as proteins) from one another. This idea is based on the notion that single nucleotide changes in DNA (point mutations) and the amino acid changes in proteins that can be produced by some point mutations occur with steady, clocklike regularity. It permits comparison of molecular sequences to estimate the time of separation between species (the more differences in sequence, the more time that has elapsed since the common ancestor).

Molecule A chemical structure composed of atoms held together by covalent bonds.

Monoclonal antibodies Defensive proteins specific for a particular antigen secreted by a clone of genetically identical cells descended from a single cell.

Monocyte The largest white blood cell. Monocytes are active in fighting chronic infections, viruses, and intracellular bacterial infections. A monocyte can transform into a phagocytic macrophage.

Monohybrid cross A genetic cross that considers the inheritance of a single trait from individuals differing in the expression of that trait.

Monomer A small molecule that joins with identical molecules to form a polymer.

Mononucleosis A viral disease caused by the Epstein-Barr virus that results in an elevated level of monocytes in the blood. It causes fatigue and swollen glands, and there is no available treatment.

Monosaccharide The smallest molecular unit of a carbohydrate. Monosaccharides are known as simple sugars.

Monosomy A condition in which there is only one representative of a chromosome instead of two representatives.

Mons veneris A round fleshy prominence over the pubic bone in a female. Part of the female external genitalia.

Morning sickness The nausea and vomiting experienced by some women early in pregnancy. It is not restricted to the morning and may be caused, in part, by high levels of the hormone human chorionic gonadotropin (HCG).

Morphogenesis The development of body form that begins during the third week after fertilization.

Morula A solid ball of 12 or more cells produced by successive divisions of the zygote. The name reflects its resemblance to the fruit of the mulberry tree.

Mosaic evolution The phenomenon whereby various traits evolve at their own rates.

Motor (efferent) neuron A neuron specialized to carry information *away from* the central nervous system to an effector, either a muscle or a gland.

Motor unit A motor neuron and all the muscle fibers (cells) it stimulates.

MRI **See** *magnetic resonance imaging.*

mRNA **See** *messenger RNA.*

Mucosa The innermost layer of the gastrointestinal tract. It secretes mucus that helps lubricate the tube, allowing food to slide through easily.

Mucous membranes Sheets of epithelial tissue that line many passageways in the body that open to the exterior. Mucous membranes are specialized to secrete and absorb.

Mucus A sticky secretion that serves to lubricate body parts and trap particles of dirt and other secretions. It also helps protect the stomach from the action of gastric juice.

Multiple alleles Three or more alleles of a particular gene existing in a population. The alleles governing the ABO blood types provide an example.

Multiple sclerosis An autoimmune disease in which the body's own defense mechanisms attack myelin sheaths in the nervous system. As a patch of myelin is repaired, a hardened region called a sclerosis forms.

Multipolar neuron A neuron that has at least three processes, including an axon and a minimum of two dendrites. Most motor neurons and association neurons are multipolar.

Multipotent A term used to describe a cell that can differentiate into many cell types.

Multiregional hypothesis The idea that modern humans evolved independently in several different areas from distinctive local populations of *Homo erectus.* Compare with *Out of Africa hypothesis.*

Muscle fiber A muscle cell.

Muscle spindles Specialized muscle fibers with sensory nerve cell endings wrapped around them that report to the brain whenever a muscle is stretched.

Muscle tissue Tissue composed of muscle cells that contract when stimulated and passively lengthen to the resting state. There are three types of muscle tissue: skeletal, smooth, and cardiac.

Muscle twitch Contraction of a muscle in response to a single stimulus.

Muscularis The muscular layers of the gastrointestinal tract. These layers help move food through the gastrointestinal system and mix food with digestive secretions.

Mutation A change in the base sequence of the DNA of a gene. A mutation may occur spontaneously or be caused by outside sources, such as radiation or chemical agents.

Myelin sheath An insulating layer around axons that carry nerve impulses over relatively long distances; it is composed of multiple wrappings of the plasma membrane of certain glial cells. Outside the brain and spinal cord, Schwann cells form the myelin sheath. The myelin sheath greatly increases the speed at which impulses travel and assists in the repair of damaged axons. The Schwann cells that form the myelin sheath are separated from one another by short regions of exposed axon called nodes of Ranvier.

Myocardial infarction A heart attack. A condition in which a part of the heart muscle dies because of an insufficient blood supply.

Myocardium Cardiac muscle tissue that makes up the bulk of the heart. The contractility of the myocardium is responsible for the heart's pumping action.

Myofibril A rodlike bundle of contractile proteins (myofilaments) found in skeletal and cardiac muscle cells essential to muscle contraction.

Myofilament A contractile protein within muscle cells. There are two types: myosin (thick) filaments and actin (thin) filaments.

Myoglobin An oxygen-binding pigment in muscle fibers.

Myometrium The smooth muscle layer in the wall of the uterus.

Myosin filaments The thick filaments in muscle cells composed of the protein myosin and essential to muscle contraction. A myosin molecule is shaped like a golf club with two heads.

Myosin heads Club-shaped ends of a myosin molecule that bind to actin filaments and can swivel, causing actin filaments to slide past the myosin filaments, which causes muscle contraction. They are also called *cross-bridges*.

Myxedema A condition characterized by swelling of the facial tissues due to the accumulation of interstitial fluids caused by undersecretion of thyroid hormone.

N

Nasal cavities Two chambers in the nose, separated by the septum.

Nasal conchae The three convoluted bones within each nasal cavity that increase surface area and direct airflow.

Nasal septum A thin partition of cartilage and bone that divides the inside of the nose into two nasal cavities.

Natural killer (NK) cells A type of cell in the immune system. These cells, probably lymphocytes, roam the body in search of abnormal cells and quickly kill them.

Natural selection The process by which some individuals live longer and produce more offspring than other individuals because their particular inherited characteristics make them better suited to their local environment.

Nearsightedness Myopia. Nearsightedness is a visual condition in which nearby objects can be seen more clearly than distant objects. Nearsightedness occurs because either the eyeball is elongated or the lens is too thick, causing the image to be focused in front of the retina.

Negative feedback mechanism The homeostatic mechanism in which the outcome of a process feeds back on the system, shutting down the process.

Nephrons Functional units of the kidneys responsible for the formation of urine. These microscopic tubules number 1 million to 2 million per kidney and perform filtration (only certain substances are allowed to pass out of the blood and into the nephron), reabsorption (some useful substances are returned from the nephron to the blood), and secretion (the nephron directly removes wastes and excess materials in the blood and adds them to the filtered fluid that becomes urine).

Nerve A bundle of parallel axons, dendrites, or both from many neurons. A nerve is usually covered with tough connective tissue.

Nervous tissue Tissue consisting of two types of cells, neurons and neuroglia, that make up the brain, spinal cord, and nerves.

Neural tube The embryonic structure that gives rise to the brain and spinal cord.

Neuroglia (neuroglial cells) Cells of the nervous system that support, insulate, and protect nerve cells; also called *glial cells*.

Neuromuscular junction The area of contact between the terminal end of a motor neuron and the cell membrane of a skeletal muscle fiber. When an action potential reaches the terminal end of the motor neuron, acetylcholine is released, triggering events that can lead to muscle contraction.

Neurons Nerve cells involved in intercellular communication. A neuron consists of a cell body, dendrites, and an axon. Neurons are excitable cells in the nervous system specialized to generate and transmit electrochemical signals called action potentials or nerve impulses.

Neurosecretory cells Specialized neurons that generate and transmit nerve impulses and make and secrete hormones.

Neurotransmitter A chemical released from the axon tip of a neuron that affects the activity of another cell (usually a nerve, muscle, or gland cell) by altering the electrical potential difference across the membrane of the receiving cell.

Neurula The embryo during neurulation (formation of the brain and spinal cord from ectoderm).

Neurulation A series of events during embryonic development when the central nervous system (brain and spinal cord) forms from the ectoderm. During this period, the embryo is called a neurula.

Neutrophil A phagocytic white blood cell important in defense against bacteria and removal of cellular debris. Most abundant of white blood cells.

Niche The role of a species in an ecosystem. The niche includes the habitat, food, nest sites, and so on. It describes how a member of a particular species uses materials in the environment and how it interacts with other organisms.

Nicotine The psychoactive component of tobacco products.

Nitric oxide A local signaling molecule that dilates blood vessels; also functions as a neurotransmitter.

Nitrification The conversion of ammonia to nitrate (NO_3^-) by nitrifying bacteria living in the soil.

Nitrogen fixation The process of converting nitrogen gas to ammonium (a nitrogen-containing molecule that can be used by living organisms). The process of nitrogen fixation is carried out by nitrogen-fixing bacteria living in nodules on the roots of leguminous plants such as peas and alfalfa.

Node of Ranvier A region of exposed axon between Schwann cells forming a myelin sheath. In myelinated nerves, the impulse jumps from one node of Ranvier to the next, greatly increasing the speed of conduction. This type of transmission is called saltatory conduction.

Nondisjunction Failure of the members of a pair of homologous chromosomes or the sister chromatids to separate during mitosis or meiosis. Nondisjunction results in cells with an abnormal number of chromosomes.

Norepinephrine Noradrenaline. A hormone secreted by the adrenal medulla, along with epinephrine, in response to stress. They initiate the physiological "fight-or-flight" reaction. Norepinephrine is also a neurotransmitter found in both the central and the peripheral nervous systems. In the central nervous system, it is important in the regulation of mood, in the pleasure system of the brain, arousal, and dreaming sleep. Norepinephrine is thought to produce an energizing "good" feeling. It is also thought to be essential in hunger, thirst, and sex drive.

Notochord The flexible rod of tissue that develops during gastrulation and signals where the vertebral column will form. The notochord defines the axis of the embryo and gives the embryo some rigidity. During development, vertebrae form around the notochord. The notochord eventually degenerates, existing only as the pulpy, elastic material in the center of intervertebral disks.

Nuclear envelope The double membrane that surrounds the nucleus.

Nuclear pore An opening in the nuclear envelope that permits communication between the nucleus and the cytoplasm.

Nucleolus A specialized region within the nucleus that forms and disassembles during the course of the cell cycle. It plays a role in the generation of ribosomes, organelles involved in protein synthesis.

Nucleoplasm The chromatin and the aqueous environment within the nucleus.

Nucleotide A subunit of DNA composed of one five-carbon sugar (either ribose or deoxyribose), one phosphate group, and one of five nitrogen-containing bases. Nucleotides are the building blocks of nucleic acids (DNA and RNA).

Nucleus The command center of the cell containing almost all the genetic information.

Nutrient A chemical found in food that is essential for growth and function.

O

Obese Having excess body fat that negatively affects health.

Oil glands Glands associated with the hair follicles that produce sebum. Also called *sebaceous glands*.

Olfactory receptor Sensory receptors that respond to odorous molecules; sensory receptors for the sense of smell.

Oligosaccharide A chain of a few monosaccharides (simple sugars) joined together by dehydration synthesis. Disaccharides, formed by the joining of two monosaccharides, are an example.

Omnivore An organism that feeds on a variety of food types, such as plants and animals.

Oocyte A cell whose meiotic divisions will produce an ovum and up to three polar bodies.

Oogenesis The production of ova (eggs), including meiosis and maturation.

Oogonium (plural, oogonia) A germ cell in an ovary that divides, giving rise to oocytes.

Opiate A pain-relieving drug derived from the opium poppy.

Opsin One of several proteins that can be bound to retinal to form the visual pigments in rods and cones.

Optic nerve One of two nerves, one from each eye, responsible for bringing processed electrochemical messages from the retina to the brain for interpretation.

Organ A structure that has a specific function and is composed of two or more different tissues.

Organ of Corti The spiral organ. The portion of the cochlea in the inner ear that contains receptor cells that sense vibrations caused by sound. It is most directly responsible for the sense of hearing.

Organ system A group of organs with a common function.

Organelle A component within a cell that carries out specific functions. Some organelles, such as the nucleus and mitochondria, have membranes, whereas others, such as ribosomes and microtubules, do not.

Origin In reference to a muscle, the end of the muscle that is attached to the bone that remains relatively stationary during a movement.

Osmosis A special case of diffusion in which water moves across the plasma membrane or any other selectively permeable membrane from a region of lower concentration of solute to a region of higher concentration of solute.

Osteoarthritis An inflammation in a joint that is caused by degeneration of the surfaces of the joint by wear and tear.

Osteoblast A bone-forming cell.

Osteoclast A large cell responsible for the breakdown and absorption of bone.

Osteocytes Mature bone cells found in lacunae that are arranged in concentric rings around the central canal. Cytoplasmic projections from osteocytes extend tiny channels that connect with other osteocytes.

Osteon The structural unit of compact bone that appears as a series of concentric circles of lacunae. The lacunae contain bone cells around a central canal containing blood vessels and nerves.

Osteoporosis A decrease in bone density that occurs when the destruction of bone outpaces the formation of new bone, causing bone to become thin, brittle, and susceptible to fracture.

OT **See** *oxytocin*.

Otoliths Granules of calcium carbonate embedded in gelatinous material in the utricle and saccule of the inner ear. Otoliths cause the gelatin to slide over and bend sensory hair cells when the head is moved. The bending generates nerve impulses that are sent to the brain for interpretation of the position of the head.

Out of Africa hypothesis The idea that modern humans evolved from *Homo erectus* in Africa and later migrated to Europe, Asia, and Australia. It suggests a single origin for *Homo sapiens*. Compare with *multiregional hypothesis*.

Outer ear The external appendage on the outside of the head (pinna) and the canal (the external auditory canal) that extends to the eardrum. It functions as the receiver for sound vibrations.

Outpatient A patient who receives health care without being admitted to a hospital or clinic for an overnight stay. Also referred to as ambulatory care.

Oval window A membrane-covered opening in the inner ear (cochlea) through which vibrations from the stirrup (stapes) are transmitted to fluid within the cochlea.

Ovarian cycle The sequence of events in the ovary that leads to ovulation. The cycle is approximately 28 days long and is closely coordinated with the menstrual cycle.

Ovary One of the female gonads. The female gonads produce the ova (eggs) and the hormones estrogen and progesterone.

Overweight Weighing more than is ideal on a standard height–weight chart. An athletic person may be overweight because of muscle development.

Oviduct One of two tubes that conduct the ova from the ovary to the uterus in the female reproductive system. It is also called a uterine tube or a fallopian tube.

Ovulation The release of the secondary oocyte from the ovary.

Ovum (plural, ova) A mature egg; a large haploid cell that is the female gamete.

Oxygen debt The amount of oxygen required after exercise to oxidize the lactic acid formed during exercise.

Oxyhemoglobin Hemoglobin bound to oxygen.

Oxytocin (OT) The hormone released at the posterior pituitary that stimulates uterine contractions and milk ejection.

P

Pacemaker **See** *sinoatrial (SA) node*.

Pacinian corpuscle A large encapsulated nerve cell ending located deep within the skin and near body organs that responds when pressure is first applied. It is important in sensing vibration.

Pain receptor A sensory receptor that is specialized to detect the physical or chemical damage to tissues that we sense as pain. Pain receptors are sometimes classified as chemoreceptors, because they often respond to chemicals liberated by damaged tissue, and occasionally as mechanoreceptors, because they are stimulated by physical changes, such as swelling, in the damaged tissue.

Palate The roof of the mouth. The front region of the palate, the hard palate, is reinforced with bone. The tongue pushes against the hard palate while mixing food with saliva. The soft palate is farther to the back of the mouth and consists of only muscle. The soft palate prevents food from entering the nose during swallowing.

Pancreas An accessory organ behind the stomach that secretes digestive enzymes, bicarbonate ions to neutralize the acid in chyme, and hormones that regulate blood sugar.

Pancreatic islets Small clusters of endocrine cells in the pancreas; also called *islets of Langerhans*.

Parasympathetic nervous system The branch of the autonomic nervous system that is active during restful conditions. Its effects generally oppose those of the sympathetic nervous system. The parasympathetic nervous system adjusts bodily functions so that energy is conserved during nonstressful times.

Parathormone See *parathyroid hormone*.

Parathyroid glands Four small, round masses at the back of the thyroid gland that secrete parathyroid hormone (parathormone).

Parathyroid hormone (PTH) A hormone released from the parathyroid glands that increases blood calcium levels by stimulating osteoclasts to break down bone. PTH, also called *parathormone*, is secreted when blood calcium levels are too low.

Parental generation The parents—the individuals in the earliest generation under consideration in a genetic cross.

Parkinson's disease A progressive disorder that results from the death of dopamine-producing neurons that lie in the heart of the brain's movement control center, the substantia nigra. Parkinson's disease is characterized by slowed movements, tremors, and muscle rigidity.

Parturition Birth, which usually occurs about 38 weeks after fertilization.

Passive immunity Temporary immune resistance that develops when a person receives antibodies that were produced by another person or animal.

Pathogen A disease-causing organism.

PCR See *polymerase chain reaction*.

PDD-NOS See *autism spectrum disorder*.

Pectoral girdle The bones that connect the arms to the rib cage. The pectoral girdle is composed of the shoulder blades (scapulae) and the collarbones (clavicles).

Pedigree A diagram showing the genetic connections among individuals in an extended family that is often used to trace the expression of a particular trait in that family.

Pelvic girdle The bones that connect the legs to the vertebral column. The pelvic girdle is composed of the paired hipbones.

Pelvic inflammatory disease (PID) A general term for any bacterial infection of a woman's pelvic organs. PID is usually caused by sexually transmitted bacteria, especially those that cause chlamydia and gonorrhea.

Penis The cylindrical external reproductive organ of a male through which most of the urethra extends and that serves to deliver sperm into the female tract during sexual intercourse.

Pepsin A protein-splitting enzyme initially secreted in the stomach in the inactive form of pepsinogen that is activated into pepsin by hydrochloric acid.

Peptic ulcer A local defect in the surface of the stomach or small intestine characterized by dead tissue and inflammation.

Peptide A chain containing only a few amino acids.

Perforin A type of protein released by a natural killer cell that creates numerous pores (holes) in the target cell, making it leaky. Fluid is then drawn into the leaky cell because of the high salt concentration within, and the cell bursts.

Pericardium The fibrous sac enclosing the heart that holds the heart in the center of the chest without hampering its movements.

Perichondrium The layer of dense connective tissue surrounding cartilage that contains blood vessels, which supply the cartilage with nutrients.

Periodontitis An inflammation of the gums and the tissues around the teeth.

Periosteum The membranous covering that nourishes bone.

Peripheral nervous system The part of the nervous system outside the brain and spinal cord. It keeps the central nervous system in continuous contact with almost every part of the body. It is composed of nerves and ganglia. The two branches are the somatic and the autonomic nervous systems.

Peripheral proteins Proteins attached to the inner or outer surface of the plasma membrane.

Peristalsis Rhythmic waves of muscular contraction and relaxation in the walls of hollow tubular organs, such as the digestive organs, that push contents through the tubes.

Pervasive developmental disorder not otherwise specified (PDD-NOS) See *autism spectrum disorder*.

PET scan See *positron emission tomography*.

pH A measure of hydrogen ion concentration of a solution; values range from 0 to 14 on the pH scale.

pH scale A scale for measuring the concentration of hydrogen ions. The scale ranges from 0 to 14. A pH of 7 is neutral, a pH of less than 7 is acidic, and a pH of greater than 7 is basic.

Phagocytes Scavenger cells specialized to engulf and destroy particulate matter, such as pathogens, damaged tissue, or dead cells.

Phagocytosis The process by which cells such as white blood cells ingest foreign cells or substances by surrounding the foreign material with cell membrane. It is a type of endocytosis.

Pharynx The space shared by the respiratory and digestive systems that is commonly called the throat. The pharynx is a passageway for air, food, and liquid.

Phenotype The observable physical and physiological traits of an individual. Phenotype results from the inherited alleles and their interactions with the environment.

Phospholipid An important component of cell membranes. It has a nonpolar "water-fearing" tail (made up of fatty acids) and a polar "water-loving" head (containing an R group, glycerol, and phosphate).

Photoreceptor A sensory receptor specialized to detect changes in light intensity. Photoreceptors are responsible for the sensation we describe as vision.

Phylogenetic trees Generalized descriptions of the history of life. They depict hypotheses about evolutionary relationships among species or higher taxa.

Physical dependence A condition in which continued use of a drug is needed to maintain normal cell functioning.

Pia mater The innermost layer of the meninges (the connective tissue layers that protect the central nervous system).

PID See *pelvic inflammatory disease.*

Piloerection Contraction of the arrector pili muscles causing hairs to stand on end and form a layer of insulation.

Pineal gland The gland that produces the hormone melatonin and is located at the center of the brain.

Pinna The visible part of the ear on each side of the head that gathers sound and channels it to the external auditory canal.

Pinocytosis A type of endocytosis in which cells engulf droplets of fluid and the dissolved substances therein.

Pituitary dwarfism A condition caused by insufficient growth hormone during childhood.

Pituitary gland The endocrine organ connected to the hypothalamus by a short stalk. It consists of the anterior and posterior lobes and is also called the *hypophysis.*

Pituitary portal system The system in which a capillary bed in the hypothalamus connects to veins that lead into a capillary bed in the anterior lobe of the pituitary gland. It allows hormones of the hypothalamus to control the secretion of hormones from the anterior pituitary gland.

Placebo In a controlled experiment to test the effectiveness of a drug, the placebo is a substance that appears to be identical to a drug but has no known effect on the condition for which it is taken.

Placenta The organ that delivers oxygen and nutrients to the embryo and later fetus and carries carbon dioxide and wastes away from each. The placenta is also called the afterbirth.

Placenta previa The condition in which the placenta forms in the lower half of the uterus, entirely or partially covering the cervix. It may cause premature birth or maternal hemorrhage and usually makes vaginal delivery impossible.

Placental stage The third (and final) stage of true labor. It begins with delivery of the baby and ends when the placenta detaches from the wall of the uterus and is expelled from the mother's body.

Plaque A bumpy layer consisting of smooth muscle cells filled with lipid material, especially cholesterol, that bulges into the channel of an artery and reduces blood flow. Another type of plaque is a buildup of food material and bacteria on teeth that leads to tooth decay.

Plasma A straw-colored liquid that makes up about 55% of blood. It serves as the medium for transporting materials within the blood. Plasma consists of water (91% to 93%) with substances dissolved in it (7% to 9%).

Plasma cell The effector cell, produced from a B lymphocyte, that secretes antibodies.

Plasma membrane The thin outer boundary of a cell that controls the movement of substances into and out of the cell.

Plasma proteins Proteins dissolved in plasma, including albumins, which are important in water balance between cells and the blood; globulins, which are important in transporting various substances in the blood; and antibodies, which are important in the immune response.

Plasmid A small, circular piece of self-replicating DNA that is separate from the chromosome and found in bacteria. Plasmids are often used as vectors in recombinant DNA research.

Plasmin An enzyme that breaks down fibrin and dissolves blood clots. Plasmin is formed from plasminogen.

Plasminogen A plasma protein. It is the inactive precursor of plasmin.

Platelet A cell fragment of a megakaryocyte that releases substances necessary for blood clotting. It is formed in the red bone marrow and is sometimes called a thrombocyte.

Platelet plug A mass of platelets clinging to the protein fiber collagen at a damaged blood vessel to prevent blood loss.

Pleiotropy One gene having many effects.

Pluripotent The ability of a cell to differentiate into nearly every cell type.

PMS See *premenstrual syndrome.*

Point mutation A mutation that involves changes in one or a few nucleotides in DNA.

Polar body Any of three small nonfunctional cells produced during the meiotic divisions of an oocyte. The divisions also produce a mature ovum (egg).

Polygenic inheritance Inheritance in which several independently assorting or loosely linked genes determine the expression of a trait.

Polymer A large molecule formed by the joining together of many smaller molecules of the same general type (monomers).

Polymerase chain reaction (PCR) A technique used to amplify (increase) the quantity of DNA in vitro using primers, DNA polymerase, and nucleotides.

Polypeptide A chain containing 10 or more amino acids.

Polysaccharide A complex carbohydrate formed when large numbers of monosaccharides (most commonly glucose) join together to form a long chain through dehydration synthesis. Most polysaccharides store energy or provide structure.

Polysome A cluster of ribosomes simultaneously translating the same messenger RNA (mRNA) strand.

Pons A part of the brain that connects upper and lower levels of the brain.

Population A group of potentially interacting individuals of the same species living in a distinct geographic area.

Population dynamics Changes in population size over time.

Portal system A system whereby a capillary bed drains to veins that drain to another capillary bed.

Positive feedback mechanism The mechanism by which the outcome of a process feeds back on the system, further stimulating the process.

Positron emission tomography (PET) A method that can be used to measure the activity of various brain regions. The person being scanned is injected with a radioactively labeled nutrient, usually glucose, that is tracked as it flows through the brain. The radioisotope emits positively charged particles, called positrons. When the positrons collide with electrons in the body, gamma rays are released. The gamma rays can be detected and recorded by PET receptors. Computers then use the information to construct a PET scan that shows where the radioisotope is being used in the brain.

Postnatal period The period of development after birth. It includes the stages of infancy, childhood, adolescence, and adulthood.

Postsynaptic neuron The neuron located after the synapse. The receiving neuron in a synapse. The membrane of the postsynaptic neuron has receptors specific for certain neurotransmitters.

Precapillary sphincter A ringlike muscle that acts as a valve that opens and closes a capillary bed. Contraction of the precapillary sphincter squeezes the capillary shut and directs blood through a thoroughfare channel to the venule. Relaxation of the precapillary sphincter allows blood to flow through the capillary bed.

Pre-embryo The developing human from fertilization through the second week of gestation (the pre-embryonic period).

Pre-embryonic period The period during prenatal development that extends from fertilization through the second week. Cleavage and implantation follow fertilization.

Prefrontal cortex An association area of the cerebral cortex that is important in decision making.

Premature infant A baby born before 37 weeks of gestation.

Premenstrual syndrome (PMS) A collection of uncomfortable symptoms, including irritability, stress, and bloating, that appears 7 to 10 days before a woman's menstrual period and is associated with hormonal cycling.

Prenatal period The period of development before birth. It is further subdivided into the pre-embryonic period (from fertilization through the second week), the embryonic period (from the third through the eighth weeks), and the fetal period (from the ninth week until birth).

Presynaptic neuron The neuron located before the synapse. The sending neuron in a synapse. The neuron in a synapse that releases neurotransmitter from its synaptic knobs into the synaptic cleft.

Primary consumer A herbivore. An animal that eats primary producers (green plants or algae).

Primary germ layers The layers produced by gastrulation from which all tissues and organs form. The primary germ layers are ectoderm, mesoderm, and endoderm.

Primary motor area A band of the frontal lobe of the cerebral cortex that initiates messages that direct voluntary movements.

Primary productivity In ecosystems, the gross primary productivity is the amount of light energy that is converted to chemical energy in the bonds of organic molecules during a given period. The net primary productivity is the amount of productivity left after the photosynthesizers have used some of the energy stored in organic molecules for their own metabolic activities.

Primary response The immune response that occurs during the body's first encounter with a particular antigen.

Primary somatosensory area A band of the parietal lobe of the cerebral cortex to which information is sent from receptors in the skin regarding touch, temperature, and pain and from receptors in the joints and skeletal muscles.

Primary spermatocyte The original large cell that develops from a spermatogonium during sperm development in the seminiferous tubules. It undergoes meiosis and gives rise to secondary spermatocytes.

Primary structure The precise sequence of amino acids of a protein. This sequence, determined by the genes, dictates a protein's structure and function.

Primary succession The sequence of changes in the species making up a community over time that begins in an area where no community previously existed and ends with a climax community.

Primordial germ cells Cells that migrate from the yolk sac of the developing human to the ovaries or testes, where they differentiate into immature cells that will eventually become oocytes or sperm.

Prion An infectious misfolded version of a host cell protein. It produces disease by causing a host protein to become misfolded and become a prion.

PRL **See** *prolactin.*

Prodrome The symptoms that precede recurring outbreaks of a disease such as genital herpes.

Producers In ecosystems, the producers are the organisms that convert energy from the physical environment into chemical energy in the bonds of organic molecules through photosynthesis or chemosynthesis. The producers form the first trophic level.

Product A material at the end of a chemical reaction.

Progesterone A sex hormone produced by the corpus luteum in the ovary. Progesterone helps prepare the endometrium (lining) of the uterus for pregnancy and maintains the endometrium.

Programmed cell death A genetically programmed series of events that causes a cell to self-destruct. Also called *apoptosis.*

Prokaryotic cell A cell that lacks a nucleus and other membrane-enclosed organelles. The prokaryotes include bacteria and archaea.

Prolactin (PRL) An anterior pituitary hormone that stimulates the mammary glands to produce milk.

Promoter A specific region on DNA next to the "start" sequence that controls the expression of the gene.

Prophase In mitosis, the phase when the chromosomes begin to thicken and shorten, the nucleolus disappears, the nuclear envelope begins to break down, and the mitotic spindle forms in the cytoplasm.

Prostaglandins The lipid molecules found in and released by the plasma membranes of most cells. They are often called local hormones (or local signaling molecules) because they exert their effects on the secreting cells themselves or on nearby cells.

Prostate gland An accessory reproductive gland in males that surrounds the urethra as it passes from the bladder. Its secretions contribute to semen and serve to activate the sperm and to counteract the acidity of the female reproductive tract.

Proteins The macromolecules composed of amino acids linked by peptide bonds. The functions of proteins include structural support, transport, movement, and regulation of chemical reactions.

Proto-oncogene A healthy gene that promotes cell division. An oncogene is a mutant proto-oncogene that can lead to the development of cancer.

Prothrombin A plasma protein synthesized by the liver that is important in blood clotting. It is converted to an active form (thrombin) by thromboplastin that is released from platelets.

Prothrombin activator A blood protein that converts prothrombin to thrombin as part of the blood-clotting process.

Protozoans A group of single-celled organisms with a well-defined eukaryotic nucleus. Protozoans can cause disease by producing toxins or by releasing enzymes that prevent host cells from functioning normally.

Proximal convoluted tubule The section of the renal tubule where reabsorption and secretion occur.

Psychoactive drug A drug that alters one's mood or emotional state.

PTH **See** *parathyroid hormone.*

Puberty The time when secondary sexual characteristics such as pubic and underarm hair develop. This period usually occurs slightly earlier in girls (from 12 to 15 years of age) than in boys (from 13 to 16 years of age).

Pulmonary arteries Blood vessels that carry blood low in oxygen from the right ventricle to the lungs, where it is oxygenated.

Pulmonary circuit (or circulation) The pathway that transports blood from the right ventricle of the heart to the lungs and back to the left atrium of the heart.

Pulmonary veins Blood vessels that carry oxygenated blood from the lungs to the left atrium of the heart.

Pulp The center of a tooth that contains the tooth's life-support systems.

Pulse The rhythmic expansion of an artery created by the surge of blood pushed along the artery by each contraction of the ventricles of the heart. With each beat of the heart, the wave of expansion begins, moving along the artery at the rate of 6 to 9 meters per second.

Punnett square A diagrammatic method used to determine the probable outcome of a genetic cross. The possible allele combinations in the gametes of one parent are used to label the columns, and the possible allele combinations of the other parent are used to label the rows. The alleles of each column and each row are then paired to determine the possible genotypes of the offspring.

Pupil The small hole through the center of the iris through which light passes to enter the eye. The size of the pupil is altered to regulate the amount of light entering the eye.

Purkinje fibers The specialized cardiac muscle cells that deliver an electrical signal from the atrioventricular bundle to the individual heart muscle cells in the ventricles.

Pyloric sphincter A ring of muscle between the stomach and small intestine that regulates the emptying of the stomach into the small intestine.

Pyramid of biomass A diagram in which blocks represent the amount of biomass (dry body mass of organisms) available at each trophic (feeding) level.

Pyramid of energy A diagram in which blocks represent the decreasing amount of energy available at each trophic (feeding) level.

Pyramid of numbers A diagram of the number of individuals at each trophic level.

Pyrogen A fever-producing substance.

Pyruvate The three-carbon compound produced by glycolysis, which is the first phase of cellular respiration.

Q

Quaternary structure The shape of an aggregate protein. It is determined by the mutually attractive forces between the protein's subunits.

R

Radioisotopes Isotopes that are unstable and spontaneously decay, emitting radiation in the form of gamma rays and alpha and beta particles.

RAS **See** *reticular activating system.*

RDS **See** *respiratory distress syndrome.*

Receptor A protein molecule located in the cytoplasm and on the plasma membrane of cells that is sensitive to chemical messengers.

Receptor potential An electrochemical message (a change in the degree of polarization of the membrane) generated in a sensory receptor in response to a stimulus. Receptor potentials vary in magnitude with the strength of the stimulus.

Recessive allele The allele whose effects are masked in the heterozygous condition. The recessive allele often produces a nonfunctional protein.

Recombinant DNA Segments of DNA from two sources that have been combined in vitro and transferred to cells in which their information can be expressed.

Recruitment A process of increasing the strength of muscle contraction by increasing the number of motor units being stimulated.

Rectum The final section of the gastrointestinal tract. The rectum receives and temporarily stores the feces.

Red blood cell **See** *erythrocyte.*

Red marrow Blood cell–forming connective tissue found in the marrow cavity of certain bones.

Reduction division The first meiotic division (meiosis I) that produces two cells, each of which contains one member of each homologous pair (23 chromosomes with replicates attached in humans).

Referred pain Pain felt at a site other than the area of origin.

Reflex A simple, stereotyped reaction to a stimulus.

Reflex arc A neural pathway consisting of a sensory receptor, a sensory neuron, usually at least one interneuron, a motor neuron, and an effector.

Refractory period The interval following an action potential during which a neuron cannot be stimulated to generate another action potential.

Relaxin The hormone released from the placenta and the ovaries. It initiates labor and facilitates delivery by dilating the cervix and relaxing the ligaments and cartilage of the pubic bones.

Releasing hormone A hormone produced by the hypothalamus that stimulates hormone secretion by the anterior pituitary gland.

Renal corpuscle The portion of the nephron where water and small solutes are filtered from the blood. It consists of the glomerulus and Bowman's (glomerular) capsule.

Renal cortex The outer region of the kidney, containing renal columns.

Renal failure A decrease or complete cessation of glomerular filtration.

Renal medulla The inner region of the kidney. It contains cone-shaped structures called renal pyramids.

Renal pelvis The innermost region of the kidney; the chamber within the kidney.

Renal tubule The site of reabsorption and secretion by the nephron. It consists of the proximal convoluted tubule, the loop of the nephron (also called the loop of Henle), and the distal convoluted tubule.

Renin An enzyme released by cells of the juxtaglomerular apparatus of nephrons. Renin converts angiotensinogen, a protein produced by the liver and found in the plasma, into another protein, angiotensin I. These actions of renin initiate a series of hormonal events that leads to increased reabsorption of sodium and water by the distal convoluted tubules and collecting ducts of nephrons.

Rennin The gastric enzyme that breaks down milk proteins.

Replication Copying from a template, as occurs during the synthesis of new DNA from preexisting DNA.

Repolarization The return of the membrane potential to approximately its resting value. Repolarization of the nerve cell membrane during an action potential occurs because of the outflow of potassium ions.

RER **See** *rough endoplasmic reticulum.*

Residual volume The amount of air that remains in the lungs after a maximal exhalation.

Respiratory distress syndrome (RDS) A condition in newborns produced by an insufficient amount of surfactant, causing the alveoli of the lungs to collapse and thereby making breathing difficult.

Respiratory system The organ system that carries out gas exchange. The respiratory system includes the nose, pharynx, larynx, trachea, bronchi, and lungs.

Resting potential The separation of charge across the plasma membrane of a neuron when the neuron is not transmitting an action potential. It is caused primarily by the unequal distributions of sodium ions, potassium ions, and large negatively charged proteins on either side of the plasma membrane. The resting potential of a neuron is about –70 mV.

Restriction enzyme An enzyme that recognizes a specific sequence of bases in DNA and cuts the DNA at that sequence. Restriction enzymes are used to prepare DNA containing "sticky ends" during the creation of recombinant DNA. Their natural function in bacteria is to control the replication of viruses that infect the bacteria.

Reticular activating system (RAS) An extensive network of neurons that runs through the medulla and projects to the cerebral cortex. It filters out unimportant sensory information before it reaches the brain and controls changing levels of consciousness.

Reticular fibers Interconnected strands of collagen in certain connective tissues that branch extensively. Networks of reticular fibers support soft tissues, including the liver and spleen.

Retina The light-sensitive innermost layer of the eye containing numerous photoreceptors (rods and cones).

Retinal The light-absorbing portion of pigment molecules in the photoreceptors. Retinal combines with one of four opsins (proteins) to form the light-absorbing pigments in rods and cones.

Retrovirus Any one of the viruses that contain only RNA and carry out transcription from RNA to DNA (reverse transcription).

Rh factor A group of antigens found on the surface of the red blood cells of most people. A person who has these antigens is said to be Rh-positive. A person who lacks these antigens is Rh-negative.

Rheumatoid arthritis Inflammation of a joint caused by an autoimmune response. It is marked by inflammation of the synovial membrane and excess synovial fluid accumulation in the joints, causing swelling, pain, and stiffness.

Rhodopsin The light-absorbing pigment in the photoreceptors called rods. Rhodopsin is responsible for black-and-white vision.

Rhythm method of birth control A method of reducing the risk of pregnancy by avoiding intercourse on all days when sperm and egg might meet.

Ribonucleic acid (RNA) A single-stranded nucleic acid that contains ribose (a five-carbon sugar), phosphate, adenine, uracil, cytosine, or guanine. RNA plays a variety of roles in protein synthesis.

Ribosomal RNA (rRNA) A type of RNA that combines with proteins to form the ribosomes, structures on which protein synthesis occurs. The most abundant form of RNA.

Ribosome The site where protein synthesis occurs in a cell. It consists of two subunits, each containing ribosomal RNA and proteins.

RNA (ribonucleic acid) A single-stranded nucleic acid that contains ribose (a five-carbon sugar), phosphate, adenine, uracil, cytosine, or guanine. RNA plays a variety of roles in protein synthesis.

RNA polymerase One of the group of enzymes necessary for the synthesis of RNA from a DNA template. It binds with the promoter on DNA that aligns the appropriate RNA nucleotides and links them together.

Rods Photoreceptors containing rhodopsin and responsible for black-and-white vision. Rods are extremely sensitive to light.

Root The part of a tooth that is below the gum line. It is covered with a calcified, yet living and sensitive, connective tissue called cementum.

Root canal A channel through the root of a tooth that contains the blood vessels and nerves.

Rough endoplasmic reticulum (RER) Endoplasmic reticulum that is studded with ribosomes. It produces membrane.

Round window A membrane-covered opening in the cochlea that serves to relieve the pressure caused by the movements of the oval window.

rRNA **See** *ribosomal RNA.*

Rugae Folds in the mucosa of the lining of the empty stomach's walls that can unfold, allowing the stomach to expand as it fills.

S

SAD **See** *seasonal affective disorder.*

Salinization An accumulation of salts in soil caused by irrigation over a long period of time that makes the land unusable.

Saliva The secretion from the salivary glands that helps moisten and dissolve food particles in the mouth, facilitating taste and digestion. An enzyme in saliva (salivary amylase) begins the chemical digestion of starch.

Salivary amylase An enzyme in saliva that begins the chemical digestion of starches, breaking them into shorter chains of sugars.

Salivary glands Exocrine glands in the facial region that secrete saliva into the mouth to begin the digestion process.

Saltatory conduction The type of nerve transmission along a myelinated axon in which the nerve impulse jumps from one node of Ranvier to the next. Saltatory conduction greatly increases the speed of nerve conduction.

Sarcomere The smallest contractile unit of a striated or cardiac muscle cell.

Sarcoplasmic reticulum An elaborate form of smooth endoplasmic reticulum found in muscle fibers. The sarcoplasmic reticulum takes up, stores, and releases calcium ions as needed in muscle contraction.

Schizophrenia A mental illness characterized by hallucinations and disordered thoughts and emotions that is caused by excessive activity at dopamine synapses in the midbrain. As a result, dopamine is no longer in the proper balance with glutamate, a neurotransmitter released by neurons in the cerebral cortex.

Schwann cell A type of glial cell in the peripheral nervous system that forms the myelin sheath by wrapping around the axon many times. The myelin sheath insulates axons, increases the speed at which impulses are conducted, and assists in the repair of damaged neurons.

Science A systematic approach to acquiring knowledge through carefully documented investigation and experimentation.

Scientific method A procedure underlying most scientific investigations that involves observation, formulating a hypothesis, making predictions, experimenting to test the predictions, and drawing conclusions. Experimentation usually involves a control group and an experimental group that differ in one or very few factors (variables). New hypotheses may be generated from the results of experimentation.

Sclera The white part of the eye that protects and shapes the eyeball and serves as a site of attachment for muscles that move the eye.

Scrotum A loose fleshy sac containing the testes.

Seasonal affective disorder (SAD) A form of depression associated with winter months when overproduction of melatonin is triggered by short day length.

Sebaceous glands See *oil glands.*

Sebum An oily substance made of fats, cholesterol, proteins, and salts secreted by the oil glands.

Second messenger A molecule in the cytoplasm of a cell that is activated when a water-soluble hormone binds to a receptor on the surface of the cell. Second messengers influence the activity of enzymes and ultimately the activity of the cell to produce the effect of the hormone.

Secondary consumer A carnivore. An animal that obtains energy by eating other animals.

Secondary oocyte A haploid cell formed by meiotic division of a primary oocyte. It is released from an ovary at ovulation.

Secondary response The immune response during the body's second or subsequent exposures to a particular antigen. The secondary immune response is much quicker than is the primary response because memory cells specific for the antigen are present.

Secondary spermatocyte A haploid cell formed by meiotic division of a primary spermatocyte during sperm development in the seminiferous tubules.

Secondary structure The bending and folding of the chain of amino acids of a protein to produce shapes such as coils, spirals, and pleated sheets. These shapes form as a result of hydrogen bonding between different parts of the polypeptide chain.

Secondary succession The sequence of changes in the species making up a community over time that takes place after some disturbance destroys the existing life. Soil is already present.

Secretin A hormone released by the small intestine that inhibits the secretion of gastric juice and stimulates the release of bicarbonate ions from the pancreas and the production of bile in the liver.

Segregation, law of A genetic principle stating that the alleles for each gene separate (segregate) during meiosis and gamete formation, so half of the gametes bear one allele and the other half bear the other allele.

Selectively permeable A characteristic of the plasma membrane because it permits some substances to move across and denies access to others.

Semen The fluid expelled from the penis during male orgasm. Semen consists of sperm and the secretions of the accessory glands.

Semicircular canals Three canals in each ear that are oriented at right angles to one another and contain sensory receptors that precisely monitor any sudden movement of the head. They detect body position and movement.

Semiconservative replication Replication of DNA; the two strands of a DNA molecule become separated and each serves as a template to create a new double-stranded DNA. Each new double-stranded molecule consists of one new strand and one old strand.

Semilunar valves Heart valves located between each ventricle and its connecting artery that prevent the backflow of blood from the artery to the ventricle. Whereas the cusps of the atrioventricular (AV) valves are flaps of connective tissue, those of the semilunar valves are small pockets of tissue attached to the inner wall of their respective arteries.

Seminal vesicles A pair of male accessory reproductive glands located posterior to the urinary bladder. Their secretions contribute to semen and serve to nourish the sperm cells, reduce acidity in the vagina, and coagulate sperm.

Seminiferous tubules Coiled tubules within the testes where sperm are produced.

Sensory adaptation A gradual decline in the responsiveness of a sensory receptor that results in a decrease in awareness of the stimulus.

Sensory (afferent) neuron A nerve cell specialized to conduct nerve impulses from the sensory receptors *toward* the central nervous system.

Sensory receptors The structures specialized to respond to changes in their environment (stimuli) by generating electrochemical messages that are eventually converted to nerve impulses if the stimulus is strong enough. The nerve impulses are then conducted to the brain, where they are interpreted to build our perception of the world.

Septum (of heart) A wall that separates the right and left sides of the heart.

SER See *smooth endoplasmic reticulum.*

Serosa A thin layer of connective tissue that forms the outer layer of the gastrointestinal tract. It secretes a fluid that reduces friction between contacting surfaces.

Serotonin A neurotransmitter in the central nervous system thought to promote a generalized feeling of well-being.

Serous membranes Sheets of epithelial tissue that line the thoracic and abdominal cavities and the organs within them. Serous membranes secrete a fluid that lubricates the organs within these cavities.

Sex chromosomes The X and Y chromosomes. The pair of chromosomes involved in determining gender.

Sex-influenced inheritance An autosomal genetic trait that is expressed differently in males and females, usually because of the presence of sex hormones.

Sex-linked gene A gene located on the X chromosome.

Sexual dimorphism A difference in appearance between males and females within a species.

Short-term memory Memory of new information that lasts for a few seconds or minutes.

Sickle-cell anemia A type of anemia caused by a mutation that results in a change in one amino acid in a globin chain of hemoglobin (the iron-containing protein in red blood cells that transports oxygen). Such a change causes the red blood cell to assume a crescent (sickle) shape when oxygen levels are low. The sickle-shaped cells clog small blood vessels, leading to pain and tissue damage from insufficient oxygen.

Simple diffusion The spontaneous movement of a substance from a region of higher concentration to a region of lower concentration.

Simple epithelial tissue Epithelial tissue with only a single layer of cells.

Simple goiter An enlarged thyroid gland caused by iodine deficiency.

Sinoatrial (SA) node A region of specialized cardiac muscle cells located in the right atrium near the junction of the superior vena cava that sets the pace of the heart rate at about 70 to 80 beats a minute. Also known as the *pacemaker*. The SA node sends out an electrical signal that spreads through the muscle cells of the atria, causing them to contract.

Sinuses Large, air-filled spaces in the bones of the face.

Sinusitis Inflammation of the mucous membranes of the sinuses, making it difficult for the sinuses to drain their mucous fluid.

Skeletal muscle A contractile tissue. One of three types of muscle in the body. Skeletal muscle cells are cylindrical, have many nuclei, and have stripes (striations). Skeletal muscle provides for conscious, voluntary control over contraction. It attaches to bones and forms the muscles of the body. Also called *striated muscle.*

Skeleton A framework of bones and cartilage that functions to support and protect internal organs and to permit body movement.

Sliding filament model A model of the mechanism of muscle contraction in which the myofilaments actin and myosin slide across one another, causing a sarcomere to shorten. When enough sarcomeres shorten, the muscle contracts.

Slow-twitch muscle cells Muscle fibers that are specialized to contract slowly but with incredible endurance when stimulated. They contain an abundant supply of myoglobin and mitochondria and are richly supplied with capillaries. They depend on aerobic pathways to generate adenosine triphosphate (ATP) during muscle contraction.

Small intestine The organ located between the stomach and large intestine responsible for the final digestion and absorption of nutrients.

Smooth endoplasmic reticulum (SER) Endoplasmic reticulum without ribosomes. It produces membrane and detoxifies drugs.

Smooth muscle A contractile tissue characterized by the lack of visible striations and by unconscious control over its contraction. It is found in the walls of blood vessels and airways and in organs such as the stomach, intestines, and bladder.

Sodium-potassium pump A molecular mechanism in a plasma membrane that uses cellular energy in the form of adenosine triphosphate (ATP) to pump ions against their concentration gradients. Typically, each pump ejects three sodium ions from the cell while bringing in two potassium ions.

Soluble fiber A type of dietary fiber that either dissolves or swells in water. This type of fiber includes the pectins, gums, mucilages, and some hemicelluloses. Soluble fiber has a gummy consistency.

Somatic cells All body cells except for gametes (egg and sperm). Somatic cells contain the diploid number of chromosomes, which in humans is 46.

Somatic nervous system The part of the peripheral nervous system that carries information to and from the central nervous system, resulting in voluntary movement and sensations.

Somatostatin A hormone secreted by the digestive tract, where it inhibits secretions of the stomach and small intestine, and by the hypothalamus, where it inhibits secretion of growth hormone. The pancreas also secretes somatostatin. Pancreatic somatostatin may regulate the secretion of insulin and glucagon.

Somites Blocks formed from mesoderm cells of the developing embryo that eventually form skeletal muscles of the neck and trunk, connective tissues, and vertebrae.

Source (donor) DNA DNA containing the "gene of interest" that will be combined with host DNA to form recombinant DNA.

Special senses The sensations of smell, taste, vision, hearing, and the sense of balance or equilibrium.

Speciation The formation of a new species.

Species A population or group of populations whose members are capable of successful interbreeding under natural conditions. Such interbreeding must produce fertile offspring.

Sperm A mature male gamete. A spermatozoon.

Spermatid A haploid cell that is formed by mitotic division of a haploid secondary spermatocyte and that develops into a spermatozoon.

Spermatocyte A cell developed from a spermatogonium during sperm development in the seminiferous tubules.

Spermatogenesis The series of events within the seminiferous tubules that gives rise to physically mature sperm from germ cells. It involves meiosis and maturation.

Spermatogonium (plural, spermatogonia) The undifferentiated male germ cells in the seminiferous tubules that give rise to spermatocytes.

Spermicides A means of contraception that consists of sperm-killing chemicals in some form of a carrier, such as foam, cream, jelly, film, or tablet.

Sphincter A ring of muscle between regions of a system of tubes that controls the flow of materials from one region to another past the sphincter.

Sphygmomanometer A device for measuring blood pressure. A sphygmomanometer consists of an inflatable cuff that wraps around the upper arm attached to a device that can measure the pressure within the cuff.

Spina bifida A birth defect in which the neural tube fails to develop and close properly. The mother's taking vitamins and folic acid before conception appears to reduce the chance of having a baby with spina bifida. Some cases can be improved with surgery.

Spinal cord A tube of neural tissue that is continuous with the medulla at the base of the brain and extends about 45 cm (17 in.) to just below the last rib. It conducts messages between the brain and the rest of the body and serves as a reflex center.

Spinal nerves Thirty-one pairs of nerves that arise from the spinal cord. Each spinal nerve services a specific region of the body. Spinal nerves carry both sensory and motor information.

Spiral organ (of Corti) The portion of the cochlea in the inner ear that contains receptor cells that sense vibrations caused by sound. It is most directly responsible for the sense of hearing.

Spleen The largest lymphoid organ; it contains a reservoir of lymphocytes and removes old or damaged red blood cells from the blood.

Spongy bone The bone formed from a latticework of thin struts of bone with marrow-filled areas between the struts. It is found in the ends of long bones and within the breastbone, pelvis, and bones of the skull. Spongy bone is less dense than compact bone and is made of an irregular network of collagen fibers surrounded by a calcium matrix.

Sprain Damage to a ligament (a strap of connective tissue that holds bones together).

Squamous cell carcinoma The second most common form of skin cancer that arises in the newly formed skin cells as they flatten and move toward the skin surface.

Squamous epithelium A type of epithelial tissue composed of flattened cells. It forms linings and coverings.

Stapes The last of three small bones in the middle ear that transmit information about sound from the eardrum to the inner ear. The stapes is also known as the stirrup.

Starch The storage polysaccharide in plants.

Statistical significance In a scientific experiment, statistical significance is a measure of the probability that the results are due to chance.

Stem cell A type of cell that divides continuously and can give rise to other types of cells.

Steroid A lipid, such as cholesterol, consisting of four carbon rings with functional groups attached.

Steroid hormones A group of closely related hormones chemically derived from cholesterol and secreted primarily by the ovaries, testes, and adrenal glands.

Stimulus Changes in the internal or external environment that a sensory receptor can detect and respond to by generating electrochemical messages.

Stomach A muscular sac that is well designed for the storage of food, the liquefaction of food, and the initial chemical digestion of proteins.

Stratified epithelial tissue Epithelial tissue with several layers of cells.

Strep throat A sore throat that is caused by *Streptococcus* bacteria.

Stress incontinence A mild form of incontinence characterized by the escape of small amounts of urine when sudden increases in abdominal pressure force urine past the external urethral sphincter.

Striated muscle **See** *skeletal muscle.*

Stroke A cerebrovascular accident. A condition in which nerve cells die because the blood supply to a region of the brain is shut off, usually because of hemorrhage or atherosclerosis. The extent and location of the mental or physical impairment caused by a stroke depend on the region of the brain involved.

Submucosa The layer of the digestive tract between the mucosa and the muscularis; the submucosa contains blood vessels, lymph vessels, and nerves.

Substrate The material on which an enzyme works.

Succession, ecological The sequence of changes in the species making up a community over time.

Summation (of muscle contraction) A phenomenon that results when a muscle is stimulated to contract before it has time to completely relax from a previous contraction. The response to each stimulation builds on the previous one.

Superovulation The ovulation of several oocytes. It is usually prompted by administration of hormones.

Suppressor T cell A type of T lymphocyte that turns off the immune response when the level of antigen falls by releasing chemicals that dampen the activity of both B cells and T cells.

Surface-to-volume ratio The physical relationship dictating that increases in the volume of a cell occur faster than increases in its surface area. This relationship explains why most cells are small.

Surfactant Phospholipid molecules coating the alveolar surfaces that prevent the alveoli from collapsing.

Suture An immovable joint between the bones of the skull.

Sweat glands Exocrine glands found in the skin. One type of sweat gland is functional throughout life and releases sweat onto the surface of the skin. Another type releases its secretions into hair follicles and becomes functional at puberty.

Sympathetic nervous system The branch of the autonomic nervous system responsible for the "fight-or-flight" responses that occur during stressful or emergency situations. Its effects are generally opposite to those of the parasympathetic nervous system.

Synapse The site of communication between a neuron and another cell, such as another neuron or a muscle cell.

Synapsis The physical association of homologous pairs of chromosomes that occurs during prophase I of meiosis. The term literally means "bringing together."

Synaptic cleft The gap between two cells forming a synapse, for example, two communicating nerve cells.

Synaptic knob A small bulblike swelling of an axon terminal that releases neurotransmitter. An axon terminal.

Synaptic vesicle A tiny membranous sac containing molecules of a neurotransmitter. Synaptic vesicles are located in the synaptic knobs of axon endings, and they release their contents when an action potential reaches the synaptic knob.

Synergistic muscles Two or more muscles that work together to cause movement in the same direction.

Synovial cavity A fluid-filled space surrounding a synovial joint formed by a double-layered capsule. The fluid within the cavity is called synovial fluid.

Synovial fluid A viscous, clear fluid within a synovial cavity that acts as both a shock absorber and a lubricant between the bones.

Synovial joint A freely movable joint. A synovial joint is surrounded by a fluid-filled cavity. This is the most abundant type of joint in the body.

Synovial membranes Membranes that line the cavities of freely movable joints and secrete a fluid that lubricates the joint.

Syphilis A sexually transmitted disease caused by the bacterium *Treponema pallidum*. If untreated, it can progress through three stages and cause death. The first stage is characterized by a painless craterlike bump called a chancre that forms at the site where the bacterium entered the body. The second stage involves a rash covering the body, and the third stage is characterized by gummas.

Systematic biology The discipline that deals with the naming, classification, and evolutionary relationships of organisms. It is also called systematics.

Systemic circuit (of circulation) The pathway of blood from the left ventricle of the heart to the cells of the body and back to the right atrium.

Systole Contraction of the heart. Atrial systole is contraction of the atria. Ventricular systole is contraction of the ventricles.

Systolic pressure The highest pressure in an artery during each heartbeat. The higher of the two numbers in a blood pressure reading. In a typical, healthy adult, the systolic pressure is about 120 mm Hg.

T

T cell **See** *T lymphocyte.*

T lymphocyte T cell. A type of white blood cell. Some T lymphocytes attack and destroy cells that are not recognized as belonging in the body, such as an infected cell or a cancerous cell.

T4 cell A helper T cell. The kind of T lymphocyte that serves as the main switch for the entire immune response by presenting the antigen to B cells and by secreting chemicals that stimulate other cells of the immune system.

Tanning The buildup of melanin in the skin in response to ultraviolet (UV) exposure.

Target cell A cell with receptors that recognize and bind a specific hormone.

Taste bud A structure consisting of receptors responsible for the sense of taste surrounded by supporting cells. Taste buds are located primarily on the surface epithelium and certain papillae of the tongue.

Taste hairs Microvilli that project into a pore at the tip of the taste bud and bear the receptors for certain chemicals found in food.

Taxon (plural, taxa) A taxonomic group, such as a genus, family, or order.

TB **See** *tuberculosis.*

Tectorial membrane A membrane that forms the roof of the spiral organ of Corti (the actual organ of hearing). It projects over and is in contact with the sensory hair cells. Pressure waves produced by sound cause the sensory cells to push against the tectorial membrane and bend, resulting in nerve impulses that are carried to the brain by the auditory nerve.

Telomerase The enzyme that synthesizes telomeres.

Telomere Pieces of DNA at the tips of chromosomes that protect the ends of the chromosomes.

Telophase In mitosis, the phase when a nuclear envelope forms around the group of chromosomes at each pole, the mitotic spindle is disassembled, and nucleoli reappear. The chromosomes also become less condensed and more threadlike in appearance.

Temporomandibular joint (TMJ) syndrome A group of symptoms including headaches, toothaches, and earaches caused by physical stress on the mandibular joint.

Tendinitis Inflammation of a tendon caused by excessive stress on the tendon.

Tendon A band of connective tissue that connects muscle to bone.

Tertiary structure The three-dimensional shape of proteins formed by hydrogen, ionic, and covalent bonds between different side chains.

Testes The male gonads. The male reproductive organs that produce sperm and the hormone testosterone.

Testosterone A sex hormone needed for sperm production and the maintenance of male reproductive structures. Testosterone is produced primarily by the interstitial cells of the testes.

Tetanus A smooth, sustained contraction of muscle caused when stimuli are delivered in such rapid succession that there is no time for muscle relaxation.

TH **See** *thyroid hormone.*

Thalamus A brain structure located below the cerebral hemispheres that is important in sensory experience, motor activity, stimulation of the cerebral cortex, and memory.

Theory A broad-ranging explanation for some aspect of the universe that is consistent with many observations and experiments.

Thermoreceptor A sensory receptor specialized to detect changes in temperature.

Threshold The degree to which the voltage difference across the plasma membrane of a neuron or other excitable cell must change to trigger an action potential.

Thrombin A plasma protein important in blood clotting that is formed from prothrombin by thromboplastin. It converts fibrinogen to fibrin, which forms a web that traps blood cells and forms the clot.

Thrombocyte **See** *platelet.*

Thrombus A stationary blood clot that forms in the blood vessels. A thrombus can block blood flow.

Thymopoietin A hormone produced by the thymus gland that promotes the maturation of T lymphocytes.

Thymosin A hormone produced by the thymus gland that promotes the maturation of T lymphocytes.

Thymus gland A gland located on the top of the heart that secretes the hormones thymopoietin and thymosin. It decreases in size as we age.

Thyroid gland The shield-shaped structure at the front of the neck that synthesizes and secretes thyroid hormone and calcitonin.

Thyroid hormone (TH) A hormone released by the thyroid gland that regulates blood pressure and the body's metabolic rate and production of heat. It also promotes normal development of several organ systems.

Thyroid-stimulating hormone (TSH) The anterior pituitary hormone that acts on the thyroid gland to stimulate the synthesis and release of thyroid hormones.

Tidal volume The amount of air inhaled or exhaled during a normal breath.

Tight junction A type of junction between cells in which the membranes of neighboring cells are attached, forming a seal to prevent fluid from flowing across the epithelium through the minute spaces between adjacent cells.

Tissue A group of cells that work together to perform a common function.

Tolerance A progressive decrease in the effectiveness of a drug with continued use.

Tongue The large skeletal muscle studded with taste buds that aids in speech and eating.

Total lung capacity The total volume of air contained in the lungs after the deepest possible breath. It is calculated by adding the residual volume to the vital capacity.

Totipotent The ability of a cell to differentiate into any cell type in that organism. A fertilized egg is totipotent.

Trabecula (plural, trabeculae) A supporting bar or strand of spongy bone that forms an internal strut that braces the bone from within.

Trachea The tube that conducts air into the thoracic cavity toward the lungs. The trachea is reinforced with C-shaped rings of cartilage to prevent it from collapsing during inhalation and exhalation.

Trait A phenotypically expressed characteristic.

Transcription The process by which a complementary single-stranded messenger RNA (mRNA) molecule is formed from a single-stranded DNA template. As a result, the information in DNA is transferred to RNA.

Transfer RNA (tRNA) A type of RNA that binds to a specific amino acid and transports it to the appropriate region of messenger RNA (mRNA). Transfer RNA acts as an interpreter between the nucleic acid language of mRNA and the amino acid language of proteins.

Transgenic organism An organism that contains certain genes from another species that code for a desired trait. It can be created, for example, by injecting foreign DNA into an egg cell or an early embryo.

Transition reaction The phase of cellular respiration that follows glycolysis and involves pyruvate reacting with coenzyme A (CoA) in the matrix of the mitochondrion to form acetyl CoA. The acetyl CoA then enters the citric acid cycle.

Translation Protein synthesis. The process of converting the nucleotide language of messenger RNA (mRNA) into the amino acid language of a protein.

Transverse tubules T tubules. The tiny, cylindrical inpocketings of the muscle fiber's plasma membrane that carry nerve impulses to almost every sarcomere.

Tricuspid valve A heart valve located between the right atrium and right ventricle that prevents the backflow of blood from the ventricle to the atrium. It is also called the right *atrioventricular (AV) valve*.

Triglycerides The lipids composed of one molecule of glycerol and three fatty acids. They are known as fats when solid and oils when liquid.

Trisomy A condition in which there are three representatives of a chromosome instead of only two representatives.

tRNA See *transfer RNA*.

Trophic level The feeding level of one or more populations in a food web. The producers form the first trophic level. Herbivores, which eat the producers, form the second trophic level. Carnivores that eat herbivores form the third trophic level. Carnivores that eat other carnivores form the fourth trophic level.

Trophoblast A group of cells within the blastocyst that gives rise to the chorion, the extraembryonic membrane that will become part of the placenta.

Tropic hormone A hormone that influences another endocrine gland.

Tropomyosin A protein on the thin (actin) filaments in muscle cells that works with troponin to prevent actin and myosin from binding in the absence of calcium ions.

Troponin A protein on the thin (actin) filaments in muscle cells that works with tropomyosin to prevent actin and myosin from binding in the absence of calcium ions.

TSH See *thyroid-stimulating hormone*.

Tubal ligation A sterilization procedure in females in which each oviduct is cut and sealed to prevent sperm from reaching the eggs.

Tubal pregnancy An ectopic pregnancy in which the embryo implants in an oviduct. This is the most common type of ectopic pregnancy.

Tuberculosis (TB) A highly contagious disease caused by a rod-shaped bacterium, *Mycobacterium tuberculosis*. TB is spread by coughing.

Tubular reabsorption The process by which useful materials are removed from the filtrate within the renal tubule and returned to the blood.

Tubular secretion The process by which wastes and excess ions that escaped glomerular filtration are removed from the blood and added to the filtrate within the renal tubule.

Tumor A neoplasm. An abnormal growth of cells. A tumor forms from the new growth of tissue in which cell division is uncontrolled and progressive.

Tumor suppressor gene A gene that codes for a protein that suppresses cancer in its normal, healthy form.

Turner syndrome A genetic condition resulting from nondisjunction of the sex chromosomes in which a person has 22 pairs of autosomes and a single, unmatched X chromosome (XO). The person has a female appearance.

Tympanic membrane The eardrum. A membrane that forms the outer boundary of the middle ear and that vibrates in response to sound waves. Vibrations of the tympanic membrane are transferred through the middle ear by three small bones (malleus, incus, and stapes; also known as the hammer, anvil, and stirrup) to the inner ear, where hearing occurs when neural messages are generated in response to the pressure waves caused by the vibrations.

Type 1 diabetes mellitus An autoimmune disorder characterized by abnormally high glucose in the blood due to insufficient production of insulin by cells in the pancreas. It cannot be prevented, and there is no cure at this time.

Type 2 diabetes mellitus A condition characterized by increased resistance to insulin by body cells. It can be prevented or delayed through changes in lifestyle.

U

Umbilical cord The ropelike connection between the embryo (and later the fetus) and the placenta. It consists of blood vessels (two umbilical arteries and one umbilical vein) and supporting connective tissue.

Undernourishment Starvation. A form of hunger that occurs when inadequate amounts of food are eaten.

Ureters Tubular organs that carry urine from the kidneys to the urinary bladder.

Urethra The muscular tube that transports urine from the floor of the urinary bladder to the outside of the body. In males, it also conducts sperm from the vas deferens out of the body through the penis.

Urethritis Inflammation of the urethra caused by bacteria.

Urinalysis An analysis of the volume, microorganism content, and physical and chemical properties of urine.

Urinary bladder The muscular organ that temporarily stores urine until it is released from the body.

Urinary incontinence Lack of voluntary control over urination. Incontinence is the norm for infants and children younger than 2 or 3 years old, because nervous connections to the external urethral sphincter are incompletely developed. In adults, incontinence may result from damage to the external sphincter (often caused, in men, by surgery on the prostate gland), disease of the urinary bladder, and spinal cord injuries that disrupt the pathways along which travel impulses related to conscious control of urination. In any age group, urinary tract infection can result in incontinence.

Urinary retention The failure to completely or normally expel urine from the bladder. This condition may result from lack of the sensation to urinate, as might occur temporarily after general anesthesia, or from contraction or obstruction of the urethra, a condition caused, in men, by enlargement of the prostate gland. Immediate treatment for retention usually involves use of a urinary catheter to drain urine from the bladder.

Urinary system The system that consists of two kidneys, two ureters, one urinary bladder, and one urethra. Its main function is to regulate the volume, pressure, and composition of the blood.

Urinary tract infection (UTI) An infection caused by bacteria in the urinary system. Most bacteria enter the urinary system by moving up the urethra from outside the body.

Urination The process, involving both involuntary and voluntary actions, by which the urinary bladder is emptied. It is also called voiding or micturition.

Urine The yellowish fluid produced by the kidneys. It contains wastes and excess materials removed from the blood. Urine produced by the kidneys travels down the ureters to the urinary bladder, where it is stored until being released from the body through the urethra.

Uterine (menstrual) cycle The sequence of events that occurs on an approximately 28-day cycle in the uterine lining (endometrium) and involves the thickening of and increased blood supply to the endometrium and the loss of the endometrium as menstrual flow.

Uterus A hollow muscular organ in the female reproductive system in which the embryo implants and develops during pregnancy.

UTI See *urinary tract infection.*

V

Vaccination A procedure that introduces a harmless form of the disease-causing organism into the body to stimulate immune responses against that antigen.

Vagina A muscular tube in the female reproductive system that extends from the uterus to the vulva and serves to receive the penis during sexual intercourse and as the birth canal.

Vaginitis An inflammation of the vagina.

Variable In a controlled experiment, the factor that differs between the control group and experimental groups.

Varicose veins Veins that have become stretched and distended because blood is prevented from flowing freely and so accumulates, or "pools," in the vein. A common cause of varicose veins is weak valves within the veins.

Vas deferens A tubule that conducts sperm from the epididymis to the urethra.

Vasectomy A sterilization procedure in men in which the vas deferens on each side is cut and sealed to prevent sperm from leaving the man's body.

Vasoactive intestinal peptide (VIP) A hormone released by the small intestine into the bloodstream that triggers the small intestine to release intestinal juices.

Vasoconstriction A decrease in the diameter of blood vessels, commonly of the arterioles. Blood flow through the vessel is reduced, and blood pressure rises as a result of vasoconstriction.

Vasodilation An increase in the diameter of blood vessels, commonly of the arterioles. Blood flow through the vessels increases, and blood pressure decreases as a result of vasodilation.

Vasopressin See *antidiuretic hormone.*

Vector (disease) An organism that transports a pathogen between hosts.

Vector (DNA) A biological carrier, usually a plasmid or a virus, that ferries the recombinant DNA to the host cell.

Vein A blood vessel formed by the merger of venules that transports blood back toward the heart. Veins have walls that are easily stretched, so they serve as blood reservoirs, holding up to 65% of the body's total blood supply.

Vena cava One of two large veins that empty oxygen-depleted blood from the body to the right atrium of the heart. The superior vena cava delivers blood from regions above the heart. The inferior vena cava delivers blood from regions below the heart.

Ventilation In respiration, breathing.

Ventral nerve root The portion of a spinal nerve that arises from the front (anterior) side of the spinal cord and contains axons of motor neurons. It joins with the dorsal nerve root to form a single spinal nerve, which passes through the opening between the vertebrae.

Ventricle One of the two lower chambers of the heart that receive blood from the atria. The ventricles function as the main pumps of the heart. The right ventricle pumps blood to the lungs. The left ventricle pumps blood to body tissues.

Ventricular fibrillation Rapid, ineffective contractions of the ventricles of the heart, which render the ventricles useless as pumps and stop circulation.

Venule A small blood vessel that receives blood from the capillaries. Venules merge into larger vessels called veins. The exchange of materials between the blood and tissues across the walls of a venule is minimal.

Vertebra One of a series of joined bones that forms the vertebral column.

Vertebral column The "backbone." It is composed of 26 vertebrae (7 cervical, 12 thoracic, 5 lumbar, 1 sacrum, and 1 coccyx) and associated tissues. The spinal cord passes through a central canal within the vertebrae.

Vesicle A membrane-bound sac formed during endocytosis.

Vestibular apparatus A closed fluid-filled maze of chambers and canals within the inner ear that monitors the movement and position of the head and functions in the sense of balance.

Vestibule A space or cavity at the entrance to a canal. In the inner ear, the vestibule is a structure consisting of the utricle and saccule.

Villi (singular, villus) Small fingerlike projections on the small intestine wall that increase surface area for absorption.

VIP See *vasoactive intestinal peptide.*

Virus A minute infectious agent that consists of a nucleic acid encased in protein. A virus cannot replicate outside a living host cell.

Vital capacity The maximal amount of air that can be moved into and out of the lungs during forceful breathing.

Vitamin An organic (carbon-containing) compound that, although essential for health and growth, is needed only in minute quantities to regulate cellular processes.

Vitiligo A condition in which melanocytes disappear from areas of the skin, leaving white patches in their wake.

Vitreous humor The jellylike fluid filling the posterior cavity of the eye between the lens and the retina that helps to keep the eyeball from collapsing and holds the thin retina against the wall of the eye.

Vocal cords Folds of tissue in the larynx that vibrate when air passes through them, producing sound.

Vulva External genitalia of a female that surround the opening of the vagina and urethra.

W

Water footprint A measure of the amount of water used by a person or population for personal use and for the production of and waste removal of products consumed.

Water-soluble hormone A hormone that cannot pass through the plasma membrane on its own, so it influences target cells indirectly, through second messenger systems. Second messenger systems initiate enzyme cascades within the cell that ultimately activate certain enzymes. Water-soluble hormones include protein and peptide hormones, such as those secreted by the pancreas and pituitary gland.

Water-soluble vitamin A vitamin that dissolves in water. Water-soluble vitamins include vitamin C and the various B vitamins.

White blood cells **See** *leukocytes*.

White matter Regions of the central nervous system that are white owing to the presence of myelinated nerve fibers. White matter is important in neural communication over distances.

X

X-linked genes Genes located on the X chromosome. Most X-linked genes have no corresponding allele on the Y chromosome and will be expressed in a male, and in a female if she is homozygous.

Y

Yellow marrow A connective tissue found in the shaft of long bones that stores fat. It forms from red marrow, and, if the need arises, it can convert back to red marrow and form blood cells.

Yolk sac The extraembryonic membrane that is the primary source of nourishment for embryos in many species of vertebrates. In humans, however, the yolk sac does not provide nourishment (human embryos and fetuses receive nutrients from the placenta). In humans, the yolk sac is a site of blood cell formation and contains cells, called primordial germ cells, that migrate to the gonads, where they differentiate into immature cells that will eventually become sperm or oocytes.

Z

Zygote The diploid cell resulting from the joining of an egg nucleus and a sperm nucleus. The first cell of a new individual.

Zygote intrafallopian transfer (ZIFT) A procedure in which zygotes created by the union of egg and sperm in a dish in the laboratory are inserted into the woman's oviducts. Zygotes travel on their own from the oviducts to the uterus.

Credits

Getty Images. **20.2(second row, right)** George Doyle/Stockbyte/Getty Images. **20.2(third row, left)** Radius Images/Alamy. **20.2(third row, right)** Ariwasabi/Fotolia. **20.2(fourth row)** Graham Dunn/Alamy. **20.4(left)** aleshin/Fotolia. **20.4(right)** Monkey Business/Fotolia. **20.9** Hattie Young/Science Source. **20.10** Radu Sigheti/Reuters/Landov. **20.12(left)** David M. Phillips/Science Source. **20.12(right)** Eye of Science/Science Source. **20.13b** Department of Entomology and Nematology Staff, University of Florida. **20.15(left)** Five P Minus Society. **20.15(right)** Douglas Chapman. **20.16b** Wellcome Images, London. **20.16c** Vince Bucci/Getty Images.

Chapter 21 CO21 Mary Altaffer/AP Photo. **21.6** Alfred Pasieka/Science Source. **21.16** Will & Deni McIntyre/Science Source. **Un. photo on p.450** AquaBounty Technologies. **21.19** National Cancer Institute. **21.A** Orchid Cellmark, Inc. **Un. photo on p.455** Orchid Cellmark, Inc.

Chapter 21A Special Topic CO21A Steve Debenport/Getty Images. **21A.1** Science Source. **21A.2a** Science Source. **21A.2b** National Institute of Health Genetics. **21A.4** David McCarthy/Science Source. **21A.5** Robert K. Moyzis. **21A.7** Dr. Judy Goodenough. **21A.9a** Deco/Alamy. **21A.9b** BSIP/Science Source.

Chapter 22 CO.22 Kumar Sriskandan/Alamy. **22.5** Stephanie Phillips/Getty Images. **22.8a** Colin Keates/Dorling Kindersley,Ltd. **22.8b** WaterFrame/Alamy. **22.10b(left)** Philip D. Gingerich. **22.10b(right)** Robert Shantz/Alamy. **Un. photo on p. 479** Steve Wilson/Shutterstock. **22.14a** Gail Johnson/Shutterstock. **22.14b** Hornbil Images Pvt. Ltd. **22.14c** Fulvio Eccardi/Photoshot. **22.15a** Dean Pennala/Getty Images. **22.15b** Henk Bentlage/Shutterstock. **22.15c** Charles taylor/Shutterstock. **22.15d** Ed Reschke. **22.18** John Reader/Science Source. **22.19a** John Reader/Science Source. **22.19b** Richard Drew/AP Images. **22.20a** The Natural History Museum/Alamy. **22.20b** Volker Steger/Science Source.

Chapter 19 CO19 Larry French/Getty Images. **19.3(top left)** Biophoto Associates/Science Source. **19.3(top right)** Biophoto Associates/Science Source. **19.5.1** Ed Reschke. **19.5.2** Ed Reschke. **19.5.3** Ed Reschke. **19.5.4** Ed Reschke. **19.5.5** Ed Reschke. **19.5.5** Centers for Disease Control and Prevention. **19.6** Rolf Ritter/Cultura Science/Getty Images. **19.7** CNRI/SPL/Science Source. **19.12** Dr. Judy Goodenough. **19.A** Design Pics Inc./Alamy.

Chapter 19A Special Topic CO19A Joe Burbank/ZUMA Press/Corbis. **19A.3** Pascal Goetgheluck/Science Source. **19A.4** Paul Clements/AP Photo. **19A.7a** The Lancet/AP Photo. **19A.7b** The Lancet/Getty Images. **19A.7c** Dr. Patrick Warnke. **19A.8** Eric Gay/AP Photo.

Chapter 20 CO-20 Africa Studio/Fotolia. **20.2(first row, left)** aleshin/Fotolia. **20.2(first row,right)** Monkey Business/Fotolia. **20.2(second row, left)** Aaron Haupt/

Index